1981

Science Year

The World Book Science Annual

A Review of Science and Technology During the 1980 School Year

World Book–Childcraft International, Inc.

A subsidiary of The Scott & Fetzer Company

Chicago London Paris Sydney Tokyo Toronto

The publishers of *Science Year* gratefully
acknowledge the following for permission to use
copyrighted illustrations. A full listing of illustration
acknowledgments appears on pages 428 and 429.

70	© 1978 John Launois, Black Star
74-75	© 1978 Martin Rogers, Woodfin Camp, Inc.
76-77	© 1978 John Launois, Black Star
182	© Doug Wilson, Black Star
182-183	© Doug Wilson, Black Star
189	© Alan Orling, Black Star
229	Booth; © 1979 The New Yorker Magazine, Inc.
248	Levin; © 1980 The New Yorker Magazine, Inc.
262	Herbert A. Blough, M.D., and Robert L. Giuntoli, M.D., from *JAMA*, © 1979 American Medical Association
279	Edward J. Kollar and Christopher Fisher from *Science*, Copyright 1980 by the American Association for the Advancement of Science
290	© 1979 Gregory Paul
295	© Alan Orling
301	© Dan Connolly
309	S. Harris; © 1979 The New Yorker Magazine, Inc.
322	Illustration by Laszio L. Meszoly. A. Shkolnik, C.R. Taylor, V. Finch, and A. Borut from *Nature*. Reprinted by permission from *Nature,* Vol. 283, No. 5745, pp. 373-375. Copyright © 1980 Macmillan Journals Limited
328	Ed Arno; © 1979 The New Yorker Magazine, Inc.
334	Dedini; © 1979 The New Yorker Magazine, Inc.
341-342	Reprint from *Popular Science.* Copyright 1980 Times Mirror Magazine, Inc.
344	Reprint from *Popular Science.* Copyright 1980 Times Mirror Magazine, Inc.

The Cover: A honeybee performs a dance that signals
the direction of a source of nectar to
her colleagues in the hive. See page 114.

Preface

Regular subscribers to *Science Year* will notice some changes in the format in this edition. Two new sections, plus a simple aid to understanding the more difficult subjects, have been added to the book. The purpose is to make *Science Year* more useful then ever to its variety of readers.

One of the new sections consists of selected reprints of scientific articles that were revised for the 1980 edition of *The World Book Encyclopedia*. The purpose of *Science Year* is to help its readers, who are primarily *World Book* owners, to keep abreast of the latest scientific developments. New *World Book* articles on science and technology are one more way to perform this service. To launch this section, the editors have chosen the subjects: "Crustacean," "Nervous System," and "Teeth."

To further broaden the usefulness of *Science Year*, a section called "Science You Can Use" has been developed. Articles in this section are aimed at the consumers of the ideas and products that have come out of the research laboratories and into our lives. Sometimes the marvels of science and technology can be confusing. So this section aims to help readers who, for example, need to know some basic things about high-fidelity equipment that can help them choose what is best for their needs. Pet owners who have been curious about whether they are feeding their dog or cat properly will find some expert advice on the subject. The energy-conscious homeowner, concerned that his fireplace may be wasting heat, will learn about special equipment designed to alleviate this problem.

Sometimes science articles are hard to follow because of the unfamiliar words used to describe the subject. Even when defined within the article, words such as *chemotaxis* or *baryon* can be stumbling blocks when they turn up again a page or two later. For this reason, selected Special Reports now include an easily located glossary that defines difficult technical terms used in the articles.

Of course, *Science Year* continues with the major familiar features that bring to its readers the wonder and excitement of science in progress. Special Reports describe in perspective the major areas of research. Science File highlights the news of the year. And People in Science stresses the human endeavors that are the foundation of all scientific discovery. Thus *Science Year* continues to be a source of information for all who wish to know what is happening in this fascinating field. [Arthur G. Tressler]

Contents

Staff

Editorial Director
William H. Nault

Editorial
Executive Editor
Arthur G. Tressler

Managing Editor
Darlene R. Stille

Chief Copy Editor
Joseph P. Spohn

Senior Editors
Patricia Dragisic
Marsha F. Goldsmith
Beverly Merz
Jay Myers
Edward G. Nash

Copy Editor
Irene B. Keller

Editorial Assistant
Lettie Zinnamon

Art
Executive Art Director
William Dobias

Senior Art Director
William Hammond

Art Director
Roberta Dimmer

Senior Artists
Joe Gound
Margaret Smith
Richard Zinn

Artist
Margot McMahon

Photography Director
John S. Marshall

Photographer
Stephen Hale

Senior Photographs Editor
Carol A. Parden

Photographs Editors
Karen M. Koblik
Jo Anne M. Martinkus

Assistant Photographs Editor
Sandra Ozanick

Research and Services
Head, Editorial Research
Lenore Glanz

Head, Research Library
Indrani Embar

Head, Cartographic Services
H. George Stoll

Index Editor
Claire Bolton

Product Production
Executive Director
Philip B. Hall

Director of Manufacturing
Joseph LaCount

Director of Pre-Press
J. J. Stack

Manager, Composition
John Babrick

Product Managers
Sandra Grebenar
Barbara Podczerwinski

Manager, Film Separations
Alfred J. Mozdzen

Assistant Manager, Film Separations
Barbara J. McDonald

Manager, Research and Development
Henry Koval

Editorial Advisory Board

Contributors

Adelman, George, M.S.
Editor and Librarian
Neuroscience Research Program
Massachusetts Institute of Technology
Neuroscience

Ahrens, Thomas J., Ph.D.
Professor of Geophysics
California Institute of Technology
Geoscience, Geophysics

Alderman, Michael H., M.D.
Professor of Medicine and
Public Health
Cornell University Medical College
Medicine, Internal
Public Health

Auerbach, Stanley I., Ph.D.
Director, Environmental
Sciences Division
Oak Ridge National Laboratory
Ecology

Bakker, Robert T., Ph.D.
Assistant Professor of Geology
Department of Earth and
Planetary Sciences
The Johns Hopkins University
Close-Up, Geoscience

Bass, Lawrence J., M.D.
Lecturer in Dermatology and
Associate Clinical Professor
University of California, Davis
Give Your Skin a Sporting Chance

Bell, William J., Ph.D
Professor of Biology
University of Kansas
Zoology

Belton, Michael J. S., Ph.D.
Astronomer
Kitt Peak National Observatory
Astronomy, Planetary

Bracewell, Ronald N., Ph.D.
Professor of Electrical Engineering and
Director, Stanford Radio
Astronomy Institute
Stanford University
Fourier's Formidable Formulas

Capece, Raymond P., B.S.E.E.
Managing Editor, Technical
Electronics
Electronics

Clark, Leland C., Jr., Ph.D.
Professor of Research Pediatrics
Children's Hospital Research Foundation
Close-Up, Medicine

Connor, William E., M.D.
Professor of Medicine
Director of Nutrition Division
University of Oregon Health
Sciences Center
Nutrition

Corbin, James E., Ph.D.
Professor of Animal Science
University of Illinois
Balanced Meals for Your
Family Pet

Counsilman, James E., Ph.D.
Professor and Swimming Coach
Indiana University
A Sport for All Seasons

Cowen, Robert C., M.S.
Natural Science Editor
The Christian Science Monitor
Tracking the Whirlwind

Cromie, William J., B.S.
Executive Director
Council for the Advancement
of Science Writing
The Secular Stargazers

Davies, Julian, Ph.D.
Professor of Biochemistry
University of Wisconsin
Biochemistry
Close-Up, Biochemistry

Dewey, Russell A., Ph.D.
Assistant Professor of Psychology
Georgia Southern College
Psychology

Edlund, Ingrid E. M., Ph.D.
Assistant Professor
Department of Classics
University of Texas
Archaeology, Old World

Eisner, Thomas, Ph.D.
Jacob Gould Schurman
Professor of Biology
Cornell University
Nature's Chemists

Gates, W. Lawrence, Sc.D.
Professor and Chairman
Department of Atmospheric Sciences
Oregon State University
Meteorology

Goldhaber, Paul, D.D.S.
Dean
Harvard School of Dental Medicine
Medicine, Dentistry

Gould, Carol Grant, M.A.
Research Associate
Department of Biology
Princeton University
The Animal Navigators

Gould, James L., Ph.D.
Assistant Professor of Biology
Princeton University
The Animal Navigators

Green, Jeffrey S., Ph.D.
Research Wildlife Biologist
USDA-Science and Education
Administration
Close-Up, Ecology

Gump, Frank E., M.D.
Professor of Surgery
Columbia University
Medicine, Surgery

Hamilton, Warren, Ph.D.
Research Geologist
U.S. Geological Survey
Geoscience, Geology

Hand, A. J., B.A.
Free-Lance Writer and Photographer
Consulting Editor
Popular Science
A Candid Look at Cameras and Film

Hanson, Richard S., Ph.D.
Professor of Bacteriology
University of Wisconsin
Microbiology

Hartl, Daniel L., Ph.D.
Professor of Biology
Purdue University
Reinterpreting Life's Blueprint
Genetics

Hester, Thomas R., Ph.D.
Professor of Anthropology and Director
Center for Archaeological Research
University of Texas at San Antonio
Archaeology, New World

Jenkins, Edward B., Ph.D.
Senior Research Astronomer
Princeton University Observatory
The Stuff Between the Stars

Jennings, Feenan D., B.S.
Director, Sea Grant Program
Texas A&M University
Oceanography

Jones, William G., A.M.L.S.
Assistant University Librarian
University of Illinois at Chicago Circle
Books of Science

Kessler, Karl G., Ph.D.
Director, Center for Absolute
Physical Quantities
National Bureau of Standards
Physics, Atomic and Molecular

Kolata, Gina Bari, M.S.
Senior Science Writer
Science
Ronald L. Graham

Lewis, Richard S., B.A.
Free Lance Writer and Editorial
Consultant
Space Exploration

Maran, Stephen P., Ph.D.
Senior Staff Scientist
NASA-Goddard Space Flight Center
Astronomy, Stellar
Close-up, Astronomy

March, Robert H., Ph.D.
Professor of Physics
University of Wisconsin
The Colorful World of the Atom
Physics, Elementary Particles

Maugh, Thomas H. II, Ph.D.
Senior Science Writer
Science
Digging for Black Gold

Meade, Dale M., Ph.D.
Head, Experimental Division
Plasma Physics Laboratory
Princeton University
Physics, Plasma

Merbs, Charles F., Ph.D.
Professor
Department of Anthropology
Arizona State University
Anthropology

Murray, Stephen S., Ph.D.
Astrophysicist
Harvard-Smithsonian
Center for Astrophysics
Astronomy, High Energy

Negele, John W., Ph.D.
Professor of Physics
Massachusetts Institute of Technology
Physics, Nuclear

Orbach, Raymond, Ph.D.
Professor of Physics
University of California, Los Angeles
Physics, Solid-State

Patrusky, Ben, B.E.E.
Free-Lance Science Writer
Solving Crime with Science

Perlberg, Mark, B.A.
Manager, Publication Department
Rotary International
Keeping Nature's Diary

Piel, E. Joseph, Ed.D.
Chairman, Department of Technology
and Society
College of Engineering and
Applied Sciences
Communications
Shopping for the Super Sound

Salisbury, Frank B., Ph.D.
Professor of Plant Physiology and Botany
Plant Science Department
Utah State University
Botany

Schneider, Eric D., Ph.D.
Research Associate
Center for Ocean Management
University of Rhode Island
Watch on the Self-Healing Earth

Silk, Joseph, Ph.D.
Professor
University of California, Berkeley
Astronomy, Cosmology

Skalka, Patricia, B.A.
Free-Lance Writer
Breast Cancer: The Options in
Treatment

Small, Donald M., M.D.
Professor of Medicine and Biochemistry
Chief, Division of Biophysics
Boston University Medical School
Close-Up, Chemistry

Smith, Bradford A., Ph.D.
Associate Professor of
Planetary Sciences
University of Arizona
Journeys to Jupiter

Snyder, Solomon H., M.D.
Distinguished Service Professor of
Pharmacology and Psychology
Johns Hopkins Medical School
Mending Shattered Minds

Snyderman, Ralph, M.D.
Chief, Division of Rheumatic and
Genetic Diseases
Duke University Medical Center
Cell Wars

Taylor, C. Richard, Ph.D.
Alexander Agassiz Professor of Zoology
Harvard University
Close-Up, Physics

Thompson, Ida, Ph.D.
Assistant Professor
Department of Geological and
Geophysical Sciences
Princeton University
Geoscience, Paleontology

Trefil, James S., Ph.D.
Professor of Physics
University of Virginia
Helping the Hearth to Heat the Home

Verbit, Lawrence P., Ph.D.
Professor of Chemistry
State University of New York
at Binghamton
Chemistry

Visich, Marian, Jr., Ph.D.
Associate Dean of Engineering
State University of New York
Energy

Ward, Harold R., Ph.D., J.D.
Director
Center for Environmental Studies
Brown University
Environment
Close-Up, Environment

Wetherill, George W., Ph.D.
Director
Department of Terrestrial Magnetism
Carnegie Institution of Washington
Geoscience, Geochemistry

Wittwer, Sylvan H., Ph.D.
Director
Agricultural Experiment Station
Michigan State University
Agriculture

Contributors not listed on
these pages are members of the
Science Year editorial staff.

Special Reports

The Special Reports give in-depth treatment to the major advances in science and technology. The subjects were chosen for their current importance and lasting interest.

Nature's Chemists

By Thomas Eisner

The bombardier beetle is one of many insects that makes and uses complex chemicals to protect itself from its natural enemies

If you love nature and have no prejudice against insects and their kin, you should try to spend a morning beside a pond or stream turning up rocks or decaying logs. You may uncover ants, millipedes, spiders, centipedes, and beetles. With any sort of luck, you may find some very special beetles, orange and iridescent-blue, usually about 1 centimeter (0.4 inch) long, which have a spectacular attribute. They are called bombardiers, and for excellent reason. When touched, bombardiers instantly shoot out visible jets of fluid from their rear and make distinctly audible popping sounds at the same time. The fluid smells terrible, burns your nostrils, and makes your eyes water.

13

Bombardier beetles are the skunks of the insect world. They use their spray to protect themselves against predators — which include a wide range of animals in various sizes, from ants and spiders to frogs, birds, and mice.

Naturalists have long known about such insect skunks. In fact, in the 1800s, British naturalist Charles Darwin found out about one of them the hard way. He was collecting beetles, and when his hands were filled, he popped one in his mouth for safekeeping. The beetle fired and, as Darwin later wrote, "burnt my tongue so that I was forced to spit [it] out."

Almost every major category of insect includes species that make chemicals for defense. Some relatives of insects, such as millipedes and arachnids, also have this chemical-making ability. The chemicals contained in the secretions are so diverse that scientists have come to think of these animals as very versatile chemists.

But bombardiers are unique. Research in recent years by various teams of scientists, including my colleagues and me at Cornell University, has shown that bombardier beetles expel their spray through chemical explosions. The fluid that they eject is very hot — as hot as boiling water.

Bombardier beetles are found throughout much of the world. There are dozens of species, most of them smaller than 2.5 centimeters (1 inch). They are usually found near water because their *larvae* (the wormlike young) live as parasites inside the bodies of water beetles.

The bombardier's secretion is produced in a pair of glands — large sacs placed side by side in the beetle's abdomen. The glands are nestled between the gut and the reproductive organs, and they open on the tip of the abdomen, like a pair of barrels on a gun emplacement. The beetle can swivel its abdominal tip in every direction, so it can aim the spray at any point on its body being assaulted.

I had always wanted to photograph the spray of bombardier beetles. When I first tried to do so more than 20 years ago, I failed (and wasted more than 20 rolls of film in the process). To hold the beetle in place, I fastened a metal rod to its back with wax droplets. Then I pinched the beetle's leg with forceps to trigger the spray, while trying to click a camera shutter at the same time. The beetle's spray was so fast — 0.03 second or less, according to sound recordings — that I could not photograph it this way.

I discussed this problem with my friend and collaborator of many years, Daniel Aneshansley, who is an engineer, and we came up with a solution. Instead of operating our camera by hand, we placed a microphone directly above the beetle and wired it to an electronic flash unit, so that the popping sound made by the beetle's ejection would trigger the flash and take the picture. We took dozens of photographs in this fashion, and they all showed the beetle's good aim. It always hit the target, no matter where our forceps had "bitten" it.

The author:
Thomas Eisner is Jacob Gould Schurman Professor of Biology at Cornell University and a member of the *Science Year* Editorial Advisory Board.

The author searches for beetles in a palmetto plant during a field expedition in Florida.

We also studied predators' responses to the spray. When we offered bombardiers to frogs in cages, the frogs attacked the beetles as they usually attack insects – by flipping their long sticky tongues at them. But as soon as the beetles sprayed, the frogs spat them out. Sometimes the beetle would be left stuck to the frog's tongue, so the frog would have to push the beetle off its tongue with its front feet.

Ants, another major enemy of bombardiers, were repelled by the spray whether they attacked singly or in groups. In 1978 and 1979, Aneshansley and I measured how quickly the beetle sprays when bitten by an ant and how quickly the ant lets go after being sprayed. To get that first measurement, we used a metal hook as an artificial ant. The hook was rigged to make a snapping noise when it clamped onto the beetle's leg and prompted the discharge. Using a microphone and a tape recorder, we timed the encounter and found that the interval between the sound of the "bite" and that of the spray's popping averaged only about 0.2 second.

Our tests with red ants and beetles showed that the entire encounter – from ant bite to beetle discharge to ant release – runs its course in about 0.3 second. We also observed that the ant cannot injure the bombardier in such a short time.

To cope with many predators, the beetle produces and stores a lot of spray. A beetle can usually fire 20 times or more, in quick succession if necessary. The total secretion amounts to more than 10 per cent of its body weight. If a bombardier were as big as a 70-kilogram (154-pound) human being, it could discharge the equivalent of 20 pop cans of spray. Even when plagued by a swarm of ants, bombardiers are able to survive. Each shot of spray lingers on the beetle's body and may take several minutes to evaporate. This residue repels the ants and keeps them from biting the beetle.

Eventually, of course, the well runs dry. We repeatedly stimulated beetles with forceps until their spray glands were completely empty. Some sprayed more than 30 times. Then we released them amid a swarm of ants. The ants overpowered the beetles and killed them. But this was an unusual situation, staged in the laboratory. In nature, the beetles probably survive most attacks.

About 24 hours after firing to exhaustion, a beetle has replenished its store of spray and can discharge again several times. Its body is evidently programmed to give high priority to the production of its defensive chemicals.

A group of West German scientists investigated the chemistry of the beetle's secretion in the 1950s. The researchers, led by organic chemist Hermann Schildknecht, who did some of his early work at the University of Erlangen, identified the main ingredient of the spray as a group of irritating and toxic compounds called quinones. At the University of Heidelberg in the 1960s, Schildknecht and his team provided the first details of how the spray works. They discovered that the bombardiers do not store quinones in their glands; they manufacture them at the moment of spraying, using other, less toxic chemicals called hydroquinones. Each gland of a bombardier has two compartments. Hydroquinones and hydrogen peroxide are stored in the inner, larger compartment. The smaller, outer compartment — called the reaction chamber — contains a mixture of enzymes. Muscles contract to force the hydroquinones and hydrogen peroxide out of the larger compartment into the reaction chamber. Then an explosion of sorts occurs in the reaction chamber. One set of enzymes liberates oxygen from the hydrogen peroxide, and another set of enzymes uses most of that oxygen to make quinones out of hydroquinones. The remaining oxygen, which is in the form of gas, propels the mixture out of the gland with a popping sound.

Aneshansley and I thought further about the German scientists' description of the explosion that occurs in the reaction chamber and decided to find out whether the explosion generates high temperatures. Evidence that the spray is hot goes back to the writings of British entomologist John O. Westwood. As early as 1839, Westwood reported that some of the large bombardiers from South America, when seized, "immediately . . . play off their artillery, burning . . . the flesh to such a degree, that only few [can] be captured with the naked hand." At one time, out of curiosity, I had tossed bombardier beetles into my mouth and found that when they fired their spray it definitely felt hot.

Aneshansley and I discussed the heat question with Cornell chemists Joanne Widom and Benjamin Widom in the late 1960s. They calculated that the chemical reactions that produce the spray should release heat. Specifically, they predicted that the temperature of the beetle's spray should be close to 100°C (212°F.), the boiling point of water.

To see if this was true, we devised various pieces of apparatus using electronic heat-sensing devices small enough to measure the temperature of the spray. For example, we used tiny thermistor beads, electronic devices that can record temperature by measuring changes in the metal's electrical conductivity produced by heat. We placed a thermistor in the path of the beetle's spray. The thermistor was hooked up to an oscilloscope, an electronic instrument with a television screen that graphically displays the changes in conductivity that occur during the spray. The thermistor measurements confirmed the Widoms' predictions — the temperature of the spray is always very close to 100°C.

Scientists do not yet know precisely how insects can produce their toxic defensive chemicals without poisoning themselves. We know that the chambers in the bombardier's glands — like similar chambers in the defensive glands of other insects — are lined with a tough membrane made of the same material as the insect skeleton. But we do not know how the cells that make the poisons, and secrete them into the chambers, are protected.

One possibility is that the cells are somehow insensitive to the poisons. But it is also possible that the cells produce the poisons in low concentrations or as relatively harmless precursors. The chemicals become fully toxic only after they have left the cells and are being secreted into the chambers. Another mystery is why the chemicals should not bother an insect when it sprays its own body parts. Bombardier beetles always hit their own legs and antennae when they spray. Why should they be able to stand this when the predators cannot?

A few years ago, we found that the spray of the bombardier beetle does not come out in a continuous stream, but is pulsed — just as water pulses from a dental "water pick." This pulsing may be part of the way nature protects the beetle itself from the spray. The pulses follow one another rapidly, at intervals of 0.001 to 0.002 second. We proved this by analyzing sound recordings of the bombardier's discharges. Using a sound spectrograph — a machine that reproduces sound graphically — we found that the sounds were not continuous. They resembled the rat-a-tat of a rapidly firing gun. We filmed the beetle's spray in 1977 at the high speed

A frog, one of the bombardier beetle's many predators, stalks a bombardier but goes away hungry. The frog approaches the beetle, *top,* tries to swallow it, *center,* but has to spit it out, *above,* and air a burning tongue now coated with the bombardier's fiery quinone spray.

17

of almost 2,700 frames per second, with the help of electrical engineer Harold E. Edgerton, an expert in high-speed photography at the Massachusetts Institute of Technology in Cambridge. The film conclusively showed the spray to be a series of short squirts, rather than one continuous stream.

We do not know yet just why the spray is pulsed. Perhaps the hydroquinones and hydrogen peroxide move into the reaction chamber in pulses, to keep it from overheating. Though the lining of the chamber is tough, the enzymes within could be harmed — literally cooked — by overheating.

The bombardier pays a price for its ability to produce a defensive chemical. Biochemists have not measured insects' metabolic "budgets" — the total energy available to an animal and how this energy is divided up among various tasks. But any living creature must expend energy to make a chemical — energy that therefore is not available for other tasks.

Biologists think that bombardier beetles derive the hydroquinones they use to make the poisons from certain amino acids in the diet. Amino acids are also the building blocks of proteins, which every animal needs just to survive. Females need them especially when they produce eggs. We can imagine a real "energy crunch" for a female bombardier. If amino acids are in short supply, does she use the chemicals mainly to produce spray for her own protection, or does she use them to produce eggs for reproduction? We do not know how the female bombardier resolves this dilemma.

The experiments with frogs and ants had led us to believe that bombardier beetles might be safe from all their enemies. But we know now that this is not so. Some species of orb-weaving spiders, including the common garden varieties of the genus *Argiope*, can cope with bombardier beetles. When a beetle flies into a spider's web and becomes entangled, the spider wraps the beetle in a tight shroud of silk before pouncing on it to kill it. It does this by revolving the beetle with one pair of legs, while another pair of legs draws sheets of silk from the spider's glands and winds the silk around the beetle.

The wrapping procedure takes place so gently that the beetle does not feel threatened and therefore does not spray. Once the beetle is wrapped, however, the spider bites it. The beetle responds by firing, but because its rear end is encased in silk, it cannot aim its spray correctly. The spider proceeds to kill and eat the beetle.

Impressive chemical defensive systems are also found in social insects such as termites. Though a dreadful nuisance to humans, termites are a delectable treat to many predators, including ants. Termites live in colonies, which sometimes contain thousands or even millions of the insects. They are often of different kinds. Some — the workers — build the nest and gather food, and others — the soldiers — serve for defense. When I was in Australia in 1974, I studied a species of termite that has a very peculiar kind of soldier. These have a

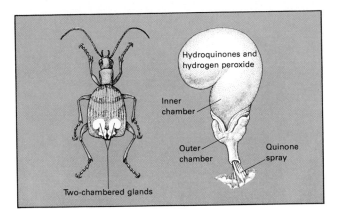

Inner chamber

Hydroquinones and hydrogen peroxide

Outer chamber

Quinone spray

Two-chambered glands

Inside a Beetle's Defense Plant

The bombardier beetle's two-part glands, *left*, produce hot spray that is measured by a tiny thermistor (at the beetle's rear), *below left*, and recorded on an oscilloscope, *below*. Spray from a closely related carabid beetle, *bottom*, reacts chemically with treated paper.

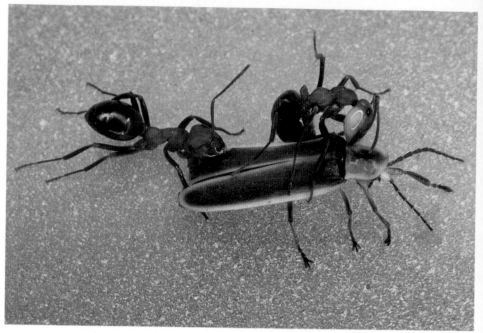

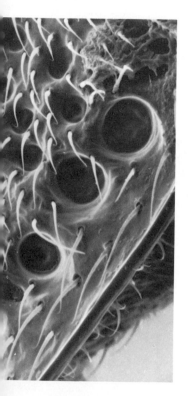

A *Photinus* firefly
defends itself by
oozing a whitish fluid
on attacking ants, *above
right*. The fluid comes
out of tiny pores in the
firefly's wing, *above*.
(Magnified 320 times.)

pointed snout that squirts a sticky secretion from a gland in the head.
The soldiers travel about with the worker termites. When a soldier is
attacked by an ant, it revolves its head to aim the fluid toward the
body part under assault, hitting the ant in the process. Chemicals in
the fluid make the predator itch; it unwittingly harms itself by
scratching and spreading the glue over the rest of its body. Any grains
of soil or other tiny particles in the environment stick to the ant and
load it down. The fluid may also clog the respiratory openings and in
extreme cases may glue the ant to the ground.

The fluid discharge is a signal for other termite soldiers to encircle
the ant. But nature is economical here — the additional soldiers in the
circle spray only if the ant has not been disabled or killed.

Ants are another group of social insects that have powerful
chemical defenses. Many ants produce a spray that contains an
acid — formic acid — that is highly irritating to predators. In some
ants, the spray contains as much as 20 per cent formic acid. Many
other insects also produce formic as well as other kinds of acid. The
champion acid producer, however, is not an insect, but an arachnid
called a vinegaroon. The vinegaroon produces acetic acid, the sour
compound in vinegar. The vinegaroon sprays this substance at a
concentration of 84 per cent. This is probably one of the most
concentrated sources of acid found anywhere in nature.

There seems to be no limit to the variety of defensive chemicals
produced by insects. A species of cockroach sprays a substance, ethyl
acrolein, that is a kind of tear gas. A number of moths, beetle larvae,
and millipedes produce hydrogen cyanide, a powerful poison. Other

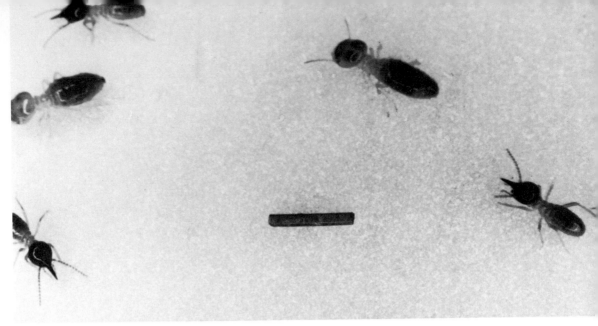

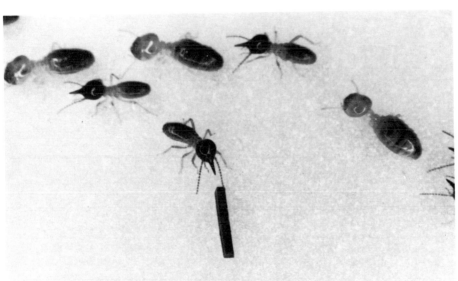

Soldier termites file
past a laboratory "ant"
(a bar magnet, remotely
controlled), *top,* until
it threatens them by
moving too close. Then
a soldier termite leaves
the line, *above left,*
and sprays a fluid on
the ant. Other soldier
termites then circle the
ant, *left,* to see if it
has been disabled or
killed by the spray.

A *Photuris* larva is eaten by a jumping spider,
above, because it has not yet acquired its defensive
chemical from other fireflies. Australian sawfly larvae,
below left, have acquired their defensive chemical from
eucalyptus leaves. When threatened by predators,
they emit it as an oily white fluid, *below right.*

A millipede, *above,* oozes a blood-red fluid that
contains quinones, powerful defensive chemicals
that discourage predators. A meloid beetle,
below, discharges a yellow fluid containing a
similarly powerful chemical, cantharidin, from its
knees when "threatened" by a laboratory forceps.

insects eject aldehydes, ketones, phenols, and similar irritating substances to protect themselves.

Some insects do not generate their defensive substances within their bodies, but get them from outside sources. These insects have the great advantage of not having to use their own energy to produce the chemicals. Some sawfly larvae, for example, feed on pine trees and use pine resin for defense. Sawflies are members of the *Hymenoptera*, the order of insects that includes bees, wasps, and ants.

Pine resin is a sticky and smelly fluid. Most insects other than sawfly larvae are repelled by it. The sawfly larvae obtain pine resin from the pine needles that they eat. As they nibble on the needles, they swallow all parts of the needles except the resin. They shunt the resin into two storage sacs attached to their esophagus. When the larvae are attacked by a predator, they discharge droplets of resin through the mouth and apply the droplets directly to the predator's body. The predators are discouraged by this.

Australian sawfly larvae feed on eucalyptus trees and use eucalyptus oil for defense just as other sawflies use pine resin. The basic storage mechanism is the same; the oil is stored in a sac attached to the esophagus until it is needed for defense.

Some insects obtain defensive materials by eating other insects. I discovered one such case in a peculiar way. My wife and I went on vacation in upstate New York in 1975 and took along our pet hermit thrush, Phogel. The thrush ate breakfast with us each morning — which meant that before we could enjoy our own meal, we had to collect more than two dozen live insects to feed to Phogel.

Over a period of four weeks, we fed Phogel more than 500 insects belonging to 100 species and dutifully recorded its reaction to each. Phogel proved to be a discriminating gourmet, consuming insects that it liked outright. Those that were chemically protected, it either rejected or ate only after many peckings and considerable hesitation. Phogel quickly learned to recognize insects that it disliked. It would simply look at these insects and ignore them. Fireflies were among the insects that it disliked most. Whatever Phogel had tasted in fireflies was obviously a potent defense, worth our efforts to identify.

The most common fireflies near Ithaca, New York, where our Cornell laboratories are located, belong to the genus *Photinus*. (Fireflies, incidentally, are beetles, not flies.) To get enough of these beetles for chemical analyses, we placed ads in our local newspapers during the summers of 1977 and 1978 asking for help. We ended up with several thousand specimens, collected for us for 5 cents apiece by more than 200 persons — many of them children. We were surprised at how many specimens we got this way, and the sum paid out cut more deeply into our research budget than expected. Still, we needed many specimens for our work, because the chemicals we were searching for occur in such a tiny amount in each insect. We obtained additional fireflies from other researchers, who needed only the abdominal tips for their biochemical studies of the light organs and were willing to spare the rest of the animals' bodies.

In the laboratory, we extracted chemicals from the fireflies and tested the extracts on thrushes. We collected insects that the birds normally eat, coated them with the extracted chemicals, and offered them to the birds. They consistently rejected insects coated with one particular extract. From this extract, my chemist friend Jerrold Meinwald and his associates isolated a group of interesting new compounds that we named lucibufagins. The lucibufagins belong to a large and varied category of compounds called steroids, but they are unlike any other known steroids except some toad poisons.

Fireflies are rejected also by predators other than birds. Jumping spiders, for example, never ate any *Photinus* that we offered to them in the laboratory, and neither did ants. The lucibufagins are highly concentrated in the blood of *Photinus.*When *Photinus* are attacked, they emit droplets of blood from pores in the margins of their wings. When these droplets ooze onto the bodies of attacking ants, the ants quickly break off the attack.

Despite these findings, we knew that the *Photinus* fireflies have natural enemies. One predator is the female of some other firefly species that belong to the genus *Photuris*. We have found that *Photuris* cannot produce lucibufagins, but acquire the chemicals for their own defense by eating the *Photinus*.

A former student in our laboratory, entomologist James E. Lloyd, now at the University of Florida in Gainesville, studied *Photuris* females and how they capture their *Photinus* prey. Fireflies use their light organs in courtship. Males of different species flash different patterns of light, and females answer with flashes of their own. Lloyd found that *Photuris* females lure *Photinus* males by flashing like *Photinus* females. Then they eat the captured males.

We offered *Photuris* females that had eaten *Photinus* males to jumping spiders. They rejected them. However, jumping spiders readily ate *Photuris* that had not eaten *Photinus*. In this way, the lucibufagins are a potent defense for the *Photuris*.

This research on the chemistry of insect defenses may have some unexpected payoffs. For example, some steroids similar to lucibufagins have been used as drugs in medicine. They stimulate the mammalian heart, including the human heart. Meinwald and I thought that lucibufagins might have a similar use. Preliminary reports from pharmaceutical laboratories indicate that lucibufagins do stimulate the human heart. However, we do not know yet if lucibufagins have undesirable side effects or are toxic to humans.

Although we are always encouraged when our discoveries have unexpected applications, as in medicine, we do not do our research because it may have applications. We like insects and are fascinated by them. What keeps us going is pure curiosity about these chemists in nature and the many ways they use their chemicals to survive.

A Sport for
All Seasons

By James E. Counsilman

**Olympic champions may be born, but the rest of us
can learn their instinctive techniques well enough
to enjoy swimming as a lifetime form of recreation**

Josh reluctantly accepts the challenge from his fifth-grade classmate, Jennifer, to a race across the pool. He knows that swimming is
not his best sport. Yet he gamely churns through the water, falling
rapidly behind as Jennifer glides effortlessly toward the other side.
Although the children are about the same height and weight and are
equally strong, Jennifer seems to be a "natural swimmer," while Josh
struggles through the water.

Why is Jennifer a much better swimmer than her friend? The
question is one that has concerned coaches, athletes, and sports fans
for centuries. Are top athletes particularly gifted, or can anyone
become a champion through determination and hard work alone?

During the last 20 years, scientists have come closer to answering
this question. We have long known that people inherit different

physical characteristics and abilities. Jennifer inherited the ability to be a good swimmer, Josh did not. As head swimming coach at Indiana University in Bloomington since 1957, I have observed and trained champions as well as ordinary swimmers. My research and that of other scientists has helped me to understand why Jennifer swims better than Josh. A swimming teacher can use the information from this research to help Josh become a competent swimmer, although probably not a champion.

The desire to become a good swimmer is as old as swimming itself. There is evidence that human beings took to the water thousands of years ago. The British Museum in London has Assyrian bas-reliefs dating to 880 B.C. that show three warriors swimming across a stream, two on inflated skins or bladders and the third using a stroke that looks like today's crawl. British explorer James Cook, writing about his 1778 trip to the Hawaiian Islands, described people who "swam and dove like fishes."

In the 1800s, however, most Europeans were reluctant to enter the water. Their attitude toward swimming was summed up in Bartholomew Parr's *London Medical Dictionary.* "Swimming is a laborious exercise and should not be continued to exhaust the strength. It is not natural to man as to quadrupeds; for the motions of the latter in swimming are the same as in walking."

But do even animals swim naturally, as Parr stated? In the mid-1960s, I decided to find out. I kept a newly hatched duck and an American alligator away from water deep enough to swim in until each was 6 months old. I also asked the owners of several newborn puppies to keep their dogs out of water until they were 6 months old.

I put each animal in a swimming pool and photographed it through an underwater window. The alligator and duck swam as though they had always been in the water. The dogs behaved quite differently. At first they thrashed about in the water, using all four legs, although they managed to keep their heads out of the water and move forward. They looked as though they were trying to walk through the water. After several sessions in the water, however, nearly all of the dogs began to swim more efficiently, learning by trial and error to tuck up their hind legs and use only their forelegs.

Each breed of dog learned at a different rate. The Labrador retriever picked up the "foreleg crawl" in only two or three sessions, but the dachshund was still swimming inefficiently, using all four legs, after 10 sessions.

Like many animals, people also learn to swim through trial and error. As Jennifer slips through the water, her senses pick up information from outside and inside her body. She feels the water pressure on her head and shoulders, sees the lane markers pass by, and hears the sound of the water rushing past her. Jennifer can also sense how tightly her muscles are contracting, how heavily she is breathing, and how rapidly her heart is beating.

The author:
James E. Counsilman, head swimming coach at Indiana University in Bloomington, has trained several Olympic medal winners. In 1979, he became the oldest person to swim the English Channel.

An Assyrian bas-relief is evidence that people swam for survival, if not sport, as early as the 800s B.C. Although one of the fleeing soldiers seems to have mastered a crawl stroke, the others are paddling to safety on inflated skins.

Her brain evaluates all the information she is gathering, and she gradually adjusts her swimming technique. She makes these adjustments unconsciously. As she swims faster, she will see the markers moving and hear the water rushing more rapidly. As her stroke becomes more rhythmic, her heartbeat and breathing rate will become more regular.

Why cannot Josh use the same information to improve his technique? Perhaps Jennifer's senses are keener than his. Perhaps her brain can better evaluate the information she receives from her senses, and her body can process it better.

This trial-and-error learning is a complex process, but it is also effortless because we are not aware that most of it is taking place. Scientists believe that humans learn most skills this way — walking is one of the first. Unlike animals, who are born with most of the skills they will need for survival, humans are born only with the desire to learn and try.

In the mid-1940s I became interested in learning not only what techniques good swimmers adopt through trial and error, but why these techniques work so well. At that time I was a graduate student in human performance physiology at the University of Iowa in Iowa City and wanted to become a swimming coach. I decided to take some courses in fluid mechanics — the study of how bodies behave as they move through air or water. I had expected to acquire information that I could immediately apply to swimming. But most of the research and problems concerned boat-propeller design or fluids being pumped

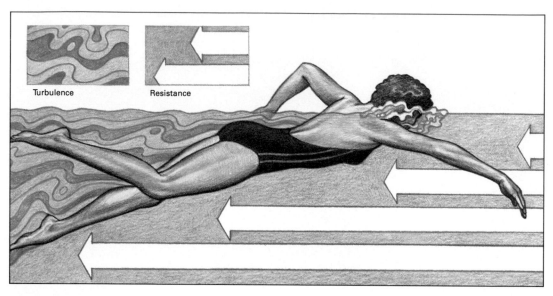

Turbulence

Resistance

Working Against Water
As she moves through the water, the swimmer must overcome two major forces – resistance from the water ahead, and the turbulence she creates that forces her to pull a certain amount of water along behind her body.

through tubes. These studies bored and disappointed me and I almost dropped the courses. Then I began to realize that the professors were teaching me the tools of the trade – the principles of fluid mechanics. It was up to me to apply these principles to the particular problems I would confront as a coach.

Fluid mechanics has indeed helped me to understand the two major, and conflicting, forces involved in swimming. One is propulsion, which sends the swimmer through the water. The other is drag, which holds him back.

Propulsion is achieved by moving the arms, and to some extent the legs, in such a way as to overcome resistance and inertia of the body. Inertia is the tendency of a body to remain in one state, either in motion or at rest. But a swimmer does not move at a steady pace. His speed fluctuates during each stroke. Each time he speeds up, he must overcome inertia. Just as stop-and-start driving uses more gasoline, these continual speed fluctuations in swimming use more energy.

A swimmer encounters three types of drag. One is head-on, or frontal, drag caused by water pushing against the swimmer's head and shoulders. Skin friction, caused by water rubbing against the swimmer's sides, is another form of drag. The third, turbulence, is created as the water first separates to allow the swimmer to move through it, then rushes back into the space behind the swimmer. The swimmer pulls some of this water along behind him in circular patterns, or eddies.

The more streamlined an object is, the less drag it encounters. When I compared films of champion swimmers and poor swimmers, I found that good swimmers maintain a much more streamlined position in the water than mediocre swimmers, and that they create a minimum of frontal drag and eddies.

For years, swimming teachers and coaches were unaware of the principles of propulsion and drag. They taught techniques that are now known to be incorrect. Nearly every book published on swimming in the 1940s told the crawl swimmer to pull his arms straight down at the side of the body, being careful not to bend his elbows.

I tried to do this when I swam competitively at the Ohio State University in Columbus before and after World War II. I'm not sure how I really did pull my arms through the water because I never saw underwater movies of my strokes. But when I became an assistant coach at Iowa in 1948, I began to train Wally Ris, a great natural swimmer. Naturally I tried to teach him the straight-armed method.

I donned a face mask and jumped in the pool to watch Ris swimming toward me. I was especially interested in analyzing his arm pull. I discovered that Ris pulled his arms through the water in a

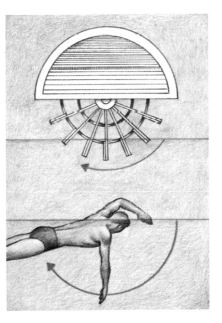 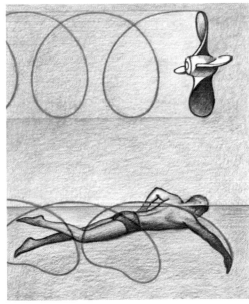 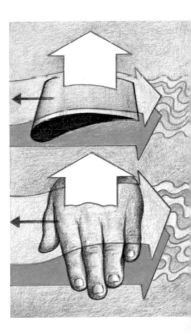

Fluid Mechanics Gets in the Swim

A good swimming stroke employs two principles of fluid mechanics. One states that maximum propulsion comes from moving a lot of water a short distance. A straight-armed stroke, like a moving paddle wheel, *left,* does not use this principle. The hand's (paddle's) straight path forces it to move water that is already in motion. In contrast, a zigzag stroke, like a propeller's spiral path, *center,* does use this principle. Since the hand's direction constantly changes, it constantly encounters still water. The zigzag stroke also enables the swimmer to make better use of the second principle, which states that the higher the speed of a moving fluid, the lower its pressure. Because the hand, like the foil, *right,* is more highly curved on the upper surface, water flows over the upper surface more rapidly and exerts less pressure on it than on the palm. This produces a lifting force, or forward pull, on the back of the hand.

Getting a Lift

The pitch and direction of the hand combine to provide maximum lift at three points in the stroke — as the hand enters the water, top, as it crosses under the chest, center, and at the side of the body, bottom.

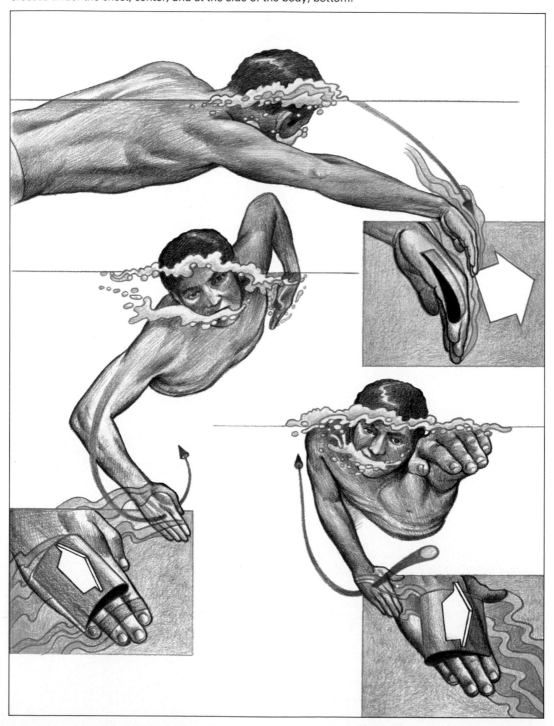

A flashing light attached to a swimmer's finger outlines the path of his hand in the crawl stroke. High-speed photographs taken from the side and front are valuable in analyzing a swimmer's stroke.

zigzag pattern and also bent his elbows. No matter how hard I coached him, he could not do it my way. Fortunately for the United States Olympic swim team, Ris never did learn my way. His "wrong" stroke — the one devised subconsciously by his superior neuromuscular system and trial-and-error learning process — carried him to a gold medal in the 1948 Olympic Games. As a result of this experience, I adopted the "Counsilman Principle": "A bad coach is worse than no coach at all."

At that point, I began to question the established methods of teaching swimming. I had to overcome the bias of my previous training and to examine the how and why of this Olympic champion's stroke. To determine how Ris performed the crawl, I took underwater motion pictures of his stroke and examined them carefully. These films confirmed that Ris, in addition to doing a zigzag pull, bent his elbow as much as 90 degrees during certain parts of the stroke. I began to photograph other champion swimmers to see if they were using similar stroke mechanics. I even watched old underwater movies of such former greats as Johnny Weissmuller and Buster Crabbe. I found that all of the great swimmers were using bent elbows and zigzag pull patterns.

Surprisingly, when I interviewed champion swimmers, they could not tell me exactly how they performed their strokes underwater. When they tried, they were invariably wrong. They had no idea how they had developed this technique and why they were such good swimmers. I gradually realized that they had learned to swim subconsciously — through trial and error. In the past 30 years, I have interviewed and coached many other world recordholders, including Mark Spitz and Shirley Babashoff, and most of them have no idea of exactly how they pull their arms through the water.

I then tried teaching less talented swimmers the techniques used by the champion swimmers. I was gratified when my students improved their speed and efficiency almost immediately. By 1950, I knew fairly well how a swimmer should swim, but I still did not know why he should swim that way.

In a proper flutter kick for the crawl, the legs cycle from a straight position to a right angle bend and back to a straight position.

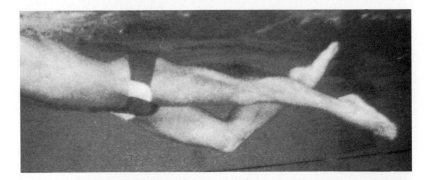

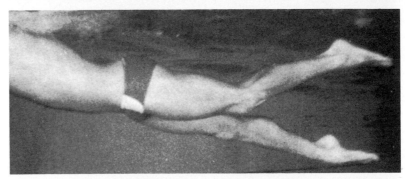

Proper breathing takes advantage of the natural rhythm of the stroke. A swimmer who breathes too late, *below,* throws his body off balance by raising his head when it should be partially submerged. A swimmer who breathes slightly earlier in the stroke, *below right,* breathes when her head is in its highest natural position.

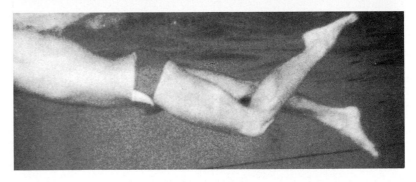

As I analyzed great swimmers' strokes, I began to draw upon my fluid mechanics courses to understand why they worked. The basic competitive strokes — the crawl, the backstroke, the butterfly, and the breaststroke — all have several mechanical factors in common. Looking at films of Jim Montgomery, an Indiana University swimmer who became a 1976 Olympic champion, I can see that he used one of these factors — the zigzag stroke pattern. He brings his arm straight into the water above his head, angles it under his chin, and across his chest. He then brings it back across his abdomen toward his side and out of the water.

There are two reasons why this is an efficient stroke pattern. One is found in a principle of fluid mechanics stating that maximum propulsion comes from moving a lot of water a short distance instead of pushing a little water a great distance. Once Montgomery's hand starts to move the water backward, it must change direction to continue to contact water that is stationary. If he had used a straight pull, his hand would be pushing water it had already set in motion.

Montgomery's zigzag stroke was good for another important reason. He moved his hand and arm laterally, or to the side, with his hand pitched so that it could push the water backward at an angle. When the hand is in this position, another effect of fluid mechanics, lift, or Bernoulli's principle, comes into play. It was discovered during the 1700s by Swiss mathematician Daniel Bernoulli, who stated that the higher the speed of a flowing fluid, the lower its pressure.

I began to understand why lift is a factor in swimming in the mid-1960s. Because water is flowing more rapidly over the back of the swimmer's hand, the pressure on the palm of the hand is greater than that on the back, resulting in lift. Since the direction in which the hand is pulling changes constantly, the pitch of the hand must also change constantly to maximize this lift.

In 1970, I presented a paper in Brussels, Belgium, at a meeting of scientists involved in swimming research. I thought my paper, "The Application of Bernoulli's Principle to Human Propulsion in Water," was the best piece of research I had ever done and expected it would revolutionize swimming. It offered hard evidence to back up my theory that lift is the main source of propulsion in world-class swimmers. Much to my disappointment, my paper was ignored. However, when this group met again in Edmonton, Alberta, Canada in 1978, about one-third of the papers presented dealt with this principle. Lift now appears to be accepted as an important propulsive force in swimming.

Montgomery would not have been able to profitably use the zigzag pattern if he had kept his elbow straight. Again from the films, I can see that although he begins each stroke with his arm straight, his elbow starts to bend as he brings his hand through the water. It continues to bend as he pulls his hand backward. When his hand reaches shoulder level halfway through the stroke, his elbow is bent at a right angle. Montgomery then begins to straighten his elbow gradually as his hand pushes backward and to the side. He makes a final push to build up momentum and carry the arm out of the water and forward for a new stroke.

Montgomery holds his elbow high during the first half of the arm pull. His hand and forearm are positioned so that they direct the force of the pull backward. The angle at which Montgomery holds his hand is also important. When his hand enters the water, it is pitched so that it knifes into the water fingertips first and does not pull down many air bubbles, which add drag. As he pulls his hand through the water, it is pitched to ensure maximum forward lift. And as it leaves the water, it slides out with very little resistance.

Montgomery's hand speed increases throughout the propulsive phase of his arm pull. He starts the pull with very little hand speed but finishes with a powerful backward thrust that propels him forward into the coasting stage of the stroke. In contrast, underwater films of poor swimmers reveal little or no hand acceleration.

A swimmer's kick is important, although it may or may not contribute to propulsion. Research shows that in the crawl and the backstroke, the kick usually only helps to stabilize and streamline the body's position. However, swimmers who do the breaststroke and butterfly rely on the kick for some propulsion.

Proper breathing techniques are also essential for efficient swimming. Montgomery swims the crawl with most of his head underwater to prevent his body from sinking lower into the water, increasing drag. He turns his head to the side and takes a breath as his arm leaves the water. This enables him to breathe without lifting his head, and to maintain the rhythm of his strokes.

Despite the natural ability to stroke, kick, and breathe correctly, even good swimmers like Jim Montgomery cannot become champi-

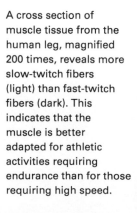

A cross section of muscle tissue from the human leg, magnified 200 times, reveals more slow-twitch fibers (light) than fast-twitch fibers (dark). This indicates that the muscle is better adapted for athletic activities requiring endurance than for those requiring high speed.

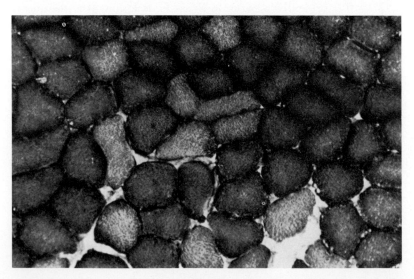

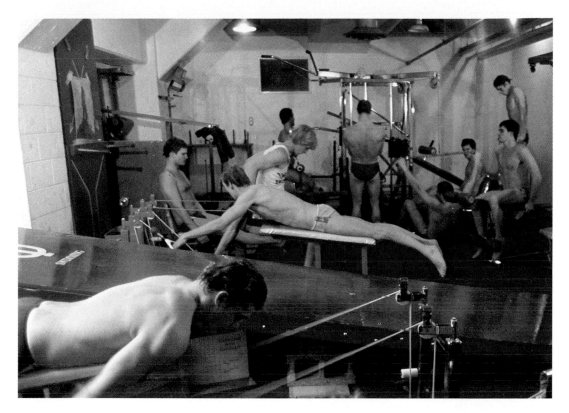

Members of Indiana University men's swim team work out with a variety of equipment designed to increase strength or flexibility in the chest, shoulder, arm, and back muscles that are used in competitive swimming.

ons without proper conditioning. In all types of athletics, conditioning or physical fitness is based on the muscles' ability to adapt to stress by becoming stronger. If Jennifer wants to become a competitive swimmer, she must develop both speed and endurance, because there are elements of both in all races.

The composition of Jennifer's skeletal muscles may determine what kind of race she will swim. Skeletal muscle cells are long fibers with many nuclei. Parallel bundles of these fibers form each muscle. There are two types of muscle fibers — fast twitch, which contract quickly but tire easily, and slow twitch, which contract more slowly but have more endurance. The slow-twitch fibers are often called red fibers because they have more myoglobin, an oxygen-storing protein that can be seen when the tissue is stained and viewed under a microscope. Athletes who have a high percentage of fast-twitch fibers are usually better sprinters, while those with a high percentage of slow-twitch fibers are better endurance athletes.

Muscle contractions are powered by the chemical adenosine triphosphate (ATP). The muscle can get ATP from three sources. One is the ATP that is stored in the muscle fibers. There is only enough ATP stored there to fuel a short burst of all-out effort, such as a 100-yard run or a 25-yard swim. When the muscles have depleted this source of ATP, they must produce the chemical by breaking down glycogen, a carbohydrate stored in muscle, and the glucose residues that glycogen contains. But when glycogen is broken down in this way, lactic acid builds up and the muscle tires. In this system, the available reserves of glycogen are used up in about two minutes. Both of these processes are anaerobic, that is, they occur without oxygen.

The third source of ATP is aerobic. When the swimmer slows down or rests, he takes in additional oxygen, which is needed to convert lactic acid back to glycogen. In the presence of oxygen, lactic acid is "burned" to carbon dioxide and water, and the energy released is used to make ATP. This can go on almost indefinitely because the swimmer is moving slower and taking in more oxygen. Because fast-twitch fibers store ATP, they are better adapted for sprinting. Slow-twitch fibers store oxygen, and are better for endurance.

Swimmers do most of their training in the water, but dry-land exercises have also become important. Until the 1960s, however, such strengthening exercises for swimmers were taboo. Coaches believed then that "long, supple muscles" were ideal for swimmers and that

Only after months of careful training and conditioning are competitive swimmers ready to leave the starting block.

weight lifting and heavy resistance exercises would shorten the muscles. We know now that strong arm muscles are strong arm muscles, regardless of how they were developed.

Today's competitive swimmers regularly lift weights and use other forms of strengthening exercises. Several machines have been developed to provide biokinetic exercises in which the muscle always works against maximum resistance. Such exercises build strength and contraction speed in muscles used in swimming. However, coaches caution against general body-building exercises. Building up muscles that are not used in swimming can add 2 to 9 kilograms (5 to 20 pounds) of useless weight to carry through the water.

A swimmer's diet is another important conditioning factor. The competitive swimmer actually follows two diets — a daily diet and a precompetition diet. His daily diet should consist of approximately 15 per cent protein, 35 per cent fat, 50 per cent carbohydrate, and enough calories to maintain his ideal weight. A swimmer's performance will suffer if he is poorly nourished.

Swimmers begin their precompetition diet two days before a scheduled meet. This diet is lower in protein and fat and higher in carbohydrates than the daily diet. The swimmer eats his last precompetition meal at least three hours before starting time, and avoids foods that are greasy or highly seasoned, and certain vegetables, such as corn and salad greens, that take longer to digest. He also avoids concentrated sweets, which draw fluids into the intestinal system, as well as beans, and "junk foods" that can produce intestinal gases.

Most people approach swimming not as a competitive sport, but as a form of exercise that can be enjoyed for a lifetime. Swimming provides a good workout for the heart and lungs without jarring or putting an undue strain on any part of the body. Thus, it can be taken up by people of almost any age and physical condition.

When I was a competitive swimmer in college, I assumed that I would never again be far from a pool. I was right, but I came to spend most of my time at the edge of the pool rather than in the water — coaching, teaching, developing training aids, and doing research. By 1970, when I was 50, this landlocked life style had taken its toll. I suffered from asthma, arthritis, chronic bronchitis, and high blood pressure. I weighed 110 kilograms (243 pounds).

Upon my doctor's advice, I began swimming for two hours a day and, in less than a year, I lost 27 kilograms (60 pounds) and felt better than I had in years. I began to train as a long-distance swimmer in March 1978, and on Sept. 14, 1979, at the age of 58, I became the oldest person to swim the English Channel.

With good coaching and proper training and conditioning, Jennifer may one day also swim the channel, or become a national sprint champion. Josh will not, but he can learn to swim well enough to enjoy it as recreation. And, 50 years from now, they can still be swimming every day.

Journeys
to Jupiter

By Bradford A. Smith

**The *Voyager* visits to the giant planet and its
four Galilean satellites have changed our views
substantially about this replica of the solar system**

The largest planet in the solar system became a star on the imaging screens at the Jet Propulsion Laboratories (JPL) in Pasadena, Calif., in 1979. Performing before the cameras aboard the *Voyager* spacecraft, Jupiter and its supporting cast – the four Galilean satellites – astounded the viewing audience of JPL astronomers with detailed scenes, many of which they had not expected to see.

As leader of the *Voyager* imaging science team, I was fortunate to be among the first scientists to share in the excitement of many new discoveries. These included the complex nature of the cloud structure and circulation of Jupiter's atmosphere; a ring of tiny particles around the planet; two new satellites; details of the surfaces of the four largest of Jupiter's 15 known satellites; and, perhaps most important, the extensive and violent volcanic activity on the satellite Io.

Our amazement at the large number of discoveries made by the *Voyager* visits to Jupiter in March and July was really just a measure of our ignorance of physical conditions in that remote corner of the solar system. Much of what we had assumed turned out to be wrong, and some things we had not even imagined were found to exist.

Jupiter dwarfs three of its satellites in a *Voyager* photo. Io is at center right; Europa is at far right; and Callisto is at bottom left.

Jupiter orbits in the cold, darker fringes of the solar system, about five times farther from the Sun than does Earth. Named for the king of the gods in Roman mythology — Jupiter, or Jove — the giant planet and its 15 known satellites make up the Jovian system. Many scientists consider it the most interesting group of astronomical bodies in our nine-planet solar system.

Because the Jovian system is so remote, until the 1970s we knew less about it than we knew about such relatively nearby bodies as the Moon and Mars. To help scientists attempting to study a planetary system so far from Earth, the National Aeronautics and Space Administration (NASA) established a long-range program in the early 1970s for the systematic reconnaissance and exploration of Jupiter and other remote planets. In 1973 and 1974, the *Pioneer 10* and *Pioneer 11* spacecraft traveled to the Jovian realm for the first time, and planetary scientists made some startling discoveries about this unique world. In 1979, the more sophisticated *Voyager* probes added immensely to our excitement and knowledge.

All of these spacecraft findings, together with new data obtained from ground-based telescopes with improved electronic detectors, are starting to provide a clearer picture of the origin, evolution, and present status of Jupiter and its four largest satellites. Astronomers are beginning to realize that this system resembles our planetary system in several ways. For many scientists, the Jovian system represents a miniature model of the Sun and its planets that may help us understand better how our solar system formed and evolved.

We are not the first observers to note the similarity between the Jovian system and the entire solar system. In 1610, Italian astronomer Galileo Galilei discovered Io, Europa, Ganymede, and Callisto — the four largest satellites of Jupiter — with a telescope he constructed. The way in which these Galilean satellites orbited Jupiter was similar to the way in which planets orbited the Sun. A few of Galileo's contemporaries believed that this supported the idea of a Sun-centered universe. This theory, put forward by Polish astronomer Nicolaus Copernicus in 1543, contradicted the popular belief that Earth was the hub around which the planets revolved.

For 345 years after Galileo's observations, the optical telescope was the only instrument available for studying the planets. As better and larger telescopes were developed, observers began to get a picture of Jupiter's basic structure.

They learned that Jupiter has a diameter of 142,800 kilometers (88,600 miles), 11 times that of Earth. Comparing facts known about the orbits of Jupiter and other solar system bodies, and applying some laws of physics, they found that its mass is 318 times that of Earth. The mass is more than twice that of all other planets, satellites, asteroids, and comets in the solar system combined. The astronomers deduced that, although its volume equals that of more than 1,300 Earths, Jupiter is only about one-fourth as dense as our planet. This

The author:
Bradford A. Smith is associate professor of planetary sciences at the University of Arizona. He was the leader of the *Voyager* imaging science team.

implied that Jupiter must be composed almost entirely of hydrogen and helium, the lightest and most abundant elements in the universe. *Pioneer 10* confirmed this.

At Jupiter's center, scientists now believe, is a relatively small solid core about one-tenth the diameter of the planet. We had only a vague idea of the composition of the core until *Pioneer* data enabled us to construct a model, and results from *Voyager* reinforced this model. We now think Jupiter's core may be made of metals, silicates, and ice.

Even before the spacecraft studies, physicists had concluded that the core is surrounded by a shell of liquid hydrogen compressed by such extremely high pressures that the hydrogen takes on the physical properties of a metal — that is, it becomes an excellent conductor of heat and electricity. Surrounding the metallic hydrogen are layers of liquid molecular hydrogen and, near the planet's surface, gaseous hydrogen. Although hydrogen is the main constituent, Jupiter's atmosphere also contains approximately 11 per cent helium and a total of less than 1 per cent methane ammonia, ammonia compounds, ethane, acetylene, and water.

Much of our improved understanding of Jupiter's atmosphere came during the mid-1970s from analyzing the close-up photos that *Pioneer* cameras beamed back to Earth. The *Pioneer* spacecraft transmitted images with five times better resolution than is obtainable with photos taken by cameras on Earth-based telescopes. For example, measurements made from Earth had persuaded scientists that near the top of Jupiter's atmosphere are layers of clouds composed of ammonia, ammonium hydrosulfide, and water ice and, below that, clouds of ammonia-water droplets. Close-up *Pioneer* photos showed

Instrument-laden *Voyager* spacecraft, *above,* performed a wide variety of experiments on the mission to Jupiter. Spectacular photos sent back by *Voyager* cameras excited an imaging team member, *above left,* who viewed them at the Jet Propulsion Laboratory in Pasadena, Calif.

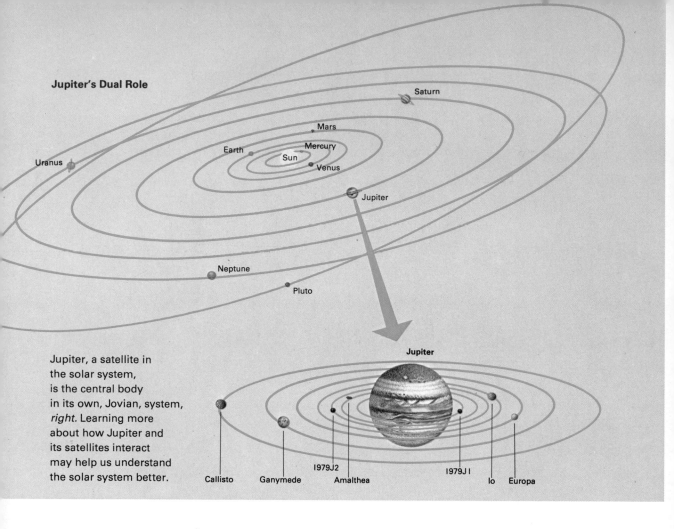

Jupiter's Dual Role

Uranus

Saturn

Mars

Earth

Mercury

Sun

Venus

Jupiter

Neptune

Pluto

Jupiter

Jupiter, a satellite in
the solar system,
is the central body
in its own, Jovian, system,
right. Learning more
about how Jupiter and
its satellites interact
may help us understand
the solar system better.

Callisto   Ganymede   1979J2   Amalthea   1979J1   Io   Europa

that some of the clouds are white or gray, while others range from
yellow and orange to brick-red. This made us think that the colors
may be caused by traces of impurities — either of elements, such as
phosphorus, or of organic compounds.

Other *Pioneer* measurements showed that the weather at the cloud
tops is windy and cold; the temperatures hover around −130°C
(−200°F.). Measuring the daily positions of the small, spotlike clouds
gave us the velocity of the winds, which varies with latitude. The
winds sometimes reach velocities of more than 600 kilometers per
hour (kph) or 375 miles per hour (mph), and tend to blow around
Jupiter from east to west or west to east, with little or no movement
toward or away from the poles.

Pioneer, and later *Voyager,* returned spectacular pictures of Jupiter's cloud system, which is organized into a series of light bands
called zones and dark bands called belts that circle the planet parallel
to its equator.

Astronomers using telescopes, long before the space probes, had
measured Jupiter's rotation period — the time the planet takes to
rotate once around its own axis. They did this by focusing on one or

more of the many small bright and dark spots within the zones and belts, and found the period to be about 9 hours 50 minutes near the equator and 5 minutes longer at higher latitudes. Because Jupiter is not a solid body, all that observers could measure were its clouds, and the clouds rotate faster at the equator than at higher latitudes. Such rapid rotation causes the equator to bulge and gives Jupiter an ellipsoid, or oval, shape. The planet's diameter at its poles is 8,800 kilometers (5,500 miles) less than at its equator.

While optical observations of Jupiter's surface continued to be rewarding, astronomers were quite excited when, in 1955, they detected with radio telescopes periodic bursts of radio energy coming from the planet. These radio emissions — the only ones at that time detected from any planet other than Earth itself — come from an interaction between Jupiter's magnetic field and high-energy particles given off by the Sun that are trapped in that field. Such an indication that Jupiter has a strong and extensive magnetic field pointed the way toward learning about the planet's deep interior, in spite of the impenetrable clouds. Radio emissions also enabled us to determine the planet's rotation period more precisely. Instead of measuring the spin of the drifting clouds, we measured the spin rate of the liquid and solid interior. Jupiter's true rotation period is 9 hours 55 minutes 29.7 seconds.

Although they are not certain just what the connection is, atmospheric scientists think that Jupiter's rapid rotation period may contribute to the creation of the surface patterns that made many of the *Voyager* pictures resemble swirling abstract paintings. The color and surface reflectivity — percentage of sunlight reflected — of Jupiter's zones and belts change over varying periods. Astronomers observing Jupiter for many years have sometimes seen dramatic changes occur within a year, and at other times have watched a feature, such as the shape of a large white oval mass of clouds, remain almost constant over a dozen years. We do not yet know what causes such changes but do not find them surprising. When we look at Jupiter, we see only meteorological events. The planet is blanketed by such dense clouds that all we see is "weather." Even *Voyager* cameras could not penetrate the cloud cover.

Although there are many small and relatively short-lived clouds in Jupiter's atmosphere, one is large and long lasting — the Great Red Spot. It was probably first noted by English physicist Robert Hooke in 1664. This huge oval-shaped feature has drifted east and west at a constant latitude in Jupiter's Southern Hemisphere, varying in color from near white to pink to brick-red. Its length has varied from 42,000 kilometers (26,000 miles) to its present 22,000 kilometers (13,600 miles). It is about 13,000 kilometers (8,000 miles) wide — slightly greater than Earth's diameter.

The nature of the Great Red Spot remained a mystery for centuries. Then planetary astronomer Elmer J. Reese and I, working at New

A massive white cloud (arrow) circles the Great Red Spot from east to west in a series of detailed *Voyager* photos. It took about three weeks to travel this far before it disappeared.

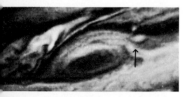

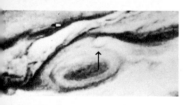

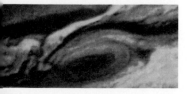

Mexico State University in Las Cruces, discovered in 1966 that this conspicuous atmospheric feature was really a giant vortex, or whirlwind, circulating in a counterclockwise direction. It is similar to one of the large anticyclones that occur in Earth's Southern Hemisphere. We discovered this when we repeatedly observed several small, dark clouds being pulled into the Great Red Spot and circulating around its edge a few times before fading away.

After detailed study of *Voyager* photos, we now think that the Great Red Spot is merely the largest member of a certain class of Jovian atmospheric features. Characteristics of all the members of this class include anticyclonic flow (clockwise in the Northern Hemisphere and counterclockwise in the Southern Hemisphere); gentle upwelling in their centers and downflow at their edges; and a more or less oval shape with an interior spiral-cloud pattern similar in structure to that of hurricanes on Earth (see TRACKING THE WHIRLWIND).

The intense radiation belts around Jupiter were a principal focus of the *Pioneer* missions. *Pioneer 10* made its closest approach to Jupiter on Dec. 4, 1973, when it came within 130,000 kilometers (81,000 miles) of the planet. It carried six experiments designed to study the radiation particles and magnetic field. *Pioneer 11,* which came within 42,000 kilometers (26,000 miles) of Jupiter on Dec. 3, 1974, largely duplicated the *Pioneer 10* experiments. Both *Pioneers'* detailed measurements of Jupiter's magnetosphere made the success of later missions possible.

Discovery of Jupiter's intense radiation environment forced the scientists and engineers who were then constructing the *Voyager* spacecraft to modify its design. Those of us working on the *Voyager* program had to make quick decisions, because the design of the spacecraft and the experiments was nearly completed. But the *Pioneer* results made it clear that Jupiter's radiation would ruin our experiments unless we modified the equipment. We had to redesign many experiments and systems and extensively revise others. For example, the glass selected for the optical systems and filters in our television cameras would have been blackened by the radiation, so we had to select new types of radiation-resistant glass. Also, many of the original solid-state electronic components would have failed. We replaced these with ones that could survive the Jovian environment.

Among the more surprising *Voyager* discoveries was a ring — a thin, disk-shaped swarm of tiny particles — surrounding Jupiter. It is made up mostly of dustlike particles that become visible only when backlighted by rays of sunlight. It was *Voyager's* good fortune to photograph the ring in this circumstance. The ring's outer edge is about 129,000 kilometers (80,000 miles) from the planet's center, and the outer 6,000 kilometers (3,700 miles) is much brighter than the rest. Jupiter's ring extends inward to the top of the planet's atmosphere.

Very weak forces that act over a long period of time, such as pressure from sunlight and interactions with Jupiter's magnetic field,

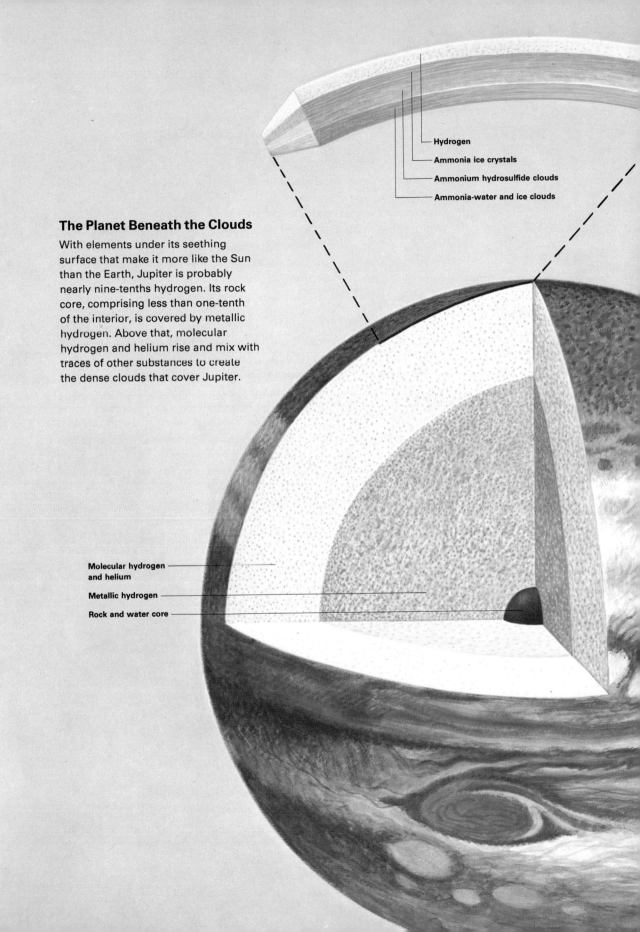

Hydrogen

Ammonia ice crystals

Ammonium hydrosulfide clouds

Ammonia-water and ice clouds

The Planet Beneath the Clouds

With elements under its seething surface that make it more like the Sun than the Earth, Jupiter is probably nearly nine-tenths hydrogen. Its rock core, comprising less than one-tenth of the interior, is covered by metallic hydrogen. Above that, molecular hydrogen and helium rise and mix with traces of other substances to create the dense clouds that cover Jupiter.

Molecular hydrogen and helium

Metallic hydrogen

Rock and water core

cause the ring particles to spiral slowly inward and ultimately settle in Jupiter's upper atmosphere. This means that there must be a source to replace those lost particles. We do not yet know whether this source is a group of larger bodies orbiting near the outer edge of the ring or dust falling inward from Io or from interplanetary space.

However, *Voyager* pictures revealed that 1979J1, the 14th satellite of Jupiter, is orbiting just inside the outer edge of the ring. This satellite has an orbital period — the time it takes one body to circle another — of only 7 hours 4 minutes, the shortest orbit of any natural satellite in the solar system. We do not yet know whether 1979J1 is a source for the ring particles or merely establishes the ring's outer boundary, but we believe it is somehow associated with the ring. In April 1980, while studying more *Voyager* photos, a JPL engineer discovered a 15th satellite, 1979J2. It circles Jupiter between the orbits of Amalthea and Io every 16 hours 15 minutes.

The *Voyager* spacecraft returned a noticeably different view of Jupiter's cloud patterns from that recorded by the *Pioneer* spacecraft. Observers using ground-based telescopes at the University of Arizona and New Mexico State University had begun to monitor extensive changes in the clouds' color and reflectivity in 1974. Between 1974 and 1979, the South Tropical Zone, which contains the Great Red Spot, grew darker while the North Tropical Zone grew brighter. Over the same interval, the equatorial region developed into a more complex structure of bright and dark clouds. However, wind speed remained about the same over the five-year period, as it had over the past several decades of careful ground-based record keeping.

This unexpected stability of Jupiter's wind currents led *Voyager* scientists to conclude that the observed winds originate in atmospheric currents far below the visible cloud layer. The dramatic changes in the visible cloud patterns that take place over a few years are really superficial events.

The *Voyager* photographs also showed that both the cloud structure and the local wind patterns are much more complex than we thought. Viewed up close, the great horizontal bands break down into a number of eddies — swirling whirlpools of air that interact with one another and with their surroundings. At first, astronomers studying Jupiter's atmosphere were not sure whether the eddies provide the energy and momentum to drive the currents or whether the currents produce the eddies. However, recent findings by atmospheric scientists continuing to study the numerical data obtained from *Voyager* photos suggest that the eddies draw their energy from Jupiter's internal heat source as warm air rises from below. This energy maintains the strong winds.

While knowledge about the Jovian system gained from *Voyager* is the newest and most newsworthy, scientists analyzing results of the space probes build upon data that many others have accumulated. For example, in 1967, infrared astronomer Frank J. Low of the

Io shows the youngest face in the Jovian system, perhaps in the solar system. Intense volcanic activity erases craters, while molten silicate under the sulfurous crust may shield a solid core.

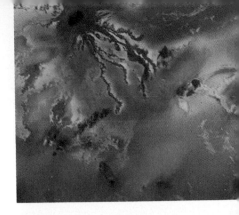

Europa's smooth surface is crisscrossed with a web of intersecting lines that may represent filled fractures in its icy crust. The crust, possibly billions of years old, may cover a solid core and a silicate interior.

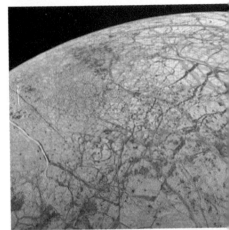

Ganymede has a grooved, twisted surface of ice that is thousands of kilometers thick. Dark patches of older crust resemble Earth's Moon, but newer bands of rays from craters are unique. It may have a soft ice interior covering a silicate core.

Callisto's ancient, heavily cratered crust has long been inactive. It is sheathed in thick, hard ice that probably covers a soft ice mantle and silicate core. Callisto has a series of concentric rings, evidence of an impact with some huge object.

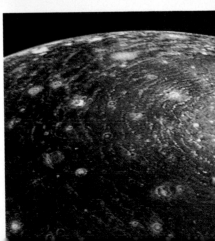

University of Arizona in Tucson measured the heat given off by Jupiter and discovered that the planet radiates about twice as much heat energy into space as it receives from the Sun. Instruments on *Pioneer 10* confirmed Low's finding. This excess energy comes not from thermonuclear reactions, as in the case of the Sun, but probably from Jupiter's very slow gravitational collapse. The planet is shrinking at the rate of 1 millimeter per year, and as it collapses, it radiates heat energy. This radiation makes Jupiter a bright, luminous body in the infrared region of the spectrum, and brings the Jovian system's resemblance to the solar system a step closer.

Some members of our *Voyager* imaging science team must have had this resemblance in mind as we watched and waited in March 1979 at JPL. Each day, as *Voyager 1* neared Jupiter and the planet's image grew larger on our television monitors, we wondered how the Galilean satellites that lay ahead would fit into the overall picture. Each of us knew that of all the planetary bodies that exploratory spacecraft had visited so far, these four large moons of Jupiter were the most mysterious. Few of us were willing even to venture a guess as to what sights we would see. Earlier observations with spectrometer-equipped ground-based telescopes had offered tantalizing hints. They indicated that three of the Galilean satellites — Ganymede, Callisto, and Europa — were covered with water ice. We believed that the ice on the first two might be more than 1,000 kilometers (625 miles) thick. Ice flows, although as slowly as cold molasses, under a persistent gravitational pull such as that on the Jovian satellites. Therefore, we feared that all the surface features on these bodies might have flowed away in glacierlike movement over the past several billion years, leaving flat, uninteresting surfaces.

We need not have worried. The low surface temperatures found in the outer solar system, at which ice becomes almost as rigid as steel, were more than a match for the smoothing effects of gravity. A wave of exuberance followed by relief swept through the *Voyager* imaging science team as the first close-up pictures of Ganymede revealed impact craters and other recognizable features in its frozen crust.

The four Galilean satellites were the only ones we knew about for nearly 300 years. Then Amalthea, Jupiter's fifth satellite, was found in 1892, when Edward E. Barnard of Lick Observatory on Mount Hamilton in California made the discovery. Orbiting 181,000 kilometers (112,000 miles) from the giant planet, Amalthea is only 200 kilometers (125 miles) across and resembles a dark-red rock. Eight more tiny satellites were discovered between 1904 and 1974. Their distance from Jupiter ranges between 11.5 million kilometers (7 million miles) and 23.7 million kilometers (14.7 million miles), and their diameters range from less than 10 kilometers (6 miles) to 120 kilometers (75 miles).

These small, remote satellites are probably asteroids, stony or metallic chunks of matter left over from the formation of the solar

Four photos transmitted
by *Voyager 2* were joined
to outline Jupiter
and reveal its ring.

system and pulled into Jupiter's orbit by the huge planet's gravitational attraction. If this is true, they do not share the same origin and evolution as the rest of the Jovian system.

Voyager 1 gave us our first close-up views of the Galilean satellites. They revealed four planet-sized worlds that differ markedly from one another, as well as from other bodies in the solar system. Through the years, scientists using Earth-based telescopes had determined the orbits and approximate sizes of the Galilean satellites. The *Voyagers* gave us the true sizes.

The four satellites are almost as large as some planets. Io, the closest to Jupiter at a distance of 422,000 kilometers (262,000 miles), has a diameter of 3,650 kilometers (2,270 miles). Europa, 671,000 kilometers (417,000 miles) from Jupiter, has a diameter of 3,130 kilometers (1,940 miles). Earth's Moon has a diameter between the two — 3,476 kilometers (2,160 miles). Ganymede, the largest of the Galilean satellites, is 1,070,000 kilometers (665,000 miles) from Jupiter and has a diameter of 5,280 kilometers (3,280 miles). Callisto, the farthest from Jupiter of the four at a distance of 1,883,000 kilometers (1,170,000 miles), has a diameter of 4,840 kilometers (3,000 miles). These satellites are similar in size to the planet Mercury, which is only 4,880 kilometers (3,030 miles) in diameter.

Like the Galilean satellites, the 14th and 15th orbiting bodies, 1979J1 and 1979J2 — discovered in *Voyager* photos — are considered integral parts of the Jovian system, even though each is less than 100 kilometers (60 miles) in diameter. Their orbits are inside those of the major satellites — 1979J1 circles Jupiter at a distance of 129,000 kilometers (80,000 miles), and 1979J2 orbits the planet at 285,000 kilometers (178,000 miles).

While we have derived a great deal of our information about the satellites from the pictures returned by *Voyager* cameras, a significant amount of knowledge has also come from the probes' spectrometers, which transmit vital data on surface composition, and from the photometer, which measures surface brightness.

Using all three methods, we learned that both Callisto and Ganymede have ancient icy surfaces that are similar, but with certain important differences. Both appear relatively dark. Callisto's surface reflectivity, calculated from brightness measurements, is only 17 per cent. Ganymede's is 43 per cent. The crater-scarred surface of Callisto appears as it must have looked 4 billion years ago. In addition to small craters, there is evidence of three major collisions.

Parts of Ganymede's surface resemble that of Callisto. But vast regions, where portions of Ganymede's icy crust were compressed and sheared into tortuous patterns of ridges and grooves, suggest internal activity long ago. Some geologists believe that this activity was similar to tectonic activity on Earth, in which immense plates of rock drift and collide, creating ocean basins and mountain ranges. On Ganymede, however, the crustal plates are made of water ice.

We also found that Europa has an icy surface, but nothing like those of Callisto and Ganymede. Europa has a thin ice crust that

A plume of an eruption on Io's surface, *right,* was first noticed on a *Voyager* photo by Linda Morabito, *far right.* It established that Io has active volcanoes. These eruptions may be caused when cold sulfur dioxide interacts with hot molten sulfur, *below,* to create pressure that ejects the material violently through the crust of the satellite.

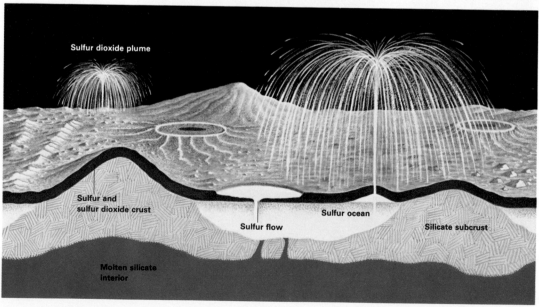

Sulfur dioxide plume

Sulfur and sulfur dioxide crust

Sulfur flow

Sulfur ocean

Silicate subcrust

Molten silicate interior

scientists believe may be only 40 to 50 kilometers (25 to 30 miles) thick. Europa's internal activity has been sufficient to destroy evidence of all but a few badly degraded impact craters. However, its frozen, nearly white surface, the brightest of all the major satellites with a surface reflectivity of 64 per cent, is crisscrossed with long bright and dark lines that resemble cracks. Although *Voyager* scientists know less about the surface of Europa than about any of the other Galilean satellites, some of them believe that Europa's surface is still mildly active. The ice covering its thin crust may still be soft and, like a glacier, it could flow over Europa's surface. This would erase all the rugged surface features.

Before the *Voyager 1* encounter, the one Galilean satellite we really felt comfortable about was Io. We had expected that its surface, lacking ice, would look much like a red-orange version of our own Moon. We could not have been more wrong. As each successively closer picture of Io appeared on our television screens at JPL without showing signs of even one lunarlike crater, we stared in utter disbelief. Clearly, some extraordinarily active process was obliterating Io's craters at a rate unknown elsewhere in the solar system. By the time the spacecraft made its closest approach to Io on March 5, we realized from the appearance of the satellite's surface that this process had to be volcanic activity. But we could hardly contain our disappointment at not seeing a single volcanic eruption in progress. As it turned out, the most remarkable finding of the entire planetary space program was about to be photographed, and its discovery was only days away.

JPL engineer Linda A. Morabito made the actual discovery on March 9. Examining some overexposed, long-range photos of Io taken for navigation purposes, she noted an enormous bright plume rising above the satellite's surface. She checked and rechecked her interpretation of the image and finally concluded that the plume did indeed mean that active volcanoes existed on Io.

Evidence for ancient and extinct volcanic activity exists on the Moon, Mars, and Mercury. But Io is the only body in the solar system, besides Earth, known to be volcanically active now. Its upheavals are more frequent and more widespread than those on Earth. *Voyager 1* observed the plumes of eight erupting volcanoes. *Voyager 2* showed that only one of those had stopped erupting four months later. However, two new centers of volcanic activity had formed during that brief interval.

Although it came as a complete surprise, scientists had a hint as early as 1973 that some very active processes, involving sodium and sulfur atoms, might be occurring either on Io or somewhere near it. At that time, physicist Robert A. Brown, then a student at Harvard University in Cambridge, Mass., used a ground-based optical telescope equipped with a spectrograph to discover a cloud of sodium around Io. Then, astrophysicist Irena Kupo and her associates at Tel Aviv University in Israel discovered a similar cloud of sulfur near the satellite in 1975. Four years later, several instruments, including charged-particle detectors, spectroscopes, and cameras on *Voyager 1* found the sulfur's source in volcanic eruptions on what is surely the geologically most active body in the solar system.

Although the explosive volcanoes on Io are much more violent than similar explosive volcanoes on Earth, the processes involved seem to be almost exactly parallel. A violent, explosive eruption occurs on Earth when ground water at a temperature of about 0° to 30°C (32° to 86°F.) comes into contact with magma — molten rock — at the exceedingly high temperature of about 1200°C (2200°F.). The water turns to steam, and the high pressure of this steam trapped underground triggers the explosion.

Similarly, I believe that violent eruptions occur on Io when cold sulfur dioxide of about −75°C (−103°F.) comes into contact with molten sulfur at a temperature of about 115°C (240°F.). Although this volcanism is "cool" compared with the kind found on Earth, it tends to be more violent. Particles and gas ejected from even the least energetic of the volcanic vents I observed on the *Voyager* views of Io had velocities of 1,800 kph (1,100 mph), and one vent ejected material at 3,600 kph (2,200 mph). By contrast, the highest velocity at which particles from a volcano on Earth travel is about 700 kph (435 mph). This is largely because of resistance from Earth's atmosphere.

According to astrophysicist Stanton J. Peale and his associates at the University of California, Santa Barbara, the energy that drives Io's volcanoes is probably associated with the tidal forces raised by nearby Jupiter. It works like this: Io's orbit around Jupiter is distorted slightly from the circular by the gravitational pull of the other satellites, especially Europa. Then, as Io periodically moves in this eccentric orbit, Jupiter's strong gravitational field pulls on it and actually stretches and flexes the satellite's crust. This friction causes huge amounts of heat to build up in Io's interior, and volcanoes are formed to get rid of the excessive heat.

Many planetary astronomers believe that such tidal heating is sufficient to melt Io's entire interior and turn it into molten silicate magma, leaving only a 20-kilometer (12-mile)-thick silicate crust covered by several kilometers of molten and solid sulfur and sulfur compounds. Io's unique surface color, ranging from reddish-orange to white and almost as bright as Europa's with 63 per cent surface reflectivity, probably results from a fallout mixture of elemental sulfur and sulfur dioxide "snow." So much solidified sulfur and sulfur dioxide snow falls from the volcanic plumes that Io's surface is probably buried and completely recycled over a time period that is remarkably short in geologic terms. Even 10 years from now, the surface of Io might be changed noticeably, and in 100 years, it might be unrecognizable.

The knowledge we gain from the detailed study of another planet may help us understand the birth and growth of Earth. Furthermore, when we try to learn more about how our solar system took form and developed, we often 'find it frustrating to have only one such system upon which to base our conclusions. Telescopic and spacecraft studies of the Jovian system may provide answers to a number of terrestrial and solar system questions.

For example, similarities between Jupiter's turbulent atmosphere and that of Earth's equatorial regions may help scientists to better understand the meteorology of those regions. The volcanism on Io, though different in several ways from the terrestrial type, provides geologists with another set of physical conditions with which to test their theories about volcanic action on Earth.

How similar are the Jupiter system and the solar system? Telescopic and spacecraft observations highlight their similarities. Most of the mass in both groups is concentrated in the central body — 99.87 per cent in the case of the Sun and 99.8 per cent in the case of Jupiter. Another obvious likeness is that several smaller bodies revolve around the central body in orbits that are nearly in the same plane. Regular spacing exists between the orbits of the smaller bodies also. There is a tendency in both systems for the density of orbiting bodies to decrease with increasing distance from the central body.

These similarities suggest that there should also be similarities in the origin and evolution of the Jupiter system and the solar system. For example, the generally accepted theory states that the central body was very hot during the early stages of its formation. As a result, the surrounding material from which the smaller bodies were formed may have undergone a kind of distilling process called fractionation. In this process, a mixture of elements is separated into portions having different properties. Fractionation seems to have resulted in those planets closer to the Sun — and satellites closer to Jupiter — being rich in refractory materials, such as metal oxides, which are very hard to vaporize, and silicates. Planets farther from the Sun — and satellites farther from Jupiter — tend to be rich in volatile, or easy to vaporize, materials, such as water.

The more examples of similar things that scientists have to study, the more they can refine their theories. The close-up views and the volumes of data on the Jovian system returned by the *Voyager* mission have doubled planetary astronomers' research opportunities.

Voyager scientists are continuing to study the more than 30,000 photos returned by the spacecraft. We still do not understand thoroughly many of the missions' remarkable findings. In order to re-examine activities that change with time and to improve our knowledge of the Jupiter system in general, NASA plans to launch two *Galileo* spacecraft in 1983. This mission will collect data on Jupiter's atmosphere and its satellites from orbit and send a probe deep into the planet's atmosphere to study its physical and chemical properties. Like *Voyager,* we expect *Galileo* to add to our knowledge and understanding of the amazing Jovian realm.

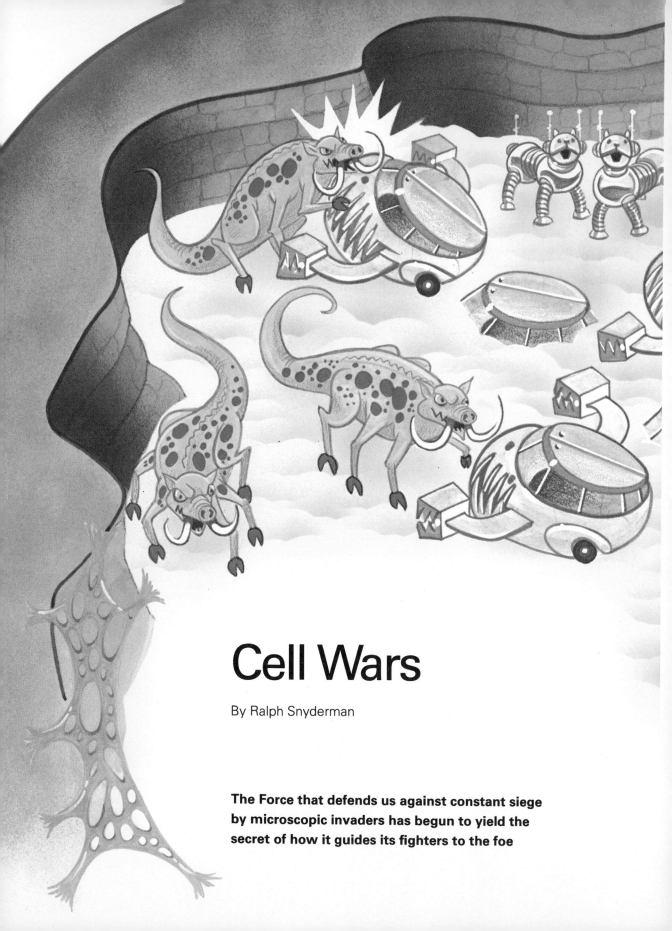

Cell Wars

By Ralph Snyderman

The Force that defends us against constant siege by microscopic invaders has begun to yield the secret of how it guides its fighters to the foe

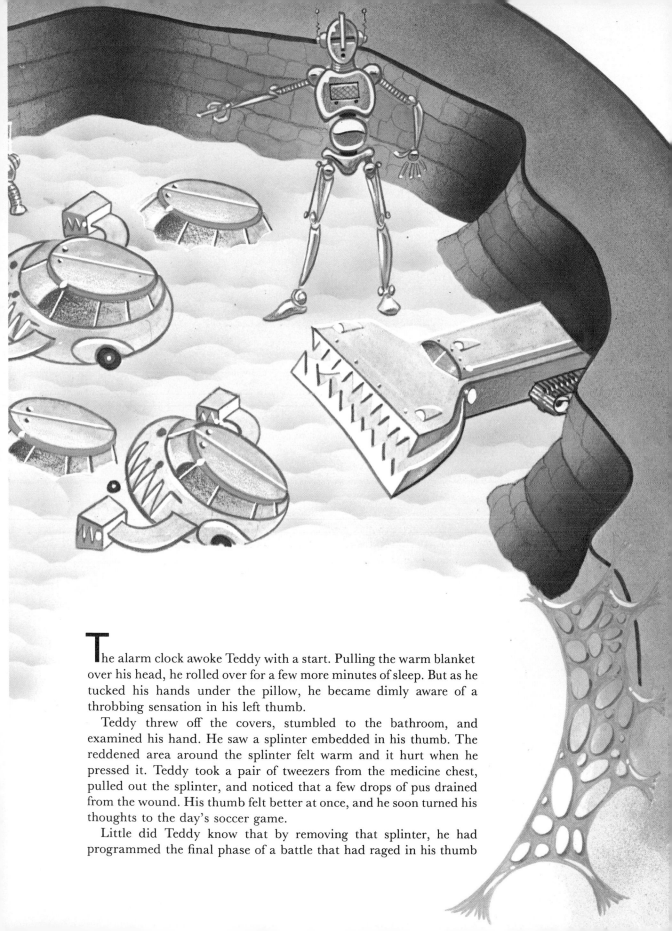

The alarm clock awoke Teddy with a start. Pulling the warm blanket over his head, he rolled over for a few more minutes of sleep. But as he tucked his hands under the pillow, he became dimly aware of a throbbing sensation in his left thumb.

Teddy threw off the covers, stumbled to the bathroom, and examined his hand. He saw a splinter embedded in his thumb. The reddened area around the splinter felt warm and it hurt when he pressed it. Teddy took a pair of tweezers from the medicine chest, pulled out the splinter, and noticed that a few drops of pus drained from the wound. His thumb felt better at once, and he soon turned his thoughts to the day's soccer game.

Little did Teddy know that by removing that splinter, he had programmed the final phase of a battle that had raged in his thumb

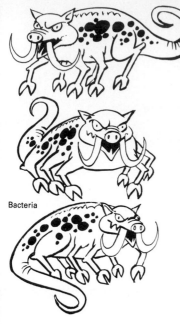

Bacteria

while he slept. Nor was he aware that his very survival had depended upon his body's ability to win that battle.

The battle in Teddy's thumb is one example of inflammation, a term applied to the wars waged in our bodies each day as we continually struggle for survival in a hostile environment. Our bodies must be constantly on guard against a host of enemy agents such as bacteria, fungi, and viruses that may enter the body through the skin or respiratory system. In the case of cancer, the enemy is our own renegade cells. Fortunately, we are protected by the immune system, a powerful army of molecules and cells, that defends us against each new attack through its constant vigilance and rapid mobilization.

Although the wars of inflammation can range from the brief skirmish triggered by a splinter to the full-scale war of a bacterial pneumonia, each battle is accompanied by the same four signs — redness, swelling, heat, and pain. Roman physicians noted these signs almost 2,000 years ago, but only in this century have scientists begun to understand exactly how the body responds during the complex process of inflammation.

When, for example, the splinter and its invading unit of bacteria penetrated Teddy's hand, a border patrol of roving molecules, or scouts, detected the invasion. They alerted the body's signal corps, a complex chemical system, to broadcast an alarm and prepare for battle. The signal corps cleared pathways to the battle site and walled off the battlefield to keep the invasion from spreading. They also called fighting divisions of white blood cells to the area.

The first fighting division to arrive on the scene was composed of neutrophils, short-lived white blood cells built for speed and a quick kill. A division of macrophages — larger and slower white cells — arrived a few hours later to wipe out bacteria missed by the neutrophils and mop up neutrophil casualties and damaged cells. Lymphocytes, a third group of white blood cells, served as field commanders during the battle. They developed the battle strategy, and made backup plans in case the initial skirmishes were lost.

As the battle against the bacteria raged, serum, the fluid in the bloodstream that transported white blood cells to the battle site, leaked into the tissues, causing the area to swell. The mounting casualties gradually formed a pool of pus — serum and white blood cells — at the center of the battle, around the splinter. The pus and swollen tissues pressed against nerve endings, producing pain. The pain, which drew Teddy's attention to his hand, eased when he removed the splinter, relieving the pressure by releasing the pus.

With the splinter removed and the bacterial invaders destroyed by the battalions of white cells, Teddy's body began to mobilize for repair. The macrophage battalion mopped up the rest of the mess and a repair crew composed of fibroblasts — cells capable of producing new connective tissue — moved into the site. Skin and capillary cells began to regenerate. The healing process was complete within a week.

The author:
Ralph Snyderman is chief, Division of Rheumatic and Genetic Diseases at Duke University Medical Center in Durham, N.C.

The intensity of the war, or inflammation, depends in part on the size, strength, and cunning of the invading army. Some invasions are taken care of simply by wandering macrophages before the inflammation process even sets in. In other cases, the invaders may be difficult to destroy or can by-pass the chemical alarm system in some way. In such cases the battle may rage on indefinitely, seriously damaging body tissues.

Of the three branches that make up the body's immune system army, the molecular scouts are the first to respond to the invasion. They must be able to quickly identify any invader anywhere in the body, but need only distinguish the invader from the body's own cells. These molecules constantly patrol the bloodstream and the spaces between the tissues and, like watchdogs responding to unfamiliar sounds or vibrations, react to electrical charges on the surface of alien molecules and sound a chemical alarm.

Lymphocytes are more complicated and have more responsibility. These cells play a dual role in the immune system. As scouts, they must be able to identify thousands of different types of invaders. They can do this because they can remember which invaders the body has encountered before. Macrophages provide information about specific invaders to the lymphocytes. The lymphocytes use that information to produce antibodies, molecules that can identify specific invaders by the antigens, or molecular dog tags, on their surfaces. Each antibody recognizes the antigen of one specific virus or bacteria that had invaded your body previously. During your lifetime, your lymphocytes will produce thousands of types of antibodies. These constantly patrol your bloodstream.

When the antibody makes contact with the antigen it has been tracking, it notifies the signal corps to call out the fighters. The signal corps is perhaps the most complex of the three branches of the immune system army. It includes a series of messenger molecules, called the complement system that circulate in the blood and tissue fluids. The complement system works something like a chain letter. Either a circulating scout molecule or an antibody combined with an antigen reacts with the first signal corps molecule in the complement system. It then reacts with dozens of second-level molecules. The activity continues until, by the time the fifth level has been activated, thousands of messenger molecules are spreading word of the invasion.

Complement messengers prepare access routes to the battle site. They produce chemical reactions that slow the blood flow around the battle area and widen the pores in blood vessel walls. This enables messengers and fighters to leave the bloodstream more easily and move to the battle site in the tissues. Some complement messengers produce a chemical beacon that radiates from the site of the invasion. Fighters follow that beacon to the battle site.

The lymphokines are another type of molecular messenger. When a lymphocyte, in its alternate role as a member of the signal corps,

Glossary

Chemotaxis: Movement of a cell toward a chemical.

Complement system: Chain of messenger molecules that directs fighter cells to the invader.

Fibroblast: Repair cell.

Lymphocyte: White blood cell that directs defense against a recognized invader.

Macrophage: White blood cell that cleans up invaders and battle debris.

Neutrophil: Fast-moving, short-lived, fighting white blood cell.

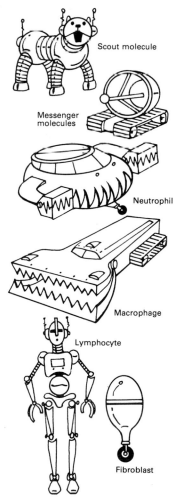

Scout molecule

Messenger molecules

Neutrophil

Macrophage

Lymphocyte

Fibroblast

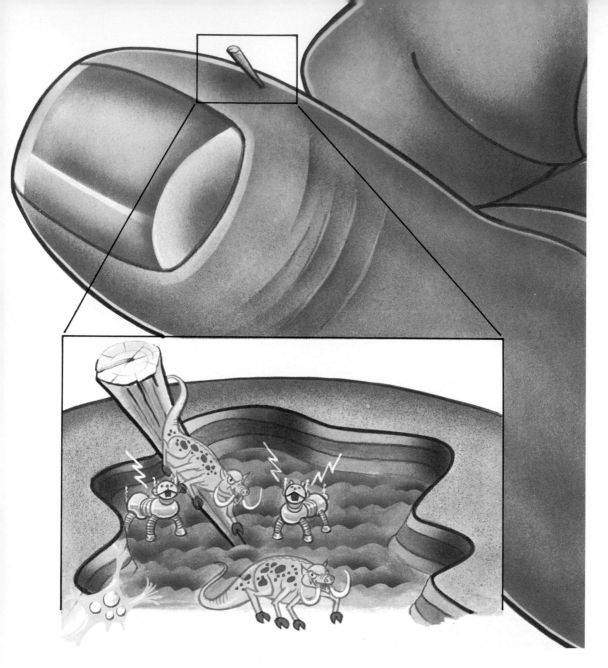

Invasion Alert
As a splinter carrying bacteria penetrates the thumb, roving scout or "watchdog" molecules detect an alien presence and sound an alert to the body's immune system.

spots a familiar invader, it produces lymphokines, which call fighter cells to the invasion area. The lymphokines also chemically activate these cells so that they are better prepared to destroy the invaders.

When challenged by an unfamiliar invader, lymphocytes rapidly divide and increase their ranks. These new lymphocytes then produce forces of lymphokines and antibodies. In this way, the immune system builds a reserve force of scouts and messengers prepared to deal with that particular invader if it ever attacks again.

The third branch of your immune system army, the fighter unit, is made up of different kinds of white blood cells that respond to the various signal corps messages. They rush through the bloodstream to the battle scene and engulf the invaders and break them down with

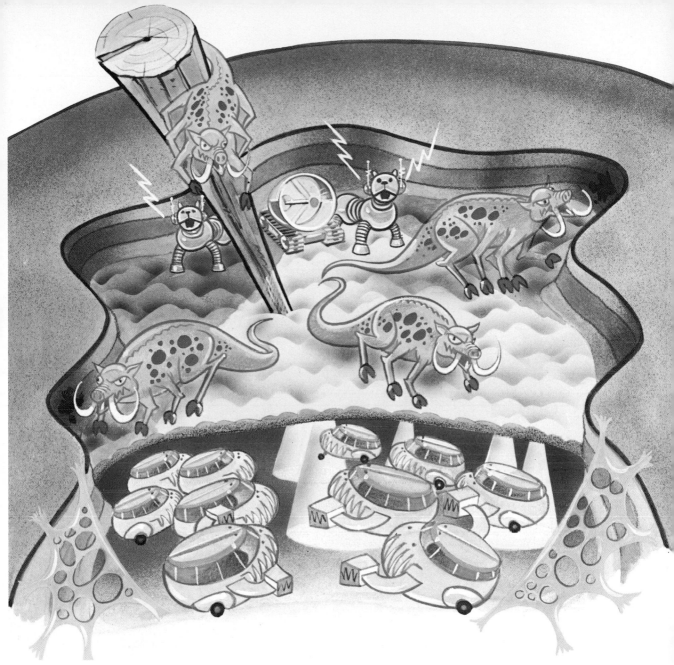

powerful enzymes, proteins that speed up the digestive process. Neutrophils are the first of these. Neutrophils are produced in the bone marrow and spend a short period of time circulating in the bloodstream. When called out, they rush into tissues to form the first line of defense, engulfing and digesting foreign invaders. When the battle is especially intense, the army's demand for fighters can become so great that neutrophils may be called up from the bone marrow before they are fully developed. A doctor sees a large number of underdeveloped neutrophils in a patient's blood count as a sign that the patient may have a severe infection. The neutrophils form a sort of suicide squad. Because they live only a few hours, none of them survives the battle.

Calling Out the Troops
The alarm activates the defense forces. A netlike wall springs up to contain the invasion (foreground), and a chemical beacon of messenger molecules directs neutrophils circulating in the bloodstream to the bacterial foe.

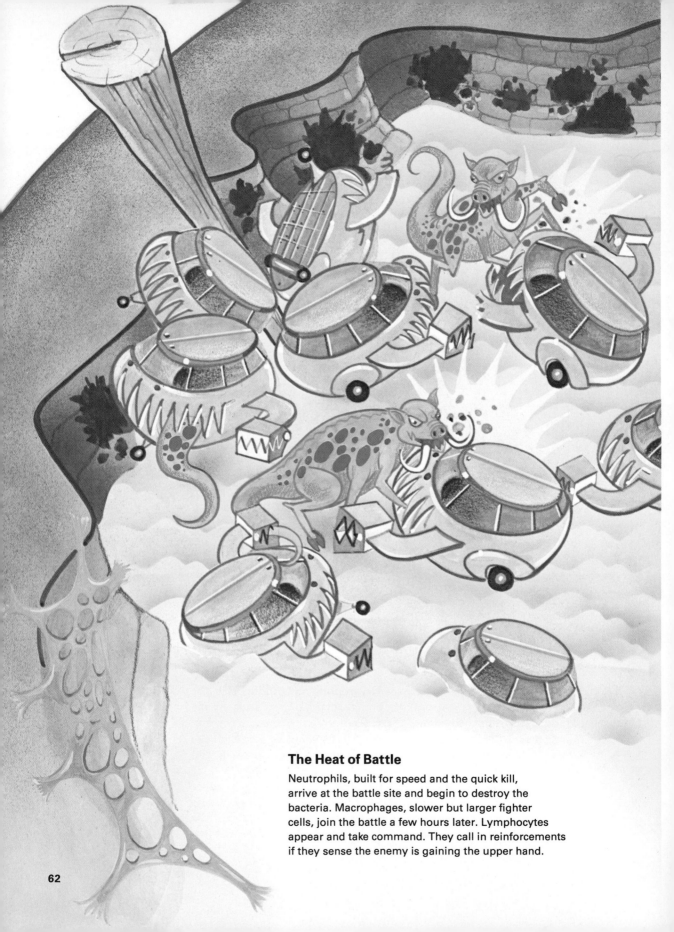

The Heat of Battle

Neutrophils, built for speed and the quick kill,
arrive at the battle site and begin to destroy the
bacteria. Macrophages, slower but larger fighter
cells, join the battle a few hours later. Lymphocytes
appear and take command. They call in reinforcements
if they sense the enemy is gaining the upper hand.

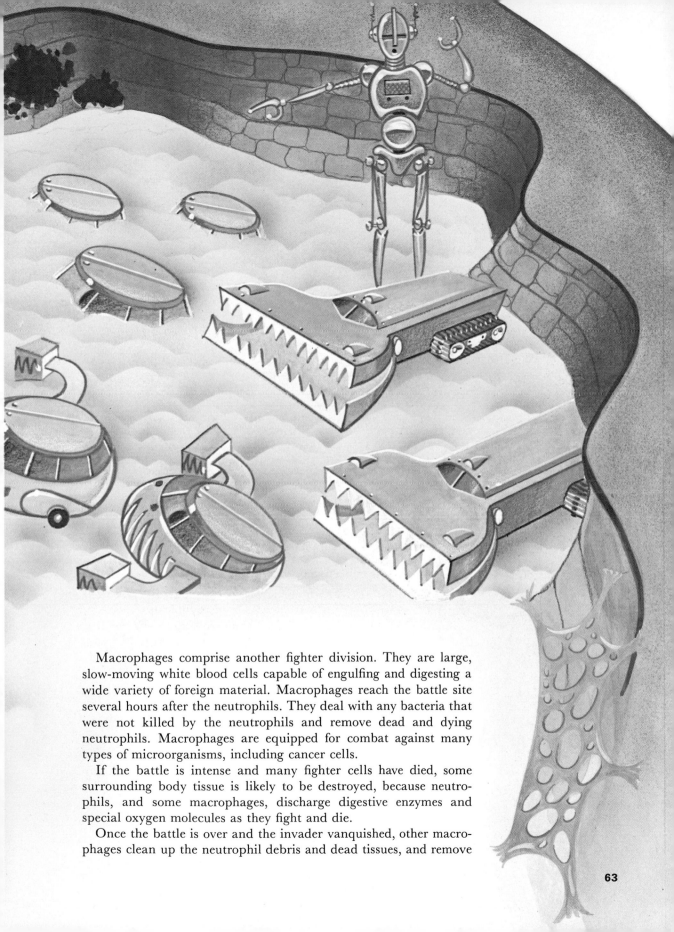

Macrophages comprise another fighter division. They are large, slow-moving white blood cells capable of engulfing and digesting a wide variety of foreign material. Macrophages reach the battle site several hours after the neutrophils. They deal with any bacteria that were not killed by the neutrophils and remove dead and dying neutrophils. Macrophages are equipped for combat against many types of microorganisms, including cancer cells.

If the battle is intense and many fighter cells have died, some surrounding body tissue is likely to be destroyed, because neutrophils, and some macrophages, discharge digestive enzymes and special oxygen molecules as they fight and die.

Once the battle is over and the invader vanquished, other macrophages clean up the neutrophil debris and dead tissues, and remove

63

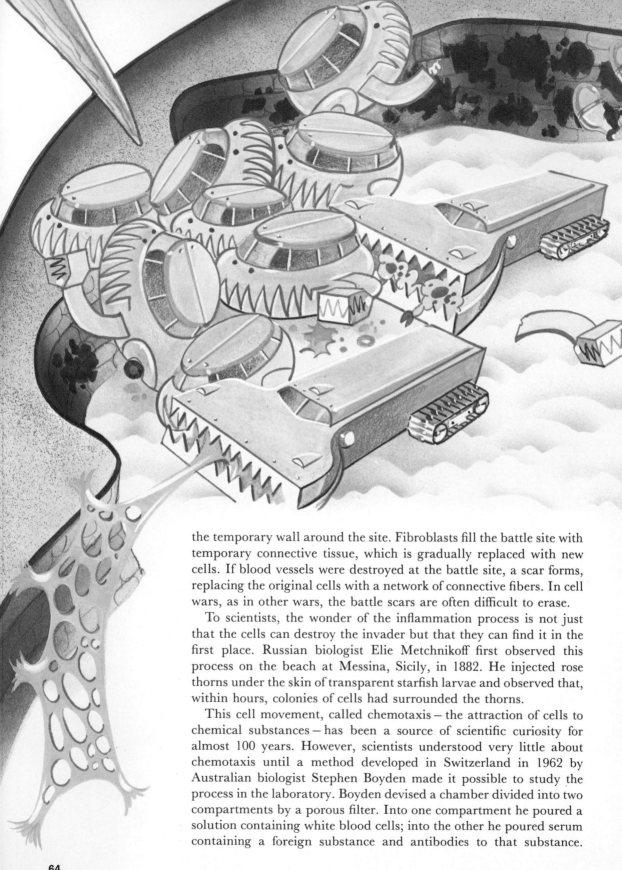

the temporary wall around the site. Fibroblasts fill the battle site with temporary connective tissue, which is gradually replaced with new cells. If blood vessels were destroyed at the battle site, a scar forms, replacing the original cells with a network of connective fibers. In cell wars, as in other wars, the battle scars are often difficult to erase.

To scientists, the wonder of the inflammation process is not just that the cells can destroy the invader but that they can find it in the first place. Russian biologist Elie Metchnikoff first observed this process on the beach at Messina, Sicily, in 1882. He injected rose thorns under the skin of transparent starfish larvae and observed that, within hours, colonies of cells had surrounded the thorns.

This cell movement, called chemotaxis — the attraction of cells to chemical substances — has been a source of scientific curiosity for almost 100 years. However, scientists understood very little about chemotaxis until a method developed in Switzerland in 1962 by Australian biologist Stephen Boyden made it possible to study the process in the laboratory. Boyden devised a chamber divided into two compartments by a porous filter. Into one compartment he poured a solution containing white blood cells; into the other he poured serum containing a foreign substance and antibodies to that substance.

When he checked the chamber a few hours later, he noted that large numbers of the cells had moved from one compartment and through the filter toward the heavier concentration of antibody molecules in the other compartment.

I became interested in how white blood cells were attracted to bacteria in 1967 while working at the National Institutes of Health (NIH) in Bethesda, Md. Using Boyden's technique, I found that chemicals released by bacterial cell walls attracted large numbers of white cells, when exposed to blood serum. By isolating several substances from the serum and testing them by the Boyden method, our group found that one substance, a fragment of the fifth-level complement molecule, was produced when the bacterial products made contact with the serum. This fragment was responsible for attracting blood cells.

Our group and another group working with immunologist Jeorg Jensen at the University of Miami in Florida also tested the effects of this complement fragment in the body. We injected it into the skin of laboratory animals and found that, within hours, the area around the injection site had become inflamed. When we analyzed skin samples taken from the site, we found many white blood cells. We concluded that bacteria did not even have to be present; the complement fragment alone could attract the cells. Similar work in our laboratory and by other researchers showed that lymphokines and other chemicals also attract white cells.

We wondered why white blood cells responded to some chemicals but not to others. My team of researchers at Duke University in Durham, N.C., in conjunction with a team led by Duke biochemist Robert J. Lefkowitz, explored this question in 1977. We knew that white blood cells were incredibly sensitive to small concentrations of certain agents. We reasoned that the white blood cells might have

Winding Down the War
As the battle comes to an end, macrophages clean up remaining bacteria and dead neutrophils and remove the wall around the battle site. Fibroblasts arrive to make temporary repairs to the damaged areas where new tissue cells will later regenerate.

65

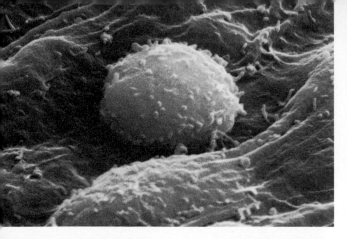

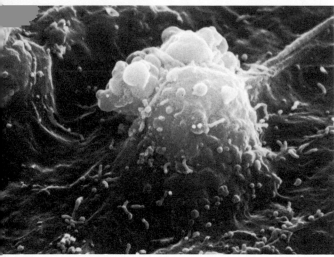

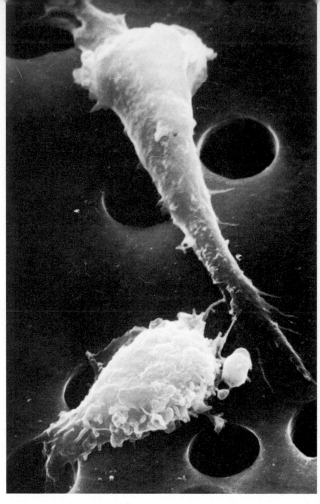

A white blood cell (magnified 10,000 times) on a blood vessel wall, *top left,* eases through the wall, *above left,* toward some nearby foreign substance. White blood cells (magnified 8,000 times), *above right,* crawl through a membrane, attracted toward a chemical that causes them to elongate, developing a broad "head" and narrow "tail."

specific *receptors* (molecules that attach to certain other molecules in a lock and key arrangement) for those particular chemical agents on their surfaces.

To test this theory, we used a valuable discovery made in 1975 by biochemist Elliott Schiffmann at NIH. Schiffmann's team found that certain molecules were chemically similar to substances released by dividing bacteria and could attract neutrophils. We labeled these molecules with radioactive markers and added them to a solution containing neutrophils. We found that the radioactive molecules attached to specific sites on the surface of human neutrophils. There are about 50,000 such receptors on each neutrophil. We found more recently that macrophages also had receptors for the same chemotactic molecules.

We began to find evidence that receptors not only receive the message that an invader is present, but that the receptors also play a role in pointing the cell in the invader's direction. Molecular biologist Marilyn C. Pike, working in our laboratory, found in 1977 that when molecular messengers bind to receptors on a particular side of the white blood cell, they change the membrane on that side of the cell.

These membrane changes cause the cell to stretch toward the highest concentration of messengers.

Studies undertaken in 1979 by Catherine Koo, a graduate student in my laboratory, suggest that when messenger molecules bind to receptors, additional receptors are called to the cell's surface. This process increases the density of receptors, and thus sensitivity to messenger molecules, on that side of the cell.

As we tracked the cells with high-powered electron microscopes, we noticed that as they moved toward the attracting chemicals, they changed shape. Once-spherical cells became longer and more streamlined. In doing so, they appeared to develop a narrow "tail" and broader "head" section.

We are currently studying how the binding process might trigger this type of white cell transformation and movement. We have observed that immediately after the messenger molecules bind to the cells, other changes occur within the cell membranes that are similar to changes in the muscle cell membranes when they contract. The similarity between white blood cells and muscle cells goes even further. White blood cells contain the proteins actin and myosin, which are critical for the contraction of skeletal muscle. We believe that these proteins may contribute to the propulsive force that drives white blood cells to the battle site.

We and others had also observed that for the white cells to move toward their target, they had to develop a kind of skeletal system. We do not yet know exactly how the white blood cells do this, but tubulin, a protein found in white blood cells, seems to be necessary for the skeleton to form. The binding of messenger molecules to white cell receptors may trigger tubulin to form bonelike structures, or microtubules, within the cell. The microtubules seem to orient the cell so that it can move directly to the highest concentration of messenger molecules and the invader. The actin and myosin filaments in the white cell contract against the microtubular skeleton to propel it in that direction.

As scientists unravel the mysteries of the normal immune system, they are learning what happens when the inflammation process occasionally goes awry, as it can at any stage. In some persons, the process is defective at birth, resulting in immune deficiency diseases. The most serious of these is called severe combined immune deficiency disease. Children born with this disorder are very susceptible to infections because their lymphocytes failed to develop normally. Their lymphocytes can produce neither the lymphokines nor the antibodies needed to direct the neutrophils and macrophages to the invaders. Unless such children are kept in a sterile environment, they usually die within months because of massive infections.

Hypogammaglobulinemia is another form of immune deficiency that results from the body's failure to produce antibodies. Many individuals with this disorder develop severe, recurrent bacterial infections because the body has no way to specifically recognize returning invaders.

Some children are born with abnormal neutrophils. In chronic granulomatous disease, for example, the neutrophils cannot produce hydrogen peroxide, one of the chemicals needed to kill many types of bacteria. Victims are plagued with recurrent skin, lung, and bone infections, and many die in early childhood.

Other diseases have been traced to the white blood cells' inability to get to the battle site. In one rare condition, the Chediak-Higashi syndrome, the sacs containing enzymes inside the cell are so much larger than normal that the fighter is too weighed down by his artillery to move. In another, the "lazy leucocyte syndrome," many of the cells seem to be unable to get out of the bone marrow and into the bloodstream to be transported to the invasion site. Victims of these conditions are very susceptible to infections.

Other immune system defects can result in continuing inflammatory diseases. For unknown reasons, the immune systems in some persons appear to identify normal body tissues as foreign, and the body's white blood cells attack and destroy these tissues as though they were invaders. Once the battle begins, it is difficult to stop it; the "enemy" is everywhere, and the body becomes host to an endless civil war. One such autoimmune disease, rheumatoid arthritis, destroys the joints. In another, systemic lupus erythematosus, almost any body organ can be attacked; and if the kidneys, brain, or heart become the target, the disease is fatal.

In addition to protecting us from viruses, bacteria, and other outside invaders, many immunologists believe that the immune system also protects us against the development and spread of cancer. It is now apparent that the immune system of a cancer patient recognizes that cancerous tissue has developed. In some instances, it can be shown that the immune system has reacted and destroyed cancerous tissue. Scientists are now beginning to understand this process. Some scientists believe that cancer develops in all of us periodically, but that our immune systems routinely detect tissues that have been transformed from noncancerous to cancerous. In fact, they believe that most cancer cells are destroyed by the immune system without the person ever knowing about it.

How, then, do some cancer cells continue to grow and to evade detection? In 1975, we began to explore the possibility that some cancer cells may have chemical passwords that allow them to sneak by the molecular scouts, so the immune system cannot detect them until they are far too numerous to destroy. We suspected that certain tumor cells produce substances that prevent macrophages from finding and destroying them.

To test this theory, we put a solution of macrophages in one compartment of a Boyden chamber and a chemical agent in the second. When we checked the second compartment a few hours later, we found large numbers of macrophages in it, indicating that the chemical was a powerful attractant for the macrophages. Then we repeated the experiment, but added a substance secreted by tumor cells to the macrophages in the Boyden chamber. When we checked both chambers after a few hours, we found that few macrophages had moved across the filter. We concluded that something in the tumor cell secretion had kept the macrophages from responding to the chemical message.

To see if this held true in the body as well, we inoculated laboratory mice with tumor cells. When the tumor cells began to multiply, we injected the mice's abdomens with a chemical that produces a localized inflammatory reaction in the skin. We injected the abdomens of tumor-free mice with the same irritant. The next day we took fluid samples from the abdomens of mice in both groups and found that many macrophages had arrived at the inflammation site in the tumor-free mice, but we found that few macrophages had clustered around the injection site in the mice with tumors. These findings confirmed our earlier conclusions.

We are now working to purify the tumor secretion responsible for blocking the macrophages' ability to respond to chemical messages. When we do so, we may be able to develop an antibody to this secretion. We hope then to use the antibody as a vaccine against this blocking action.

During the 1970s, scientists discovered some ways to strengthen and restrain the immune system army, but our understanding is still quite limited. Periodic injections of gamma globulin, a blood protein containing many antibodies, can reinforce the army in victims of hypogammaglobulinemia. We are still trying to find out exactly how aspirin, a valuable weapon in the war against arthritis, reduces inflammation. It may scramble the chemical message that mobilizes white cells against the victim's own tissues. We have found that corticosteroids, a group of hormones, can offer some protection to lupus and arthritis victims against their rebel immune forces, but we know very little about how they do so. Teams of researchers also are investigating the possibility that interferon, a natural antiviral protein, (see THE ELUSIVE PROMISE OF INTERFERON, *Science Year,* 1980) and certain synthetic drugs can improve the immune system's ability to kill cancerous tissues.

The more we learn about the body's defense system, the more we realize what a marvelous force it is. Scientists are continuing to discover new ranks of soldiers in the immune system army and to observe greater complexity in its maneuvers. In addition to gathering information about this army, we are trying to find ways in which we can come to its aid when necessary. Perhaps, when we can more skillfully control its maneuvers, we may be better able to prevent and treat severe recurrent infections, control chronic inflammatory diseases, and even cure cancer.

Watch on the Self-Healing Earth

By Eric D. Schneider

The coast of Brittany has become an international ecological laboratory in which scientists are studying the long-range effects of a massive oil spill

I stood on the high dunes east of the village of Portsall in November 1979 and surveyed the Brittany coast of northwestern France. It is one of the most beautiful coasts in the world, with broad, sandy beaches, great rock formations and cliffs, and many small estuaries where the sea flows inland to meet rivers. But when I looked at the shore carefully, I saw traces of sticky black oil on the rocks and oozing from muddy sediments. About 1,800 meters (6,000 feet) offshore loomed the broken bow of the supertanker *Amoco Cadiz* – a mute reminder of the massive oil spill that occurred here 20 months before.

For centuries, this rocky coast at the entrance to the English Channel has been the site of shipwrecks. High winds, rough seas, and near-record tides in the area have carried many ships off course onto its rocky coast or one of the many offshore islands. This had been the fate of the *Amoco Cadiz,* a supertanker about 365 meters (1,200 feet) long, which went aground on offshore rocks on March 17, 1978. The tanker broke in two and dumped about 1.6 million barrels of Arabian and Iranian crude oil into the sea.

I first saw the wreck on March 24, 1978, almost a week after the tanker went aground. As director of the United States Environmental Protection Agency's (EPA) Environmental Research Laboratory at Narragansett, R.I., I had been asked to bring a team of investigators to aid French scientists in assessing the impact of the spill.

As the wind and cold fog bit into my face on that late winter day, I surveyed a scene of havoc. The tanker looked like a beached and broken sea monster, with each cresting wave carrying more brown fluid from its bleeding body. Oil covered the water, coated the coast, and generated gases that filled the air. Storms and fierce winds had raged for days, and the oil was being pushed and carried by the same treacherous tides and currents that had driven the *Amoco Cadiz* aground in the first place. In places, the heavy thickness of the oil caused the waves to churn the oil into the sediments — layers of sand and silt — both offshore and onshore. Contrary to the old saying, oil and water do mix in an oil spill. The ocean waters, by mixing with the oil, hasten its distribution. Each tide or shift in the wind carried the oil in some new, unpredictable path, spreading the oil slick from beach to beach and into the river estuaries. Oil poured from the wreck for about 14 days and eventually polluted more than 645 kilometers (400 miles) of shoreline. Because of the high winds and tides, virtually no oil was collected at sea.

All along the coast, I saw men, women, and children pushing, shoving, and carrying oil off the beaches. Thousands of French troops joined local residents in a hopeless struggle to keep the seemingly endless waves of oil from flooding ashore. Other soldiers blocked roads to keep away the curious. I cannot forget their unhappiness and despair, nor can I forget their determination as they toiled in the cleanup effort.

As an ecologist, I tried to imagine the reaction of animals to the oil's rude intrusion. How does a sponge, which cannot wander from its home on the sea floor, react to the first taste of oil? Is it numbed painlessly to sleep, or does it scream at the threat and try to cling to life? Local ornithologists said later that the land birds smelled the oil coming and left their nesting grounds. Some fish species probably also smelled the oil in the water and fled. Other fish apparently confused the taste or smell of the oil with natural organic compounds in the water and were trapped by the black tide.

For years, scientists have debated the potential impact of oil spills. They have studied small spills and recorded the impact of oil on animals in laboratory experiments. The results of such studies were either contradictory or inconclusive. Some scientists thought that oil accidents, such as the huge leak from an underwater well off Santa Barbara, Calif., in 1969, caused little biological damage. Others

The author:
Eric D. Schneider is a research associate at the Center for Ocean Management, University of Rhode Island at Kingston.

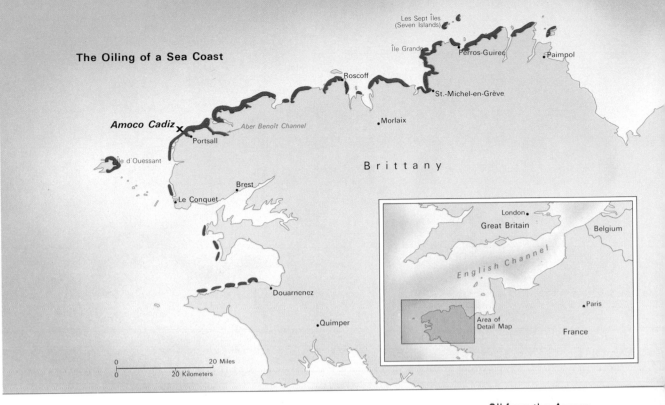

The Oiling of a Sea Coast

Les Sept Îles
(Seven Islands)

Île Grande

Perros-Guirec

Paimpol

Roscoff

St.-Michel-en-Grève

Amoco Cadiz ✕

Aber Benoît Channel

Morlaix

Portsall

Île d'Ouessant

Brittany

Brest

Le Conquet

London

Great Britain

Belgium

English Channel

Paris

France

Area of
Detail Map

Douarnenez

Quimper

0   20 Miles
0   20 Kilometers

Oil from the *Amoco Cadiz* spill spread along the Brittany coast of France in March 1978. The shaded area marks the 393 kilometers (244 miles) of coastline covered by the oil a few days after the spill.

reported that even a small spill such as that from a fuel-oil barge off Falmouth, Mass., in 1969 took a high toll among some species. In laboratory studies, scientists found that some species of small fish can live in fairly high concentrations of oil in seawater, while other marine animals, such as the lobster, do not feed properly even when the levels of oil contamination are very low.

The *Amoco Cadiz* tragedy was the first major oil spill to be studied thoroughly. The government of France asked an international team of scientists to assess the impact of what local residents called *marée noire* (black tide) on their ecosystem — the complex of living and nonliving things, including animals, plants, rocks, sediments, and water that occupy the area. In Brittany, the ecosystem includes humans and their fishing industry, as well as oyster beds, birds, tiny marine animals, aquatic plants, the ocean, rivers and their estuaries, sandy beaches, and the rocky coast. The coast of Brittany had become a giant macabre laboratory and scientists would witness mass changes in this complex marine ecosystem.

I spent that first day driving and walking along the coast. I saw oil everywhere — on the high rocky cliffs, in small estuaries, and on sandy beaches. That evening, my team and I — along with French government officials, industry representatives, and other scientists — received a full briefing on the spill. The meeting was held near Brest at the research headquarters set up at the French National Oceanographic Laboratory known as Centre Oceanographique de Bretagne (COB). We learned about studies that were already underway. For

example, a team of scientists from the United States had landed in France just hours after the *Amoco Cadiz* went on the rocks. These were members of the Spilled Oil Research Team of the U.S. National Oceanic and Atmospheric Agency (NOAA). They hired a helicopter and a light plane soon after they arrived and began producing daily maps showing the progress of the oil along the shore. Some of them measured the thickness of the oil along the coast, mapped its spread, and observed damage to plants and animals, photographing the scene in detail.

Claude J. M. Chasse, head of marine research at the University of Western Brittany, described his biological observation program. More than 600 of his students were counting dead animals at 180 stations along 200 kilometers (125 miles) of the coast. Chasse's students continued to monitor the shoreline populations for months

and his studies later proved to be among the most valuable in following the developments caused by the spill.

We heard from a representative of the Society for the Study and Protection of Nature of Brittany, which organized volunteers to collect birds that had been covered with oil. He reported that most of the birds were dead, but surviving animals were taken to bird-cleaning "hospitals" run by volunteers.

Scientists from the Roscoff Laboratory, about 50 kilometers (31 miles) up the coast, told how they were doubly affected. With more than a century of data collected from these waters, they felt a kinship with the marine organisms of the Brittany coast. And their facility — located right on the coast — had been inundated by the spill. The government tried to erect floating booms — air-filled tubes — to wall off the oil from their laboratory, but the strong winds and tides blew

The oil spill ravaged a normally scenic Portsall beach in Brittany, *above left*. An oil-soaked razorbill, *top*, was just one of thousands of birds — most of which died — that were victimized by the spill. Limpets, *above*, which were also covered with oil, usually survived.

Joining in a cooperative, but futile, effort to clean the area, French army troops, *above,* dispose of newspapers used to soak up the oil from the beach. While local fire fighters, *above, right,* wash down an embankment with high-pressure hoses, other citizens scrub oil from nearby rocks, *left.*

Volunteers try to clean
an oil-soaked guillemot
at a bird hospital
set up at Trégastel
just after the spill.

the booms about like straw. The Roscoff staff then had to close down
their beach-front aquariums to keep out the ocean, now laden with
oil, that normally supplied them with water. They also told us that
local oyster farmers had to destroy more than 100 million oysters
because the oyster beds were coated with oil.

At the end of the briefing, biologist Lucien Laubier, director of the
COB laboratory, invited the participating scientists to form an
international team to study the long-range effects of the spill. We
agreed to develop an integrated study that would tie together all
relevant factors. The kinds of questions that needed to be asked
included: Were there enough oil-eating bacteria in the area around
the Brittany coast to remove a substantial amount of the spilled oil?
What impact would the oil spill have on such economically valuable
species as fish, lobster, oysters, mussels, and seaweed?

The need for a team of experts in several fields was obvious. For
example, crude oil is a complex mixture of organic compounds, and
care must be taken to distinguish natural hydrocarbons normally
found in seawater from the hydrocarbons of the oil. Organic chemists
can measure petroleum-derived compounds to a very precise level of
one part per billion. However, they need the most up-to-date

equipment, and the cost of analyzing a single seawater sample can exceed $1,000.

The chemists' preliminary analyses indicated the need for further studies. They informed us that some of the oil was vaporizing, becoming gas, so that about 40 per cent of the hydrocarbons were moving into the atmosphere. The gases created a strong odor, noticeable as far as 32 kilometers (20 miles) inland, and some researchers said that the fumes had caused mild illness among residents along the coast.

The next morning, my U.S. team of EPA and university scientists decided we could best aid the French by splitting into two field teams to visit coastal areas and sample the organisms in the sediment. We had come prepared with special sampling equipment and storage containers so that we could take samples from France and analyze them later at our laboratories in the United States. Only one member of our group spoke fluent French. The rest of us had to rely on high school French and lots of arm waving to get past the military road-blocks along the coast.

The work went on for two weeks. Every evening our field teams would meet to report on the day's results. The "beach boys," an NOAA team, usually covered more ground than did other groups. On the fourth day, they reported that they had found a salt marsh flooded with oil near the town of Île Grande, about 160 kilometers (100 miles) from the site of the wreck. With the wind blowing hard for days, the marsh — at the end of a long bay — had become a catch basin for the oil. Such tidal flats can hold oil in their sediments for years.

The following day, three of us drove to Île Grande. All along the coast, people were still mopping up oil. No sooner was a beach cleaned than the next tide or wind change would bring in another blanket of oil.

Near St. Michel-en-Greve, the shore seemed to be littered with white shells. When we stopped and walked across an oil line left by the last highest tide, we saw that the beach was a giant graveyard, with millions of dead sea urchins, razor clams, and cockles lying on the sand. Biologist Jeffrey L. Hyland of our EPA lab had visited this beach the day before and had seen no evidence of such a kill. That evening, we learned that chemists had measured oil dispersed in the ocean water at levels ranging from 100 parts per billion to 4,000 parts per billion. Apparently, the higher concentrations had killed the sea urchins, razor clams, and cockles — bottom-dwelling organisms that live in one spot and cannot move.

Curiously, the tidepools of a nearby beach teemed with life. Evidently, the beach was located in a place that was sheltered from the prevailing winds.

Despite the damage we had seen in many places, we were not prepared for what we saw at the Île Grande salt marsh. It had become just a cove of oil. Only the tips of the taller plants stuck up above the

Biologist Louis Cabrioch
(right) and an associate
on the deck of the
research ship *Pluteus II,
above,* examine some
sediment from the ocean
floor to see what effect
the oil may have had on
the tiny plants and
animals living there.
In a cabin below, Serge
Berne, *left,* maps the
spreading of the oil.

oil. A few days later, after the tides and the oil had receded, the marsh looked like a burned-out hayfield.

Another damage site was especially moving – the Seven Island Bird Sanctuary north of the Brittany coast. Oil from another wrecked supertanker, the *Torrey Canyon,* had hit these offshore islands in March 1967. Thousands of birds that had come to the sanctuary for spring mating were caught by that oil as they fed in the ocean water. Now another black tide was menacing the birds.

Our French colleagues arranged for us to meet ornithologists at the Seven Island Bird Sanctuary, so that we could learn how the *Amoco Cadiz* spill had affected the islands. We traveled there in a small boat from the village of Perros-Guirec, accompanied by young French scientists and a retired French colonel, president of a local bird sanctuary. The colonel was anxious to learn the fate of the puffin, a cute black-and-white bird that looks somewhat like a penguin but has a bright red beak. The colony of puffins on the Seven Island Sanctuary represented the southernmost outpost of the bird, which ranges as far north as the Shetland Islands and Iceland. The French considered the puffin an endangered species on the Brittany coast because the *Torrey Canyon* spill had killed more than 10,000 of them, leaving only about 1,400.

As we left the harbor at Perros-Guirec, we noticed patches of oil floating past our boat and oil-coated rocks along the high-tide lines. Approaching the islands, we saw birds circling overhead. Thousands of cormorants and guillemots crowded onto the cliffs. We did not see many dead birds floating in the water, probably because dead birds always sink quickly. Only a small percentage of them ever wash ashore. Guillemots dived into the sea, sometimes picking up oil-coated pieces of seaweed for their nests. I wondered if the oil in the nests would affect their eggs.

As we traveled from island to island, we searched the cliffs and rocks in vain for nesting puffins. Finally, late in the day, a French ornithologist excitedly pointed up at a lone puffin flying with a flock of other birds. It was the only one we saw.

When we returned to Perros-Guirec, we went to the colonel's home, which had been converted to a makeshift bird hospital. Volunteers worked silently there, removing oil from sick-looking birds. They used special solvents and heat lamps to warm the animals. One of the workers told us they could save only 5 per cent of their patients, but they felt the effort was worthwhile.

After the two weeks were up, we had concluded the first portion of our studies. Before leaving, we arranged to meet again in three months. Our French colleagues agreed to host our next meeting at the COB laboratory — a one-day seminar on all the results obtained as of that time, including our U.S. studies and the continuing monitoring program in France. I had been named chairman of an international working group on spilled-oil research.

When we returned to our laboratories in the United States, we found our work had just begun. For example, chemist James Lake and his technicians at our EPA lab in Rhode Island began the time-consuming task of analyzing water samples and oil-contaminated sediments and organisms. Then they had to coordinate results with those from laboratories at NOAA in Seattle, the University of New Orleans, and the French government.

When we all met again in Brest in June 1978, I and my fellow scientists from NOAA, the EPA, and several U.S. universities reported on our in-depth analyses outlining the events that followed the grounding of the *Amoco Cadiz*. Much data had been collected by the French and reported to us over the three-month period. The studies showed that deadly quantities of oil stayed along the coast for weeks after the wreck. Oil levels were highest in the estuaries. Spring high tides along with rough seas had worked the oil down into muddy sediments offshore and in the estuaries. In coastal waters, oil-degrading bacteria flourished and aided the cleanup with their natural destruction of the crude oil. But some oil was hidden under seemingly clean sands, waiting to be exposed later by fall and winter storms. Some heavily oiled algae were still clinging to coastal rocks, but the scientists did not know if the algae would live and reproduce.

We began to see evolving patterns that shed light on the impact the oil had on the smaller ecosystems in the area. Chasse reported that some species that lived in heavily oiled areas were almost completely wiped out. Several species hung on tenaciously, while others appeared to thrive once the heavy concentration of oil was dispersed.

Species with fast regeneration times — which produce new generations often — recovered most rapidly. For example, phytoplankton, tiny plants that live in the water, reproduce in a matter of days. Also, tides constantly sweep new phytoplankton into the area from cleaner areas.

Zooplankton, tiny animals that live in the water, have longer regeneration times — weeks to months. Their population remained low in the more heavily oiled areas. It was still difficult three months later to predict how other species would fare, so we agreed to continue the scientific inquiry.

Some scientists would keep checking the levels of oil in the sediments and in key marine organisms. Some biologists would continue their studies of commercially valuable species, such as fish and shellfish, and of key ecosystems along the coast. We agreed to meet again in 18 months, after we had followed several more life cycles of the creatures in this ecosystem.

That meeting, a four-day symposium held in Brest in November 1979, was sponsored by the French National Oceanographic Ministry and the Ministry of the Environment.

Chemist John L. Laseter of the University of New Orleans began by presenting data on sampling he had done in 1978 for hydrocarbons in the atmosphere. His analyses were so accurate that he could differentiate between organic compounds found in normal urban air, pollution caused by automobiles, and oil-derived hydrocarbons from the spill. He concluded that gaseous fumes from the oil had polluted the air in many coastal towns and villages.

French and U.S. scientists had closely followed changes in the chemistry of the oil as it broke down into various compounds. They reported that the oil generally stayed in sediments for some time;

Twenty months after the spill, a salt marsh on Île Grande shows little evidence of having recovered from its bout with the black tide.

Twenty months after the spill, oil still coats
the rocks of coastal Brittany, *left*. It lurks
a few centimeters below the sand, *below left*,
to ooze into a footprint on the beach, *above*.

some heavier and more toxic oil compounds remained in sediments
longer. Their data showed that oil incorporated into the muddy
sediment of the estuaries remained longest. In addition, they found
that the waves and tides churned up the sediments during winter
storms, releasing the oil into the ocean waters—in effect, starting
another spill months after the wreck.

Apparently, oil-eating bacteria—normally present in the area—
flourished in great numbers all along the coast after the spill. Two
scientists estimated that bacteria may have eaten or degraded 0.5
kilogram of petroleum hydrocarbons per hectare per day.

French scientists reported that offshore phytoplankton and zooplankton populations had changed little in the 20 months since the
spill. Their fast regeneration time and the constant entry of new
organisms with the tides had apparently left them healthy. But plants
growing on the shore suffered a different fate. The oil killed many
such plants, greatly decreasing the total number along the coast.
Nevertheless, scientists were optimistic about the ultimate fate of the
plants because not one of the 76 species of marine plants in the area
was totally destroyed.

Damage was just beginning to appear among lichens, plants that
cling to rocks. Scientists reported that the photosynthesis rate of
coastal lichens—a measurement of how plants use light for growth—
was 33 per cent lower than the rate for lichens in a nearby area
unaffected by the oil.

However, some plant species not only weathered the accident, but
may have even profited by it. Chasse pointed out that the seaweed

fucus was sprouting and growing normally less than 1 kilometer (0.6 mile) from Portsall and had grown 10 to 12 centimeters (4 to 5 inches) in the first few months after the spill.

Some green seaweeds such as *Enteromorpha* flourished in spots, as did some threadlike bacteria. The scientists suggested that some plants probably thrived because of increased nitrogen in the water, which resulted from the bacterial breakdown of animals and other dead plants. Other plants probably thrived because of the almost complete absence of gastropods, tiny plant-eating animals that scrape seaweeds from the surface of rocks.

Representatives of the Roscoff Laboratory presented some of the most interesting and somber data at the symposium. Marine ecologist Louis Cabrioch, a native of this coast and now deputy director of the biological station, reported that offshore amphipods, small shrimplike organisms, were a major casualty. These creatures, a prized food for many species of offshore fish, decreased from 23 species to 1, and the number of amphipods per square meter decreased from 7,000 to 15. Cabrioch was concerned about how the amphipod species could be replenished, because they live on the ocean floor and do not move far from their initial home. They lay their eggs in bottom mud, and their young emerge as crawling creatures. Although adult amphipods swim, they do so very slowly and usually over short distances. Cabrioch was not sure whether they could migrate at all.

Some animals on shore survived the spill well, others did not. Although we had seen the massive kills of sea urchins and razor clams initially, French scientists reported at the November conference that most limpets—many with their caplike shells coated with oil—survived. Clams were driven out of the sand on the beaches by the oil and some died. Others, covered with oily sediment by the tides, had to recuperate from the effects of toxic oil in their bodies. Analyses of their body tissue 20 months later showed much scarring and destruction of cells in important internal organs. Some shrimp and worm species moved into territory previously occupied by now-dead competitors and thrived. One scientist reported that the number of species for some animals even increased for a period of time.

Fisheries biologist Y. Desauneray of the Scientific Institute for Fisheries presented his fishery-trawling data from the bays of Morlaix and Lannion. He noted that in several species of ground fish, including the sole and the flounder, those that would have hatched in 1978 were missing. He concluded that the oil either killed the young larvae in the water or killed their food source. This was the first known incident where oil had seriously damaged a fishery.

In some cases, Desauneray said, fish became severely malformed. Some were covered with sores, while flounders and others suffered fin-rot diseases. About 90 per cent of the fish caught off Brittany in December 1978 had fin rot, but this figure dropped to 73 per cent by May 1979 and to 2 per cent by October 1979. Desauneray concluded

Human reaction to the oil spill ranges from outrage, as expressed in French posters, *right,* to despair, as expressed on the face of a citizen gazing at an oily beach, *far right.*

that there was a low incidence of disease in October because most of the surviving fish had been born after the heavy oil had dispersed.

The mullet, another important commercial fish, decreased from 30 to 80 per cent by the 1978-1979 season, depending on the location of the fishery. Diseased mullet caught in the estuary Aber Benoit had large heads on shriveled, sore-covered bodies. Sadly, these normally fast-swimming fish became easy prey for children, who caught them with their bare hands in coves around the coast.

Scientists who had interviewed fishermen reported that crabs were smaller than normal and not marketable. The lobster yield near Portsall was normal, but the females had lost between 25 and 87 per cent of their eggs early, and egg-bearing females were only half as fruitful as normal. The valuable offshore beds of *Laminaria,* or kelp, a giant type of seaweed, survived the spill and continued to grow and reproduce. No analysis for hydrocarbons had been made of *Laminaria* tissue. Some scientists were concerned about this because that seaweed is a source of iodine and other pharmaceutical substances.

Zoologist J. Y. Monnat of the Zoology Laboratory of Brest offered an analysis of the spill's effect on sea birds. He concluded that 15,000 to 20,000 sea birds were killed in the first week after the spill. Four species made up 85 per cent of the total — puffins, the small penguin, the troil guillemot, and the tufted cormorant.

Even before the spill, Monnat wondered whether pollution of the sea was contributing to a decline in bird colonies in the area. He wrote, "The repeated massive accidental spills of pollutants in our region cannot but precipitate the decline and disappearance of our marginal colonies." I recalled the lone puffin we saw over the Seven Islands in April 1978 — was he the last of "a marginal colony"?

I concluded that the oil spill survivors were apparently chosen at random in a gruesome game of Russian roulette. In some cases, survival appeared to depend on whether shelter happened to be available. In other cases, evolutionary genetics made the difference. One animal was immune to the toxic chemicals of the oil and another was not. Survival for some animals depended on whether their prey had been contaminated by the oil.

Even though we could explain changes in the species in an ecosystem and their relationship to each other after the fact, we generally agreed that we could not have predicted events as they had unfolded. Some species died, but others quickly moved into their territory and flourished there. Many species adapted and filled empty ecological niches.

The scene was similar to that in a forest that has suffered a major fire. Months after the fire, weeds and seedlings compete for the nutrients left in the ashes. Within two years or so, dark burned stalks are the sole reminder that a forest once stood there. Different animals inhabit the scrub, and together the different species evolve into new ecosystems. Off Brittany, shifts in species have taken place but, like the high trees in the forest, it will be years before some of the important species grow back to their original proportion in the community.

It will take time for some effects to show up clearly. Animals that normally have long life spans may die long after the spill, not directly from poisoning by oil but from aftereffects, such as gonadal cancer. Ecologists do not know how many generations it takes for a sharply reduced population of longer-lived species to return to normal, but most scientists assume that it would require three to five life cycles.

What have we learned from this giant study of a spill? The more information we collected, the more we became convinced that the *Amoco Cadiz* — and every other — oil spill is probably unique. Different species of plants and animals are involved in different geographic areas and each has different abilities to withstand the effects of the oil. The effect of the spill would also vary with the season.

As scientists, we know that ecosystems are always in a state of flux, with or without oil spills. Species shift with the seasons, with long-term changes in climate, and with man-made changes. Why then have scientists devoted so much effort to the issues of coastal pollution? The answer has to do with the basic relationship of all species — human beings, other animals, and plants — the world over.

The Brittany coast is only one region that is being affected by massive pollution. In April 1980, Mexico's Ixtoc I oil well spilled into the Gulf of Mexico more than twice as much oil as the *Amoco Cadiz* spilled into the Atlantic. And another tanker spilled oil on the Brittany coast in March 1980. Because of the delicate balance of life, we can only wonder what future changes will be wrought there. Which "marginal" species will disappear from the earth forever? Nature has some ability to recover from such accidents as oil spills, but some losses are final.

Tracking the Whirlwind

By Robert C. Cowen

Widespread sources of hurricane information, from satellite photos to eyewitness reports, help scientists to better predict the paths of these savage storms

Wind and rain are no strangers to Massachusetts, but this rain was torrential and unrelenting. The wind blew so hard that the oak tree under which my mother and I sought shelter made the ground heave ominously as it bent before recurring gusts. The memory of myself as a wondering 10-year-old in Boston is vivid more than 40 years later. The great New England hurricane of Sept. 21, 1938, was one of the worst natural disasters in the area's history.

After my mother and I struggled to the relative safety of our apartment that blustery day, we could see why hurricanes are called the greatest storms on earth. Roofs of several nearby buildings were torn off like box tops and dropped into the street. Signs and billboards, ripped from their moorings, sailed off and landed a block or two away. Trees fell and electrical wires came down. We learned later that the storm left more than 600 persons dead throughout New England, as well as on Long Island, New York. It also forced 63,000 others to seek emergency aid and shelter, and caused property damage estimated at $387 million.

Yet this was not an exceptionally powerful storm. On the hurricane intensity scale of 1 to 5, it ranked 3. Its strongest sustained winds, measured at 193 kilometers per hour (kph) or 121 miles per hour (mph), were far below the 320 kph (200 mph) that hurricane winds can blow. The storm's unexpected movement made it unusual.

The hurricane was sighted off Cape Hatteras, North Carolina, at sunrise on the day we felt its fury. Like many hurricanes coming from the south, it had been expected to veer toward the northeast and pass east of Cape Cod, Massachusetts. However, it came in over Long Island and up the Connecticut River Valley, catching even Weather Bureau forecasters off guard. Hurricanes normally advance at speeds of 16 to 48 kph (10 to 30 mph) and a few may travel at 50 kph (35 mph). This storm had unexpectedly accelerated and raced into New England at 96 kph (60 mph). Tracking facilities were inadequate in 1938, and meteorologists had to rely on eyewitness accounts from ship captains and, occasionally, airplane pilots for reports on the progress of a storm at sea.

Today, a hurricane could not take an entire region by surprise because a widespread network of sensors such as radar and instruments on satellites and planes monitor the approach of such storms at all times. Data from this network, along with reports from ships at sea and island weather stations, give us a good idea of what to expect from a particular storm. Nevertheless, prediction of its path and behavior cannot be completely accurate because scientists still do not know all they would like to about these savage weather systems. Meteorologists continue to study hurricanes in an effort to determine precisely what triggers them, how and where they are likely to form, and what path they are most apt to follow.

From their studies over the years, scientists have amassed considerable information. They know that a hurricane is a powerful tropical cyclone, a whirling storm with heavy rain and winds of 119 kph (74 mph) or more. In the Northern Hemisphere, hurricane winds blow counterclockwise, or cyclonically, in a tight spiral around the eye — the storm's central region of low atmospheric pressure. In the eye of a hurricane, which is usually 32 kilometers (20 miles) or more in diameter, winds are light or calm, rain ceases, and the sun may shine through broken clouds.

A tropical cyclone is a large-scale atmospheric disturbance whose main circulation takes the shape of a nearly circular vortex, or whirlwind. The National Weather Service (NWS) has designated terms for the various phases of such a storm. The beginning phase is a tropical depression, in which the strongest winds blow at less than 62 kph (39 mph). The depression becomes a tropical storm when winds rise to between 62 and 119 kph (39 and 74 mph). The storm becomes a hurricane when the strongest sustained winds exceed 119 kph.

The author:
Robert C. Cowen is natural science editor for *The Christian Science Monitor*.

These powerful storms are called *hurricanes* only in the Atlantic Ocean and off Mexico's west coast. They are called *typhoons* in the North Pacific Ocean; *baguios* in the Philippines; *cyclones* in the South Pacific and Indian oceans; and *willy-willies* in Australia.

While meteorologists can describe the structure of such a storm, they still cannot explain all the details of how one behaves. But they are fairly certain about how the storm maintains its power once it has been set in motion. A hurricane acts as a giant pump in the atmosphere. It sucks up warm, moist air from near the sea's surface. The air rotates upward through the chimneylike eyewall, a curtain of clouds surrounding the eye, or center, of the storm. Then it disperses horizontally at the top of the system.

Mature hurricanes measure from 96 kilometers (60 miles) to more than 1,600 kilometers (1,000 miles) in diameter. They contain thousands of tall, vertical clouds. At lower levels, winds spiral in toward the eye, gaining speed as they go. Then, in an area about 16 to 32 kilometers (10 to 20 miles) around the eye, the air turns and flows upward through the clouds of the eyewall. Winds tend to blow most fiercely around the eyewall, attaining speeds of 240 kph (150 mph) or more. Outside this circle of high winds are rainbands — spiral cloud bands containing many rainshowers. These often appear in satellite photos as a pinwheel of spiraling clouds.

Near the top of this hurricane system, at altitudes of 12,000 to 18,000 meters (40,000 to 60,000 feet), the air flows out horizontally. When the outflowing air reaches the edge of the storm, it starts to sink and disperses.

The vigorous circulation — in at the bottom, up through the clouds, and out at the top — moves about 1 million metric tons of air per second through a typical hurricane. In one day, a typical large hurricane condenses about 18 million tons of water gathered from the warm moist air. The power to do this comes largely from the rate at which heat is released when the water vapor condenses and water-drops freeze in the rain-producing clouds inside the storm. The power required to lift that much air that high is about 300 times the total electrical generating capacity of the United States. Any system with that much power can easily become a destructive force.

Hurricanes wreak their havoc with their violent winds and flood-producing rains. They also cause a local rise in ocean waters called a storm surge. Storm surges claim 9 of every 10 hurricane victims. They form when hurricane winds blowing onshore sweep water before them with the average water level increasing 5 meters (15 feet) or more. Combined with the usual tide, this surge creates a hurricane storm tide. Wind-driven waves may add another 2 to 4 meters (6 to 12 feet) of advancing water. Huge surges cause severe flooding that demolishes buildings, washes out beaches and highways, and drowns people.

Winds, while usually quite strong, may be the least destructive agents of a hurricane's power. Nevertheless, recurring gusts can

The awesome power of hurricanes can almost totally demolish a Caribbean village, *above,* and, *clockwise,* tear the roofs off houses, level a restaurant, and create a huge surge of water that destroys buildings and beaches boats.

topple tall structures, such as radio towers and church steeples, and winds can pick up and hurl debris, such as broken-off tree limbs and even pieces ripped off buildings, with great force. They can also cause tornadoes around the hurricane's edges.

Some scientists think that hurricanes may be an important element in nature's effort to balance the earth's energy budget. By pumping heat and moisture to high altitudes, these storms help to redistribute energy from the tropics. The ocean-atmosphere system is like a vast heat engine driven by the temperature difference between the tropical "firebox" and the polar "icebox." If there were no circulating winds, storms, or ocean currents to redistribute excess heat in the tropical zone, that area would heat up unbearably, while more northern regions, darkened by unending winter night, would always be frozen. However, global circulation in the form of prevailing winds mixes the earth's atmosphere to temper the effects of the firebox and the icebox. It works like this: Heated air rises over the equator and moves toward the poles. Because of the earth's rotation, it travels in a swirling motion rather than in a straight line. This rotation creates a force that makes the air swirl to the right in the Northern Hemisphere and to the left in the Southern Hemisphere. The force does not exist at or near the equator. As the rising air moves toward the poles, cooler surface air replaces it. This movement of air creates the trade winds, two belts of constantly blowing winds that circulate between the equator and about 30° north and south latitude.

Because warm air, like that over the equator, is lighter than cold air, it presses less heavily on the earth. So the regions where warm air circulates often form low-pressure centers — also called lows, cyclones, or depressions — around which winds blow. Hurricanes develop from these tropical depressions. Cold air creates high-pressure areas, called highs or anticyclones. Air tends to move, in the form of wind, from high-pressure areas to low-pressure areas — the greater the pressure difference, the stronger the wind.

Highs are generally associated with clear weather, because their air currents move downward. The air is compressed and heated and evaporates clouds. Lows bring stormy weather because their air currents move upward. The cooling air encourages cloud formation.

Air pressure is registered on a barometer, a vertical glass tube closed at the top, with its open bottom end in a cup of mercury. The tube is marked with a scale in either inches or millibars (mb), special units of pressure. The normal height to which air pressure forces mercury up the tube at sea level is 29.53 inches, representing 1013 mb pressure. As air pressure rises, so does the mercury in the tube; when the pressure falls, so does the mercury. So a high millibar measurement indicates fair weather, and a low measurement may mean that a storm — possibly a hurricane — is brewing.

Just north of the equator, where the belts of northern and southern trade winds meet, is a zone of low pressure. This zone follows the sun.

A Tropical Low Forms

Cold polar winds (blue), *right,* flow toward the equator, and become warm (red). At the same time, the earth's rotation force twists those from the north and some of those from the south into the easterly trade winds. As their air rises and cools, *below,* some of it returns to the poles. Other air currents rise in place, cool, descend, are warmed, then rise again, forming circular belts. These belts split, and their horizontal parts converge just north of the equator, *below right.* The earth's rotation twists them around each other, resulting in a low-pressure area.

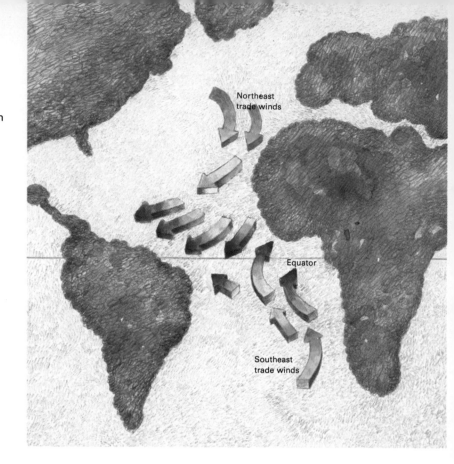

Northeast trade winds

Equator

Southeast trade winds

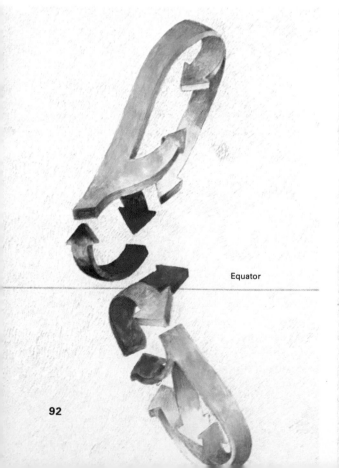

Equator

Equator

Storm clouds

A Hurricane Develops

Warm moist air flowing into a low-pressure area rises and twists into a spiral, *left,* cooling and forming tall storm clouds. The process continues, creating a hurricane, *below.* The air spirals upward in a counterclockwise, or cyclonic, direction, through a chimneylike eyewall. Rainbands surround the eyewall. At the top, the cooled air spreads out horizontally in an outflow cloud that moves in a clockwise, or anticyclonic, direction.

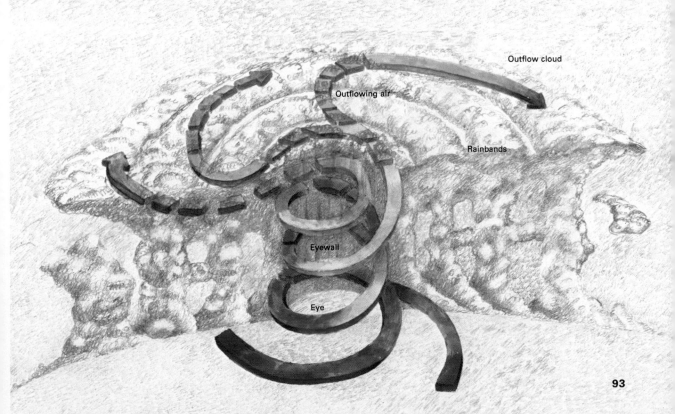

Outflow cloud

Outflowing air

Rainbands

Eyewall

Eye

Sept. 9, 1979

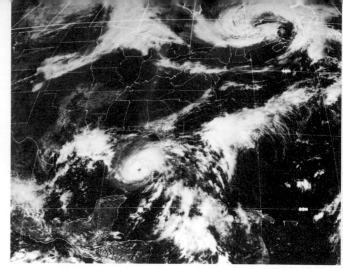

Sept. 11, 1979

Sighted on September 9 as a ball of clouds off Cuba's coast, Tropical Storm Frederic was tracked in a series of satellite photos. The storm strengthened as it moved northwest across the warm Gulf of Mexico waters. As Frederic neared the Mississippi-Alabama coast on September 12, it had become a powerful hurricane organized around a large, ragged eye. After it passed over land the next day near Mobile, Ala., the storm began to break up.

Starting in February each year, it begins to move northward, reaching its farthest point, about 12° north latitude, in August. When the low-pressure zone is near the southern end of its range, it is not much affected by the earth's rotation. But as it moves north, the rotation force becomes strong enough for depressions to form that can become the violent winds of a tropical cyclone, or hurricane system.

During the summer and fall, when the factors necessary to form hurricanes are abundant in the North Atlantic, the Atlantic Hurricane Warning Service at the National Hurricane Center (NHC) in Coral Gables, Fla., and the Environmental Science Services Administration (ESSA) Weather Bureau Hurricane Warning offices in San Juan, Puerto Rico; New Orleans; Washington, D.C.; and Boston maintain a constant watch for tropical disturbances that could develop into destructive cyclonic storms.

On Aug. 22, 1979, the NHC office in San Juan received photos taken by earth-orbiting weather satellites that showed a concentration of billowing cumulus clouds and other organized cloud patterns. These formations indicated that an atmospheric disturbance was moving westward from Africa over the Atlantic Ocean. By August 25, this disturbance had intensified enough to be called a tropical depression. The next day, when it was halfway between the Cape Verde Islands and the Lesser Antilles, it was named Tropical Storm David. David reached the hurricane stage on August 27.

The storm was surveyed intensely through the five days it took to become a full-blown hurricane. The National Meteorological Center in Suitland, Md., issued summaries of weather conditions in the Northern Hemisphere. ESSA satellites photographed the clouds in the system, and weather ships and reconnaissance aircraft radioed reports to NHC headquarters.

NHC forecasters, who usually prefer to use ship or plane reports to confirm a storm's status, found it easy to classify David on the basis of satellite data alone. Photos of the spiraling cloud bands around the eye clearly showed hurricane strength. From the photos, the forecasters could determine how fast the clouds – and the storm – moved.

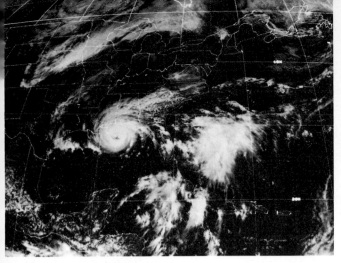

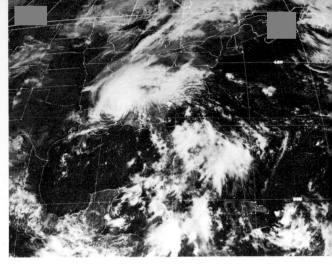

Sept. 12, 1979   **Sept. 13, 1979**

NHC relies mainly on satellite data to track a hurricane if the storm poses no threat to land. But David was headed straight for the Caribbean islands, so closer surveillance was vital. Therefore, the first reconnaissance plane went into action on August 27. The United States Air Force (USAF) supplies the planes and crews for hurricane surveillance. Flying back and forth through the storm, the crews pinpoint the latitude and longitude of the storm's eye and report wind speeds and air pressure there.

When hurricane watchers identified David as a tropical depression on August 25, they estimated its central pressure at 1008 mb and clocked its maximum winds at about 48 kph (30 mph). By the time they upgraded David to hurricane status on August 27, the central pressure was down to 980 mb and dropping 1.5 mb per hour. Winds were blowing at 119 kph and rising. David was ready to join the ranks of memorable hurricanes.

David caused massive flooding and wind damage as it moved across the tiny eastern Caribbean island of Dominica on August 29. The storm grew even stronger as it moved across the Caribbean Sea sucking up warm moist air. It reached its greatest intensity, with a central pressure of 924 mb and winds of 278 kph (173 mph), south of Puerto Rico on August 30. Moving west-northwestward, the storm smashed the Dominican Republic the next day. It caused flooding that swept away villages, killed more than 1,000 persons, left more than 200,000 homeless, and caused damage of about $2 billion.

At that point, the storm clearly posed a threat to the United States. So the U.S. National Oceanic and Atmospheric Administration (NOAA), parent agency of the NWS and NHC, inaugurated Project Hurricane Strike. In a Strike operation, meteorologists monitor the hurricane in research planes from NOAA's Research Facilities Center at Miami International Airport. They maintain constant aerial surveillance for 40 hours before the storm's expected landfall in the mainland United States.

Each Strike plane can stay aloft for 10 hours, and it spends much of that time flying through the storm at levels ranging from 460 to 7,300 meters (1,500 to 24,000 feet). The crews use a variety of instruments to obtain information for immediate use on the present storm and for future research. Radar gives a three-dimensional view of raindrops or ice crystals within the storm clouds. A laser beam scans cloud droplets passing through a wing-mounted instrument to determine their size and type. Probes dropped at various altitudes measure the air's temperature and moisture content. As they descend, other probes dropped into the sea measure water temperature to a depth of about 600 meters (2,000 feet). Instruments also gather data on wind speed and direction and on air pressure at sea level. All of this information, along with the airplane's latitude and longitude and the observation time, is recorded automatically every minute. The Strike crew feeds data into computers on the plane, recording their observations on such things as the diameter of the hurricane's eye and the state of the sea surface. Every half-hour, this information is relayed by a communications satellite to NHC. This up-to-date account in effect puts the office-bound forecasters inside the storm.

Meanwhile, the storm gives Strike crew members one of the wildest rides in aviation. Winds buffet the plane, tossing it from side to side. A

Hurricane Strike planes, *below,* from the Research Facilities Center in Miami, Fla., gather data on storms in the Atlantic Ocean and Caribbean Sea. An airborne hurricane hunter plots the storm, *right,* and relays data to the hurricane center.

Meteorologists at the National Hurricane Center in Coral Gables, Fla., ponder reports received from a wide network of hurricane watchers. They use the information to help them predict where dangerous storms will strike the land.

sudden downdraft can drive it down 300 meters (1,000 feet), only to have an updraft heave the plane back to its original altitude. In nearly 20 years of hurricane probing, the United States has not lost a plane. Yet, as senior hurricane researcher Robert C. Sheets, who has made 250 hurricane flights, observes, "Anyone who tells you they are not anxious before making one of these flights is not really telling the truth. Basically, we are going into the most powerful thing nature has to offer." Nevertheless, Sheets, who works at the National Hurricane and Experimental Meteorological Laboratory (NHEML) in Coral Gables, says that the exhilaration of getting a close look at their research subject overcomes any apprehension. "That's what keeps us coming back," Sheets says, "it's not like studying numbers at a desk. You're experiencing the data directly."

The Strike force, along with observers on ships and at island and mainland stations, made David the most intensely monitored hurricane in history. The storm followed an erratic course from September 1 through 6 that took it from the Dominican Republic to New England. Rainfall from David caused much flooding along its overland route through the United States. The hurricane also spawned tornadoes in Delaware, Maryland, New Jersey, Pennsylvania, and Virginia. Wind and rain caused widespread power failure, and millions of people along the Eastern Seaboard were temporarily without electricity. David lost strength as it moved over land and could no longer replenish itself with warm, moist, tropical air. By September 7, it became a storm that NHC no longer tracked.

A band of trees was planted through the center of a Florida trailer park as a test of hurricane protection. When high winds hit, the trees tempered their full force. Mobile homes in the sheltered area (bottom) were little affected. Those on the windward side (top) suffered severe damage.

Meanwhile, a new storm, Frederic, had become the main concern of NHC forecasters. Developing from a disturbance that moved west from Africa on August 27, Frederic more or less followed in David's track across the Atlantic. Although not so fierce as David had been, it caused floods in the Dominican Republic, Haiti, and Cuba. It also spawned a few tornadoes in the Virgin Islands and Puerto Rico. The major reason for Frederic's mildness was that Hurricane David slowed its growth. The cold outflow of air from David descended over Frederic and kept it from developing. When Frederic reached Cuba on September 6, it was still only a tropical depression with winds of 56 kph (35 mph) and central pressure of 1006 mb.

However, Frederic was invigorated by a very warm sea surface of 30°C (86°F.) near Cuba and gained hurricane power on September 10. Frederic moved across the Gulf of Mexico, and swept ashore near the Mississippi-Alabama border on September 13 as a major hurricane with 950-mb central pressure and 208-kph (130-mph) winds. It did most of its damage in the Southern States by creating a storm surge along the entire coastal region from Santa Rosa Island, Florida, to Pascagoula, Miss.

Even though scientists do not fully understand hurricanes, they have tried to modify them. In 1961, NHEML researchers started a program called Stormfury for seeding hurricane clouds, much as ordinary clouds are seeded to increase rainfall. Aircraft fly above and beside the storm clouds and drop tiny silver iodide crystals into them, triggering rainfall. This seeding also makes clouds grow taller. According to the theory, seeding cumulus clouds — slightly away from the storm's center of maximum winds — would increase their height above the existing eyewall. This would form a new "chimney" that would give the powerful inward-spiraling, low-level winds a new place to rise. The old eyewall would dissipate, while the new one, away from the storm's center, would produce winds that were not so intense and damaging.

The Stormfury researchers first tried this seeding technique on Hurricane Esther in 1961, then on Hurricanes Beulah (1963), Debbie (1969), and Ginger (1971). Seeding had small effect on Beulah and Ginger. But Debbie's maximum wind speed dropped 31 per cent after seeding, and this seemed to support their theory. However, the wind decrease could have been an unpredictable variation typical of the strange behavior of hurricanes.

Stormfury seeding, suspended in 1972, produced no conclusive results. But the scientists are ready to try again. They have the three aircraft used in Strike operations, plus a USAF propeller plane and a National Aeronautics and Space Administration (NASA) jet aircraft that can fly at altitudes of 9,000 to 12,000 meters (30,000 to 40,000 feet) in and over storms. In addition, computer simulations of seeding experiments and other research have given them a better idea of what to expect in real storms.

Even without Stormfury, NOAA's investment in its flying laboratories is paying off as Strike operations gather valuable research data for forecasters. Responding to a hurricane warning by boarding up buildings, shutting down businesses, and evacuating people is expensive. So Strike researchers hope to better pinpoint the areas endangered by a hurricane where people will have to take these precautions. This can save millions of dollars and avoid much inconvenience for people living in hurricane-prone areas. Strike researchers are also planning a new project called Chase, in which NHEML will work with the Electric Power Research Institute (EPRI) of Palo Alto, Calif., to gather data from near the ground as a hurricane comes onshore. EPRI scientists want to find out how winds affect power lines. They will use instruments, mounted on poles on the beach and for a few kilometers inland, to measure the wind's strength and its changes as the storm moves inland. Chase is part of a larger study that should help in drawing up more rigorous building codes.

NHEML is also trying to learn more about hurricane-induced flooding to help predict storm surges. NWS is now preparing 20 computer models for regions stretching from the Gulf Coast to Massachusetts for use in Project SLOSH (Sea, Lake, and Overland Surges from Hurricanes). Each model will include local topographical information, such as height of land and shapes and sizes of lakes and river basins and their normal water levels. Three-dimensional maps will locate levee systems, roads, and other geographic features. When wind and pressure data from an incoming storm are fed into the program, forecasters will be able to predict where the expected storm surges will strike and how big they will be.

Forecasters need all the help they can get. NHC Director Neil Frank has said that forecast accuracy has not improved since the early 1970s. He explained that "in many coastal areas where we need more lead time with the most accurate forecasts — 24 hours instead of 12 hours — we are just not going to be able to provide it. If there is going to be any increase in the effectiveness of the hurricane-warning system," Frank added, "it's got to come from the people."

This means more than heeding warnings, boarding up property, and evacuating. It means using hurricane-resistant building designs and restricting the development of areas that are vulnerable to flooding and storm surges. Millions of people have risked their lives needlessly during the last 20 years by moving into exposed areas along the Gulf Coast and Eastern Seaboard of the United States.

Recognizing this growing danger, the American Meteorological Society (AMS) in 1976 asked, "Is the United States building toward a hurricane catastrophe?" Acknowledging that "the beach offers a beautiful way of life," the AMS issued a "plea for realistic hurricane preparedness plans at state, county, and local levels." In coping with the greatest storms on earth, the informed concern of the people is critical in making the most of the scientists' forecasting ability.

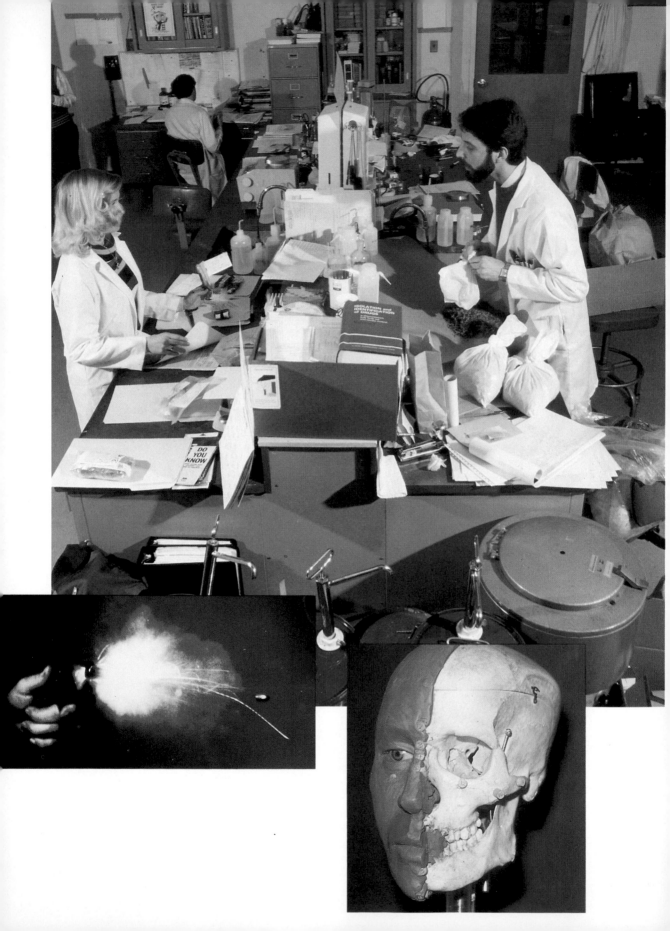

Solving Crime with Science

By Ben Patrusky

The trail now leads through the laboratory as the scientist joins the detective in tracking down clues that will lead to the guilty party

The 1978 rape-murder of a 2½-year-old girl in southern California ranks as one of the most bestial crimes on record. Using a pincerlike gripping tool, the murderer mutilated his victim and dumped her body in a secluded spot in Los Angeles' Topanga Canyon.

The jury did not deliberate long. On Dec. 15, 1979, it found Theodore Frank, a previously convicted child molester, guilty of "Murder One with Special Circumstances." Frank would never commit another such horrible crime because the verdict carried a mandatory sentence of either death in the gas chamber (if capital punishment is reinstated in California) or life imprisonment with no possibility of parole. Yet law-enforcement officials shuddered to think that only a few years earlier, under the very same circumstances, Frank would have gone free.

"Five or 10 years ago, we probably wouldn't have been able to arrest this guy, let alone get him indicted and brought to trial," said Richard H. Fox, chief criminalist of the Ventura County Crime Laboratory. "We just wouldn't have been able to produce the evidence we needed to link Frank directly to the crime. No doubt about it, he would have walked away, free to commit God knows what other atrocities."

Like Frank, many criminals are now brought to justice who would almost certainly have escaped retribution less than 10 years ago. Without question, the credit for this dramatic turnabout must go to the rapid and recent growth of forensic science — science as it applies to the law and the courtroom.

Even the shrewdest criminals leave some trace of their illicit activities, as fans of Sherlock Holmes well know. Sir Arthur Conan Doyle's fictional English detective solved many crimes in the late 1800s and early 1900s on the basis of a particular kind of mud on a suspect's shoe, or a certain type of tobacco ash from a cigar.

In 1980, law officers have an astonishing array of new techniques and instruments to help them make use of even the most fragmentary evidence — a tiny speck of blood, a strand of hair, or a wisp of gunshot residue. With these new techniques, police can detect *latent* (invisible) fingerprints on a corpse and identify the unique "signatures" of weapons. This new forensic arsenal gives police a significantly greater capacity to "individualize" crime — to match clues to specific persons. It has also helped them clear innocent people who have been wrongly accused of crimes.

However, this advance in the ability to identify criminals and others — such as plane crash victims, whose identification can be exceedingly difficult — hinges on more than improved technology. An equally crucial element has been the development of highly trained scientists who can use the new technology and interpret its results. An ideal crime-fighting science team is likely to include such specialists as a forensic pathologist, who performs autopsies to determine the cause of death; a forensic odontologist, who makes identifications by examining bite marks and other dental evidence; a forensic anthropologist, who identifies skeletal remains; and a criminalist, who analyzes physical evidence such as fingerprints, hair, gunshot powder, and body fluids. Most of the work in state and local forensic laboratories deals with violent crimes, robberies, and drug cases. Local law-enforcement agencies investigating such "white-collar" crimes as computer fraud, industrial espionage, and bribery usually employ outside experts from federal departments and agencies or private investigating companies.

The full-time staff of a crime laboratory varies widely from community to community and state to state. Small cities and towns may depend heavily on state services. Large cities such as New York City, Chicago, and Los Angeles have highly sophisticated labs of their own. The federal government, of course, has the laboratories of the Federal Bureau of Investigation and other agencies. Besides the staff in these labs, there is a kind of free-lance pool of experts, many of whom work part time at crime investigation. These specialists may find themselves working in Florida one week, and giving evidence in a trial in Montana or teaching a short course in criminology in New York the next.

The author:
Ben Patrusky is a science writer who specializes in medical topics.

To a great extent, the sudden growth of forensic science results from landmark decisions made by the Supreme Court of the United States in the 1960s. The high court's rulings in *Escobedo v. Illinois* (1964) and *Miranda v. Arizona* (1966) diminished the courtroom value of the confession, long the basis of many criminal convictions. Essentially, these two cases affirmed that a criminal suspect has the right to remain silent and the right to have a lawyer present during questioning. If the suspect is not informed of these rights, any testimony or confession he gives may not be used against him in court. Writing for the court majority in the Escobedo case, Justice Arthur J. Goldberg put the issue in perspective: "We have learned the lesson of history, ancient and modern, that a system of criminal-law enforcement which comes to depend on confession will, in the long run, be less reliable than a system which depends on *extrinsic* [outside] evidence independently secured through skilled investigation."

The message was clear, and it revolutionized police procedures. The police would have to do better at developing good, hard, objective physical evidence. And that called for better technology and more skilled investigators. These requirements have been paying off, both in terms of convicting the guilty and protecting the innocent.

Consider the Frank case. "We had reason to think Frank might be our man," says Fox, who led the scientific team on the case, "but the evidence was really skimpy." Then detectives found the key piece of evidence during a search of the suspect's home several months after the murder. They turned up a viselike hand tool commonly used by auto mechanics to grip and twist metal.

A crime-lab technician uses a scanning electron microscope, *top,* to examine gunshot residue. The sample, in the cylindrical chamber at left, is bombarded by electrons to produce an image on the screen at right of a residue particle, *above,* magnified 4,500 times.

Criminalist Fox realized that the device had teeth that could have produced the patterns found in wounds on the little girl's body. "Our only possible direct link was this viselike tool." But was this the tool that savaged the child, or merely one just like it? "We needed to demonstrate that this was the very same tool if we were to convince ourselves, let alone a jury, that Frank was the killer," says Fox.

Every such tool, Fox explains, has its own distinct "signature" – unique patterns formed on its jaws by chance during its manufacture. And these peculiarities, if detected, ought to be reflected in the tool marks left on the girl's body. Fox knew that the tool would have to be very highly magnified and clearly defined to bring out the most subtle details. An optical microscope would not do the trick. So Fox had the tool examined under a scanning electron microscope (SEM), a powerful scientific research instrument developed in the 1960s.

The SEM produces a beam of high-energy electrons that knocks other electrons out of the test specimen. The specimen's topography – its peaks and valleys – determines the intensity of this secondary emission, which is used to form a detailed, point-by-point image of the tool's gripping surface. The beam scans the specimen in much the same way that the beam in a television set travels across the picture tube to produce an image. The SEM magnifies pictures as much as

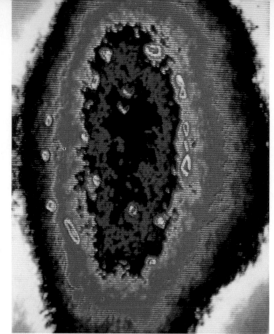

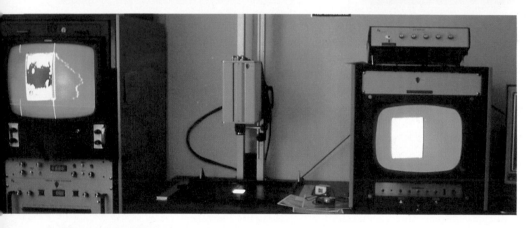

A video image enhancer, *above,* electronically combines two images of the same bite photo to emphasize detail in the faint tooth impressions, *top left.* By assigning false colors to various intensities of gray in the photo, the same instrument produces a vivid picture of the bite pressures on the skin.

1,000 times more than does an optical microscope. It also has an extraordinary depth of focus, so the tops of peaks and bottoms of valleys on a surface can be seen in focus simultaneously — a property that gives its images a startling three-dimensional quality.

Ronald Taylor, a top-flight electron microscopist in the Los Angeles Coroner's Office, conducted the SEM analysis on the Frank hand tool. The pictures he obtained left little room for doubt. They revealed the tool's signature — a series of unique tooth edges, chips, and craters that had left their unmistakable mark on the little girl's body. This striking, new-technology evidence sealed Frank's fate.

Many forensic experts believe that the SEM's magnifying power and capacity for detail has made it the most dependable means for determining whether a suspect has recently fired a gun. When a gun is fired, it leaves traces of gunpowder on the gunman's hand. These bits of gunshot residue are usually sphere-shaped and the electron microscope can detect them in trifling amounts.

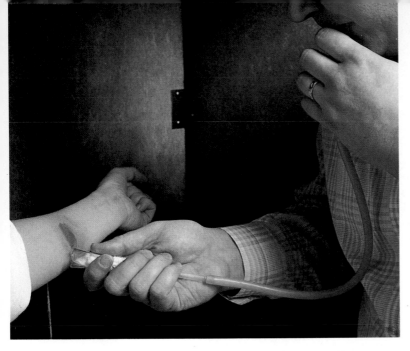

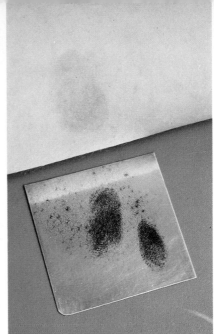

Searching for fingerprints, a police aide blows iodine vapor onto a victim's arm, *above.* When pressed against a silver plate, the stain reacts chemically to transfer the fingerprint to the plate, *above right.*

A microscopic comparison of soil samples from Ohio, *right,* and Pennsylvania, *bottom right,* helped establish the scene of a murder. The Ohio soil contained such minerals as tourmaline (T), garnet (G), and olivine (O), but mud stains on the body, found in Ohio, did not. These matched the soil from Pennsylvania where the murder weapon was found. Photomicrographs, *below,* also helped to match a mark on a metal door pried open in a burglary (left) with patterns on a crowbar (right) that police suspected was used in the crime.

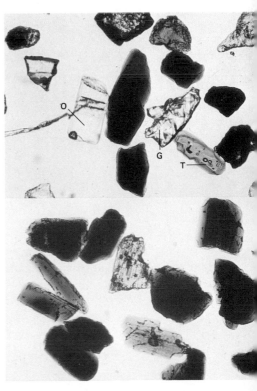

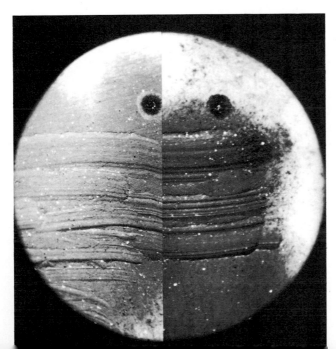

The SEM can also identify the chemicals in a specimen. Gunshot residue, for example, contains the chemicals barium, lead, and antimony from the bullet's shell casing. To identify the constituents of the residue, technicians attach a simple detector to the SEM to monitor X rays, which the specimen releases when it is bombarded by the high-energy scanning electron beam. Every chemical element in the sample emits its own distinct X-ray signature. The presence of both characteristics on a suspect's hand—shape and chemical content—constitutes proof that he or she has recently fired a gun.

Most detectives probably feel that the best evidence is fingerprints of the accused at the scene of the crime. In strangulation, for example, the ultimate evidence would be the murderer's fingerprints on the victim's neck. But skin does not register fingerprints—at least they were not detectable with the old powder-dusting methods of print detection, which worked only on flat, hard surfaces. Recent experimental studies with a newly devised detection technique, however, show that latent fingerprints on a cadaver may last for up to 24 hours. If the body is refrigerated, the prints will last even longer.

In this technique, iodine vapor is blown over the area on the skin of the cadaver where prints may be lurking—the neck of a strangulation victim, for instance. The iodine dissolves in the criminal's exuded body oil, which carries the fingerprint, causing the area to turn purple. The technician then applies liquid iodine and presses a silver plate on the site. The resulting chemical reaction produces silver iodide, which reveals the fingerprint pattern when exposed to light.

In 1979, a Florida jury convicted a Miami Beach health-spa owner of the murders of one man and two women found shot in the spa. The conviction was based largely on a fingerprint from the middle finger of the left hand found on the body of one of the women. The case was the first in which prints lifted from the skin of a dead person were admitted as evidence in court.

Perpetrators of violent crimes, especially sexual assault and child abuse, are likely to leave another kind of calling card—bite marks. According to Lowell L. Levine, a forensic odontologist in New York City's Medical Examiner's Office, bite marks are just as unique as fingerprints. Even identical twins leave distinctly different bite impressions. So, match the bite marks to the bites and you are likely to have the culprit.

Levine has done just that. His testimony proved pivotal in the much-publicized 1979 multiple murder trial of Theodore R. Bundy in Florida. Bundy was accused of bludgeoning and strangling two women students. The crucial clue in the case was a faint bite mark found on one of the alleged victims. Levine sent photographs of the mark to Homer Campbell at the University of New Mexico for computer photoenhancement, a process developed to sharpen photos transmitted from spacecraft. Campbell was able to bring out details that were not apparent in the photos at first. These prints—showing, among other things, clear evidence of a chipped tooth — matched the defendant's bite precisely, and the jury convicted Bundy. According to Levine, "The Bundy case was as good a case as you could hope [to find] to prove the forensic worth of dental evidence."

Levine suggests that dental records will prove even more valuable as time goes on in identifying criminals, as well as in identifying missing persons and victims of crimes and accidents. The dental-information bank continues to grow through such avenues as health insurance plans, many of which require dental examinations. This dental data, says Levine, properly cataloged and stored in central computers, could give law-enforcement personnel a powerful new investigative tool.

Blood turns up as evidence in many criminal cases. But that has not always helped police much. Early blood typing was restricted to the well-known genetically based ABO system consisting of blood groups A, B, AB, and O. (The letters are given to certain markers on the surface of red blood cells.) Suppose, for example, that a burglar cuts himself and leaves a trace of blood at the burglary scene. Police arrest a suspect and find by a chemical test that he has type O blood, the same as the blood sample taken from a stain found at the scene of the crime. The problem is, however, that some 45 per cent of the people in the United States would also test positive for O. Naturally, this is not very convincing evidence. But ABO typing still has forensic value. If, for example, a murder victim was found in a pool of AB blood and a suspect was found to have AB bloodstains on his shirt, then police would have reason to be suspicious. Only about 5 of every 100 persons in the United States have this relatively rare blood type.

In addition to ABO, other red blood cell markers are now commonly included in tests at a forensic blood lab, such as the MN system, consisting of types M, N, and MN, and the Rhesus or Rh system, with at least five different subgroups. The MN or Rh markers alone have the same limited value to forensic scientists as ABO. But all these systems are genetically unrelated; each is inherited independently of the other factors. So, by classifying a bloodstain according to

90°

60°

30°

10°

The shapes of blood spatters depend on the angle at which the blood fell and thus provide clues to the victim's position or movement at the time of the crime.

Proteins from 12 blood samples form banded patterns, or "blood prints," when subjected to electrical current during electrophoresis. This process gives police a highly accurate way to match blood types.

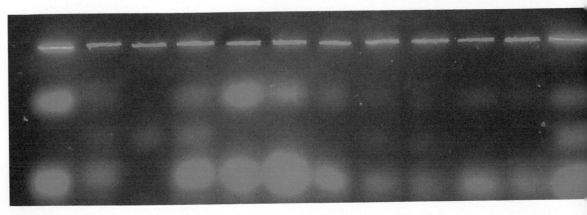

all three systems, scientists can make a much better guess as to its origin. The probability of two persons having the same type of ABO is 1 in 3, while the chances of such a coincidence occurring in all three systems is 1 in 40.

Forensic scientists know that the hundreds of genetically determined biochemical substances in the blood could theoretically serve to distinguish one individual from another, much as fingerprints do. But pinpointing the source of blood is much more difficult because of its great complexity. Moreover, the distinguishing differences can be uncovered only by complicated, time-consuming laboratory tests. Nevertheless, science has recently made giant strides toward this goal. Says Robert C. Shaler, director of serology and criminalistics in the New York City Medical Examiner's Office, "We still can't answer the question, 'Whose blood is it?' but we've sure gotten a lot better at establishing a probable source."

There are tests, for example, that reveal individual differences in enzymes within the blood cell and proteins in the blood plasma. These tests have increased the odds for a correct identification of a blood source to a remarkable degree. Forensic specialists now study eight such enzymes and proteins, as well as the ABO, MN, and Rh systems. Taken together, they can increase the odds of a correct blood match-up to as great as 75,000 to 1.

Specialists type enzymes and proteins by a process called electrophoresis. They dissolve the blood sample in a saline solution, place the mixture on a gel, and subject it to an electrical current for a few hours. Each protein or enzyme in the sample moves through the gel toward either the positive or negative pole at a rate that depends on

Civil authorities and forensic experts begin the painstaking job of piecing together and identifying the 274 victims of the tragic 1979 plane crash near Chicago's O'Hare Airport.

its molecular size and electrical charge. When all of the molecules are separated, the gel is stained. This produces visible bands of each enzyme or protein on the gel — a biochemical profile of the blood. This "blood print" can then be compared with a blood print obtained from the suspect.

This much-improved blood-typing capability is holding up in court. It was crucial in the 1978 case of a 70-year-old woman who was bludgeoned to death in her Bronx, N.Y., apartment, apparently during an attempted holdup. Police sent a suspect's clothing to Shaler's laboratory for analysis. Shaler found two penpoint-sized spots of dried blood on the suspect's shirt, and managed to get a biochemical profile of the blood, which "just about coincided" with the blood taken from the dead woman. In this case, Shaler testified that there was only 1 chance in more than 70,000 that two persons could have the same blood marker, enzyme, and protein characteristics. The evidence was instrumental in getting a conviction.

Bloodstains help convict criminals in still another way. By studying how blood has been spilled at the scene of a killing, forensic specialists can often reconstruct some of the circumstances surrounding the crime.

Much of the credit for establishing the value of blood "spatter" goes to criminalist Herbert L. MacDonnell of Corning, N.Y., who began an intensive investigation in the early 1970s of how blood travels as a result of impact from a high-velocity bullet or the thrust of a knife. He also studied the kinds of bloodstains produced when blood splashes against various kinds of surfaces. Among other things, his studies disproved the long-held idea that drops of blood break up into

To reconstruct a face from its skull for identification, small numbered plugs, showing the thickness of tissue, are placed at points on the facial bones and then connected by strips of clay, *below left*. The rest of the "flesh" is then filled in and coloring and hair added to produce the likeness of the victim, *below*.

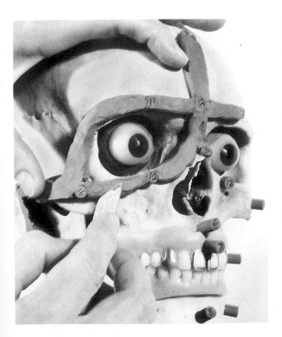

smaller droplets when they fall through the air. He demonstrated that a globule of blood remains a globule until it strikes the ground, even when dropped from a tall building.

Since 1972, evidence derived from the analysis of bloodstain patterns has figured importantly in several cases. Testimony by MacDonnell helped to acquit a veterinarian accused of shooting his assistant in 1968. There had been bad feeling between the two men for some time. On the day of the shooting, the assistant called the vet and threatened him and his family. He later arrived at the vet's house in his car; the vet, fearing for his children's safety, grabbed a loaded shotgun and ran out to the car. An argument followed, during which the shotgun went off and the assistant was killed. The vet, who claimed it was an accident, was arrested for murder. There were no witnesses to the incident.

In his testimony at the trial, MacDonnell was able to prove that the pattern of bloodstains both outside and inside the car showed that the victim must have suddenly shoved open the car door against the vet. This accidentally set off the shotgun. Thus the assistant contributed to his own death.

Richard Fox described a Ventura County stabbing case in which the alleged assailant denied the attack and insisted that he had never been close enough to the victim to inflict the wound. A single drop of blood on the suspect's shoe was enough to refute his story. The nature of the spatter indicated that it could only have been produced by the blood falling perpendicularly, proving that the suspect had, in fact, been standing quite close to the victim when the wound was inflicted. The man later confessed.

Other body fluids also have tales to tell. Nearly 80 per cent of people are secretors. In other words, ABO blood types are revealed in their saliva, perspiration, tears, and (in men) seminal fluid. San Diego criminalists – with an assist from a forensic odontologist – made good use of this information in solving the fatal shooting and stabbing of a man in his home in 1976. Police arrested two women acquaintances as suspects in the case. They had found one woman's fingerprints at the murder scene but they had no physical evidence to link the other woman directly to the crime. Then a detective, checking the murder site one more time, noticed a wad of chewing gum on top of a bureau.

The detective sent the gum first to odontologist Norman D. Sperber in the San Diego County Coroner's Office, and then to the crime lab for testing. Sperber noted marks in the gum that greatly resembled irregularities he later spotted in the second suspect's bite. And at his suggestion, laboratory tests were done that showed that the gum had been chewed by a secretor with the relatively rare AB blood type – the blood type of the second suspect. The case never went to trial. Shortly after these findings came to light, the two women admitted their guilt.

"Whodunit?" is a major concern of forensic science. But so is "Who was it?" When police must identify skeletal remains, they usually call in forensic anthropologists, those specialists trained to extract information from human remains.

From an examination of bones — their shape, size, and density, for example — these experts can usually determine if the remains are human and deduce the approximate age at death, as well as sex, stature, and race. They often spot other distinguishing characteristics, such as bone fractures or whether the person had suffered from polio or arthritis — information that could prove vital to identification.

Forensic anthropologists also practice a special kind of wizardry. For example, Clyde Snow of the Federal Aviation Administration's Aeronautical Center in Oklahoma City, Okla., is known for his genius in reconstructing mutilated bodies. Given a mere remnant of skull, Snow has used sculptor's clay to produce with remarkable precision a likeness of the victim that next of kin can identify.

Another practitioner is Jean-Pierre Leharry, chief technologist in the New York City Medical Examiner's Office. Leharry's skills have

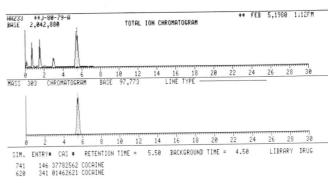

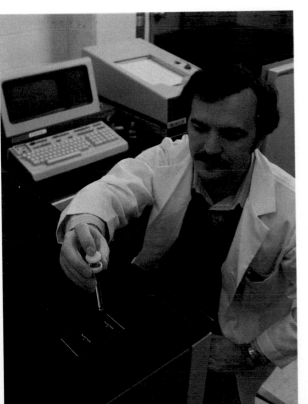

Cocaine and heroin crystals, *top left and right,* reveal their structures when magnified 100 times under a microscope. By placing a suspected sample of cocaine in a gas chromatograph-mass spectrometer, a technician can analyze it and compare it with examples taken from the crime lab's library of known drugs, *left.* The readout, *above,* shows a peak in the sample that matches the one in pure cocaine, thus identifying the sample. The smaller peaks represent impurities.

Future criminalists learn how to reconstruct faces using casts of skulls in a course dealing with forensic anthropology at Colorado State University, Fort Collins.

earned him the nickname "Merlin of the Morgue." Leharry has had no formal medical training. But his astonishing firsthand knowledge of anatomy, acquired during nearly 20 years of morgue work, has allowed him to puzzle out what would seem to the untutored eye an altogether unsolvable mystery.

Consider the case of the unidentified, badly mutilated, one-armed torso found in the Bronx near the New York Botanical Garden in 1978. In just a few hours, Leharry established that the torso was that of a 60-year-old man who was 178 centimeters (5 feet 10 inches) tall, weighed 77 kilograms (170 pounds), and had a 102-centimeter (40-inch) chest span. With this information, the police matched Leharry's description to that of a man listed as a missing person a few weeks earlier. A chest X ray obtained from the health records of the missing man revealed details identical to those seen in X rays of the torso. Barely 24 hours after discovering the torso, police had a positive identification.

Because of their unusual skills, Snow and Leharry are regularly called to the scene of plane crashes to sort out the remains and identify the bodies. So, too, are qualified forensic odontologists like Levine. In fact, these men joined forces with a corps of other top-flight forensic specialists in May 1979 to help identify the 274 persons killed when an American Airlines DC-10 crashed and burned while taking off from Chicago's O'Hare International Airport. Essentially, they had to deal with 15,000 body parts. There were not many fingerprints; fire had destroyed most of this evidence.

The investigators went to work in a jerry-rigged hangar at O'Hare that rapidly became, in Levine's words, "the largest institute of forensic science in the world." Levine served as consultant to 18 local dentists who were drafted into service by the Cook County medical examiner. The team tried to match up the odontological evidence gathered at the crash site with dental records obtained from the families of passengers known to be on the plane.

Pathologists carefully examined the remains — scorched bodies and body parts — for all manner of clues: Was the person a nail-biter? Were the ears pierced? Were there any medical problems that would be detectable from organs that may have survived reasonably intact, such as the uterus and prostate—well protected by the pelvis? Were there scars, either from surgery or accidents?

Radiologists in the hangar clicked off X-ray pictures of the remains for later comparison with medical records. As if laboring over some ghoulish jigsaw puzzle, the anthropologists tried to match body parts. They worked very carefully. "In such disasters," says Leharry, "we have to be sure the numbers add up. We have to worry whether the body parts all came from passengers or whether some were from ground victims who also have to be identified."

Within three weeks, the forensic team had identified 240 of the 274 victims. As is generally the case in such mass disasters, the teeth, the most durable part of the body, held the key to most identifications.

Crime specialists often have to answer a third fundamental question: What is it? Is the powder taken from a suspected drug dealer an illicit substance and, if so, which one? Do the paint chips recovered at the site of a hit-and-run accident match paint samples taken from the suspect's automobile?

Many answers come from two laboratory mainstays—the gas chromatograph and the mass spectrometer, which are often used together to identify substances. The gas chromatograph enables chemists to analyze the components of substances that can be converted to gaseous form, such as petroleum products, smog, and smoke. The mass spectrometer also breaks down the chemical components of various substances and analyzes them. In the newest versions of these instruments, each produces a graphic printout of the various chemicals. These printouts are then compared to printouts of known chemical substances stored in a computer library; a good match provides the proper identification.

Forensic chemist Ken C. Raiser of the Illinois Department of Law Enforcement's crime lab in Joliet, Ill., describes how the two machines help in the battle against illegal drugs. Not only can they identify the drugs themselves, they can also identify the other chemicals that dealers often use to "cut," or dilute, drugs such as heroin and thus increase their profits. These substances may range from inexpensive drugs such as atropine and methapyrilene, which mimic heroin in certain simple chemical tests, to plain sugar. The identification of certain chemicals may help pinpoint a particular drug dealer as the source, and sometimes even locate the origin of the drug. Brown Mexican heroin, for example, can often be traced to a particular part of Mexico by the substances used to cut it. Such information is invaluable to law-enforcement agencies.

Sherlock Holmes's knowledge of anatomy, chemistry, and geology helped solve many fictional crimes. Today's forensic scientists —better trained, and armed with vastly more sophisticated equipment—are solving real ones. In a complex, imperfect society, they cannot eliminate crime, but they are making it much more difficult for the criminal to escape justice.

The Animal Navigators

By James L. Gould and Carol Grant Gould

Magnetic material found in the bodies of honeybees and homing pigeons may play a role in how they, as well as animals that migrate, consistently find their way home

An isolated mountaintop in central Mexico is covered each winter with orange-and-black monarch butterflies that have come from eastern North America. Some have traveled as much as 3,900 kilometers (2,400 miles) to winter in the mild, humid jungle. The ruby-throated hummingbird starts in the Northern United States or southern Canada and flies 800 kilometers (500 miles) across the Gulf of Mexico and back each year. The arctic tern, a large sea bird, flies from New England to Antarctica and back again — 35,000 kilometers (21,700 miles) each year, or the equivalent of seven trips across the continental United States. The large green sea turtle travels from its feeding grounds along the coast of Brazil to a tiny island in the Atlantic Ocean where it buries its eggs in the

warm sand. Then it swims laboriously back home across the ocean, for a total trip of about 2,000 kilometers (1,200 miles).

It is astonishing, not only that these animals travel such distances but also that they find their destinations with such accuracy. Scientists actually know little about how animals perform their navigational feats. We and others have analyzed and written about specific aspects of animal migration. Yet researchers are a long way from explaining animal navigation in precise detail.

For example, scientists long thought that migrating birds guide themselves north in the spring and south in the autumn simply by following the stars in the night sky. But then they found that many birds orient themselves correctly even when the stars are hidden by heavy clouds. Scientists also thought honeybees use the sun exclusively to find their way back to the hive after they have located flowers containing nectar and pollen. But bees, too, continue to navigate correctly under overcast skies.

When humans first began to sail the seas about 3200 B.C., they too navigated by the sun and stars. But they were unable to do so under cloudy skies. Then, in the 1000s or 1100s, humans devised the compass — an instrument that determines direction using the earth's magnetic field. This field, which stems from the earth's core, has force lines that run from magnetic north to magnetic south. The earth's magnetic poles differ slightly from its geographic poles. A compass is essentially a magnetized needle mounted in such a way that it can swing freely. It will always point to magnetic north. The compass provides a reference that travelers can use to determine in which direction they are moving.

Is it possible that migrating animals also use the earth's magnetism to find their way? Microbiologist Richard P. Blakemore, now of the University of New Hampshire, made a major breakthrough in 1975 that linked living creatures other than humans to the earth's magnetic field. He reported that some bacteria have particles that act as magnets in their one-celled bodies and use them to point themselves along the earth's magnetic field lines, a course that takes them to the mud in which they find food. At that point, scientists stepped up their search for a magnetic compass in migratory animals.

To learn how animals might use magnets, scientists first had to understand the basics of animal navigation. Migrating birds are not good subjects because they make only two major flights a year — south to their winter home and then back north again in the spring. So, to repeat any experiment enough times to ensure accurate results, a scientist would have to spend years gathering data.

We first worked on animal navigation in 1970 under biologist Donald R. Griffin of Rockefeller University in New York City, tracking the movements of migrating birds. The purpose of the project was to see if migrating birds, which travel at night, fly in a straight line even when it is cloudy and they cannot see the stars. We

The authors:
James L. Gould is assistant professor of biology at Princeton University in New Jersey and Carol Grant Gould is a research associate in Princeton's biology department.

A honeybee, *right,* which travels between its hive and sources of nectar many times a day, and pigeons, *below,* which can find their home lofts from great distances, are useful subjects for research in animal navigation.

worked in a field in upstate New York every dismally cloudy and cold evening in early spring and late fall to monitor the flocks migrating south and then flying north again. Our colleagues tracked the birds' paths on a Korean war-surplus ground-radar unit, and their tracking determined that during the few kilometers we could follow them, the birds kept on a straight course. We also used special equipment that measured the exact height of the clouds in the area and determined that the migrating birds were not flying above the clouds — where they could have seen the stars.

But simply knowing the birds can fly accurately without visual cues still does not tell us just how they navigate. So, like many experimenters before us, we turned to creatures that perform the same feats again

A dancing bee, *left,* holds center stage as it signals the location of some nectar. Gluing a number to a bee, *center,* helps to monitor the dance on a television screen fitted with a special grid for measuring the dance angle, *bottom.*

and again, over an observable distance. One is the honeybee, which uses its strikingly intricate navigational behavior to make repeated trips between the hive and food sources. The homing pigeon, which can be trained to fly to its home loft from hundreds of kilometers away, is another ideal subject for the study of animal navigation. Unlike migrating birds, the homer repeats its journey every time it is taken away from home.

Pigeons and bees each have their advantages and disadvantages as research subjects. Pigeons, being larger than bees, are easier to train and study. Also, pigeons are interesting because they have as complex a navigation system as any known to exist in nature. For example, we know they have a built-in map sense — the ability to know where they

are in relation to where they are going — because a trained homing pigeon can get home even from an unfamiliar location.

A honeybee, unlike a homing pigeon, cannot find its way back if you move it far from its normal neighborhood — the exact distance depending on the forager's age and experience. Still, bees are excellent experimental subjects, performing their feats far more often and reliably than pigeons. Bees are social insects, and a foraging bee looks for food for the whole hive — sallying forth 25 to 100 times a day to locate suitable flower patches nearby.

In nature, bees build their hive in a tree, with vertical combs on which they deposit the nectar they bring in. Modern beekeepers generally use wooden box hives filled with partially built vertical combs that mimic the bee's own. This encourages the bees to finish the job. The man-made hive has a small opening which the bees use as a door. Scientists generally use observation hives with glass walls that make it easier to observe our research subjects — the hive's 5,000 to 30,000 foragers.

Austrian biologist Karl von Frisch, who won the 1973 Nobel prize for physiology or medicine for his studies of honeybees, determined the basic navigational abilities of the honeybee in a series of experiments in the 1940s. First, he showed that the bees generally use the sun as a compass. But he also demonstrated that, even if the sun is hidden behind a cloud or a line of trees during all or part of the bee's flight, the bee has some compass sense that enables it to find its way back to the hive. The forager keeps track of its position with respect to home throughout its journey and compensates for the sun's westward movement, which varies at different times of the year. In the course of their foraging, honeybees are frequently faced with strong winds and must aim themselves well off course to compensate for the wind's effect. The bee does all this with a blurred kind of vision.

A flower patch, *below left,* is located at a 40° angle from a bee hive — measured horizontally, using the sun's position as a reference. Inside the hive, *below right,* a honeybee, who has visited the patch, translates that angle to the vertical plane with a dance that uses the pull of gravity as a reference.

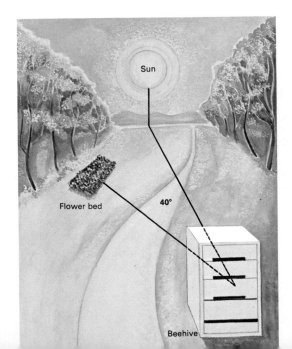

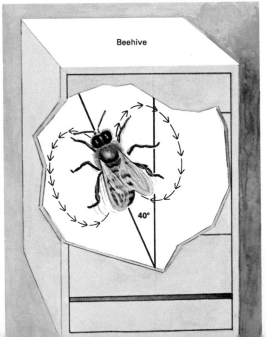

A Helmholtz coil creates a magnetic field around a laboratory beehive. Bees within the flight chamber — the net enclosure — are studied to see what effect changes in the field have on their navigational ability.

But the most remarkable — and useful — of all the bee's amazing feats is the way it "tells" the other foraging bees in the hive how to get to the food it found. Bees do a "waggle dance" that encodes all their complex computations into a few bodily contortions and a brief burst of sound. Frisch observed and described the dance in 1944. The bee makes a short, straight, waggling movement, then waggles itself completely around in a loop. It then makes another waggling movement in the other direction. The maneuver looks like a rough figure "8" set on its side.

Frisch demonstrated that a bee dance uses the sun as a reference point. He had already found that bees see in a part of the spectrum that ranges from orange-yellow to ultraviolet; that is, they cannot see red, as humans can, but they see ultraviolet — which we cannot. So he observed the dance using red light, which would not affect the bees. Dancing on vertical sheets of comb hanging from the top of an enclosed and totally dark hive, the bee uses gravity as a reference point, moving as if "up" were the direction of the sun outside the hive. For instance, if the sun is directly in front of the hive entrance, and the flower patch the bee has found is 40° to the left, the returning forager performs the dance 40° to the left of vertical on the comb. Frisch showed that the length of time of the waggle indicates the distance to the food; the longer the waggle lasts, the farther away the food is.

Once researchers decoded the bee dance, they were able to tamper with bees or their environment in various ways, to see how the tampering affected the bees' "calculations." For instance, Frisch and his student Gertraud Schifferer glued a tiny lead weight on a forager in a series of tests in the 1950s, and found that the bee almost always overestimated the distance to the food. By turning a hive on its side, and allowing the dancing bees a full view of the sun and sky, Frisch and his colleagues zoologists Martin Lindauer and Herbert Martin of Frankfort, West Germany, found that the bees pointed their dances directly at the food.

Other experiments have underlined the sun's importance to bees. When Martin and Lindauer used mirrors to reverse the actual position of the sun as seen by dancers in a horizontal hive, they found that the bees reversed their dances. When they obscured the sky completely by covering the hive, the dances became disoriented. So the bees were using the sun as their compass. But if the dancing bees could see a part of the blue sky, without the sun, they oriented properly. The bees must also find navigation cues in just a small patch of sky.

Frisch found the secret to this additional system in 1949. He allowed horizontally dancing bees to view a small piece of the sky — but not the sun — through various color filters. Most colors did not affect the dancers, but when he used a filter that masks ultraviolet light, the dancers became disoriented. Frisch then filtered out all light but ultraviolet and polarized that light. Polarizing light, in effect, filters out selected waves of the light's radiation. The bees reoriented their dances and danced correctly. When he turned the polarizer, the dancers changed the angle of their dance accordingly. Frisch concluded that bees can see patterns of ultraviolet polarized light in the sky fanning out from the sun. These patterns are visible to bees — though

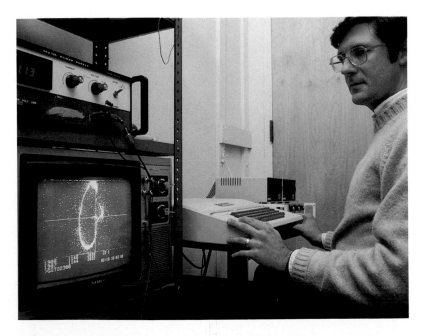

The daily variation in the local magnetic field displayed on the television monitor is part of the input to the computer that regulates the Helmholtz coil.

not to humans – even in a small patch of clear sky. Bees can use them to navigate according to the direction of the sun even when the sun is not directly visible. This is obviously helpful to an animal that often moves about under cover of leaves or branches, where it cannot see the sun, but can see patches of sky.

Thus, the bee uses not only the sun as its main compass, but also a backup system based on the sun – patterns of ultraviolet polarized light. On cloudy days, however, the sun is obscured; and, although ultraviolet light penetrates all but the heaviest clouds, the polarized patterns do not. Yet bees manage to forage, return to the hive, and do their dance. The bee has some clue other than the sun or the polarized light patterns. Along with biologist Michael L. Brines of Rockefeller University, we concluded that this additional backup system may use some form of magnetism.

Biologists determined about 1970 that bees are sensitive to the earth's magnetic field. Lindauer and Martin learned this while studying a nagging problem uncovered by Frisch about 20 years earlier – dancers signaling the angle between the sun and the food source rarely get the angle exactly right. For example, all foragers may dance 5° to the right of the correct direction at noon, but 10° to the left at 3 P.M. To test whether magnetism affects the dance error, Lindauer and Martin arranged a set of Helmholtz coils around a laboratory hive in such a way as to cancel the earth's magnetic field in the hive. They placed a grid over the glass-sided hive and then measured the angles of the dances from the grid. To their surprise, the usual dance error disappeared. In another experiment, when they turned the hive on its side, forcing the bees to dance on a horizontal surface without their normal cues from the sun or sky, the dance was at first disoriented. But after the hive had been on its side for several weeks, the bees – which continued to circulate outdoors to gather and store food – began dancing to only four compass points – north, south, east, and west. However, when the magnetic field in the hive was canceled, the dance again became disoriented. Scientists could not explain these results, but the findings suggested that bees respond in some way to the earth's magnetic field.

As we got more involved in searching for the bee's magnetic compass, we realized that our work was related to research being done on the navigation systems of homing pigeons. This work, too, covered a period of many years.

Homing pigeons have been bred as racers or message carriers for hundreds of years, but still each young bird must be trained before beginning its career. To teach a bird to home, a trainer takes it a short distance from its home loft, releases it, and makes sure it gets back to the loft. Over and over again, the trainer takes the bird a little farther away, until it can get home from many kilometers away.

British biologist G. V. T. Matthews, then of Cambridge University in England, developed a systematic method in the 1950s for training

A homing pigeon appears to set its course for home using magnetic north as a reference.

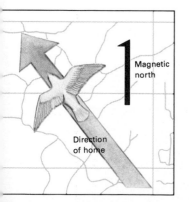

Magnetic north

Direction of home

Homing pigeons are
released in the first
stage of an experiment
in tracking the birds'
navigational patterns.

pigeons for scientific research. He used the conventional training sequence but, in addition, he carefully recorded data for each bird – including the direction in which it took off, and the exact distance covered on each release. Once Matthews had trained the birds, he began experimenting with various factors that might affect their homing ability.

Like other scientists who have followed Matthews in studying pigeon navigation, we have observed that working with homing pigeons is a time-consuming, tedious, but often amusing chore. Sometimes the pigeons are moody. Despite the greatest preparation and manipulation, they simply refuse to fly. Or they may rest in a nearby tree after release, waiting for a companion to fly with them.

The time-honored method of determining if a bird is a good homer has been to follow its path out of sight with binoculars as it disappears over the horizon. This method gives a fairly accurate reading, but it limits release sites to high points free of trees and brush that might conceal the observer's view of a departing bird. Also, it tells researchers nothing about what happens to the pigeon between the time it vanishes from their sight and the time it returns to the loft.

Biologist Charles Walcott of the State University of New York in Stony Brook and Martin Michener, his student, equipped pigeons with tiny radio transmitters in the mid-1960s and then tracked the

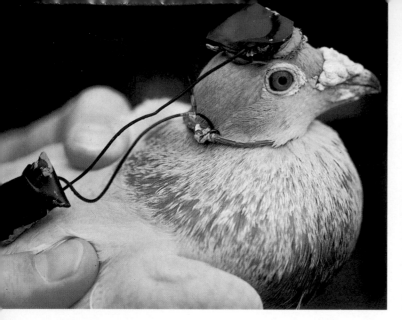

A tiny Helmholtz coil on a pigeon's head, *above,* affects the bird's ability to find its way home. This evidence that pigeons use the earth's magnetic field in some way led to the examination of pigeon tissue in a superconducting magnetometer, *above right,* which showed that the tissue contains magnetic material.

signals as the birds flew off. They also tracked the birds with an airplane to record their exact paths, following them but never moving so close as to disturb their subjects.

When techniques had been worked out for studying the birds' paths, scientists concentrated on finding out what compasses the birds use and how their mysterious map sense brings them home from unfamiliar locations.

Scientists have been trying for years to link the homing pigeon's navigational skills to some type of magnetic compass within them. Results of early experiments seemed to point away from a magnetic effect. We know now this was because a magnetic compass is a secondary system for the homing pigeon — just as it is for the honeybee. It took many experiments by many scientists to sort out some basic facts about the pigeon's use of magnetism. For example, biologists have frequently released birds with magnets attached to their heads. There was no hard evidence that the head contained the system that the pigeons might use to detect magnetic fields, but it seemed a likely spot to begin. The magnet-equipped pigeons still flew off in the right direction. If the birds were using a magnetic compass, it would have been distorted by the magnets they were wearing.

A series of experiments called "clock shifts" — first devised by zoologist Klaus O. Schmidt-Koenig of Tübingen, West Germany, in the 1950s — helped pinpoint how pigeons use the sun in their navigating. The clock shift took advantage of circadian rhythm, the built-in clock, that tells an animal what time it is and therefore what it should be doing — such as eating, sleeping, or waking. Circadian clocks are set naturally by the day, starting with sunrise, so humans can tamper with a pigeon's clock by putting it in a room and turning the lights on and off according to an artificial schedule. In this way, researchers can make the pigeon think it is any time they wish — in effect, resetting their clocks.

In a typical clock-shift experiment, researchers kept pigeons in a dark room and turned on the lights at noon, to simulate dawn or about 6 A.M. When the pigeons were released a few minutes later, 160 kilometers (100 miles) west of their actual home loft, the sun was high in the sky. The pigeons, calculating that it was dawn, expected the sun to be to the east. But the sun was to the south. When they could see the sun, the pigeons automatically used it as a navigational clue and flew off to the south, thinking that they were flying east toward home. Evidently, they could not take into account the fact that the sun was high above the horizon to the south — as it normally is at noon — instead of just rising on the horizon to the east.

Clock-shifted birds were not fooled on cloudy days, however. They flew straight home, indicating that they had some backup navigational system that did not involve the sun.

Intrigued by the idea of a secondary compass, biologist William T. Keeton of Cornell University in 1972 began to test various possibilities. On both clear and cloudy days, he released some pigeons wearing magnets on their heads to distort any natural magnetic system, and some control pigeons wearing brass weights to account for the weight of the magnets. On sunny days, the magnet-equipped birds homed as well as their brass-weighted comrades. But the magnet-equipped birds could not find their way home on cloudy days. At this point, the idea that pigeons could sense something as subtle as the earth's magnetic field lines seemed believable.

Attempting to pin down this effect, Walcott outfitted his pigeons in the early 1970s with tiny Helmholtz-coil helmets, which produce a local magnetic field that in effect cancels any existing magnetic field. With these helmets, he could control precisely the magnetic field that surrounded each bird's head as it flew. Sure enough, as he reported in 1974, the birds navigated correctly on sunny days. On cloudy days, the pigeons flew away from home when the coil was arranged to produce a field with the north pole pointing up through their heads. But when the south pole pointed up, they flew directly home. This indicated that the birds were using magnetic north as a reference for their calculations on cloudy days.

It occurred to us that honeybees and homing pigeons might have some permanent magnetic material in their bodies — like the iron ore magnetite of which early compass needles were made — to produce this sensitivity to the earth's magnetic field. Marine biologists had already discovered that the electrosensitive organs of such fish as sharks and rays, used to find the tiny electrical fields generated by potential prey hidden in mud on the ocean floors, can also detect the current that the earth's magnetic field induces in them as they swim through the ocean.

Scientists had long thought that no animal could manufacture magnetite. But in 1962, paleoecologist Heinz A. Lowenstam of the California Institute of Technology reported that the chiton, a

Homing pigeons released over a major disturbance (shaded circle) in the earth's magnetic field had difficulty in finding their way home, reinforcing the theory that they use the earth's field to navigate under certain conditions.

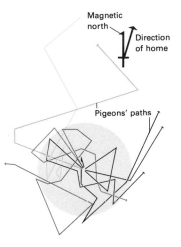

125

Monarch butterflies, *below,* which travel between North America and Mexico annually, and green sea turtles, *bottom,* which find their way across the Atlantic Ocean each year, are candidates for future research in migration by magnetism.

tiny marine animal, makes its teeth of magnetite so that they will be hard enough to scrape algae from rocks. And Blakemore's 1975 report on bacteria made a crucial link between magnetite and navigation. He photographed the bacteria through an electron microscope and saw the magnetite particles that keep the bacteria aligned with the earth's magnetic field.

In our view, magnetite particles in bees and pigeons would give the animal a built-in reference system to the north-south lines of the earth's magnetic field. The animal's mysterious inborn navigational information would then tell it how to proceed from the north-south reference point — for example, east or southwest.

But we could not imagine how to locate the traces of magnetic material that bees and pigeons would need. We calculated that an animal's magnetic field detector could operate successfully with no more than 1,000 magnetic domains. A domain is the smallest group of atoms that can act as a magnet.

The solution to our search for animal magnets came in 1978 — and not in a laboratory but at a dinner party. We explained to friends that we were searching for a technique to detect magnetism in bees. Our host, geologist Kenneth S. Deffeyes, a Princeton colleague, and geologist Joseph L. Kirschvink, then a graduate student, suggested we look for the magnetite as a geologist would. They explained that geologists use a cryogenic magnetometer, an exquisitely sensitive instrument, to detect minute magnetic fields in rocks. They arranged with colleagues at the United States Geological Survey (USGS) Paleomagnetics Laboratory in Flagstaff, Ariz., for us to put some bees through their magnetometer. We analyzed our bees there for the first time in March 1978.

We lowered the bees, encased in small lucite boxes, into the magnetometer, and the computer connected to it announced that most of our specimens were indeed magnetically "hot." Using plastic knives and pieces of broken glass — nonmagnetic tools that would not disturb any natural magnetism in the sample — we then divided the bees into head, thorax, and abdomen sections to see which part contained the magnetic material. First, we tried the heads, as the most likely location; then we tried the thorax sections. We finally located magnetic material in the bees' abdomens.

Back at Princeton, Kirschvink used the data from the magnetometer to calculate that each bee has a total of about 100 million domains of magnetite — many more than we had predicted.

We returned to the USGS magnetometer at Flagstaff with a suitcase full of specimens in May 1978, including bees, bats, beetles, and two of Walcott's homing pigeons. We found magnetic tissue between the brain and skull in the pigeons' heads.

To verify our results, we made several trips in 1978 and 1979 to the Woods Hole Oceanographic Institute in Massachusetts, which has a magnetometer sensitive enough to handle our samples. There, in collaboration with Walcott and Kirschvink, we located and removed tissue containing magnetite from about 24 pigeons. We also determined that the homing pigeon, like the honeybee, has many magnetite domains — about 100 million more than are actually needed for a "magnetic compass."

In the future, we plan to experiment with these animals and others to see why they might need so many sensitive detectors. The most obvious possibility is that bees and pigeons may need to measure the strength of the earth's magnetic field with great precision. The earth's field varies in intensity from place to place. The place to place variations may be important to the map system of the homing pigeons. Also, the earth's field varies in intensity over time, though by a very small amount. There is some evidence that bees set their circadian rhythms to the small daily variation in the earth's field strength, and the bees would need some way to read these variations.

Walcott performed an experiment in the 1960s with homing pigeons that shows they are disoriented by a major disturbance in the earth's field. He released birds near an iron mine, and they could not get their bearings. Some returned home despite their initial confusion, others never did. But an iron mine produces a huge magnetic disturbance. No one yet knows how the pigeons are equipped to detect and deal with smaller variations in the field.

We are eager to try our new-found techniques — the results of a union between biology and geology — on such animals as monarch butterflies, salmon, and green sea turtles. These animals might also be carrying tiny magnets ready to tell their nervous systems which way to fly, swim, or crawl. We look forward to finding further answers to the mystery of animal navigation.

Mending Shattered Minds

by Solomon H. Snyder

The ravages of schizophrenia can now be controlled by drugs whose effects also shed light on the complex chemistry of this terrible mental illness

She felt her brain rotting and exploding. She felt more guilty than the worst criminal on earth and at the same time she was impelled to destroy the human race. Bizarre thoughts, weird visions, and strange voices perplexed and terrified her. Underlying it all was an overwhelming anxiety.

In *Autobiography of a Schizophrenic Girl* (1951), Marguerite Sechehaye says, "In waking fantasies I constructed an electric machine to blow up the earth and everyone with it . . . . With the machine I would rob all men of their brains . . . . I was abominably, intolerably guilty, without cause and without motive. Any punishment, the very worst . . . could never deliver me of the load. The [voices] ordered me to burn my right arm or the building in which I was . . . . If I refused to obey, I felt guilty and cowardly and the anguish mounted . . . . I could find no rest, for horrible images assailed me, so vivid that I experienced actual physical sensation . . . . It seemed that my mouth was full of birds which I crunched between my teeth, and their feathers, their blood and broken bones were choking me. Or I saw people whom I had entombed in milk bottles . . . and I was consuming their rotting cadavers. Or I was devouring the head of a cat which meanwhile gnawed at my vitals. It was ghastly, intolerable."*

The everyday world can become a nightmare for the schizophrenic, as the disease distorts ordinary things and events into a horrible new "reality."

*From *Journal d'une Schizophrène* by Marguerite Sechehaye, © Presses Universitaires de France.

This young girl's experience is typical of the torment that schizophrenics endure. The psychic pain is so great that many victims would rather have terminal cancer. Many schizophrenics commit suicide to escape their mental anguish.

Until the mid-1950s, acute schizophrenics were doomed to suffer for most of their lives. There was no cure, not even a treatment that could ease the symptoms. I recall my first visit in 1958 to a large mental hospital in Washington, D.C., when, as a freshman medical student, I was beginning research on the psychology of schizophrenia. Reviewing records, I came upon case after case of individuals who had entered the hospital between 1910 and 1920 and were still there. These cases were not simply instances of institutional neglect. I found these patients to be in a state of hopeless mental deterioration, consumed with the voices only they could hear.

Because of its frequency and the horror of its acute symptoms, schizophrenia is generally regarded as the most severe psychiatric disorder. At least 1 per cent of the population of the United States suffers from a severe form of schizophrenia and another 2 to 3 per cent probably is afflicted with more moderate versions. Before the mid-1950s, a diagnosis of schizophrenia was a life sentence without a possibility of parole. But the introduction of effective antischizophrenic drugs called neuroleptics radically changed this situation.

In 1955, about 634,000 patients were in mental hospitals in the United States, at least half of them schizophrenic. The number of patients was increasing at a rate of more than 13,000 each year. About 1956, chlorpromazine, the first neuroleptic, was introduced into U.S. mental hospitals, and the trend abruptly reversed. Over the next 15 years, the number of patients in mental hospitals actually fell 50 per cent while the total U.S. population rose steadily. Treatment for other mental disorders also improved, but such a massive decrease in hospitalized patients would not have been possible without the use of neuroleptics to treat schizophrenia. The drugs have led also to new research on the causes and mechanisms of schizophrenia, and greatly increased our understanding of the disease.

Like many physical illnesses, mental illnesses can be classified in several ways. However, because we know less about brain structure and function than about other areas of the body, classifications of mental illnesses are less precise. Brain disorders involve interwoven disturbances of thought and feeling, and the border between sanity and insanity is frequently a blurred one. Moreover, cultural prejudice against "crazy" people and popular misconceptions about the nature of various mental illnesses also cloud the issue. For example, many people believe that schizophrenia involves "split," or multiple, personalities, similar to those exhibited by the main characters in books and motion pictures such as *The Three Faces of Eve* and *Sybil*. It does not. The schizophrenic has an entirely different mental problem. He has a single personality — but it is a shattered one.

The author:
Solomon H. Snyder is a professor of psychiatry and pharmacology at the Johns Hopkins University School of Medicine.

One broad way to classify mental disorders is by the degree of the patient's contact with reality. A minor form of mental illness is known as a neurosis. Neurotics have contact with reality most of the time. However, they may have an obsession or fear, such as a dread of crowded places. Or they may be anxious or depressed for reasons that they cannot define. A severe form of any mental illness is called a psychosis. Psychotic individuals have essentially lost all contact with reality. A psychotic schizophrenic may think that he is Jesus Christ or Napoleon, or hear voices telling him to kill all human beings.

Mental disorders can also be classified by their symptoms. For example, manic-depressive illness has quite different symptoms from those of schizophrenia. Manic-depressive patients may be extraordinarily elated at times but severely depressed at other times. Sometimes the episodes of mania and depression alternate with clocklike regularity every few days, weeks, or months.

Schizophrenia has so many symptoms that psychiatrists are not sure whether it is a single disease or a grab bag of many disorders. However, most psychiatrists consider schizophrenia to be a chronic, or long-term, disorder in which thinking, feeling, and behavior become severely disorganized. The most distinctive symptom is a disturbance in thinking that usually shows up in the way patients talk. Their statements are often rambling and unrelated, or connected in only a limited way. The most easily recognized thought abnormalities are delusions of persecution or grandeur. A typical schizophrenic delusion of persecution is a feeling that "the FBI is out to get me." In a delusion of grandeur, a patient may be convinced that he is some great historical figure, such as Jesus Christ or Napoleon. Some are convinced that their thoughts are being broadcast to the world, or that some outside agency is inserting thoughts into their mind.

Hallucinations, in which the person hears or sees something that is not really there, are the most dramatic symptoms of schizophrenia. For example, the patient may hear "voices" that speak directly to him and comment critically on his behavior. Patients may also have hallucinations of taste or smell.

Despite the variety of symptoms, psychiatrists have grouped schizophrenics in this manner. Those most concerned with delusions of persecution or grandeur are called paranoid schizophrenics. Patients who are rigidly immobile and totally mute, as if in a stupor, although sometimes wildly hyperactive, are called catatonic schizophrenics. The most deteriorated patients are hebephrenic schizophrenics. They usually behave childishly, speaking incoherently and giggling inappropriately much of the time.

Depending on when and how the disease begins, psychiatrists also distinguish between process and reactive schizophrenics. Process schizophrenics never behave quite normally, even as small children. They gradually withdraw from other people and, by late adolescence, begin to lose contact with reality. They seldom display dramatic

Glossary

Amphetamines: A class of drugs used as stimulants and appetite depressants.

Barbiturates: A class of sleep-inducing drugs.

Catatonic schizophrenia: A condition characterized by withdrawal, rigid immobility, muteness, and occasional excessive activity.

Depression: A mental disorder characterized by deep, prolonged periods of dejection and despair.

Hebephrenic schizophrenia: A condition characterized by incoherent speech, inappropriate giggling, and childish behavior.

Neuroleptics: A class of drugs used to treat schizophrenics.

Neuron: A nerve cell.

Neurosis: A mild mental disorder characterized by depression, anxiety, obsessions, and fears.

Neurotransmitters: Chemicals that transmit messages between neurons.

Placebo: A pill or other medical treatment with no active ingredients, used as a control in tests of new medicines.

Paranoid schizophrenia: A condition characterized by delusions of grandeur and persecution.

Psychosis: A severe mental disorder that deeply disrupts normal behavior.

symptoms, but quietly "fade into the woodwork." By contrast, reactive schizophrenics may adjust to life fairly normally until they have a sudden, often dramatic, breakdown as young adults.

Few process schizophrenics ever achieve normal behavior despite careful and extensive treatment. Many reactive schizophrenics, on the other hand, recover within a few months and are able to lead normal lives, even without treatment. They may never suffer a relapse.

Family studies suggest that process and reactive schizophrenia may be different diseases. Relatives of process schizophrenics are often schizophrenic themselves, but relatives of reactive schizophrenics are rarely schizophrenic. However, they frequently become manic-depressives, suggesting that reactive schizophrenia is an unusual form of manic-depressive psychosis.

Scientists are not sure what causes schizophrenia, or whether the causes are purely environmental, or biological, or both. Some researchers have speculated that extreme pressures exerted by the parents — from emotional neglect to a smothering closeness — might cause a child to develop schizophrenia. This implies an environmental cause for the disease. Others argue that schizophrenia is a biological disease that is inherited and that abnormal parental behavior merely reflects a parent's own schizophrenic tendencies. Studies over the past 50 years suggest both factors are involved.

Studies of twins, in particular, indicate the presence of both factors. Monozygotic, or identical, twins come from the same egg, and have

Schizophrenics suffer many torments, ranging from (*left to right*) an inability to fit their thoughts together logically; persuasive hallucinations of voices that criticize their actions or direct their behavior; withdrawal from their surroundings; feelings of grandeur.

virtually identical genetic makeup and physical appearance. Dizygotic, or fraternal, twins develop from two separate eggs and have no greater genetic similarity than do other brothers and sisters. If one identical twin has a disease with a genetic cause, it is highly likely that the other will develop it. There is much less chance of this with fraternal twins.

Studies show that the identical twin of a schizophrenic has a 50 per cent chance of developing the disease. For fraternal twins, the probability is only about 15 per cent. Clearly, these studies indicate an important genetic role in schizophrenia. But since the probability that both identical twins will be schizophrenic is only 50 per cent — despite their genetic identity — there must be environmental factors operating as well.

Researchers have explored the births and early childhoods of sets of identical twins where one twin later developed schizophrenia. Psychiatrist William Pollin of the National Institute of Mental Health in Bethesda, Md., found that the twin who developed schizophrenia almost invariably weighed less at birth and tended to be clumsier as a small child. He concluded that one environmental factor in schizophrenia is the environment in the womb.

In work begun in 1962, Seymour S. Kety, Harvard Medical School professor of psychiatry, and other workers have examined adoption records to evaluate the role of genetics in schizophrenia. They conducted most of their studies in Denmark, where carefully detailed

U.S. Population

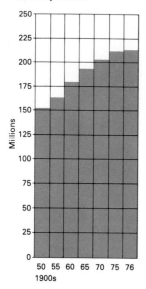

Schizophrenics in State and County Mental Hospitals

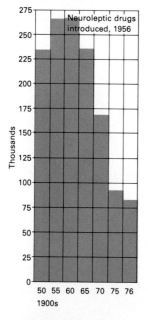

Neuroleptic drugs introduced, 1956

Despite the rise in population, *top,* people hospitalized for mental illness has steadily declined since 1956, when neuroleptic drugs were first used to treat schizophrenia, *above.*

records of the entire population are kept. The scientists searched out people who had been adopted at birth, found out which of these had become schizophrenic, and then located both their biological and adoptive parents. The investigators found a much higher incidence of schizophrenia among the biological than among the adoptive parents. This indicates that genetics plays an important role in schizophrenia.

Since genes direct the synthesis of proteins, which in turn regulate all of the body's chemical reactions, a specific biochemical abnormality must be involved in schizophrenia. The problem was to find it.

Neuroleptic drugs played a leading role in the search for this abnormality. When chlorpromazine was introduced, physicians thought it was just a supersedative to calm agitated schizophrenics. However, in studies conducted four years before, in 1952, French psychiatrists Jean Delay and Pierre G. Deniker had found that chlorpromazine did much more than calm patients. In addition to relieving the agitation of overactive patients, it seemed to make withdrawn patients more active. Moreover, it did not seem to affect all schizophrenic behavior equally. Anxiety, overactivity, and hostility, for example, were not altered immediately. The first prominent drug-induced improvement the French researchers found was in the schizophrenic thought disorder. They speculated that chlorpromazine is more than just a sedative. It must act specifically on the symptoms of schizophrenia.

Subsequent research has borne this out. When researchers began to compare the effects of chlorpromazine to those of *barbiturates* (a class of sedative drugs) in the early 1960s, they found the barbiturates were no more effective against schizophrenia than were placebos — sugar pills. Moreover, while the first neuroleptics acted as sedatives, those developed later did not. But they proved to be just as effective in relieving schizophrenic symptoms.

Psychiatrists found themselves in a curious position — they were using a drug that clearly worked against schizophrenia, although it did not cure it, but they did not know how the drug worked. What parts of the brain did it affect? What biochemical systems did it alter? If they could answer these questions, perhaps they could identify the basic causes of schizophrenia.

When scientists tested chlorpromazine in the laboratory with various biochemicals known to operate in the brain, they found that it reacted with almost all of them. As a number of other neuroleptics, all chemically related to chlorpromazine, were developed, researchers also tested their biochemical reactions to see if they correlated with each drug's relative ability to control schizophrenia. Only one of the tests showed any relationship to the neuroleptics' ability to control schizophrenia. This test involved the chemical dopamine.

In 1962, pharmacologist Arvid P. Carlsson of the University of Göteborg in Sweden measured the amounts of various neurotransmitters in brains of rats treated with neuroleptics. Neurotransmitters are

Diseased Branches on the Family Tree

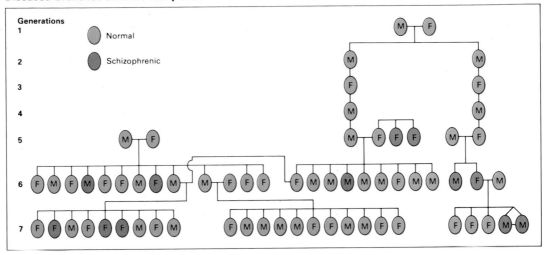

The family tree of two Swedish families joined by marriage shows a high incidence of schizophrenia, suggesting that the disease runs in families and thus has a genetic basis. Of the 68 individuals in this family, 12 suffered from schizophrenia, a disease rate nearly 18 times greater than normal.

chemical messengers released by one neuron, or nerve, and sent to another. This transmits information from nerve to nerve. Practically all information-processing in the brain involves neurons communicating with each other via various neurotransmitters.

After sacrificing rats that had been treated with neuroleptics and removing their brains, Carlsson mixed the brain tissue in a test tube with chemicals that fluoresced or glowed when they reacted with neurotransmitters. This allowed the neurotransmitters to be measured. In his experiments, he found that the levels of these chemicals in the drug-treated brains were no different from those in untreated rat brains. However, Carlsson also measured the breakdown products of these neurotransmitters — the compounds into which they change after transmitting their chemical message from one nerve to another. He found that the drugs did alter concentrations of the breakdown products of one neurotransmitter — dopamine. Carlsson also found that different neuroleptics influenced these dopamine-related chemicals in proportion to their ability to control schizophrenia. He concluded that he was on the track of finding where neuroleptics perform their antischizophrenic actions.

Carlsson speculated that the biochemical patterns he had observed indirectly indicated that the neuroleptics blocked the nerve-cell receptor sites for dopamine. Receptors are molecules on the surface of cells such as neurons that recognize and accept only certain biochemicals that are sculpted to fit them as a lock fits a key. A test of Carlsson's hypothesis would require direct measurement of receptor sites for dopamine.

In the 1970s, my research team developed a technique to measure how much of the neurotransmitter attached to brain membranes that contain the proper receptors. Using compounds — either neurotransmitters or related drugs — tagged with a radioactive substance, it

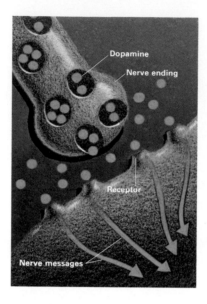 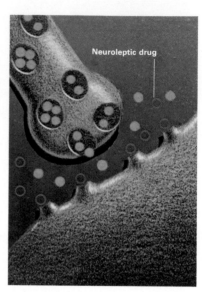

Dopamine

Nerve ending

Neuroleptic drug

Receptor

Nerve messages

A Drug Blockade
Dopamine molecules released by one nerve fit into receptors on another to transmit their neurochemical message, *right*. To control schizophrenia, neuroleptic drugs fit into the same receptors, thus blocking dopamine transmissions, *far right*.

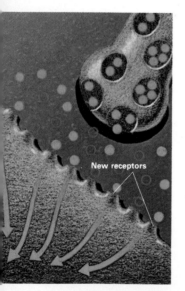

New receptors

Molecular Counterattack
Long-term drug treatment causes nerves to develop more dopamine receptors. The resulting increase in dopamine sensitivity may cause tardive dyskinesia.

became possible to count the neurotransmitter or drug molecules bound to the brain membranes. After grinding up normal rat brains, we isolated the brain membranes containing the receptors and mixed them in a test tube with the radioactive compound to be tested. When we filtered this mixture, only the membranes and the molecules of the compound that had bound to the receptors remained. A radioactive counter then measured the amount of the test compound that had been picked up by the brain. When we used this technique with different neuroleptic drugs, we were able to compare the relative effectiveness of the various compounds.

Unfortunately, the concentrations of receptors for any given neurotransmitter in the brain are extremely low, amounting to only about one-millionth by weight of brain tissue. And, the drugs and neurotransmitters can also bind to all sorts of other proteins, fats, and carbohydrates on brain membranes as well as to the actual receptors. This indiscriminate binding would vastly exceed the small amount of binding to the true neurotransmitter receptors. However, technical improvements in the early 1970s increased the ability to detect true receptor-drug interactions.

We applied these techniques to find receptors for most of the known neurotransmitters in the brain. In 1975, postgraduate students Ian Creese and David Burt and I measured dopamine receptors in the brain by monitoring the binding of radioactive neuroleptic drugs to brain membranes. Philip Seeman of the University of Toronto in Canada independently obtained similar results. Soon, my team and Seeman's group were able to test the theory proposed 13 years earlier by Carlsson. We tested 30 or more neuroleptics that were being used to treat schizophrenics. Their relative ability to block dopamine receptors in the test tube was closely linked to how well they work in treating schizophrenia. Thus neuroleptics seem to work by blocking dopamine receptors in the brain.

Another line of investigation, involving amphetamine drugs, also pointed toward a role for dopamine as a factor in schizophrenia. Amphetamines have long been used as stimulants and appetite suppressants. Because of the euphoria they produce, they have also been widely abused. Addicts must take increasingly larger doses of the drug to produce a "high," and they experience a profound depression when they stop taking the drug. After large doses, amphetamine addicts frequently develop a mental disorder that closely mimics paranoid schizophrenia. Indeed, many addicts have been diagnosed as schizophrenics until doctors learned that they were taking these drugs. So, many psychiatrists concluded that amphetamine psychosis is very much like at least some forms of schizophrenia.

Psychiatrist John M. Davis of the University of Chicago found in 1972 that small doses of amphetamines — amounts that students might take to keep themselves awake the night before an exam — produce striking effects in schizophrenic patients. When controlled schizophrenics were given small doses of amphetamines, their symptoms got dramatically worse. This did not happen when he gave equal doses of amphetamines to persons with other mental illnesses.

The Field of Battle
Many of the nerve paths that use dopamine to carry their messages lead into the limbic system, a primitive part of the brain that is believed to control emotions. It may hold the key to conquering schizophrenia.

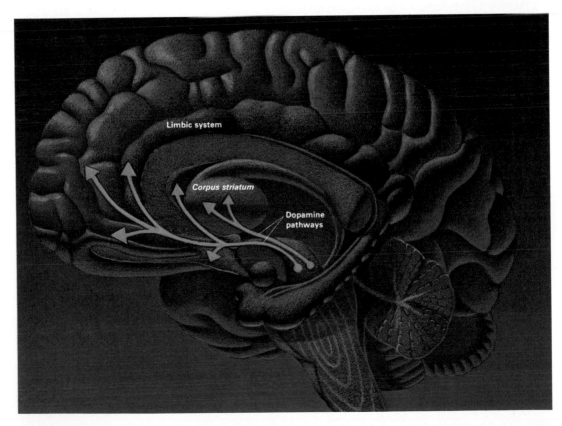

In addition to Davis' work, research in the 1960s and 1970s indicated that most of the effects of amphetamines result from the release of dopamine and similar neurotransmitters from the nerves that normally store them. By blocking dopamine receptors, neuroleptics reduce the action of dopamine and diminish schizophrenic symptoms. Amphetamines have the opposite effect. They increase dopamine release onto the receptors—making schizophrenic symptoms more severe. They even produce schizophrenic symptoms in persons who are not schizophrenic.

Since several lines of research point to dopamine as an important biochemical factor in schizophrenics, it is important to know the area of the brain in which this neurotransmitter operates. Some of the most prominent dopamine neuronal pathways are in the limbic system, a region of the brain that regulates emotions. Dopamine neurons extend to several limbic areas. Researchers still do not know which, if any, of these areas is the site of the antischizophrenic action of the neuroleptics. In looking for the answer, they have turned to some unwanted properties of the neuroleptics.

Neuroleptic drugs produce serious side effects that are also linked to the dopamine systems. When first treated with these drugs, many schizophrenics develop abnormal muscular movements throughout the body, symptoms that closely resemble those of Parkinson's disease. Victims of Parkinson's disease become quite rigid and have difficulty in walking, talking, and moving their arms.

No one knows the precise cause of Parkinson's disease. Many scientists blame it on a virus that affects certain brain structures. The major brain abnormality found in patients with Parkinson's disease is the degeneration of a dopamine pathway associated with a part of the brain called the *corpus striatum,* which regulates motor activity. Research has shown this degeneration to be the source of the symptoms of Parkinson's disease. When the dopamine levels are restored by treating these patients with L-dopa—the amino acid precursor, or forerunner, of dopamine—those who were previously immobile regain normal movement.

An even more serious side effect of neuroleptics also involves dopamine neurons in the corpus striatum. The effects that resemble Parkinson's disease occur early in neuroleptic treatment. However, after months or even years of treatment with high doses, some patients develop what seems to be an opposite array of symptoms. In this reaction, called tardive dyskinesia, their lips, tongues, arms, and legs move in an uncontrolled flailing pattern. The mouth and facial muscles can move so violently that patients cannot even eat.

In some ways, this reaction is more serious than the Parkinson-like side effects. When the neuroleptic dose is lowered, the Parkinson symptoms vanish. This does not happen with tardive dyskinesia, however. Reducing the dose of neuroleptics often makes the symptoms worse. Although increasing the dose alleviates symptoms temporarily, tardive dyskinesia appears to be an irreversible – but not universal – side effect of neuroleptic treatment.

The disease is so disfiguring and disabling that some researchers consider it worse than schizophrenia itself. Tardive dyskinesia occurs, depending on individual dosages, in 5 to 30 per cent of schizophrenics treated with neuroleptics. Some doctors thus believe that neuroleptics should not be used in treating schizophrenia, because they carry the risk of permanent neurological damage. See NOURISHING OUR NEURONS, *Science Year,* 1980.

The fact that tardive dyskinesia seems like the opposite of Parkinson's disease and, in fact, is alleviated somewhat by increasing neuroleptic doses, suggests a possible explanation of what changes occur in the brain. After being blocked by high doses of neuroleptics for a long time, perhaps the neurons become excessively sensitive to dopamine. What might cause such supersensitivity? Could there be a change in the dopamine receptors themselves?

My research team obtained direct evidence in 1975 that this happens. We developed an experimental animal model of tardive dyskinesia simply by treating rats with neuroleptics. Using the same laboratory techniques we used originally to measure the binding of dopamine to receptors, we found that the drugs provoked an increase in the numbers of dopamine receptors in the rats' corpus striatum. Thus, we suspect that, in tardive dyskinesia, the chronic blocking of dopamine receptors stimulates the neurons that contain them to make more dopamine receptors. The result is an uncontrolled motor activity resembling that caused by an excess of dopamine.

One of the major goals in schizophrenia research is to develop more effective neuroleptics with less damaging side effects. The ability to measure dopamine receptors in test tubes is helpful. A researcher can now screen dozens of drugs in one day to test their ability to block dopamine receptors. The drugs that block dopamine most effectively are also generally more powerful in treating the disease.

What direction is schizophrenia research likely to take in the future? Scientists need to know whether particular abnormalities in dopamine or other systems in the brain lie at the heart of the schizophrenic disorder. They must pinpoint the part of the brain involved in the disease.

Researchers must also try to find other drugs that might relieve schizophrenic symptoms. We now know of at least 25 distinct neurotransmitters in the brain. Most of these have been discovered in the last few years, and, as yet, we know of no drugs that enhance or block their effects. One important task for future research will be to develop drugs that act selectively upon each of the neurotransmitter systems in the brain.

In pursuing this work, researchers have two aims. As scientists, they hope to learn how schizophrenia operates. As doctors, they hope to relieve the awful human suffering.

Hall 26

PATTERNS
OF
PARADISE

Keeping Nature's Diary

By Mark Perlberg

Crammed with the things of this earth — animal, vegetable, and mineral — natural history museums look at past and present life to see the future.

At 6:49 A.M. on Feb. 13, 1980, the sun rises out of Lake Michigan and illuminates Grant Park downtown on Chicago's lakefront. At the south end of the park, Field Museum of Natural History begins its day. The bronze doors at the north and south entrances, through which most of the public enters the vast building, are still locked. Guards on the night shift have made their last rounds along nearly four dozen long corridors of exhibits, laboratories, and storage and work areas. Some of the night guards pause in their patrols of the dark halls to enjoy a favorite exhibit in solitude by flashlight. Others are more aware that the building, completed in 1921, moans and creaks like any older building. The occasional bang of a ventilator flap or knock in a steam pipe can still startle them. But their night-long vigil is almost over.

Field Museum is one of a handful of the world's great natural history museums. Like kindred institutions — such as the American Museum of Natural History in New York City, the National Museum of Natural History (a part of the Smithsonian Institution) in Washington, D.C., the British Museum (Natural History) in London, and others in Toronto, Mexico City, Paris, Berlin, and Leningrad – Field Museum plays many roles. All of these institutions share the same kinds of tasks and problems. What is said of Field Museum can, to some degree, be said of all the others.

To the general public, the museum is a series of exhibits that show the earth as it was and is. It provides a visual history of the planet and its life. But a museum is much more than that. To the amateur collector, it is a place where a hobby or interest can be turned into useful scientific work. To the visiting scientist, it is a catalog of earth's history, a place where evidence is kept. Just as a county clerk's office holds a community's birth, marriage, and death certificates, a museum holds the records of life on earth. To the curators in charge of taking care of these records, the museum is the source of much of their own scientific research.

By 7:30 A.M., staff members begin arriving through the west entrance of the Field Museum. The cooks brew fresh coffee in the newly refurbished cafeteria. The day engineer checks the heating levels in the building. The receiving dock is opened so that supplies and specimens for the museum's collections can be delivered.

The collections – the heart of any museum – illustrate how little the public sees of a museum. Collections consist of "things" – birds, beetles, arrows, spears, bones, seeds, plants, shells, rocks – grouped together because of some sort of relationship. Field Museum has 13 million things grouped, numbered, and named in its catalogs. Of these, only about 65,000 objects – 0.5 per cent of the total – are on display. The rest of these specimens are stored in nonpublic areas in drawers, on cabinet shelves, or in bottles and tanks filled with preserving fluid. Some of these objects have already been studied and are being held for the record; others are now being studied. Some specimens in the collections may not be worked on for years to come.

A few minutes before 8 A.M., guards open the bronze doors for early arriving curators and other staff members. Among the arrivals are artists who design the new and temporary exhibitions; artisans who build models and exhibit cases and install the temporary shows; and technicians who mount plant specimens on sheets of acid-free paper or clean and assemble the bones of prehistoric animals. Maintenance workers also arrive, along with those who work in the print shop and

The author:
Mark Perlberg is a Chicago-based editor and free-lance writer.

such departments as business, personnel, and public relations. By 8:30 A.M., Field Museum's staff of 300, including the administrators charged with the difficult tasks of running this complex enterprise and finding the money to keep it going, is at work.

At 8:45 A.M., the day-shift security guards assemble and get their assignments. A veteran guard forecasts a slow day. It is cold and there may be some snow. Besides, February is not a big tourist month in Chicago and it is early in the semester for school trips, although some

Long lines of visitors filed into Field Museum when the record-breaking Egyptian exhibit, "The Treasures of Tutankhamon," was featured in 1977.

are scheduled for today. He recalls a February day during a blizzard more than 10 years earlier when exactly 31 people visited the museum. On the other hand, there were more than 12,000 visitors on the day after Thanksgiving 1979.

Upstairs, on the third floor, departmental coffeepots are perking. Scientists and technicians gather in a geology workroom to warm up with their morning cups. Their conversation ranges from politics, traffic, and basketball scores to professional topics such as the feeding habits of various extinct South American mammals.

At 9 A.M., the visitors begin to arrive. By any standards, what they see is impressive. They walk up a flight of white marble steps, pass through a row of white marble columns that flank the entrance and enter Stanley Field Hall.

The museum's focal point, Stanley Field Hall is as long as a football field, 21 meters (68 feet) wide, and 23 meters (75 feet) high. Light pours down through the skylighted ceiling and is reflected off the white marble floor and white walls. On both sides, graceful arches open onto halls of exhibits that lead to the east and west wings of the museum. At the south end of the hall, two curving stairways lead to the second floor, where the same pattern of side halls and wings is repeated. More exhibits are on display on the ground floor beneath

A museum curator, *right,* places colorful insect specimens with their kin in a collection drawer. An array of formidable-looking rhinoceros beetles, each about nine centimeters (four inches) long, awaits study, *below.*

Measuring facial bones in an extensive museum collection of prehistoric human remains helps an anthropologist trace the anatomical development of the human skull.

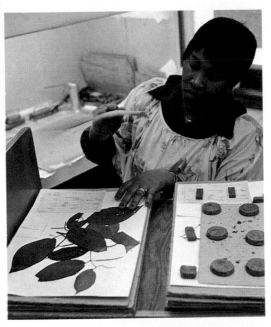

A botany assistant, *above left,* glues dried plant specimens to herbarium sheets, while in a nearby anthropology storeroom, *above,* another worker checks woven baskets collected from Indian tribes of North America's northwest coast. In a zoology storeroom for large animal skins, *left,* a museum aide examines a leopard skin.

145

Museum scientists visiting the field sift through the biologically rich tidal mud of Panama to gather marine worms and other animals to add to their museum's collection.

Stanley Field Hall. Storage and work areas are on the ground, third, and fourth floors and in several new facilities behind exhibits. In all, the building has 8 hectares (20 acres) of floor space, of which 3.2 hectares (8 acres) are devoted to the exhibits.

Stanley Field Hall has only a few symbolic displays, three of them monumental in size. Each represents one of the scientific departments of Field Museum.

Zoology is represented by a pair of fighting bull elephants, a display constructed in 1908 by Carl E. Akeley, the father of modern taxidermy. This exhibit set new standards for taxidermy because it showed that even very large animals could be mounted in dramatic, lifelike poses.

Anthropology is represented by a pair of giant totem poles 12 meters (40 feet) tall that were carved out of red cedar by American Indians in British Columbia. Several large masks from New Guinea stand at the south end of the hall.

To symbolize geology, a mounted skeleton of *Gorgosaurus,* a nasty-looking meat-eating dinosaur, stands over its fallen prey, a *Lambeosaurus* that met its end in a riverbed in Alberta, Canada, some 45 million years ago. While the fearsome head and teeth of *Gorgosaurus* look frighteningly real, the visitor is actually looking at a plaster cast. The real head, about 91 centimeters (36 inches) long, lies in a storeroom on the third floor. It is a large specimen and museum officials feared that it might fall off the mounted skeleton and smash to pieces on the floor.

Botany does not fare as well as the other departments in Stanley Field Hall, for a natural reason. The museum tried to find a large tree for the hall, but each one chosen needed more light than could be obtained from the natural light that filtered through the skylights overhead. So the botany department had to be content with

smaller trees whose major botanical virtue is that they can grow in the light available.

At 10:30 A.M., a bus carrying first-graders from a suburban school pulls up at the west entrance. The children, accompanied by a teacher and several parents, are ushered into the Place for Wonder on the ground floor.

The Place for Wonder is an excellent place to introduce youngsters to the world of museums. It has specimens that can be touched, smelled, and in one case, even struck. Two small girls spot a large mounted diamondback rattlesnake. They squeal, pick it up, run their hands over the creature's scales, and put it down—quickly. With evident pleasure, a boy in a wheelchair shakes a small plastic box that contains rattles taken from similar diamondback rattlers. Another boy inspects spectacularly colored rocks; and a third picks up a meteorite. A dark-haired girl picks up a mallet and strikes a Chinese gong that hangs in a section of the room labeled "Country of the Month."

Meanwhile, college students and other researchers are arriving at the museum's library on the third floor. The library has 185,000 volumes and an impressive collection of scientific journals, some of which date back more than 100 years. It is considered among the best in the world. The library also has a rare-book collection that contains priceless books on natural history, some dating almost from the beginning of printing in the 1400s. One volume, the "Elephant Folio" of paintings of North American birds by John J. Audubon, is on display in a second-floor lounge area. Each week, a page is turned to reveal a new example of the great 19th-century naturalist's art.

At 11 A.M., members of a family from suburban Evanston stare solemnly at a row of mummies and mummy cases from ancient Egypt in Hall J on the ground floor. Behind the onlookers is an enormous black sarcophagus, or stone coffin, covered with hieroglyphics. Nearby is a cedarwood funeral ship, 10 meters (32 feet) long, built in 1842 B.C. to ferry

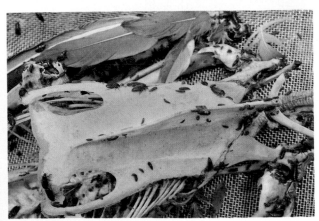

Piecing together the corkscrew-shaped fossil cast of a beaver tunnel, millions of years old, *top,* or cleaning a modern American Indian rug, *center,* require human hands, but the cleaning of a bird's carcass is done best by beetles and larvae, *left.*

147

the body and burial party of King Sesostris III down the Nile River from Memphis, the first capital of ancient Egypt.

In 1979, just under 1 million persons visited Field Museum, and it is a safe bet that most of them trooped downstairs to gaze at these and other relics of a complex civilization, some of which date back nearly 6,000 years.

The "mummies are the most popular permanent exhibit in the museum," says botanist Lorin I. Nevling, Jr., assistant director for science and education. "There just seems to be a universal appeal for the things of ancient Egypt. I think that was borne out by the great success of the King Tut show here and everywhere in the United States." The "Treasures of Tutankhamon" exhibit, 55 objects from the tomb of King Tutankhamon, toured museums in the United States on loan from the Egyptian government. About 1.3 million persons saw the exhibit in Field Museum from April to August 1977. Crowds of similar size jammed museums in Washington, New Orleans, Los Angeles, Seattle, New York City, San Francisco, and Toronto, Canada.

"It had all kinds of things that interest people," Nevling explains. "It had gold, it had death, it had the promise of immortality. The mummification process, after all, is really an effort at reaching immortality. The Tut show seemed to us to have all the elements that one would hope to have in an exhibit."

While Field Museum has an outstanding collection of material from ancient Egypt and other early Near Eastern civilizations, other museums, such as the Metropolitan Museum of Art in New York City, have more extensive holdings of such artifacts. But few museums can match Field Museum's displays and collections on North and South American Indian cultures. Even fewer can rival its holdings in masks, weapons, ornaments, clothing, and objects of art from the vast Pacific Island world of Micronesia, Polynesia, and Melanesia.

It is this richness that enabled the museum to mount its latest show "Patterns of Paradise," which was to open in early March 1980. It is a unique display of tapa, cloth made by tropical peoples around the world from tree bark, and used in clothing, costumes, masks, blankets, and hats. Much of it is richly colored with bold geometric designs. Most of the samples in this first extensive museum show of tapa came from Field Museum's own collection.

At 11:30 A.M., Hall 26 on the second floor, where "Patterns of Paradise" is being installed, is dimly lighted to protect the colors in the cloths, which are fixed between flat pieces of plastic framed in red Honduras mahogany. Some of these frames hang from the ceiling and others are placed in neat plastic cases on the floor.

Designer Donald R. Skinner has come down from his fourth floor office to oversee the installation. "We wanted to build a lot of

Conservation specialists examine a massive Northwest Coast Indian totem pole restored to its original unpainted beauty after weeks of hard work.

ambiance — atmosphere — into this show," he says, "so I put in all the ambiance we could afford. I sat down and drew some sketches and came up with the idea of 'islands' — that is, of displaying the cloth in islands of clear plastic that we hope will seem to float in the darkened room. To carry out the theme, we built structures resembling ships' booms, from which we'll hang wooden, lanternlike lights. And we had a tape recording made in Samoa of village sounds, voices, the sounds of people beating bark to make cloth and of the surf . . . to play during the show."

John E. Terrell, associate curator of Oceanic archaeology and ethnology, is in charge of the new exhibit. "We are the only museum in the country that could put this show on using primarily material from its own collection," he says proudly.

The idea for the show was born in 1976 during a "Members' Night," when the museum allows members a peek at its storerooms and laboratories. That night, Terrell displayed samples of tapa in a room across from his office. The interest in the colorfully patterned cloth surprised him so much that he asked Anne W. Leonard, a museum volunteer, to make a thorough search of the department's tapa collection. Leonard grew so engrossed in the task that she and Terrell decided to write a book on tapa, because no definitive work existed. Another staff member then suggested that they might as well put on a tapa show. Now, after years of planning and work, the exhibit was taking shape.

At lunchtime, a pleasant hubbub of voices fills the museum's cafeteria. A boy about 8 talks loudly about dinosaurs. He wants to go upstairs after lunch to see the skeleton of *Apatosaurus,* more usually, but less correctly, called *Brontosaurus,* a giant stretching 22 meters (72 feet) from tail to nose. "The dinosaurs are the second most popular exhibit in the museum," Nevling reports. "You'll usually find young children leading their parents by the hand to see them. It seems to be an age-related thing."

Museum curators and staff members also eat lunch in the cafeteria. The curators — the keepers of the collections — and their technical assistants perform the basic scientific work of the museum. There are 33 full-time curators at Field Museum, and their activities vary considerably.

John B. Kethley, curator of insects, spent the morning at a staff meeting and hopes to work after lunch on a grant proposal requesting federal funds for research. Tomorrow he will work on his mites and ticks. Eugene S. Richardson, curator of fossil invertebrates, spent the morning choosing photos for an album of fossils collected from the Mazon Creek area southwest of Chicago, an important site for collecting fossils of soft-bodied animals. Richardson and others, including hundreds of enthusiastic "rock hounds" — amateur collectors — have made this 300-million-year-old site one of the best known in the world.

Melvin A. Traylor, Jr., chairman of the zoology department, has been struggling to complete the final volume of *Peter's Checklist of the Birds of the World*. Many noted ornithologists have worked on this 15-volume project, begun in 1931. When completed, it will list nearly all the known species of birds, their descriptions, known ranges, relationships, and all previously published scientific literature about them. It will be a base line for future bird studies all over the world.

Telephone calls, letters, and visits interrupt the curators at their reading, writing, measuring, and cataloging. A schoolchild has dug up something in the backyard and wants it identified. Is it an Indian arrowhead? A newspaper reporter wants to know when the 17-year cicadas will appear again in northern Illinois. A gardening group is looking for a speaker for its March meeting.

Some of Field Museum's curators are working elsewhere on this February day. Edward J. Olsen, curator of mineralogy, just back from a tour of Antarctica with museum members, is at the University of Chicago, studying tiny dust grains found in certain meteorites. Olsen believes that these grains represent the earliest form of solid matter in the solar system and is analyzing their chemical makeup. Donald Whitcomb, newly appointed assistant curator of Near Eastern archaeology, is digging and surveying an ancient Red Sea port at Quseir al-Qadim in Egypt. Botanist Timothy C. Plowman is also on expedition, studying the Indians' use of plants in medicine in the upper Amazon Basin in Brazil. After his evacuation from Bolivia in November 1979 during a political coup, anthropologist Michael E. Moseley went to Peru, where he is studying the ancient and extensive canal and irrigation systems that were built by the native pre-Columbian civilizations.

Work at the museum continues in the afternoon. Volunteer Vicki Hlavacek, an American Airlines stewardess, is spending another of

Looking for the fine details of bone structure, an ichthyologist examines the stained and preserved skeleton of a tropical fish, *above left.* A museum worker adjusts a scanning electron microscope to examine the even finer details of the contents of a tadpole's stomach, *above.*

her days off in the white-walled zoology preparation laboratory on the third floor. Dressed in a white coat and wearing plastic gloves, she is dissecting a colobus monkey that recently died in a Chicago zoo. When she removes as much flesh, skin, and fur as possible with surgical tools, she will place the skeleton in a lidded 38-liter (10-gallon) fish tank that is swarming with black *Dermestes* beetles and their larval young. The beetles will pick the skeleton clean. "This gives us a completely clean skeleton without any damage to the fine bones," says Michael L. Reed, a technical assistant in charge of the "bug room." When the beetles have done their job, the skeleton will be placed in a freezer to kill any beetles or larvae remaining on it. Then it will be cleaned and added to the museum's collection. Flesh is removed from the bones of larger animals, such as antelopes, by cooking them in special vats in a combination of hot water and an enzyme detergent.

The volunteers and technical assistants make an important contribution to the museum. The 260 or so regular Field Museum volunteers have donated thousands of hours of work over many years, and some have become as knowledgeable in their particular fields as many professionals. They are a diverse group — retired executives, homemakers, hobbyists, and interested students. Technical assistants typically have some prior training in their work. Many have done graduate work in science, or in special fields such as museology, conservation, and microscopy.

Not far from the bug room on this afternoon, for example, several technicians are using the museum's scanning electron microscope

Richly decorated tapa, or bark cloth, is mounted in mahogany display cases, *below.* Along with masks and other tapa artifacts, *below right,* it becomes an exhibit on the uses of bark cloth in South Pacific cultures, *opposite page.*

(SEM) to study flower pollen. With its high magnifications and clear image resolution, the SEM can bring out structural differences in the pollen of plant species, thus helping botanists to distinguish between the parent plants and establish their relationships.

The ordering of plants, animals, or even minerals, by their relationships to one another is called classification. It is a museum's fundamental scientific work. William E. Burger, chairman of the botany department, has made several trips to Costa Rica to study, collect samples, and classify that country's unusually rich *flora* (plant life). It is no accident that Burger made the forests of that small Central American country his beat. The botany department has always specialized in Central and South American flora. Its herbarium, the fifth largest in the United States, already contains the world's most complete collection of specimens from Guatemala and Peru among its collection of 2 million dried plants. Over the years, the department has produced one very large work, *The Flora of Guatemala,* a description of the known plants of that country, and is working on *The Flora of Peru,* begun in the 1930s. Together, the books amount to 14,000 pages of plant descriptions and classifications.

But Burger is not content simply to maintain and add to the herbarium. His own research deals with the origin, success, and enormous diversity of flowering plants, a group that developed only about 130 million years ago, relatively late in the 3-billion-year plus history of life on earth.

Three stories below Burger, on the ground floor, Harold K. Voris, associate curator of amphibians and reptiles, is analyzing data

For children eager to get a feel for nature, a museum is a matchless introduction to the earth and its wondrous life.

accumulated on trips to the South China Sea and Malaysia on the feeding habits of a little-known predator, the poisonous sea snake. Voris spent last summer determining the size of fish swallowed by sea snakes. He studied the remains of fins found in snakes' stomachs and learned that both the larger and smaller sea snakes are preying on small fish, even though the bigger snakes could take larger prey. No one knows why the animals behave in this way.

Thousands of bottles containing specimens of snakes, frogs, and fish in alcohol solution are lined up outside Voris' office. On racks against a wall are alligator skins and skulls. Voris picks up one of the smaller bottles, containing a frog in a solution of ethyl alcohol. Like others in this work, he sees museums as a vehicle for preserving knowledge of species that may soon be extinct. "It is right, in a way, to compare the museum to a great library of the natural world," he says. "But really, the museum is unique, because there aren't an infinite number of copies of what it collects and studies, and they can't be reprinted. This little frog is not only an individual end point but a representative of its species. Maybe if it weren't in a museum, it would be unknown to us. After all, more and more species are going extinct, and except for the fossil record, which is far from complete, nature is very unforgiving. She hasn't spent a lot of time preserving her own materials."

It is 3 P.M. A young zoologist hurries to the third floor to talk with biogeologist David M. Raup, curator of geology and chairman of the department. She is writing her doctoral dissertation on a method of determining the sex of mollusks in the North Sea by examining their shells. She wants to talk to Raup because he has written on the evolution of shell forms. In fact, he has programmed computers to display images of shells so that their design similarities – and hence their evolutionary relationships – can be studied with mathematical precision. Raup discusses his work at length with her, and, later, with another visitor.

"What is really interesting about this procedure," he says, "is that we have been able to draw forms that don't occur, either living or in the fossil record, and then to ask the very interesting question, 'Why didn't they occur?' In some cases, they don't occur because they would be poorly adapted from an engineering standpoint – they would make a lousy shell. In other cases, we can't figure out why a certain shape hasn't been tried. It may be the result of simple evolutionary chance – the animal just hasn't gotten there yet. Maybe it will in the future."

As the afternoon shadows lengthen across a table in Raup's office, the visitor ponders the uses of the museum. All the things in this enormous building – and all the people studying them – tell us much about life's past and present. But many scientists think that the real importance of a museum lies in giving us some hint of the future. They believe that museums provide bedrock research for other scientific fields – in medical research, for example, where an exact identification of an insect parasite may be essential in learning how a disease spreads. The thousands of plants and animals not yet discovered, described, or studied may hold the key to many biological puzzles and provide unexpected economic and social benefits. The evolution of our own society may be illuminated by information on the behavior of more primitive societies. The long course of life itself may hold clues to the direction future life may take.

Much of Raup's work, for example, deals with mass extinctions of life that occurred long ago, the largest about 225 million years ago, the most recent about 65 million years ago. Do such events suggest another die-off in the future? "Fortunately," says Raup, "these events occur at widely spaced intervals in our time scale."

On that time scale, the museum's day is ending. In the exhibit areas, it has been a slow day – only 871 visitors, less than a third of yesterday's total. By 5 o'clock, they and most of the staff are gone. A few curators work late in the darkened building and there are night classes scheduled on such subjects as Egyptian hieroglyphics, scientific illustration, and birdsong. By 8 or 9 P.M., the building will be inhabited only by the guards, the past, and, perhaps, the future.

The Stuff Between the Stars

By Edward B. Jenkins

Clouds of dust and patches of high-temperature gas abound in a universe once considered empty and cold

On a clear night, the sky appears to be filled with stars. You can see more than 2,000 of them distinctly. Millions more make up the white splash of the Milky Way, the glistening stellar cascade that gives its name to our galaxy. But the stars that we see, and the innumerable other stars beyond our vision, occupy only a tiny part of the universe. For example, if we were to scale things down so that each star floating through the immensity of space were no bigger than a grain of sand, which, oddly enough, has a similar density, the average distance from grain to grain would be about 50 kilometers (30 miles).

Because early astronomers could see nothing in the considerable "clearings" between the stars, they wondered whether the huge interstellar void was a perfect vacuum. Within the last 100 years, however, investigators have found evidence that the stars in our galaxy are immersed in a vast sea of gas and dust. And within the last 10 years, thanks to radio and space telescopes, we have discovered much about the nature of this intriguing stuff between the stars.

Most of the gas in this interstellar medium (ISM) is hydrogen, the most abundant element in the universe. There are also measurable amounts of other elements. In addition, there are infinitesimal particles of dust, which probably consist of silicates, graphite, and

If our galaxy lacked the gas and dust of the interstellar medium (ISM), the Milky Way would appear in the night sky as a narrow band of bright stars.

water ice. But this material is spread so thinly between the stars that interstellar space does come close to being a vacuum. The average density of the ISM, only one atom per cubic centimeter, is more than 10 billion times thinner than the "empty space" a good laboratory vacuum pump can achieve. If we were to look through a tube from a platform above the earth's atmosphere toward the most distant star we can see, 3,000 light-years (9.5 trillion kilometers) away, we would be looking through the same amount of gas as if we peered through a similar tube only 1 meter (39 inches) long at sea level.

Where did the stars and the gas and dust between them come from? Both the stars and the ISM are part of a cycle of heavenly birth, death, and regeneration that began about 13 billion years ago. Many cosmologists believe that a huge explosion, a big bang, took place then. Immediately after the explosion, radiation energy formed an expanding sphere called the primordial fireball. Most of the fireball became matter, chiefly hydrogen and a little helium gas. The matter continued to expand and, in time, separated into great clumps. Under the relentless influence of gravity operating over billions of years, the clumps fell together and turned into galaxies, including our own Milky Way. Smaller clumps inside the galaxies collapsed even further and became stars. As a result, matter is very unevenly distributed throughout the universe.

Stars continue to form in the same way. Gas and dust in the ISM contract under the force of gravity and form a compact, luminous ball. Heat is created as the gaseous and dusty matter becomes compressed, and an internal pressure builds up. When the temperature is high enough to sustain nuclear burning and the internal pressure equals the gravitational force, the infall of matter ceases and a star is born. This pause in the compression — the life of a star — lasts for millions or billions of years depending on how massive the star is. Nuclear reactions in the star's interior create additional heat energy that keeps it burning and prevents it from contracting further.

While some of the interstellar gas may consist of primordial matter that was left over from the original big bang and chanced to escape the gravitational plunge to stars and galaxies, astronomers believe that most of it originated from earlier generations of stars. Stars may return a good portion of their material to the ISM in one of two ways. Some types continue the cycle in a relatively mild manner, sending a stellar wind of escaping matter out into space. Others, notably the supernovae, undergo sudden radical changes climaxing in explosions that blow the stars' outer layers back into space.

Our knowledge of the composition of the ISM confirms its chiefly stellar origin. In addition to hydrogen, the ISM and the surface layers of stars recently formed from it contain several elements that are produced almost exclusively by nuclear reactions inside stars. If the interstellar gas were primordial — that is, matter that came from the big bang but never became part of a star — it would consist almost

The author:
Edward B. Jenkins is a senior research astronomer at the Princeton University Observatory.

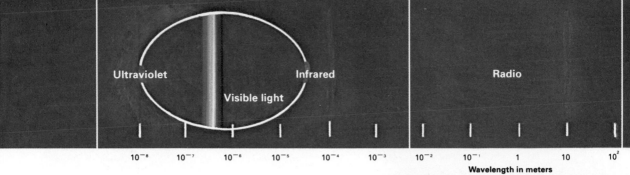

totally of hydrogen and helium. It would contain none of the heavier elements such as carbon, nitrogen, and oxygen. Because we do find traces of these elements in the ISM, we know it was processed through stars.

When did astronomers become convinced that space is filled with highly dispersed matter? As early as 1847, it was apparent to German-born astronomer Friedrich G. W. Struve at the Pulkovo Observatory near Leningrad, Russia, that the number of stars seen at different levels of apparent brightness did not conform to a uniform distribution of stars in space. Laws of physics predict how dim a star should be in proportion to its distance. Struve found the more remote stars were dimmer than they should have been. One explanation for this could have been that the stars were not uniformly distributed; another, that the light just became "tired" of traveling such great distances. But even in the mid-1800s, Struve thought that some sort of semitransparent substance in space could be absorbing some of the light.

In 1910, Edward E. Barnard of the Yerkes Observatory in Williams Bay, Wis., reported on his study of dark patches in the Milky Way where there seemed to be almost no stars. He suggested that the stars were there but that they were hidden by light-absorbing material.

From 1930 through 1932, astronomers Robert J. Trumpler, Edwin P. Hubble, and Peter van de Kamp studied a number of objects, such as globular star clusters — concentrations of many stars — or other galaxies, away from the plane of the Milky Way galaxy. They found far fewer of these when they looked through the plane of the Milky Way. The astronomers concluded that interstellar dust was obscuring these objects and that the dust is distributed throughout the galaxy. In essence, then, we look out at the universe through a vast layer of haze.

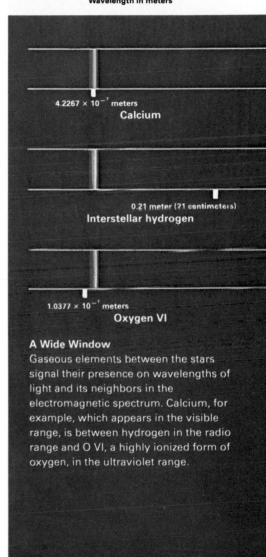

4.2267×10^{-7} meters
Calcium

0.21 meter (21 centimeters)
Interstellar hydrogen

1.0377×10^{-7} meters
Oxygen VI

A Wide Window
Gaseous elements between the stars signal their presence on wavelengths of light and its neighbors in the electromagnetic spectrum. Calcium, for example, which appears in the visible range, is between hydrogen in the radio range and O VI, a highly ionized form of oxygen, in the ultraviolet range.

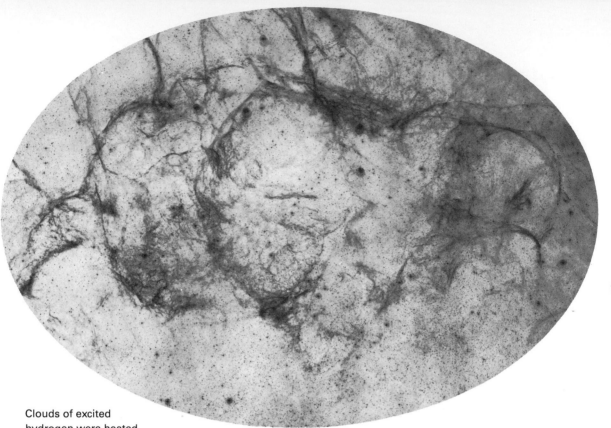

Clouds of excited hydrogen were heated to a visible state by powerful shock waves of an exploding supernova. The hot hydrogen lights up as wispy filaments of the supernova remnant.

Astronomers detected the interstellar dust by direct visual observation. Later, using entirely different observations, they found evidence of gaseous material, which we now know accompanies the particles that obscure starlight.

How can we identify the elements that exist thousands of light-years away? Fortunately, heavenly objects give off huge amounts of energy that reaches earth as electromagnetic radiation or waves. Light is the most familiar form of this radiation, but it is only a small part of the entire range, or spectrum. This spectrum extends from the long wavelengths of radio waves, microwaves, and infrared rays through the visible to the short wavelengths of X rays and gamma rays. The visible spectrum appears as a band of colors because our eyes see the different wavelengths of light as colors, ranging from red for the longest waves to violet for the shortest.

Because every element radiates in its own characteristic way, astronomers can find out what stars are made of by analyzing their electromagnetic radiation. The elements either emit or absorb radiation, which appears as bright or dark lines in the spectrum. When astronomers analyze the radiation from stars with a spectroscope, the lines tell them which gaseous elements are present. Bright spectral lines, called emission lines, represent energy being given off by excited, or hot, gases. Alternatively, absorption lines appear at the very same places in the spectrum when these gases absorb light energy from some other source, such as a star.

After astronomers began attaching spectroscopes to telescopes, they could focus on a star and record the absorption lines from substances in its outermost layers. The pattern of the lines identified elements in these layers and indicated whether or not the atoms had been ionized — had lost some of their electrons through collisions at high temperatures. Astronomers studied many stars and detected many elements in them in the early 1900s, but one astronomer, Johannes F. Hartmann, at the Potsdam Observatory in Germany, made a surprising discovery when he studied binary stars.

Binary, or double, stars and multiple star systems, where two or more stars are in mutual orbit, show periodic Doppler shifts in their absorption lines. A Doppler shift is the apparent change in frequency, or wavelength, caused by motion to or away from an observer. Astronomers study how the absorption lines of binary stars appear to increase or decrease in wavelength — toward the red or blue ends of the spectrum — as the stars move away from or toward us.

In 1904, Hartmann noticed that most of the absorption lines in the spectrum of a bright binary star system in the constellation Orion showed the expected Doppler shift, but two sharp lines — those of ionized calcium — did not seem to shift. He concluded that the calcium was not in the star but in front of it. Astronomer Vesto M. Slipher of the Lowell Observatory near Flagstaff, Ariz., offered strong support for Hartmann's conclusion by reporting in 1909 that he had observed many binary stars whose spectra had a few nonshifting calcium lines.

Most astronomers accepted this interpretation. They embraced the new viewpoint that the stars did not exist in a perfect vacuum and that gaseous elements distributed through space caused the spectral absorption. But a few people questioned this conclusion. They argued that the absorption lines must come either from another massive star close to the binary system or from a tight cocoon of gas surrounding the orbiting stars. The existence of interstellar gas became indisputable only after astronomers collected a massive amount of data on the spectra of calcium. From these studies, they learned that absorption lines were stronger for more distant stars because the farther away they were, the more gas there was between them and us. Also, the gas did not move with the stars.

Until the mid-1900s, astronomers derived all their knowledge about the heavens from optical telescopes. But the visible band is only a narrow window within the wide span of the electromagnetic spectrum. New types of telescopes now enable us to collect information from all types of radiation. We use infrared instruments and giant antenna arrays to monitor the longer infrared and radio waves, while other telescopes gather data from the shorter ultraviolet waves, X rays, and gamma rays. Whatever the wavelength of the radiation we study, we are still looking principally for those telltale emission and absorption lines.

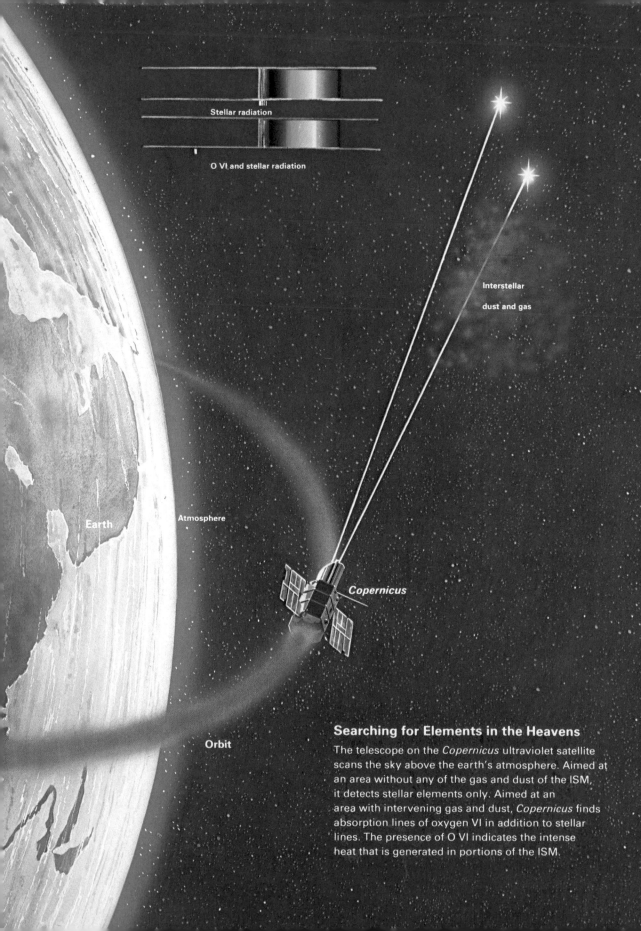

Stellar radiation

O VI and stellar radiation

Interstellar

dust and gas

Earth

Atmosphere

Copernicus

Orbit

Searching for Elements in the Heavens

The telescope on the *Copernicus* ultraviolet satellite scans the sky above the earth's atmosphere. Aimed at an area without any of the gas and dust of the ISM, it detects stellar elements only. Aimed at an area with intervening gas and dust, *Copernicus* finds absorption lines of oxygen VI in addition to stellar lines. The presence of O VI indicates the intense heat that is generated in portions of the ISM.

Visible spectroscopic studies showed that hydrogen is the predominant element in the makeup of stars, so astronomers theorized that it should also be the most abundant gas in space. But visible spectroscopic studies could not detect interstellar hydrogen. Elements emit or absorb energy at more than one wavelength. Dutch astronomer Hendrik C. van de Hulst suggested in 1945 that hydrogen should also radiate in the radio region, and would probably be found at a wavelength of 21 centimeters.

Harold I. Ewen and Nobel prizewinning physicist Edward M. Purcell of the Harvard College Observatory in Cambridge, Mass., first registered the radio spectral line of atomic hydrogen in 1951, using a simple radio telescope. The most intense radio signals came from a narrow band centered on the Milky Way, which turned out to be a region of huge clouds of hydrogen. During the following years, astronomers mapped this emission carefully, studying the shapes, movements, and distribution of the hydrogen clouds. Because radio waves could easily pass through the dusty haze layer that mingled with the stars and blocked optical studies, the scientists were able to trace the structure of our entire galaxy for the first time.

In 1963, astronomers detected signals that showed a great abundance of molecules in addition to single-atom elements in many of the denser clouds. After these discoveries, simple compounds like hydroxyl (OH) and carbon monoxide (CO) seemed to be commonplace in the sky. But in order for complex molecules to form, a number of atoms must meet and cling together. Scientists thought this could not occur in space because the atoms are so widely scattered and have few opportunities to join. Therefore, when observers first used radio astronomy to search for molecules, they spent little time tuning into possible frequencies of molecules with more than two atoms; they believed that such substances would be destroyed almost as fast as they were created because of the harsh interstellar environment.

However, in 1968, astronomers abandoned the notion that interstellar chemistry is confined to building very simple compounds. Then scientists at the University of California, Berkeley, discovered radio emission lines of gaseous ammonia (NH_3) near the center of our galaxy. This finding triggered a rash of new discoveries of increasingly complex organic compounds in space. Among them were formaldehyde (H_2CO), isocyanic acid (HNCO), cyanoacetylene (HC_3N), formic acid (HCOOH), methyl cyanide (CH_3CN), acetaldehyde (CH_3CHO), and methyl mercaptan (CH_3SH).

By 1980, radio-emission lines from more than 50 different compounds had been detected and identified. As a rule, these complicated molecules seem to be found only in the centers of clouds that are extraordinarily dense by interstellar standards. Slow atomic collisions that can form the molecules occur there frequently. Also, the thick layers of dust in the clouds serve to shield the molecules against the disruptive ultraviolet radiation.

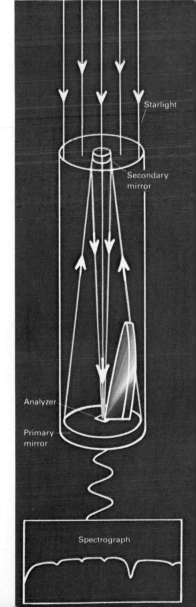

Starlight enters the *Copernicus* telescope, hits the primary mirror, is reflected to the secondary mirror, then is divided into its component colors by a spectrograph. This information, converted to data form, is transmitted to the earth where it appears as a graph, or spectral tracing.

Starlight

Secondary mirror

Analyzer

Primary mirror

Spectrograph

Just how productive interstellar molecule factories can be was seen when the University of Maryland's Benjamin M. Zuckerman in 1974 found ethyl alcohol in the interstellar cloud Sagittarius B2, near the center of our galaxy. The finder of the "heavenly hooch" reported, "Preliminary estimates indicate that the alcoholic content of this cloud. . . if purged of all impurities and condensed, would yield approximately 10^{28} [10 billion billion billion] fifths at 200 proof. This [far] exceeds the total amount of all man's fermentation efforts since the beginning of recorded history."

During the 1970s, studies of the distribution of emission from carbon monoxide molecules indicated that the inner spiral arms of our galaxy contain many gigantic, dense clouds of gas that are richer in molecules than they are in free atoms.

Nature often rewards us when we take the trouble to view our surroundings from a different perspective. For example, radiation in the far-ultraviolet end of the spectrum cannot penetrate the upper layers of the earth's atmosphere. So when astronomers could mount observing instruments on satellites that orbit above the earth's atmosphere, they opened new windows on the observing spectrum. Now they can record diverse forms of radiation, and they have discovered astrophysical phenomena that once went completely undetected by even the best ground-based telescopes. A telescope on

A computer-generated picture of the invisible interstellar gas in the Milky Way, placed against a photo of visible stars, is based on data from a radio telescope. The colors indicate the direction in which the gases are moving relative to the earth: red gases are receding; blue gases are approaching; and green gases are stable.

the *Copernicus* satellite, an automated observatory launched in August 1972, revealed that the ISM had its share of surprises in both its composition and physical state. The 80-centimeter (32-inch) diameter telescope on *Copernicus* contains an ultraviolet spectrometer for recording the detailed pattern, with changing wavelengths, of ultraviolet light. Just as in the visible stellar spectra, particular interstellar atoms or ions absorb the light at special wavelengths. This allows astronomers to detect many more substances in the ultraviolet.

My colleagues at Princeton University and I, who are responsible for operating *Copernicus,* have collected a large volume of data on various elements in space. We included observations of some elements at different levels of ionization — that is, elements whose atoms have varying numbers of electrons removed. When we first identified various absorption lines, we found evidence of O VI — oxygen atoms with five of the eight electrons removed. This is a surprisingly high level of ionization for an atom in the ISM. A great deal of energy is required to separate these five electrons, with their negative charge, from the positive charge of the atom's nucleus. The removal of the electrons one after another requires more energy each time because the atom's positive charge is increased.

We first thought bombardment by cosmic rays, extremely fast-moving subatomic particles, might provide the energy. However, we

Supernova remnant

Tunnels

Supernova

dismissed this possibility when we noticed that the width of the absorption lines of ionized oxygen differed from lines of the other substances in interstellar clouds. We surmised that these lines were wider because the atoms were moving rapidly in random directions, much as they would if the gas were very much hotter than usual. We now believe the oxygen atoms can be so highly ionized because they are located in entirely separate, special regions of the ISM where the temperature is extremely high — somewhere between 100,000°C and 1,000,000°C. At this temperature, the free electrons in a gas move so rapidly that they can knock off an atom's electrons when they strike it. As temperatures increase, the average number of electrons that can be removed also increases.

Tunnels of Heat
Powerful shock-wave fronts from two or more supernovae — massive exploding stars — set up a network of tunnels of hot gas in the cooler ISM. Successive exploding stars maintain the heat of these tunnels.

In 1974, Debra A. Meloy, then one of my undergraduate students at Princeton, and I followed up on the initial discovery of O VI by examining the spectra of many stars observed by *Copernicus*. To our surprise, we found the absorption lines of O VI, which were sometimes rather broad and weak and therefore difficult to recognize, in the spectra of almost all the stars we studied. Princeton astronomer Donald G. York looked for other kinds of highly ionized atoms and found the weak lines produced by N V — nitrogen atoms with four electrons removed. Evidence was mounting that the high temperature regions were relatively numerous. They were also distinct from the previously identified areas that contained denser, lower-temperature gas. In essence, the ultraviolet spectra revealed, for the first time, that the ISM has areas that are very hot.

These areas are about 1,000 times less dense than the cooler areas to compensate for the high temperature and keep the pressures in approximate balance. The contrast in density between the hot and cold interstellar matter is about the same as the ratio of the densities of air and water — about 1,000 to 1.

When we published the results of our studies in 1974, it was as if we were reliving the experience of Hartmann and Slipher in the early 1900s. Just as skepticism greeted their discovery of nonstellar calcium absorption lines, our interpretation of the results of our study of O VI was challenged by some scientists.

One group of astrophysicists at the University of Colorado in Boulder was investigating what happens when a stellar wind slams into the surrounding gases. John J. Castor, Richard McCray, and Robert Weaver found in 1975 that the wind's force creates a cavity, or bubble, in the cooler interstellar gas. This bubble is a type of shell around the star. The impact of the hot star's high-speed gas stream on the inner wall of the bubble creates enough energy to heat the gas to more than 100,000°C.

The Colorado scientists believed that the O VI we found might arise from the tight shell of hot gas surrounding the star or group of stars we observed with the *Copernicus* instrument, and not from a pervasive network of hot gas in space. They suggested that the hot gas

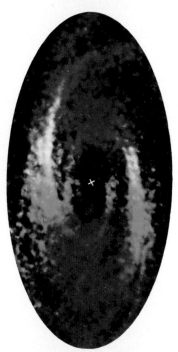

M81, a nearby galaxy, *top,* in radio view, *above,* displays gases that move between the stars just as they do in the Milky Way galaxy.

seemed to be pervasive because of a coincidence arising from the necessary limits on our star sample. The only stars hot and bright enough to have their spectra measured in the ultraviolet are the same ones that have strong stellar winds. The Colorado researchers theorized that if we could have observed stars that lacked strong stellar winds, we would have found that the hot gas did not exist throughout interstellar space.

By 1978, however, using the *Copernicus* telescope, I amassed sufficient evidence to show that the presence of O VI was related to a star's distance from us rather than to the type of star involved. The strength of the absorption lines we recorded generally increased in the case of more distant stars because there was more hot gas between us and them. Also, the lack of apparent movement of the gas, as determined by studying the Doppler shift of the stars, seemed more consistent with widely distributed material that was not linked specifically to individual stars.

Additional support for a broad distribution of the hot gas came from observations reported in 1974 by scientists at the University of Wisconsin in Madison, followed by studies at Massachusetts Institute of Technology in Cambridge and Tokyo University. Using instruments on sounding rockets, which carry instruments above our atmosphere for a short time, these researchers observed a diffuse, patchy glow of low-energy X rays all over the sky. They suggested that the glow came from a widely distributed high-temperature gas.

How is the gas heated in the first place? One source of heat is shock waves in the ISM generated by supernova explosions. Donald P. Cox and Barham W. Smith of the University of Wisconsin calculated in 1974 that the extraordinarily powerful blast waves from exploding stars occur frequently enough and spread widely enough to establish a network of hot gas tunnels through the cooler, denser interstellar gas. These tunnels are maintained as shock waves spread out from one explosion after another, overlap at their edges, and reheat the gas. Observations confirming that there is more hot gas in the vicinity of known supernova remnants than elsewhere in the ISM support the supernova origin of the heating. Christopher F. McKee of the University of California, Berkeley, and Princeton University's Jeremiah P. Ostriker arrived at an even stronger conclusion in 1977. McKee and Ostriker believe that if the cool ISM were clumpy to begin with, instead of smoothly distributed, the supernova explosions would be even more far reaching. The hot gas would then occupy most of interstellar space, leaving the cooler, denser gas and dust confined to isolated small clouds immersed in the hot medium.

At this point, we might wonder, "If we're practically surrounded by gas at temperatures of up to 1,000,000°C, why aren't we being roasted?" Hot things transfer their heat to cooler things by conduction — the heat traveling from atom to atom by a succession of direct collisions — or by radiation, in which the heat is carried through space by electromagnetic waves. Conduction is most efficient where atoms are densely packed and can easily collide and so transfer energy. Radiation is most efficient in a dark, nontransparent object. Because the gas has an average density of only about 1 ion per liter (1,000 cubic centimeters) and is also highly transparent, it conducts and radiates heat poorly. Thus, we are not burned up because the gas is extremely thin. This thinness also keeps the gas from cooling rapidly. Scientists have estimated that the hot gas takes from 1 million to 10 million years to lower its temperature by a measurable fraction of its original value.

In their investigation of the ISM, astronomers have detected gases at two extremes of density and temperature — ranging from the cool, dense molecular clouds with about 100,000 molecules per cubic centimeter and a temperature of about −200°C to the hot, low-density, highly ionized material with about 1 ion per 1,000 cubic centimeters and a temperature of 1,000,000°C. Intermediate density and temperature values have also been detected. But more remains to be discovered. For example, while we are reasonably certain of the amount of gases in the different portions of the ISM, we have had difficulty measuring the relative amount of space each portion occupies. We want to learn more about these percentages to increase our understanding of the key evolutionary processes of the ISM.

Investigators active at the frontier of research on gaseous matter in space are now studying material in various forms from more distant parts of the universe. Astronomers have already connected radio telescopes into arrays to map the atomic hydrogen emission in other galaxies. Blair D. Savage and Klaas D. de Boer at the University of Wisconsin used the International Ultraviolet Explorer satellite in 1979 to observe the brightest stars in the Magellanic Clouds, two small galaxies that lie near our own galaxy. They found that hot gas extends far beyond the plane of the Milky Way.

The next great leap in our understanding of the universe will probably come from observations by the National Aeronautics and Space Administration's (NASA) Space Telescope. It is scheduled for launch by the space shuttle in 1984. Its 238-centimeter (94-inch) diameter primary mirror will make it the largest astronomical instrument ever placed in space. Using the most advanced sensor systems available, this orbiting observatory will collect extremely faint light signals from distant sources and analyze them very precisely. It will be able to observe a spectrum ranging from the far-ultraviolet to the near-infrared.

It is almost certain that we shall uncover new surprises about the tempestuous gaseous sea in our own galaxy, and perhaps even make unimagined discoveries about the realm of intergalactic space. The Space Telescope may extend our vision to the very edge of the universe, offering views of galaxies so distant that astronomers will see them as they were when the universe was formed.

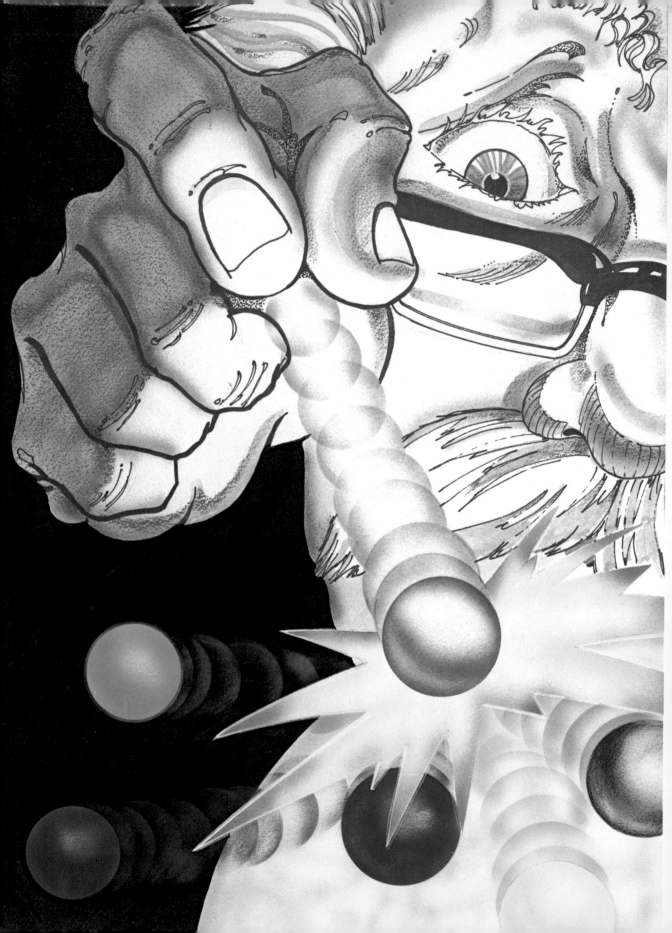

The Colorful World of the Atom

By Robert H. March

**A new theory of charge patterned after the physics
of color explains how particles called gluons
hold quarks together in nature's mightiest grip**

There is much wisdom in old folk tales. One of these, "The Sorcerer's Apprentice," aptly illustrates the frustration of physicists who search for the truly elementary particles, the most basic building blocks of the universe.

In this tale, as adapted by Walt Disney in the motion picture *Fantasia* (1940), a young man apprenticed to a great wizard is given a boring, backbreaking task. While his master is away, he must fill a huge tank by drawing water from a well, one bucket at a time. Confident of the magic he has learned so far, the apprentice casts a spell on a broom, making it sprout arms and legs and take over the tedious job.

But the apprentice does not know how to stop the magic broom, and soon the tank is overflowing. Driven to desperation, he attacks the broom with an ax. But his ax stroke splits the broom, magically, into two brooms, each as big as the original. He attacks again and again, but succeeds only in creating more brooms.

A high-powered electron blasts a proton apart, giving up energy
that condenses into a colorful cascade of subatomic particles.

Soon, the frustrated apprentice faces an army of brooms, each hauling buckets of water. His master's castle is flooded. Of course, the sorcerer returns eventually to set things right, leaving our young apprentice sadder but wiser.

And so it has gone in the world inside the atom. For nearly 20 years, theoretical physicists have suspected that protons and neutrons, the building blocks of the nucleus of the atom, are not truly elementary particles, but that they have smaller parts called *quarks*. The name was coined in 1964 by Murray Gell-Mann, a physicist at the California Institute of Technology in Pasadena. The obvious way to test this theory was to chop loose a quark and examine it. Instead of axes, researchers use gigantic particle accelerators, the most powerful tools of modern physics. These machines, the largest of which measures about 2 kilometers (1⅓ miles) in diameter, speed up tiny projectiles such as protons or electrons to velocities approaching that of light — 300,000 kilometers (186,000 miles) per second — and aim them at nuclei.

Experimental physicists have tried to break quarks loose from protons and neutrons in target nuclei by blasting them with electrons or protons. But they have had no more luck than the sorcerer's apprentice had with his ax. Every blow they have delivered has simply generated more particles — other protons or neutrons and other objects that are just as big and complex as the originals. What has been going on?

The answer can be found in the folk tale. The experimenters have indeed chopped quarks loose, but these particles do not remain alone for long. Each quark quickly creates new partners for itself and emerges from the experiment not as a loose quark, but as part of a new combination of quarks.

But physicists do not believe in magic. This description of quark behavior is intolerable because it does not explain exactly how a proton "magic broom" replaces its missing quark. Theoreticians have found the answer in a newly formulated fundamental force known by the initials QCD and by the name of the elementary particle that transmits it, the gluon.

In the peculiar world of subatomic particles where this force acts, the rules by which we understand nature in our day-to-day lives do not apply. Energy takes many forms in our ordinary world, and we often change its form to suit our purposes. For example, by burning gasoline, we convert the chemical energy that holds its molecules together to mechanical energy that propels an automobile. We can take mechanical energy from gasoline, but we cannot reverse the process to make gasoline out of mechanical energy. In the subatomic world, however, the conversion of energy to mass and vice versa is commonplace. For example, when two subatomic particles collide, part of their energy of motion can be converted to mass in the form of new particles. The mass of any particle, including a quark, simply

The author:
Robert H. March is a professor of physics at the University of Wisconsin and the author of the Special Report, "The Quandary Over Quarks," in the 1975 edition of *Science Year*.

represents the investment of energy required to create it. Similarly, a more massive subatomic particle can break up into a less massive combination of particles, with the excess mass converted to energy of particle motion.

Another peculiar feature of the subatomic world is that a truly elementary particle must be something like a point in geometry — it must have no size. What distinguishes one elementary particle from another is not size or shape, but how this curious little point concentration of energy responds to various forces.

A third peculiarity is the existence of antimatter. Each type of particle of matter has a corresponding antiparticle of antimatter that is equal to it in mass but opposite in electrical charge and certain other properties. An elementary particle can be created only if an elementary antiparticle is made at the same time. Similarly, a particle can be destroyed only if it encounters an antiparticle. Electrons obey this rule, and so do quarks.

Some particles are neither matter nor antimatter, however. The photon, or particle of light, is the most familiar example. Photons can be created freely, as long as energy is available. When they are absorbed, their energy changes the motion of the absorbing object or creates particle-antiparticle pairs. Likewise, the gluon, carrier of the QCD force, is neither matter nor antimatter.

Photons and gluons have a special role in the subatomic world. Some other kinds of particles can freely create or absorb them, so they serve as messengers, transporting little bundles of energy from one particle to another. This process of trading energy generates the forces that bind particles to one another. Electromagnetic forces, such as the attraction that binds an electron to an atomic nucleus, are transmitted by photons. The attraction is not a long, smooth pull, but a series of short, intense pulses. Gluons hold quarks together in protons and neutrons by similar pulses of energy.

The subatomic world did not seem nearly so peculiar in 1932, when British physicist Sir James Chadwick discovered the neutron. Our picture of elementary particles seemed well in hand. Atoms had nuclei containing protons that carried an electrical charge of $+1$ and uncharged neutrons. Orbiting the nuclei were electrons that carried an electrical charge of -1. Theoreticians completed this picture with a fourth elementary particle, the neutrino, an electrically neutral counterpart of the electron. The neutrino accounted for certain kinds of radioactivity, but experimentalists did not actually detect this particle until later.

It became clear by the 1950s that this picture was incomplete. Theoretical physicists still regarded the electron and neutrino as elementary particles, as they do today, but they recognized that protons and neutrons are much more complex. The experimenters had discovered that protons and neutrons are not the only particles of their kind, but simply the longest-lasting members of a vast particle

Glossary

Antimatter: Material made up of particles identical to those in ordinary matter, except for their electrical charges and certain other properties, which are the opposite of those in ordinary matter.

Antiquark: An elementary particle that is identical to a quark, but with the opposite color charge.

Baryon: A particle made up of three quarks — a neutron or a proton, for example.

Color: The charge that gluons carry between quarks as the gluons transmit the QCD force.

Electron: An elementary particle that orbits an atom's nucleus and has an electrical charge of -1.

Elementary particle: A subatomic object that is not made up of smaller objects.

Gluon: An elementary particle that transmits the QCD force between quarks, keeping them locked together in hadron combinations.

Hadron: One of a family of subatomic objects that includes baryons, antibaryons, and mesons.

Meson: An object made up of a quark and an antiquark.

Neutrino: A particle that takes part in certain kinds of radioactivity.

Neutron: A particle in an atom's nucleus that is made up of three quarks and has zero electrical charge.

Particle accelerator: A machine that greatly increases the speed of particles and directs them at a target.

Photon: An elementary particle that transmits electrical and magnetic forces. Certain photons make up ordinary light.

Proton: A particle in an atom's nucleus that is made up of three quarks and has an electrical charge of $+1$.

Quantum color dynamics (QCD): The theory of how gluons and quarks interact.

Quark: An elementary particle that exists only in groups called hadrons, which the QCD force holds together.

In 1932, Professor Krauq, a fictitious elementary particle physicist, viewed the atom as a combination of protons, neutrons, and electrons. He also sometimes saw an additional particle, the neutrino, which took part in some atomic reactions.

family known as *hadrons*. All other hadrons, which are produced in accelerators or by cosmic rays, are short-lived. None lasts as long as one ten-millionth of a second, so they play no role in ordinary matter. But researchers have found nearly 300 different kinds so far. All of these hadrons have a basic family resemblance that led Gell-Mann and his colleague, physicist George Zweig, to suspect that hadrons were merely different combinations of a few simple parts. The two researchers proposed in 1964 that each proton and neutron contains three smaller objects — Gell-Mann's quarks. In creating this idea, Gell-Mann and Zweig did something akin to figuring out how many different kinds of pieces are in a Tinkertoy set by studying things that are built with them, even though they could not see the individual pieces themselves.

According to their proposal, quarks combine to form two kinds of hadrons. One is a *meson* — a quark and an antiquark. Mesons contain both matter and antimatter, so they quickly annihilate themselves. The other kind of hadron, which has three quarks, is called a *baryon*. The proton and neutron are the least massive baryons and the only baryons that exist in ordinary matter. More massive baryons become protons or neutrons as soon as they are created by shedding their excess mass as energy. The baryon has an antimatter counterpart, the antibaryon, which is made of three antiquarks. Antibaryons are quickly annihilated by confrontations with baryons.

As the theory explains, protons and neutrons are made of two kinds of quarks, designated u and d for *up* and *down*. These labels have nothing to do with the everyday meaning of the words *up* and *down*. They are simply names that distinguish one kind of quark from another. The u's carry $+\frac{2}{3}$ of the fundamental unit of electrical charge — the amount carried by a proton or an electron — and the d's

By the 1950s, Professor Krauq was working with more than 200 additional subatomic particles. He understood that they had no place in ordinary atoms, but he could not see them well enough to explain how they were related to one another.

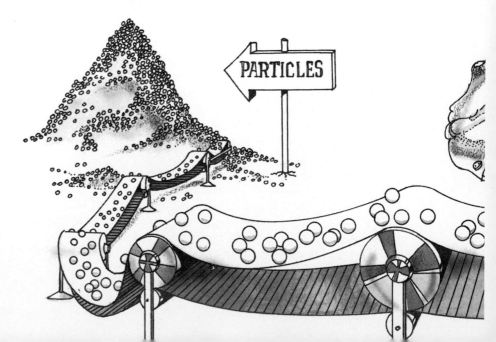

carry $-\frac{1}{3}$. A proton is made up of two u quarks and one d quark. Its electrical charge is the sum of the quarks' charges, $+1$. The neutron's combination is udd, so it contains equal amounts of positive and negative charges.

The theory proposed by Gell-Mann and Zweig accounted for all the hadrons and their charges, but it had two serious defects. First, the forces binding quarks together were strong, but they hardly seemed so potent that particles from a powerful accelerator could not overcome them. Yet, in 15 years of trying, no experimenter has knocked a quark out of a proton so that it emerged from the experiment as a loose quark. Physicists who had mastered the problems of pulling electrons loose from atoms and splitting the nucleus

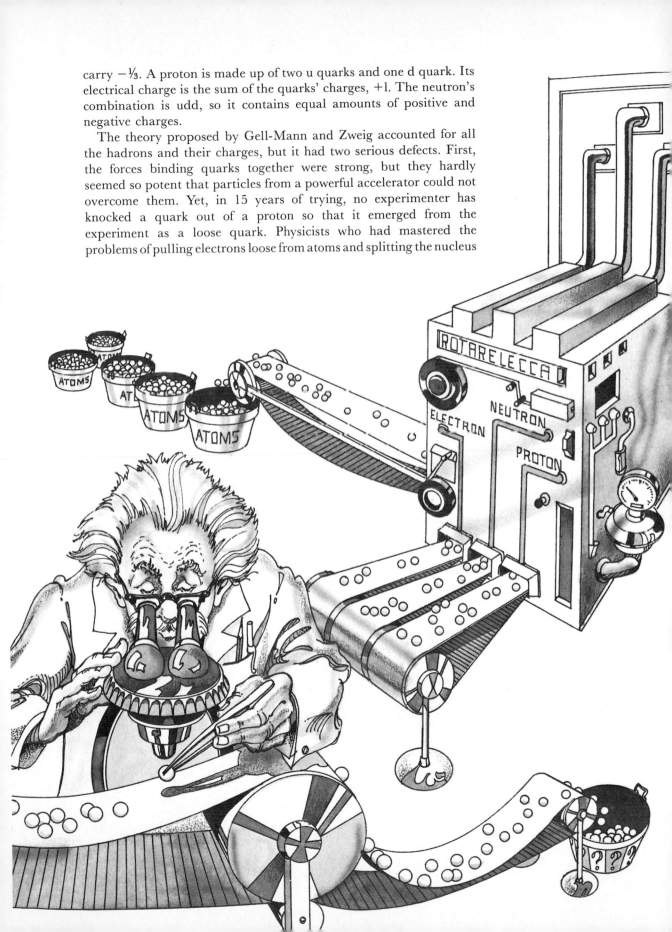

itself were at a loss to explain this. The second defect in the theory was that while it described all existing hadrons so well, it did not explain why experimenters had not discovered two-quark or four-quark hadron combinations.

Over the past five years, however, theoreticians have corrected both of these defects by adding the gluon to the theory. The theory says that gluons, like photons, always move at the speed of light. But there is one crucial difference between photons and gluons that explains the hold that gluons exert on quarks. A photon leads a short, simple life inside an atom. It is emitted by one electrically charged object and absorbed by another. In fact, we can define electrical charge as the ability to create or absorb photons. The photons themselves do not possess this characteristic of charge. They are electrically neutral, so they cannot create other photons. But a gluon can produce another gluon, sharing its energy with its offspring. As gluons travel back and forth between quarks, they proliferate rapidly and are absorbed equally rapidly by the quarks. And the more gluons there are, the more powerful is their grip on the quarks.

As a result, each proton or neutron contains a swarm of gluons traveling between quarks. In fact, scientists estimate that as much as half of a proton's or neutron's energy is tied up in this swarm. It serves as the reservoir of energy that makes a proton or neutron a "magic broom."

To see how a swarm of gluons operates, look at what happens when experimenters try to knock a quark loose from a proton by hitting the quark with an electron in a particle accelerator. The quark receives a swift jolt of energy and starts off as if it were free to escape. But the quark cannot outrace the speeding gluons, which travel at the speed of light — the absolute speed limit for any material object. The gluons re-establish their grip, gradually applying the brakes to the quark. The gluons that this quark emits use energy that they take from the quark's motion to create more gluons. These form a slender neck connecting the wayward quark to its relatives back in the proton. Inside this neck, the gluons become so concentrated that pairs of quarks and antiquarks begin to form. These particles cannot escape because they are also trapped in the gluon swarm, so they quickly find one or two partners and form new mesons, baryons, or antibaryons.

The neck splits into a jet of hadrons, all moving in approximately the same direction. The swiftest particle in the jet usually contains the quark that was struck by the electron. This quark picks up an antiquark or two quarks as partners. At the base of the neck, another quark replaces this quark in the proton, restoring the original baryon.

All of this activity takes place in less than one-billionth of one-trillionth of one second. The struck quark has turned into hadrons by the time scientists can observe the tracks of the particle jets on their instruments. But physicists can reconstruct the motion of the struck quark from these particles' motions. The experimenter never sees a quark or gluon. But the jets contain particles that last long enough to travel many meters in the accelerator laboratory. Physicists can see these particles' tracks in photographs of a bubble chamber — a closed vessel filled with very cold liquid under pressure and mounted so that the jets strike it. Charged particles going through the liquid make visible bubbles that can be photographed.

Researchers also use more complex detectors that emit an electrical impulse when a particle passes through them. The impulses are fed to a computer that calculates the paths of the particles that caused them. By studying the paths of a jet of particles, physicists can obtain a fairly accurate indication of the quark's original motion. And by studying thousands of such jet formations, they can unravel the

When Krauq viewed the proton through a more powerful instrument in the 1970s, he saw that it was not one particle but a combination of particles — three quarks held together by a cloud of gluons.

Keeping Color Balance

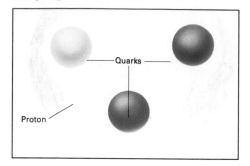

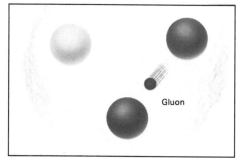

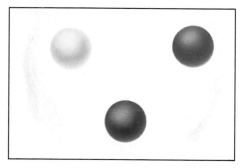

Krauq saw that the quarks were red, blue, and yellow, *top.* When a quark emitted a gluon and changed color, *center,* another quark quickly absorbed a gluon to restore the color balance, *above.* Quarks emit and absorb gluons constantly, *below.*

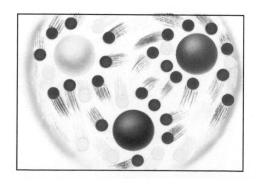

details of how the QCD force controls the interactions of the particles.

So the "magic" is complete. A quark has been knocked out of a proton, but it has not been set free. Where there was one hadron — a proton — there are now several, just like the brooms in "The Sorcerer's Apprentice." The electron's jolt has created additional protons, just as the blows of the ax made more brooms.

Theoretical physicists added a property shared by quarks and gluons called *color* to the theory to explain why there could not be two-quark and four-quark combinations. This name was chosen because of a neat analogy with the rules of color mixing. It has nothing to do with real colors as we know them.

In the theory, the term *color* refers to a property like electrical charge. Just as charge means the ability to create or absorb photons, *color* means the ability to create or absorb gluons. There are two kinds of electrical charge — one plus and one minus. There are six kinds of color, however — three pluses and three minuses. Quarks carry three plus colors — the three primary colors red, yellow, and blue; and antiquarks carry three minus colors — minus-red, minus-yellow, and minus-blue. The color a quark carries does not affect its mass or other properties, and all colors are equally able to create or absorb gluons.

The theorists say that a hadron must be made up of quarks whose colors are the same as the real colors of light beams that combine to make white light. There are only two ways to make white light with beams of the six real colors that correspond to the quarks' imaginary colors. Three colors can be combined: red, yellow, and blue; or minus-red,

The Gluon's Unbreakable Grip

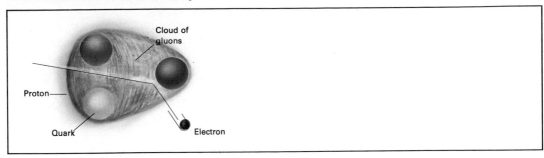

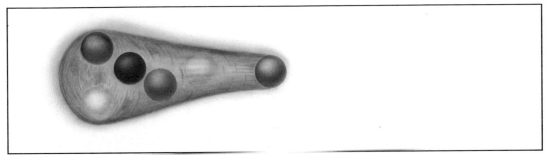

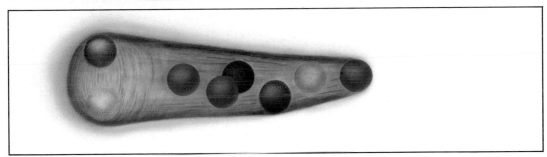

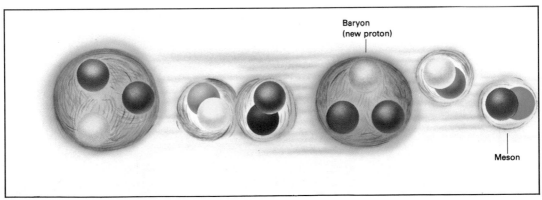

An electron that has been boosted to high energy can knock a quark
out of a proton, but the quark does not become free. The gluon cloud
stretches to hold onto it. More quarks form from the remaining energy.
They quickly combine in twos and threes, forming some of the particles
that had puzzled Professor Krauq. One new quark becomes part of the
original proton. The departing quark becomes part of a new combination.

minus-yellow, and minus-blue; or a color can be combined with its opposite, as in a blend of red and minus-red.

A baryon is simply a combination of one red, one yellow, and one blue quark. But a quark does not keep its color. Quarks change colors continually by emitting and absorbing gluons. The gluon exchange maintains the color distribution — one red, one yellow, and one blue quark. For example, if a red quark emits a gluon and turns yellow, changing the color distribution to two yellow quarks and one blue quark, then the other yellow quark will quickly absorb a gluon and turn into a red quark.

A meson is a combination of a quark and an antiquark of opposite colors — a red quark with a minus-red antiquark, for example. But a meson's quark and antiquark do not keep their colors, either. Emitting a gluon changes the color of a quark, so each quark and antiquark spends equal time bearing each of its three possible colors. But the colors of the pair are always opposites. For example, when a red quark emits a gluon and turns blue, its minus-red partner quickly absorbs a gluon and turns minus-blue. Two- and four-quark combinations obviously could not follow the rules of mixing colored light, so the theory now excludes them. And the theory now matches the experimental evidence further by explaining why colorless particles such as electrons and neutrinos do not feel the QCD force.

Physicists still believe that ordinary matter is made up of only four building blocks, as they did in 1932, but the elementary particles now are known to be electrons, neutrinos, u-quarks, and d-quarks. QCD, which is the theory of gluons that explains quarks' behavior, stands for quantum color dynamics, or quantum chromodynamics. *Quantum* specifies that the force is transmitted in bundles — in this case, gluon bundles; *chromo* comes from the Greek word for *color;* and *dynamics* is the name applied to any theory of force.

Professor Krauq's 1980 model of the atom includes the familiar electron and neutrino, but now he sees that the proton and neutron are combinations of two kinds of quarks, called *up* and *down*.

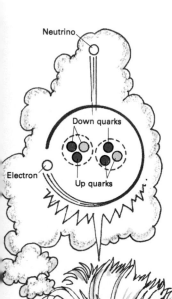

Neutrino

Down quarks

Electron

Up quarks

As powerful as QCD is, it still sheds no light on one remaining mystery of the subatomic world — the existence of the so-called *heavy* quarks named *strange,* and *charmed,* and *bottom* or *beauty,* and other massive elementary particles. Some of the rare, fleeting products of violent collisions triggered by accelerator beams or cosmic rays are hadrons made of heavy quarks. Similarly, there exist short-lived particles that are like electrons and neutrinos, except that they are more massive. For example, the electron's more massive counterparts are the muon, which is 207 times as massive as an ordinary electron but otherwise identical to it, and the tau, which is 3,700 times as massive as the electron. But the muon and the tau are unstable and turn into electrons in less than one-millionth of a second by shedding energy. The same goes for heavy quarks such as the strange quark, which is 1.6 times as massive as the d quark, and the charmed quark, which is 5 times as massive as the u quark. Neither heavy quark lasts more than one ten-millionth of a second and, therefore, neither do the hadrons that contain them. They turn into other particles by shedding energy.

QCD has not solved the mystery of the more massive elementary particles, but the theory may help solve one of the deepest mysteries of the universe — the relationships among what presently appear to be fundamental forces. Theoretical physicists have long wanted to explain all of nature's basic forces as forms of one fundamental force, much as British mathematician and physicist James Clerk Maxwell created a unified picture of electricity, magnetism, and light as different forms of electromagnetism in 1864.

Since the 1930s, scientists believed that there were four fundamental forces: gravity; electromagnetism; the strong interaction that binds protons and neutrons together in nuclei; and the weak interaction that accounts for certain kinds of radioactivity. Physicists now recognize that the strong interaction is not a fundamental force after all. It is derived from the QCD force in the same way that chemical binding forces that hold a molecule's atoms together are the combined result of electrical attractions and repulsions of individual electrons and nuclei inside atoms. The strong interaction is a more complicated force simply because many objects are involved. And theoreticians working in another branch of physics showed that the electromagnetic force and the weak interaction are really two forms of one force. So by the summer of 1980, the number of fundamental forces stood at three — gravity, the combined electromagnetic and weak force, and the QCD force. But the similarities between gluons and photons suggest that scientists may be able to combine separate theories of the electromagnetic and QCD forces. Such a theory would suggest that these forces are simply different versions of the same force. Physicists could then take up the final task that occupied the last 25 years of Albert Einstein's life — a theory uniting the forces of electromagnetism and gravity.

Digging for
Black Gold

By Thomas H. Maugh II

**Oil firms in the Western Hemisphere are extracting
liquid fuels from sticky black sand and dirt
that can rival the stocks of Middle East petroleum**

Giant excavators mine the surface of the Canadian wilderness for tar sands — raw materials for synthetic crude oil.

From the air, they looked like toys — the excavating machines digging up the Athabasca tar sands at the Syncrude Ltd. surface mine north of Fort McMurray in Alberta, Canada. As I drove from the airport toward the site, even from 5 kilometers (3.1 miles) away, the machines did not seem unusually big. Only when I stood beside one of the mammoth dragline excavators could I appreciate the enormity of the machines and the Athabasca tar sands project.

The dragline is somewhat like an ordinary power shovel, but it is much larger and it is shaped differently. The cab, the dragline's control center, is manned by three operators. It houses the controls, 24 electric motors, a lunchroom, and even showers. A steel-frame arm as long as a football field reaches outward and upward from the base of the cab. Steel cables hung over pulleys at the end of the arm are attached to a digging bucket. The bucket is big enough to hold the

Hydrocarbons that can be made into liquid heating and automotive fuels exist in a spectrum of forms, ranging from crude oil, the easiest to refine, to coal, the most difficult.

Crude oil

Tar sands

The author:
Thomas H. Maugh II is senior staff writer for *Science* magazine.

15-passenger van in which my hosts and I toured the site, with room left over for a Volkswagen Rabbit or two. A cable winch in the cab provides the digging force. Six of the electric motors, each capable of exerting 970 kilowatts (1,300 horsepower) of power, rotate the winch which pulls the bucket along the pit surface toward the cab as the bucket's thick metal teeth tear out the sticky black sand. The arm cables then lift the digging bucket and its load out of the pit, dump the sand onto a pile that runs along the pit's edge, and lower the bucket for another bite.

Syncrude has four such draglines gnawing a hole 4 kilometers (2.5 miles) long and 60 meters (200 feet) deep in northeastern Alberta's landscape. Following each dragline is a bucket-wheel excavator about eight stories high. The buckets, moving in a circle like Ferris-wheel seats, pick up sand from the pile and dump it onto a steel-corded rubber conveyor belt about 1.8 meters (6 feet) wide. Each bucket-wheel excavator loads about 7,000 metric tons (7,700 short tons) of black sand onto the belt in an hour. The sand moves on a series of such conveyor belts that carry it 5 kilometers (3.1 miles) to the processing plant.

"Everything about this project is big," said Robert E. McRory, Syncrude's senior adviser for public affairs. "The eight machines use as much electricity as a city of 300,000 persons."

The project is big because the stakes are big. Energy experts describe the Syncrude operation as the energy plant of the future, a way to help overcome the energy shortage that threatens the industrialized world. Each day, McRory said, the dragline excavators remove 66,000 cubic meters (2.3 million cubic feet) of overburden—topsoil and other material—to expose the oil sands and mine 200,000 metric tons (220,000 short tons) of the black ore. Syncrude extracts from this amount of ore 100,000 barrels of liquid that refiners can convert to

Oil shale

Coal

gasoline, heating oil, and kerosene. This is barely a trickle compared with the world's 1979 petroleum production of about 61 million barrels per day (bpd), but tar sands hold an abundance of this liquid.

The Alberta tar sands (also called oil sands) alone contain enough material to provide the energy equivalent of six times the petroleum resources in Saudi Arabia's oil fields. And world stocks of petroleum are dwindling. New discoveries have barely kept up with production and consumption, and most experts expect the discovery rate to continue to decline. Moreover, the producing countries are already limiting production to keep prices up and make supplies last.

New sources of energy will be required to make up for the dwindling petroleum stocks. Nuclear power and solar energy will be used in some power-plant and household applications, but they cannot replace liquid fuels. Coal can be converted into liquid fuels relatively simply, but most experts agree that the cost is too high. For the immediate future, the most promising alternate liquid fuels source is tar sands. Tar sands in Alberta contain the equivalent of about 1 trillion barrels of petroleum. A similar deposit in Venezuela holds as much as 2 trillion barrels. There are at least another 1 trillion barrels elsewhere, most of it in Russia.

Tar sands are near one end of a spectrum of deposits in the earth that contain hydrocarbons — chemical compounds made almost entirely of the elements carbon and hydrogen. This spectrum includes gaseous, liquid, semisolid, and solid hydrocarbons that have different compositions and contain different kinds of impurities.

The lightest are the natural gases, in which methane, a single hydrocarbon, is the most plentiful. Liquid hydrocarbon deposits — petroleum or crude oil — contain mixtures of hundreds of hydrocarbons. They can be classified by *viscosity* (resistance to flow) as light crude, medium crude, and heavy crude.

Semisolid hydrocarbon deposits are more complex. These are mixed with rock, silt, or sand. The hydrocarbons of oil shale, for example, are contained in a waxy, dark-brown substance that is mixed with light-brown silt in rocks made of compressed layers of clay, or silt and minerals. The hydrocarbons of tar sands are contained in bitumen, a semisolid made of about 83 per cent carbon. The remainder consists of hydrogen and various impurities, including nitrogen and sulfur. Bitumen is also found in oil shale and soft coal.

Coal is made up of various solids. No two coal deposits are exactly alike, but all contain carbon, hydrogen, nitrogen, oxygen, and sulfur. Coal is classified by its carbon content, which ranges from 98 per cent for anthracite, the hardest coal, to 30 per cent for brown coal.

All hydrocarbon deposits are products of decay and pressure. Coal formed from swamp plants that died from 1 million to 440 million years ago. Over the years, the dead swamp plants were covered by soil and compressed into coal; the higher the pressure, the greater the amount of carbon in the coal.

Petroleum and natural gas began as marine plants and animals that lived in shallow water along the coasts of ancient oceans. The organic material first sank to the floors of the oceans and was covered by sediments that kept the air out, preventing the material from decomposing immediately.

Bacteria, heat from the earth's interior, and pressure convert the organic material into tiny drops of oil and bubbles of gas, which then move into surrounding rocks. Usually the oil and gas rise through layers of porous rock to the earth's surface and are lost. Sometimes, however, a layer of nonporous rock forms above the oil and gas deposit and prevents the hydrocarbons from escaping. This rock layer acts like an overturned bowl, trapping the oil and gas.

If gas continues to be formed in this natural trap, enormous pressures may develop. In fact, some oil wells operate for long periods

The West's Sticky Riches
Both Canada and Venezuela have much more oil locked up in their bitumen than the Middle East has in its petroleum reserves.

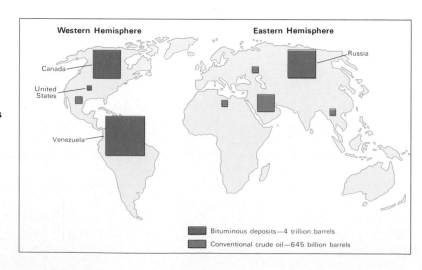

Western Hemisphere   Eastern Hemisphere

Canada
United States
Venezuela
Russia

Bituminous deposits—4 trillion barrels
Conventional crude oil—645 billion barrels

Bucket-wheel excavators transfer mined tar sands from storage
piles to conveyor belts that carry them to the processing plant.

of time without pumps, because the pressure is great enough to drive the oil to the surface. Before oil drillers learned to control this pressure, it used to drive newly struck oil out of the ground in wasteful gushers that spewed high into the air, sometimes for days.

The ease of extracting petroleum depends on the reservoir rock's *permeability* (ease with which liquid can pass through it) and, more importantly, on the viscosity of the substance. Light crude oil flows as freely as household machine oil at room temperature, and pumps can remove it from the ground without any special treatment. Medium crude flows like automobile engine oil. Some can be pumped out directly, but most of it must be heated to thin it. Heavy crude has the consistency of molasses, so it must be given more heat than medium crude before it can be pumped.

Tar sand bitumen developed in the same manner as petroleum, but at some point along the way it lost its less viscous hydrocarbon molecules and became thick and heavy. Some scientists think that the molecules evaporated when the deposits were exposed to the atmosphere. Others believe that oil-eating bacteria may have eliminated them. As a result, tar sands deposits are too thick to pump. But those that lie near the surface can be strip-mined.

The Athabasca tar sands are a mixture of 84 to 88 per cent sand and clay, 8 to 12 per cent bitumen, and 4 per cent water. Bitumen does not flow at room temperature, but it flows freely when it is heated to about 80°C (180°F.).

Nature made the Athabasca tar sands easy to process. The bitumen, or the petroleum from which it developed, formed elsewhere, perhaps many hundreds of kilometers away. This material migrated to Athabasca and seeped into the wet sand there. Since oil and water do not mix, the ingredients of these tar sands formed an unusual arrangement. A thin film of water surrounds the sand grains and separates them from the bitumen. When this tar sand is placed in hot water, the bitumen quickly separates from the sand and floats to the surface of the water, where it can be skimmed off. The sand sinks to the bottom and is discarded.

The Athabasca tar sands were first reported in 1778 by Peter Pond, an American fur trader who established a trading post near the present town of Fort McMurray. He saw the Indians waterproof their canoes with bitumen from the sand along the riverbank. Commercial interest in the sands began in 1897, when the Geological Survey of Canada started drilling to determine the size of the reserves.

The Canadian government and several private companies tried to exploit the sands. The effort intensified in the 1920s, when researchers developed much of the fundamental technology used today. Some speculators drilled wells looking for oil pools in the 1920s and 1930s, while others built small plants to extract the oil, but no tar sands industry developed at that time because its product would have been much more expensive than ordinary petroleum.

Canada's snows quickly cover equipment left idle overnight, *left.* But winter work continues even when abrasive tar sands freeze so hard that they wear out a bucket-wheel excavator's thick steel teeth, *above.*

The first tar sands developer was Great Canadian Oil Sands (GCOS), a subsidiary of the Sun Company of Philadelphia. In 1964, GCOS began to build a 45,000-bpd facility about 30 kilometers (19 miles) north of Fort McMurray. The task was formidable. Because of the site's isolation, GCOS had to build new roads and improve existing ones. All the construction equipment, supplies, and workers had to be brought in from the outside, and the workers had to be fed, housed, and provided with recreational outlets to combat the gloom of the subarctic winters. Construction was completed in 1967 at a cost of about $300 million, but the company has been operating at a profit only since 1978.

The greatest expense and difficulty in producing bitumen lies in mining the tar sand and conveying it to the processing plant. The deposits are covered by as much as 6 meters (20 feet) of muskeg, a swamplike mass of partially decayed vegetation. "The first step," said GCOS manager of operations A. R. Allen, "is to clear off the scraggly growth of tamarack and black spruce trees that grow in the muskeg. We can do this efficiently only in the winter when the muskeg is frozen deeply enough to support equipment. Operations in the summer tended to concentrate more on retrieving sunken equipment than removing material. But work in winter is difficult. The hours of daylight are short, visibility is restricted by fog, and the temperature can drop to −45°C (−49°F.)." GCOS now drains the water from the muskeg by means of ditches. Then the muskeg and other overburden — sand, gravel, and shale — can be removed in the summer.

"In summer," said Allen, "tar sands can only be described as smelly and sticky." The viscous fluid film between the sand grains, said GCOS President Stanley A. Cowtan, binds the mass together like a fine-grained asphalt road mix. Bitumen is "almost gluelike and

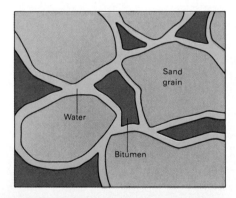

Sand
grain

Water

Bitumen

The Athabasca tar sands deposits formed with a thin film of water surrounding the sand particles, *left.* Huge drums tumble a mixture of tar sands and hot water, *below left.* The bitumen then floats to the top in tanks while the sand settles out, *below.*

sticks to everything. It clogs the cooling systems of vehicles, sticks to conveyor belts, and piles up at transfer points on the belts. The bitumen also slowly dissolves the natural rubber in tires, conveyor belts, and other equipment."

"Tar sand is highly abrasive," added Cowtan, "because the sand in it is 95 per cent quartz, which is extremely hard. In winter, undisturbed, frozen tar sand resembles a grindstone. During our first winter, the bucket-wheel teeth glowed red as the machine worked. Sometimes the thick steel buckets were ripped and the teeth torn from their sockets. And when big chunks of frozen sand were dropped on conveyor belts, the belts broke."

The company overcame most of the problems of winter mining by dynamiting the tar sands during the summer. "Blasting fluffs up the sand bed and lets air get into the sand so that it can act as an insulator," Cowtan explained. "Not as much water gets in and so the sand does not freeze as solidly in the winter. In addition, the heavy-equipment manufacturers redesigned bucket-wheel teeth and scraper and bulldozer blades to minimize friction, and used metals that resist wear better. The rubber companies developed more resistant materials for tires and conveyor belts. And we made up new vehicle-maintenance schedules, which we observe strictly."

Like Syncrude, GCOS uses conveyor belts to carry the tar sands to the extraction plant. The sands are then mixed with chemically treated water at 80°C (112°F.) in four horizontal rotating drums, each 5.2 meters (17 feet) in diameter and 15.6 meters (51 feet) long. The mixture then goes into four separation cylinders, each 13.4 meters (44 feet) in diameter and 7.8 meters (25 feet) deep, where the sand and clay settle to the bottom and the bitumen floats to the surface. The sand and water are carried off to a 168-hectare (415-acre) artificial pond next to the plant. The bitumen goes into a chamber where it is heated by 500°C (910°F.) *coke* (bitumen that has been converted to almost pure carbon). This heating causes gases in the bitumen to evaporate. Distilling these gases — cooling them until they condense into liquids — forms naphtha, kerosene, and gas oil, each of which is treated with hydrogen to remove sulfur. The liquids are blended to form synthetic crude oil and then are pumped through a 41-centimeter (16-inch) pipeline to refineries in Edmonton, about 480 kilometers (300 miles) to the south.

The GCOS facility produces 45,000 bpd and will be enlarged to a capacity of 58,000 bpd early in 1982. The $2.5-billion Syncrude plant, which opened in 1978, produces 100,000 bpd and may reach 129,000 bpd by 1984. Alsands, which is owned by Shell Canada — a unit of the Royal Dutch-Shell Group — and several other oil companies, announced in January 1980 that it would begin work on a $5-billion, 400,000-bpd plant near Fort McMurray that will take seven years to build. Imperial Oil Company and Petrofina Canada Ltd. have plants on the drawing boards. And in April 1980, Shell Canada applied to

Tar sands processing has added unwanted features to the landscape — a sulfur dump, *above,* and a pond of hot water with a surface film of bitumen, *above right.* A scarecrow keeps birds from becoming casualties of the pond.

the Alberta Energy Resources Conservation Board for a permit to build near Edmonton what it says will be the world's first refinery that will produce only synthetic crude oil.

Considering the large size of the tar sands plants, the environmental impact has been slight, Syncrude officials say. The tar sands contain 4 to 6 per cent sulfur, and processing removes most of it. Unfortunately, much of the sulfur goes into the air. Alberta's government has set a limit of 287 metric tons (316 short tons) of sulfur dioxide emissions per day for Syncrude. This amount, company officials argue, is virtually insignificant in northeastern Alberta. But an Edmonton-based environmental group called Save Tomorrow, Oppose Pollution (STOP) contends that dangerous quantities of sulfur dioxide might build up in the winter because of frequent temperature inversions, which occur when a layer of warm air settles over cool air that is near the ground, trapping pollutants. STOP says that this danger will be even greater when more plants are operating.

STOP also contends that Syncrude's *tailings* (residue) pond poses a danger to the area's water supply. The group claims that the pond contains substantial quantities of organic chemicals and metals that could pollute the Athabasca River 5 kilometers (3.1 miles) to the east. The company contends that the pond is too far from the river to pollute it significantly.

Another problem is the thin coat of bitumen on the pond surface that sticks to migratory birds that land there. Syncrude attempts to solve this problem by removing bitumen from the surface. A vacuum hose from a boat draws off the pond's top layer and then a centrifuge on board the boat separates the bitumen from the water. Syncrude also uses electrified scarecrows in an attempt to discourage birds from landing on the pond.

The greatest environmental impact has probably been on Fort McMurray, which is on the site of an old trading post. The population was less than 1,000 when GCOS arrived in 1964. Today, Fort McMurray is a bustling community of more than 30,000 persons, complete with parking and urban-congestion problems, and very high land and housing prices. GCOS and Syncrude have built new housing and recreational facilities in the area, but the rapid growth has been painful for both long-time residents and newcomers.

The United States has no tar sands deposit as big or as rich as those in Alberta. U.S. deposits in California, New Mexico, and Texas equal about 30 billion barrels of petroleum. Here, the young tar sands industry faces a technical challenge that the Canadians have not had to face. No U.S. deposit has the thin film of water between the bitumen and sand found at Athabasca, so the separation process is much more difficult.

Perhaps the closest U.S. equivalent of the Athabasca tar sands is a unique deposit near McKittrick, Calif., about 70 kilometers (43

Modern town houses and high-rise apartment buildings have sprung up on the edge of Fort McMurray near a 19th-century log cabin — a symbol of the rustic life in the days before the mining boom.

miles) west of Bakersfield. There, large deposits of diatomaceous earth — an absorbent material containing silicon used in such products as swimming-pool filters and cat litter — are saturated with an average of about 12 per cent oil by weight. The Getty Oil Corporation plans to mine and extract synthetic crude and gas from this material.

Sometime in 1980, said Getty project engineer Boyne Grainger, the company will begin to build plants to test the two most efficient ways to separate oil from diatomaceous earth. "One method uses a rapidly evaporating hydrocarbon that resembles cigarette-lighter fluid to wash the oil from the earth," said Grainger. "The oil and solvent are then separated, the solvent is recycled, and the oil is piped to refineries. In the second process, the diatomaceous earth is heated to about 650°C (1200°F.) to evaporate the hydrocarbons, which are then distilled and chemically treated to produce crude oils and gas."

When Getty decides which process to use, Grainger added, it will build a 20,000-bpd plant near McKittrick. The company expects to operate the plant for 48 years and extract a total of 380 million barrels of oil. Kernridge Oil Company also has holdings in the area.

The American Mining and Exploration Company, a small firm in Albuquerque, N. Mex., may begin building a plant in 1980 to test another solvent-extraction technique on tar sands deposits near Santa Rosa, N. Mex. If the test is successful, the company plans to build a 10,000-bpd plant that would recover more than 160 million barrels of oil from the deposit, the largest in New Mexico.

Most of the tar sands in the United States and Canada lie at least 45 meters (150 feet) beneath the surface — too deep to be strip-mined. So petroleum companies have been searching for ways to thin the bitumen in the ground so that they can pump it to the surface like ordinary petroleum.

The first deep tar sands that will be mined are at Cold Lake, about 200 kilometers (124 miles) northeast of Edmonton in eastern Alberta.

Tapping Deep Deposits
Bitumen that is too far underground to strip-mine and too thick to pump can be thinned by steam-heating, *right,* then pumped to the surface, *far right.*

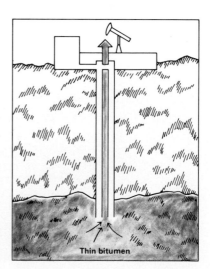

Imperial Oil Company has conducted test projects there since 1964 and is now producing about 5,000 bpd by a steam-heating process called "huff and puff." Steam is injected into the tar sands at 350°C (662°F.) and a pressure of 140 kilograms per square centimeter (2,000 pounds per square inch) (huff) through a group of wells. Four to six weeks of heating thins the bitumen so that it can be pumped to the surface (puff) for as long as six months.

Private companies have invested more than $150 million on such experimental *in situ* (on the spot) projects, most of them in Alberta. These companies and Alberta's government are expected to invest another $250 million during the 1980s. At least 18 pilot projects are operating in Alberta and six in the Southwestern United States, all designed to heat the bitumen in the ground.

Imperial plans to build a $5-billion in situ plant at Cold Lake that will produce as much as 160,000 bpd. The project calls for drilling about 10,000 wells over at least 20 years. Up to 2,500 of these wells will operate at any given time. Energy for producing the steam to be pumped into the wells will be provided by burning either 5 million metric tons (5.5 million short tons) of coal annually or 25,000 bpd of the bitumen. Every barrel of synthetic crude produced will require about 5 barrels of fresh water to provide steam and for use in the separation operations. Imperial plans to recycle the water. The plant will emit about 60 metric tons (66 short tons) of sulfur dioxide per day into the atmosphere.

Many companies are watching Imperial's progress at Cold Lake as they observed GCOS at Athabasca. Alberta officials speculate that success at Cold Lake will spark a series of large in situ projects, just as success at Athabasca spawned a series of strip-mine projects.

Meanwhile, the private companies and the Canadian government are trying to sell their successful technology to the rest of the world, and at least one tar sands plant may open outside North America. Venezuela announced in December 1979 that it will mine the mammoth bitumen deposits in the Orinoco River Basin in the eastern part of the country.

The major limitations in 1980 are the high cost of such mining and the demands of other energy projects for technological expertise, construction workers, and money. As long as the price of crude oil continues to increase, however, the technology and money for tar sands mining will probably be found. Strong tar sands industries would greatly increase the world supply of liquid hydrocarbons. This would decrease the industrialized nations' dependence on high-priced Middle East petroleum and would give the energy researchers many more years to develop alternative fuels.

Nevertheless, the cost of removing hydrocarbons from tar sands is much higher than the cost of pumping oil or natural gas from the ground. So, although a tar sands industry will increase our supply of energy, it will not lower its cost.

Reinterpreting Life's Blueprint

By Daniel L. Hartl

**The discovery of split genes in higher forms of life
is tantalizing biologists with new questions —
and perhaps new answers — to the puzzle of heredity**

In the mid-1970s, molecular biologists were as smug as the ancient astronomers who were sure that the heavens revolved around the earth. These biologists had reason to be quite satisfied with themselves and their accomplishments. In a mere 25 years, they had uncovered many of life's deepest secrets. Never in the history of science had so many important discoveries come so quickly.

This era began in 1953, when biologists James D. Watson and Francis H. C. Crick, working at Cambridge University in England, discovered the molecular structure of deoxyribonucleic acid (DNA). This is the substance that conveys genetic information from one generation to the next and determines how all organisms, from bacteria to birch trees to beluga whales, look and function. By the late 1970s, biologists had learned so much about genes and how they operate that they thought only minor details were needed to complete the whole picture.

Then, in 1977, came a revelation almost as shocking as Copernicus' pronouncement over 400 years ago that the planets revolve around the sun. Two teams of researchers discovered independently that certain genes are not packaged in neat, continuous segments of DNA but are interrupted by apparently meaningless stretches of the molecule. These so-called split genes bewildered scientists. It was as if they had looked up the word *split* in the dictionary and found it spelled *spljkmpoqit*. But although the idea of split genes was revolutionary, it was soon embraced wholeheartedly. Crick spoke for all molecular biologists when he wrote in the April 1979 issue of *Science* magazine, ". . . in September 1976, I had no idea that a typical gene might be split into several pieces and I doubt if anybody else had." He went on to note that, only two years later, the existence of split genes was universally accepted.

If split genes are the rule rather than the exception, why had scientists not discovered them earlier? The answer is simple. Most biologists had been carrying out detailed genetic research only in procaryotes, organisms such as bacteria and blue-green algae whose cells have no nucleus. Genes are not split in procaryotes. So no one had expected genes to be split in eucaryotes — organisms such as plants, animals, and humans whose cells do have a nucleus. However, in the 1970s, scientists developed the laboratory procedures necessary to carry out detailed genetic studies in eucaryotes. By late 1979, such studies had uncovered split genes for 12 different eucaryotic proteins in almost as many organisms. Contrary to what everyone had supposed for a decade, genes in apes are constructed very differently from those in algae.

Genes in all organisms consist of DNA. This two-stranded molecule resembles a long spiral ladder or, more precisely, two half-ladders. Each strand, or half-ladder, is composed of a sidepiece of alternating phosphate and sugar molecules, with half-rungs of molecules called bases that jut out from each sugar. Each half-rung can be any one of four chemical bases — adenine (A), guanine (G), thymine (T), or cytosine (C). In a complete DNA molecule, the two strands are lined up with their bases joining in the middle to form rungs. Since the bases are of different lengths, only two combinations of bases — A and T, and G and C — can meet properly in the middle.

The order of the bases in a DNA strand determines the genetic information in the gene, much as the sequence of letters determines the meaning of a word. This information tells the cell how to manufacture particular types of proteins, the complex compounds that are needed to keep cells alive.

The protein ordered up by a particular gene is manufactured in a two-step process. In the first step, called transcription, the DNA segment comprising the gene splits into two strands. Only one strand contains the genetic information for a particular protein. That strand becomes a set of instructions for building a strand of ribonucleic acid

The author:
Daniel L. Hartl is a professor of biology at Purdue University. He also contributes the Genetics article in *Science Year*'s Science File section.

(RNA). RNA is almost identical to DNA, and their two strands fit together. However, in an RNA strand, the base thymine is replaced by another base, uracil (U).

The RNA strand is put together in sections consisting of alternating sugar and phosphate molecules with a base attached to each sugar. As these segments link together one by one to form the RNA strand, each RNA base — A, G, U, or C — joins with its complementary DNA base to form the rungs of a hybrid RNA-DNA ladder. The completed RNA strand, a blueprint of the DNA strand, separates from the DNA. It is then ready to participate in the next step in protein manufacture.

Translation is the second step in protein manufacture. The cell now uses the information in the RNA as a set of instructions to build a particular type of protein. Proteins are composed of amino acids, and each kind of protein consists of large numbers of amino acid molecules linked together like boxcars on a train. The order of the amino acids in a protein is determined by the order of the base molecules in the RNA strand.

A tiny particle in the cell called a ribosome "reads" the RNA and carries out its instructions. The ribosome attaches to one end of the RNA strand and moves along toward the other end, three bases at a time. These three-base steps, called codons, are the "words" in the RNA set of instructions.

As the ribosome reads each codon word, it adds one particular amino acid to the protein that is being manufactured. Since there are only 20 amino acids and 64 possible codons, more than one codon can specify some amino acids. For example, codons UUU, UUC, UUA, and UUG all specify the same amino acid in much the same way that "cease," "desist," "halt," and "quit" are all synonyms for "stop."

I n procaryotes, translation can take place while transcription is still going on. Ribosomes can attach to the end of an RNA strand as soon as it is made, and they begin to manufacture proteins while the rest of the RNA strand is still forming. This overlap does not occur in eucaryotes, however. The two stages are separate because eucaryotes have a nucleus. RNA is produced only within the nucleus, where the DNA is located. Then, because the nucleus does not contain ribosomes, the completed RNA strand must leave the nucleus to carry its instructions to the ribosomes.

By the 1950s, scientists began to notice something very peculiar about the genetic material in the cells of eucaryotes. They saw that the strands of RNA in the nucleus were much longer than the strands of RNA outside the nucleus. In fact, it looked as if only about one-fifth of the RNA was leaving the nucleus to be translated.

They also observed that the RNA strand produced in eucaryotes undergoes certain processing before it leaves the nucleus to be translated. All RNAs are "capped" by one special base molecule, a chemically modified guanine, at the "top" end of the strand where the ribosome will later attach to begin translation. Most RNAs are

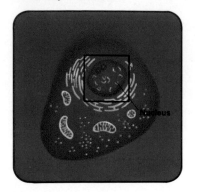 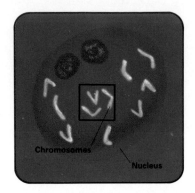 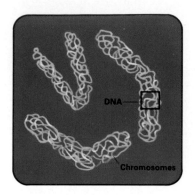

also finished at the "bottom" end by a string of 150 to 200 consecutive adenine bases. Until the late 1970s, many molecular biologists believed that the shortened RNA that emerged from the nucleus had been trimmed off at the ends by enzymes before it was capped and finished. Nobody wanted to believe that large pieces were removed from the middle of the RNA strand.

Until 1977, no one had observed the actual shortening process. That year, groups working at the Massachusetts Institute of Technology (M.I.T.) in Cambridge, Mass., and at Cold Spring Harbor Laboratory in Long Island, N.Y., decided independently to study the process using adenovirus 2. This virus, which causes short-term respiratory infections in humans and can affect other animals, has genes for several different proteins. The M.I.T. group, composed of molecular biologists Susan Berget, Claire Moore, and Philip Sharp, focused on a particular type of RNA that, when translated, produces a protein called hexon. This protein forms a major part of the coat of adenovirus 2. Like all viruses, when adenovirus 2 infects a cell, it uses the host cell's machinery to manufacture the proteins it needs to replicate itself. The scientists chose to study this particular viral protein because large amounts of its RNA can be extracted from infected animal cells.

To carry out their study, the M.I.T. group first had to obtain the RNA that is translated to produce hexon protein. The RNA that leaves the nucleus is known as messenger RNA (mRNA), and the scientists knew that hexon mRNA was most abundant about two days after cells had been infected with adenovirus 2.

To obtain the mRNA, they added adenovirus 2 to human cells growing in culture dishes. Two days later, they ground up the cells and separated the mRNA that was attached to ribosomes. To see if the mRNA was actually hexon mRNA, they added it to an artificial mixture containing ribosomes and other ingredients necessary for making proteins. When they added their mRNA to this mixture, hexon protein was produced.

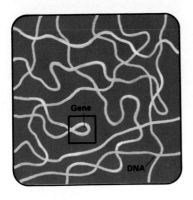

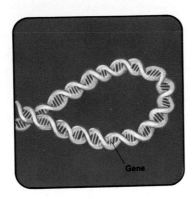

In a microscopic voyage into the cell, *from left to right starting on the opposite page,* the nucleus first appears as a marbled sphere. Closer inspection reveals a collection of chromosomes that, in turn, seem to be a thick mass of DNA. At closer range, the DNA appears as a long thread formed by two strands entwined in a double helix. A gene is one segment of this thread.

The next step in the study was to determine how the hexon mRNA matched up with the DNA in the hexon gene. To do this, the researchers used a procedure developed in 1975 by biochemists Raymond L. White and David S. Hogness at Stanford University in Palo Alto, Calif., called the R-loop technique. In this technique, scientists extract double-stranded DNA from cells and add segments of it to a special solution that causes the strands to repeatedly come apart briefly and then rejoin. Then the researchers add an mRNA strand that they know codes for a particular protein. The mRNA strand matches up with the complementary section of DNA during one of the DNA's separations. This DNA-mRNA hybrid does not come apart in the chemical solution, so the unmatched DNA strand can only rejoin its partner above and below the hybrid.

When scientists view the mixture through an electron microscope, they see an area that appears as a narrow loop or as a thickened region in a DNA strand. This region is thicker because it is made up of three strands — a strand of DNA entwined with a strand of mRNA and the unpaired strand of DNA that makes a short detour around the two. Because this thickened region may sometimes appear as a loop, it is called an R-loop. Scientists know that, in transcription, the DNA had produced RNA and that the resultant RNA had been transformed into the mRNA with which the DNA is paired in the R-loop. They can then conclude that the DNA is the gene for the particular protein and that the mRNA codes for that protein.

To match up the hexon mRNA with the hexon gene, the M.I.T. group had to obtain the hexon gene. To do this, they added a restriction enzyme to adenovirus 2 DNA. Restriction enzymes cut a DNA molecule only at particular places. There are 11 such places in the adenovirus 2 DNA, so the enzyme cut it into 12 pieces. The scientists used the largest piece because they knew from earlier work that it contained the hexon gene.

When they mixed hexon mRNA with hexon DNA and viewed the mixture through an electron microscope, they saw that most of the mRNA had joined the DNA to form an R-loop. As expected, the stretch of 150 A's at the bottom of the mRNA did not match up with the DNA because it had been added to the mRNA after transcription. They did expect the mRNA to match the DNA at the top, however, because the one capping base added to the mRNA would have been too small to see. But they did see something, and it did not match. A length of mRNA trailed off at the top, just as the string of A's had trailed off at the bottom. The M.I.T. scientists performed this experiment again and again, hoping to uncover a laboratory error that had prevented them from arriving at the "right" result — that is, finding all of the mRNA neatly contained in a single R-loop. Yet, at the end of each test, the unmatched segment appeared mockingly at the top of the mRNA. The researchers could neither explain its existence nor make it go away.

While the M.I.T. group was tracking down the source of that mysterious segment, the Cold Spring Harbor molecular biologists — Louise Chow, Richard Gelinas, Thomas Broker, Richard Roberts, and Daniel F. Klessig — were studying the R-loops that were formed not only by the mRNA for hexon but also for several other adenovirus 2 proteins. These researchers, too, were amazed by their R-loop findings. Each one of the mRNAs that they studied seemed to have an unmatched segment at its top.

Neither group knew it at the time, but both the M.I.T. and the Cold Spring Harbor teams had decided to use the same research strategy to search for the source of the mysterious segment. They hoped to find a small piece of adenovirus 2 DNA among the 12 pieces that would match up with this mysterious segment of mRNA. If they could find such a piece, they could conclude that it had been used to transcribe the segment. The discovery of this piece would indicate that the mRNA for hexon and the other adenovirus 2 genes the groups were studying had been transcribed from two separate segments of DNA — the large DNA segment from the first R-loop, and a smaller segment from another part of the strand. It would mean that these adenovirus 2 genes were split.

To obtain pieces of DNA to use in these experiments, they again cut adenovirus 2 DNA with restriction enzymes and separated the resulting 12 pieces according to length. Then, in a series of R-loop procedures, they tried to match up each of the smaller DNA pieces with the mysterious mRNA segment. They expected this trial-and-error method to produce one — and only one — additional R-loop.

The M.I.T. scientists, who were working with the hexon gene, were in for another surprise. One DNA piece indeed reacted, but it formed three R-loops. This indicated that three separate sections of DNA had transcribed the mysterious mRNA segment. The biologists concluded that the hexon gene is not only split, but it is split into four pieces — three pieces for the unmatched segment at the top of the mRNA and one piece for the rest.

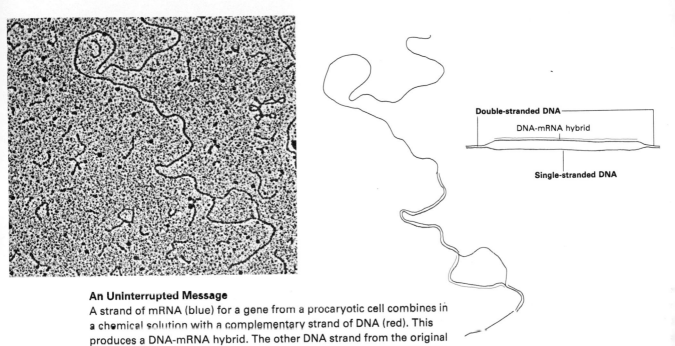

An Uninterrupted Message
A strand of mRNA (blue) for a gene from a procaryotic cell combines in a chemical solution with a complementary strand of DNA (red). This produces a DNA-mRNA hybrid. The other DNA strand from the original pair is displaced. The DNA segment in the hybrid is the actual gene that carries the instructions for producing a protein. In procaryotic cells it is one continuous segment. (Magnification 18,000 times.)

An Excess of Information
A eucaryotic mRNA strand (blue) combines with the DNA strands (red) in separate areas. Only these sections, called exons, carry instructions for producing proteins. The intervening sections of double-stranded DNA, called introns, that split the gene have no known function.

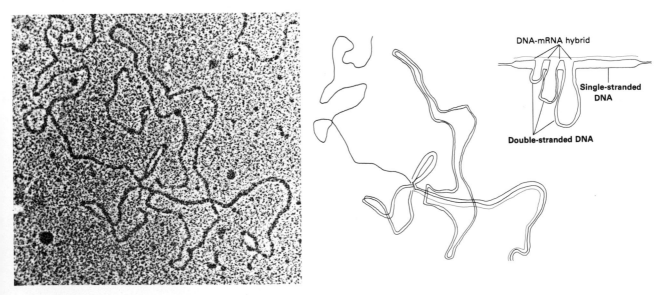

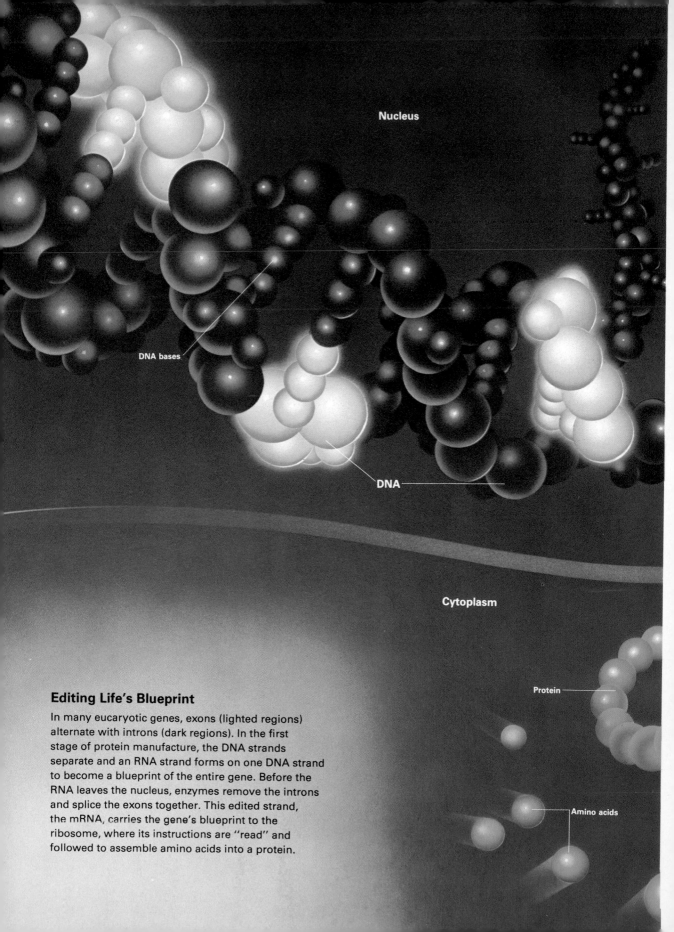

Nucleus

DNA bases

DNA

Cytoplasm

Protein

Amino acids

Editing Life's Blueprint

In many eucaryotic genes, exons (lighted regions) alternate with introns (dark regions). In the first stage of protein manufacture, the DNA strands separate and an RNA strand forms on one DNA strand to become a blueprint of the entire gene. Before the RNA leaves the nucleus, enzymes remove the introns and splice the exons together. This edited strand, the mRNA, carries the gene's blueprint to the ribosome, where its instructions are "read" and followed to assemble amino acids into a protein.

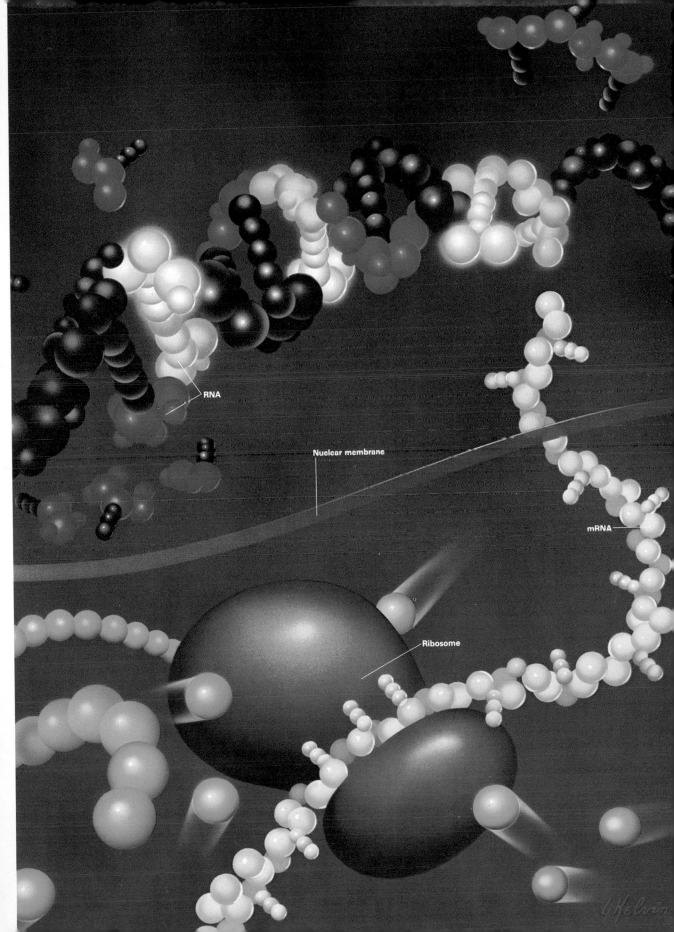

RNA

Nuclear membrane

mRNA

Ribosome

The Cold Spring Harbor group that was studying several adenovirus 2 genes obtained the same results. However, they found something else even more amazing. The same piece of DNA that formed three R-loops with the top of the hexon mRNA also formed three R-loops with the top end of the mRNA for several other proteins. This indicated that the top ends of all of these mRNAs are transcribed from the same piece of DNA.

Klessig found in 1978 that the identical top end of each protein's mRNA is a "leader sequence," which may act as a start signal that ribosomes need in order to become attached and begin translation. The actual mRNA coding sequence that determines the order of amino acids in the protein is different for each protein. The leader sequences and the coding sequences are all present on the very long first RNA strand that is produced in the nucleus. However, the leader and coding sequences of the RNA in the nucleus are separated from each other by other segments of DNA that do not occur in the final mRNA. Biochemist Walter Gilbert of Harvard coined the name *introns* for the segments that are not found in the final mRNA and *exons* for those parts that remain to create the protein.

Scientists now believe that the introns are cut out of the RNA by enzymes similar to restriction enzymes. Then other enzymes join or splice the cut ends of the leader to the coding sequences. When all the introns have been removed and the leader and coding sequences have been properly spliced, the RNA is capped at the top, finished with a chain of A bases at the bottom, and released from the nucleus as mRNA. The introns left behind are apparently broken down by different enzymes.

There was still some hope for anyone who wished to uphold the simple, procaryotic picture of unsplit genes. Perhaps split genes occur only in certain viruses such as adenovirus 2, or perhaps introns occur only at the end of coding sequences. But by the end of 1977, molecular biologists studying other eucaryotic genes had showed that split genes are a common feature of eucaryotes and that introns can occur anywhere in a gene.

Teams at the National Institutes of Health (NIH) in Bethesda, Md., and at the University of Amsterdam in the Netherlands found that in mice and rabbits, the gene for hemoglobin, the oxygen-carrying protein in red blood cells, contains two introns within the coding sequence. Scientists at the Basel Institute for Immunology in Switzerland and at Harvard University discovered that the coding sequence is split in a mouse gene involved in immunity. Groups at the Institute of Biological Chemistry in Strasbourg, France, and at Baylor College of Medicine in Houston found in 1978 and 1979 that the ovalbumin gene in chickens, which codes for a major protein in egg white, is split into seven pieces. Finally, a research team at the University of Washington in Seattle discovered an intron in a gene for a yeast protein in 1979.

Why are these genes split? By the summer of 1980, no one was certain. In some cases, exons correspond to different parts of a protein. For example, one of the exons in hemoglobin codes for the central part of the protein, which is the part that carries the oxygen. The mouse protein immunoglobulin, which is involved in immunity, has four functional parts; its gene is also split into four corresponding parts. However, in the ovalbumin gene, exons and functional parts of the protein are not related.

Gilbert suggests that introns may play a role in the evolutionary process. He theorizes that introns may serve a purpose just before reproductive cells are formed. At this point, DNA strands form into rods, or chromosomes. The chromosomes pair off and join together briefly to exchange DNA. During this exchange, an intron-exon-intron unit from one gene may move into a place on another gene formerly held by an intron alone. This would provide eucaryotes with a powerful method of adding new functions to genes. For example, the hemoglobin gene may have been created by the accidental insertion of the exon that codes for the oxygen-carrying part of the protein into the middle of another gene. This might have made it possible for higher forms of animal life to evolve by providing, in the hemoglobin molecule, a way to carry oxygen to cells of an organism.

According to another theory, introns may be required for normal gene function. In 1979, NIH molecular biologists Dean H. Hamer and Philip Leder chemically removed the introns from the DNA of a tumor virus called SV40, which infects both monkey and human cells. They cut the DNA into introns and exons with restriction enzymes, then used a linking enzyme to join the exon pieces in the right order. However, when they used this DNA without introns to infect monkey cells, they found that the DNA was transcribed into RNA in the nucleus, but the RNA was rapidly broken down by enzymes before it could leave the nucleus to translate the virus genes into protein.

Because introns are found so frequently in eucaryotic genes, many scientists now believe that they may have several functions. Molecular biologists hoping to find clues to their functions are comparing the positions and base sequences of introns in a wide variety of genes. Perhaps introns may be necessary to ensure that an RNA transcript will be processed into mRNA and released for translation. Perhaps some introns are simply leftovers from the gene's creation with no present function.

Although scientists offer conflicting explanations for them, they seem to agree that the discovery of split genes in eucaryotes is one of the most important findings in molecular biology in the last 20 years. Biology laboratories all over the world are electric with curiosity and excitement. There are important problems to be solved and important discoveries to be made. These days, molecular biologists are anything but smug.

Fourier's Formidable Formulas

By Ronald N. Bracewell

**Mathematicians of the early 1800s called Joseph
Fourier's equations impossible and impractical but
modern researchers consider them indispensable**

A mathematical discovery announced in 1807 and digital computer techniques developed in the 1960s have teamed up in a new kind of X-ray machine that is revolutionizing certain types of medical diagnosis. The machine, called a computerized axial tomograph (CAT) scanner, produces clear X-ray pictures of the inside of a living human body in cross section — like photographing a slice of bread while it is still in the loaf without photographing the slices next to it.

Neurosurgeons have used the CAT scanner since 1972 to find brain tumors and its use is now spreading to other medical fields. Lung surgeons are using it to pinpoint cancers. Internists examine CAT scans to see whether internal organs have become enlarged. Other physicians use scans to analyze the spinal column one tiny slice at a time. Every part of the body is open to the CAT scanner's invisible probe. This instrument has already been so beneficial to humanity that British electronics engineer Godfrey N. Hounsfield and United States physicist Allan M. Cormack won the 1979 Nobel prize for physiology or medicine for developing it.

The scanner's computer program depends on the 1807 mathematical discovery called the Fourier Transform, which is named after its inventor, French mathematician Jean Baptiste Joseph Fourier. Fourier Transforms help 20th-century scientists study the universe in

Ordinary X-ray photographs, *opposite page,* record a human skull's bone and soft tissue as if all of this material were located on the skull's surface. But a computerized axial tomogram (inset), produced by Fourier mathematics, shows the distribution throughout a section of the skull.

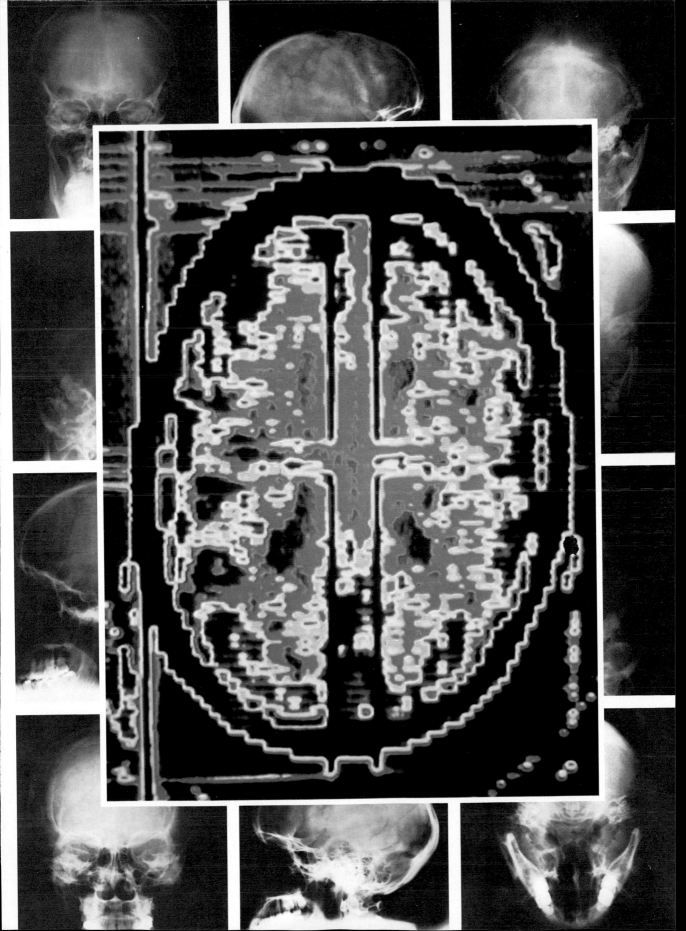

many ways. They assist astronomers in mapping the vast reaches of outer space; help microbiologists build models of tiny creatures, such as viruses, that inhabit the microscopic world; and aid communications technicians in sharpening photographs of the earth's surface sent back from artificial satellites.

They also enable an instrument called a Fourier spectrometer to analyze a glowing object's light rays so that scientists can identify the object's molecular makeup. Technologists use the spectrometer to control the quality of industrial materials and to monitor the purity of drinking water, foods, and medicines. Even music has felt the effect of Fourier Transforms. The Moog synthesizer, a popular keyboard instrument, uses this mathematical discovery to produce music without the aid of any ordinary musical instrument.

Fourier Transforms are an advanced example of how scientists and engineers use the mathematical equations of physical laws to study and control the universe. A design engineer who knows the equations that apply to a certain kind of structure or motion can design the advanced parts of a machine without having to design the basic parts by trial and error.

Some simple equations have a surprising range of applications. For example, the parabola is a curve whose height is proportional to the square of its width. This shape may be difficult to visualize, but the next time you use a drinking fountain, notice the form of the rising and falling water stream — it is a parabola. Suspension-bridge cables follow a curve that matches the stream's curve turned upside down. A section sliced through the center of a microwave-relay reflector is also a parabola. The relationship linking a simple geometrical shape, a stream of water, a hanging cable, and a reflector is the simple equation of the parabola.

Fourier also used a simple geometrical figure — the sine wave — at the beginning of the mathematical research that led him to the discovery that bears his name. Unlike the parabola, the sine wave does not appear in any form that is visible to the naked eye. But you can make something very close to a sine wave by anchoring one end of a long rope and moving the other end up and down rapidly with your hand until one or more points along the rope stand still while the rest of the rope vibrates.

Many common objects vibrate in a way that mathematicians describe by graphs of sine waves, even though their vibrations do not form sine waves in space as does the rope. For example, the graph of an object that swings back and forth like a pendulum is a pure sine wave. The distance it moves is plotted on the vertical axis and time is plotted on the horizontal axis. The highest points on the graph are called crests, and the lowest points are troughs. The sine wave is a periodic wave — one that repeats itself over a period of time, just as the pendulum repeats its swing. The crests and troughs are an equal distance from the horizontal axis.

The author:
Ronald N. Bracewell is director of the Radio Astronomy Institute and professor of electrical engineering at Stanford University.

The waves of musical sounds are also *sinusoidal* (in the form of sine waves). A tuning fork vibrates with a simple back-and-forth motion like a pendulum swing, so a graph of its sound is a sine wave. But most musical instruments do not vibrate so simply. A violin string, for example, vibrates as a whole and in parts at the same time. Each half of the string, each third of the string, and even smaller fractions may vibrate separately. The graphs of the whole string and those of the fractions of the string are all sine waves. The combined graph of the whole-string and fractional vibrations is a periodic wave made up of a large wave with smaller troughs built into it as ripples on the curve. Mathematicians say that this complex curve is the sum of the sine curves.

Fourier applied the mathematics of such complex sinusoidal waves to problems of heat conduction that were important to the industries of his time, such as lumber, ceramics, and chemicals. For example, sawmill operators wanted to know how heat flowed through boards so that they could determine the most efficient way to dry lumber — how long to heat a board, how much heat to apply, and where to apply it. Mathematically, this was a problem in cooling — in determining how each tiny concentration of heat applied at a point on the board's surface would cool itself by spreading out into the board and by escaping into the air.

Scientists and mathematicians applied mathematics to many cooling problems. They considered shapes such as rods, spheres, cubes, cylinders, and wedges — geometrical forms that resembled material and equipment used in such industrial processes as drying clay, seasoning timber, and cooling vats. First, they imagined that a solid object of a simple geometrical shape was heated and cooled in a certain way. Then they used mathematics to try to determine heat distribution and rates of warming and cooling in that object.

One of the problems they wrestled with was the heat distribution along a rod that had been heated nonuniformly, such as a poker that was red-hot at one end but cool throughout the rest of its length. Scientists tried to figure out how the heat would flow so that they could predict how the temperature would rise and fall at some point along its length — at the handheld end, for example.

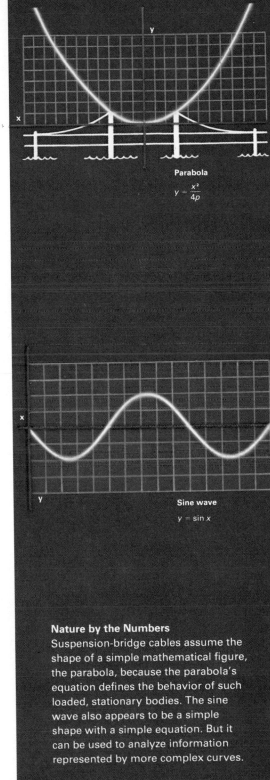

Parabola

$$y = \frac{x^2}{4p}$$

Sine wave

$$y = \sin x$$

Nature by the Numbers
Suspension-bridge cables assume the shape of a simple mathematical figure, the parabola, because the parabola's equation defines the behavior of such loaded, stationary bodies. The sine wave also appears to be a simple shape with a simple equation. But it can be used to analyze information represented by more complex curves.

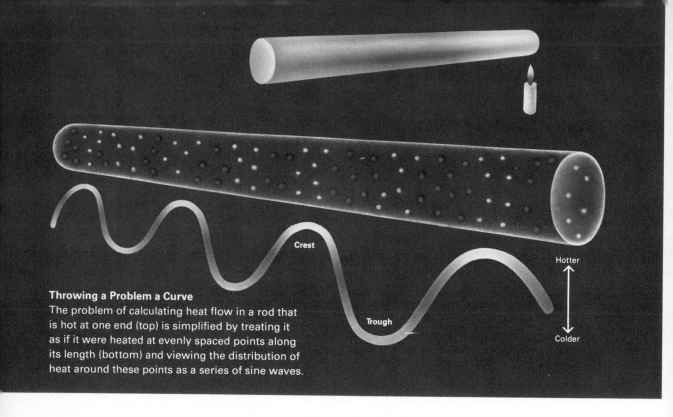

Throwing a Problem a Curve
The problem of calculating heat flow in a rod that is hot at one end (top) is simplified by treating it as if it were heated at evenly spaced points along its length (bottom) and viewing the distribution of heat around these points as a series of sine waves.

Crest

Trough

Hotter

Colder

Fourier first simplified the problem by imagining that the rod had been heated at evenly spaced points along its length, rather than just at one end. He graphed each tiny concentration of heat in the bar as the crest of a sine wave and each cooler region between hot spots as a trough. Fourier imagined that, as time passed, each heat concentration would become cooler because heat would flow to the cooler regions, which would become warmer. So the crests would fall as the troughs rose. Fourier's greatest insight was in understanding that he could plot the heat distribution in the bar at any time after the initial heating by adding up the sine waves of all the concentrations.

Fourier developed a new mathematical equation, called the diffusion equation, that described the flow of heat from an object's warm parts to its cool parts and invented a method—the Fourier Transform—for solving it. He then applied his new mathematics to the original problem of the poker heated at one end and to problems of heat distribution in objects of more complex shapes.

Other mathematicians of his time accepted Fourier's results. But then Fourier took his mathematical analysis a step further. He had begun with the idea of adding up sine waves to form periodic curves, but before long the method was extended to nonperiodic curves. Fourier said that any wave form could be synthesized, or built up, by combining a set of sine waves, and any wave form could be analyzed, or broken down, into sine waves. He understood that sine waves of many different sizes would be needed, all rising and falling in a certain sequence. And he recognized there was only one way to analyze a complex curve into sine waves.

But this idea was not accepted immediately. When Fourier presented his new theory to the Paris Academy in 1807, the great mathematician Joseph Louis Lagrange declared it was impossible. Other authorities agreed, so the theory was not immediately published. However, over the next few years, Fourier convinced mathematicians of its validity, and its usefulness became obvious. The scientific community's uneasiness soon gave way to enthusiasm. "Fourier's theorem is not only one of the most beautiful results of modern analysis," British physicist William Thomson, later Lord Kelvin, wrote in 1867, "but it may be said to furnish an indispensable instrument in the treatment of nearly every recondite [difficult to understand] question in modern physics."

Fourier's analysis was little used at first, because such a large amount of arithmetic — additions and multiplications — to graph a complex wave had to be done by hand. First, the wave had to be divided into a series of vertical strips of uniform width, each strip represented by a point on its part of the curve. The amount of arithmetic that had to be performed depended upon the number of data points needed to describe the wave. The number of additions equaled the number of points and the number of multiplications equaled the number of points squared. For example, analyzing a complex wave specified by 1,000 points taken at regular intervals would have required 1,000 additions and 1 million multiplications.

So the effort to use Fourier mathematics was made only when the results justified the effort. About 1910, scientists bombarded crystals with X rays and analyzed the results with Fourier Transforms to determine where the crystals' atoms were located. The same technique was used a little later to analyze proteins. In both cases, dozens of clerks had to do the tedious computing on mechanical calculators.

Some applications of Fourier's mathematics required so many computations that engineers had to build gigantic mechanical devices — complex assemblies of disks, wheels, cylinders, and gears — to perform them. The results were recorded on mechanical counters like an automobile's mileage indicator. The British Admiralty Board used such a mechanical computer in the 1880s to compute tide tables for the world's principal ports. A ship's captain approaching a foreign port could consult these tables to see how high the water would be at his scheduled time of arrival. Electronic digital computers developed in the 1950s were much faster and more compact than mechanical computers. They could easily handle the enormous number of calculations necessary to compile the tide tables, so in the 1960s they took over this computational work.

The small, mass-produced digital computer greatly extended the use of Fourier's techniques. For example, it enabled scientists to build a Fourier spectrometer in the mid-1960s. United States physicist Albert A. Michelson conceived the idea of the spectrometer about 1900. He knew that a molecule that is heated to a high temperature

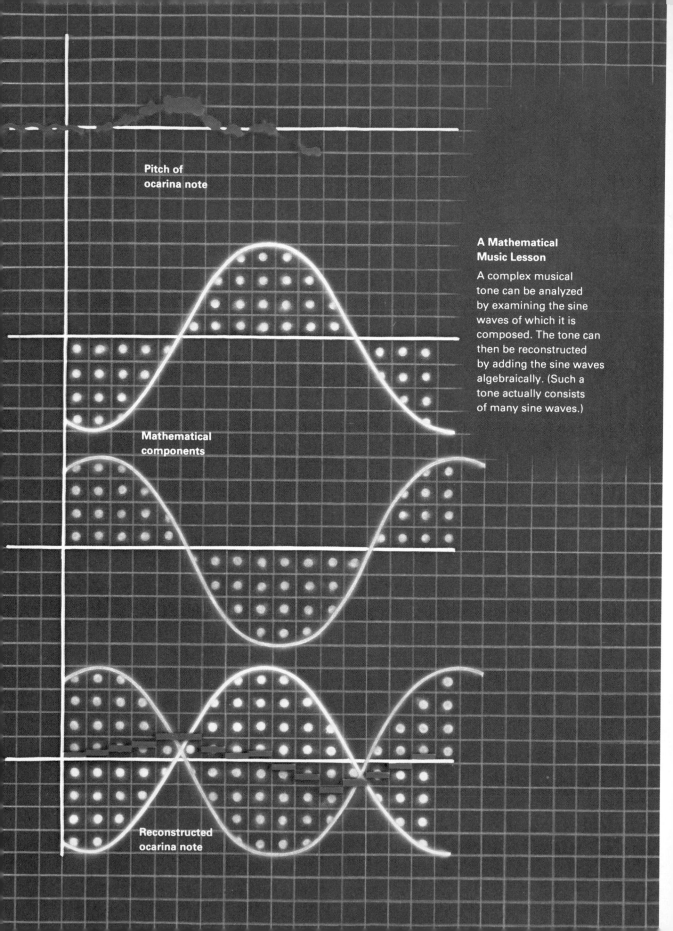

Pitch of
ocarina note

**A Mathematical
Music Lesson**

A complex musical
tone can be analyzed
by examining the sine
waves of which it is
composed. The tone can
then be reconstructed
by adding the sine waves
algebraically. (Such a
tone actually consists
of many sine waves.)

Mathematical
components

Reconstructed
ocarina note

gives off a pattern of light waves of various wavelengths — distances between crests. The pattern is different for each kind of molecule, so a scientist can identify a molecule if he knows the wavelengths of the light that it emits. But a heated object emits light of all the wavelengths in its pattern at once.

Michelson thought of a way to sort out the wavelengths. He envisioned a coated glass plate that would split a beam of light coming from the object into two parts. Each would travel a separate path before mirrors directed them to a light detector. The length of one path would be adjustable.

A scientist using the spectrometer would first set the paths at the same length. The crests of the light waves of a given wavelength would arrive in the order in which they left the heated object. The detector would record the light intensity as if the beam had not been split. Then the scientist would make the path lengths slightly different. The crests from half of the beam would now arrive after the crests from the other half and the detectors would record a different intensity. Further path-length changes would cause further intensity changes.

The results of all this would be plotted on a graph of intensity and distance. The operator would use Fourier Transforms to analyze the graph into sine waves that would represent the wavelengths of the light emitted by the heated object.

Michelson's idea was scientifically sound, but the calculations would have taken too long for the computers of his time to perform them. So the idea had to wait until the electronic digital computer was developed. Fourier spectrometers are now widely used in chemical research.

Scientists extended the range of Fourier mathematics even further during the late 1960s by using the Fast Fourier Transform (FFT). This was developed by James W. Cooley of International Business Machines Corporation's Thomas J. Watson Research Center in Yorktown Heights, N.Y., and John W. Tukey of Bell Telephone Laboratories in Murray Hill, N.J., and Princeton University in New Jersey in 1965. This technique organized the calculations much more efficiently, causing a revolution in computing.

The FFT saves time by decreasing the number of multiplications needed to analyze a complex curve. It divides the curve into a large number of equal segments and analyzes each segment separately. The number of multiplications needed to analyze the entire curve decreases by one-half for each doubling of the number of segments. For example, suppose we divide the 1,000-digit curve we analyzed with regular transforms into two segments of 500 points each. The number of multiplications needed to analyze each segment is 500 squared, or 250,000. The second segment requires the same number, so the total is 500,000, or half of the original 1 million required before. We can continue subdividing the curve until we are left with 500 segments of 2 points each, requiring a total of only 9,000 multiplications.

$$F(\nu) = N^{-1} \sum_{\tau = 0}^{\tau = N - 1} f(\tau)e^{-i2\pi(\nu/N)\tau}$$

$$f(\tau) = \sum_{\nu = 0}^{\nu = N - 1} F(\nu)e^{i2\pi(\nu/N)\tau}$$

Using the FFT technique on complex waves that contain many more data points provides even more dramatic savings. For example, about 1 million points define the wave form of the voltage that forms one frame of a television picture. Building up the wave form by the direct method would require 1 trillion multiplications, but the FFT technique cuts this to 19 million. So FFTs enable a scientist to synthesize a television image that is as sharp as the finest pictures available from commercial broadcasters at only a tiny fraction of the cost of building up the same image with ordinary Fourier Transforms.

The FFT technique enables the CAT scanner's computer to handle a complete scan of about 10,000 points in less than two minutes. Ordinary X-ray machines photograph everything in the path of the X-ray beam. A picture of the lungs, for example, also shows the ribs that lie in front of and behind the lungs, and the spine. These details complicate the job of a surgeon who examines the picture trying to locate a suspected lung cancer. X-ray tomography, developed in 1921, produces cross-sectional pictures in clear focus of the part of the body to be studied. However, it does not remove the unwanted foreground and background, it merely blurs out the detail. But computer-assisted tomography produces clear pictures of the desired slice of the body, free from clutter. To do this, the scanner's X-ray tube shoots rays through the body section from many angles. X-ray detectors on the other side of the body translate the strengths of the rays that reach them into electrical impulses, which a computer combines to produce the clear tomogram.

The scanner's X-ray source and X-ray detector are mounted opposite each other on a large metal ring. The patient lies on a table that slides inside the ring. First, the table is positioned so that the ring is around the section of the body to be scanned. Then the ring sends X rays through that section and they are picked up by the detector. Moment by moment, the detector reports the strength of X rays received to the adjacent computer. Then the ring rotates one degree and the scan is repeated in the new orientation.

This process continues until the body section has been scanned 360 times, once for each degree in a circle. In any single scan, background and foreground are telescoped together as in an ordinary X-ray picture, but the telescoping occurs at different angles because of all the different orientations. The computer then manipulates the series of data points that represent how X-ray strength varied with ring

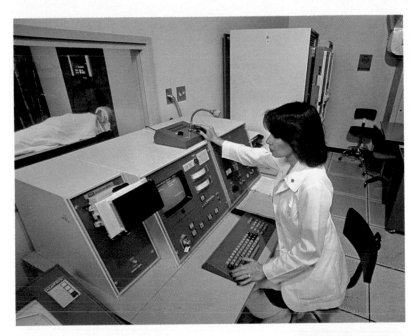

A technician sets a computerized axial
tomograph's controls, *above,* to begin
an X-ray scan of a patient inside a huge
detector ring, *right.* The machine's
computer then uses Fourier mathematics
to analyze the data gathered by the ring
and produce a television picture of
a cross section of body tissue, *below.*

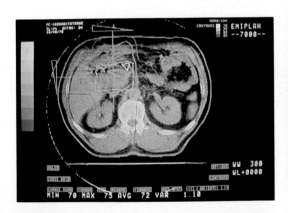

Fourier synthesis of sound builds music mathematically in a Moog synthesizer, *right.* Fourier analysis of sound led to the development of artificial voices in machines that can read to the blind, *below right,* or can help children to learn to spell, *below.*

An experimental speech printer detects
the sound waves of spoken words, then
uses Fourier mathematics to analyze these
waves so that it can print the words.

Fourier mathematics combined data from
electron photographs of a virus only 24
micromillimeters in diameter, *below,* so
that a detailed, three-dimensional model
of the virus could be built, *right.*

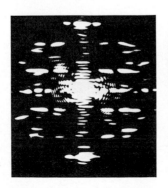

orientation and the part of the body being scanned. It divides this series into segments which it then multiplies, adds, reassembles, and sends to a television tube that displays a picture of the body section.

Scientists had previously used Fourier Transforms in this way to probe objects that ranged from the cosmic to the microscopic. I had used such a technique in the mid-1950s to locate sources of certain kinds of radiation coming from the sun. The sun and the earth change their orientation with respect to each other as they rotate, so I obtained data points at various orientations by scanning the sun with a radio telescope several times during the day. I then applied a Fourier program that I had developed and thus located the sources of this solar radiation.

Not by Math Alone

Jean Baptiste
Joseph Fourier

The man who invented Fourier analysis and synthesis was also a prominent French scientific and governmental administrator. Jean Baptiste Joseph Fourier was born on March 21, 1768, in Auxerre, France, southeast of Paris, the 19th child of a tailor. Orphaned when he was 8 years old, he was educated by the local Benedictine monks and became a teacher in Auxerre in 1789. He became active in local affairs during the French Revolution of 1789. His defense of victims of the Reign of Terror of 1793 and 1794 led to his arrest in 1794. He was released later that year and went to Paris to study mathematics. When the Polytechnical School was founded in Paris in 1795, Fourier joined its staff as an assistant professor of mathematics. His reputation as a mathematician grew so rapidly that he was chosen as one of a band of learned men who accompanied Napoleon Bonaparte on a 1798 military expedition to Egypt. Fourier soon became secretary of the Institute of Egypt.

After the French left Egypt in 1799, Napoleon appointed Fourier prefect of the department (governor of the state) of Isère in southeastern France. His duties included collecting taxes, supervising military recruiting, and law enforcement. He worked to smooth over bad feelings remaining from the Revolution of 1789 and supervised the draining of 80,000 square kilometers (31,000 square miles) of swamps and the building of the French section of the road from Isère's capital, Grenoble, to Turin, Italy. Fourier did most of his mathematical work on heat-transfer problems while at Grenoble. Napoleon, who had become emperor, made him a baron in 1808.

But when Napoleon abdicated in 1814 and set out for Elba, a tiny island off the coast of Italy, Fourier found himself in a difficult position. Grenoble was on the emperor's route and Fourier knew that greeting his old master would jeopardize his standing with the new king. Louis XVIII might not look favorably on old associates and appointees of the departing emperor. Fourier used his political powers to get Napoleon's route changed, and thus kept his job.

Napoleon returned to France in 1815 in an attempt to reconquer his former empire. This time he did march through Grenoble, but Fourier left the city to avoid him. Napoleon made Fourier a count and appointed him prefect of the department of the Rhône, three days later.

Napoleon's rule this time lasted only 110 days. Fourier's days in provincial politics ended then and he moved to Paris to concentrate on science. He was elected to the Academy of Sciences in 1817, appointed permanent secretary in 1822, and named to the French Academy in 1827. Fourier died in Paris on May 16, 1830.   [R.N.B.]

British biologist Aaron Klug used Fourier Transforms in 1968 to obtain a picture of the internal structure of the tobacco mosaic virus. This virus is only 24-millionths of a millimeter in diameter, therefore, it is much too small to be seen through an ordinary microscope. But a transmission electron microscope can produce a picture of such a virus by shooting electrons through it just as an X-ray machine shoots X rays through an object.

Klug operated the electron microscope like a CAT scanner's ring, first scanning the virus, then changing the microscope's orientation and scanning again. He repeated the process until he had finally scanned all around the virus and along its entire length. Klug then used Fourier Transforms in a computer program that manipulated the microscope's data just as the CAT scanner's program manipulates its information. The resulting picture showed the inside as well as the outside of the object. Klug used this picture to build a three-dimensional model of the virus for study.

The U.S. National Aeronautics and Space Administration uses Fourier mathematics to provide clear, detailed pictures of planets and satellites taken in space. These pictures look like regular photographs, but they are transmitted by radio from space line by line, in the same way that a television picture is produced. Each line is transmitted as a series of radio impulses that a computer can process by Fourier techniques to tailor the scene in ways that would otherwise be extremely difficult, if not impossible.

The computer takes the information apart, adjusts the pieces of data according to its program, and puts them back together so that the pictures are clearer than they would otherwise have been. This computer program can filter background fog, increase and decrease contrast, and sharpen blurred edges.

Musicians have joined scientists in the use of Fourier Transforms. The Moog synthesizer is an electronic instrument that generates a variety of sounds. This instrument has a computer that manipulates electronic impulses that correspond to simple sine waves. It then forms combinations of impulses that it sends to speakers, which produce complex sound waves. The synthesizer can build up any complex wave, so it can duplicate the sound of any ordinary musical instrument. It also can produce sounds that are beyond the reach of such instruments. Composers have already begun to use these extraordinary sounds to write computerized music.

Thus, a mathematical technique that was developed to solve industrial heat-flow problems touches our lives in an astonishing variety of ways. As a quality-control tool, it affects the food we eat, the water we drink, and many of the manufactured products that we use every day. As a medical tool, it can save our lives. As a sound-building technique, it affects the music we hear. And as a means of analyzing scientific data, it enhances our understanding of the universe.

Jean Baptiste Joseph Fourier would be amazed.

For Further Reading

Additional information on some of the subjects covered in the Special Reports may be found in these books and magazine articles.

A Sport for All Seasons
Counsilman, James E. *Competitive Swimming Manual for Coaches and Swimmers.* Counsilman Company, Incorporated, 1977.
Counsilman, James E. *The Science of Swimming.* Prentice-Hall, Incorporated, 1968.

Journeys to Jupiter
Hartmann, William K. "Moons of the Outer Solar System Become Real, Although Weird, Places," *Smithsonian* Magazine, January 1980.
Science, June 1, 1979.
Science, November 23, 1979.
Soderblom, Laurence A. "The Galilean Moons of Jupiter," *Scientific American,* January 1980.

Cell Wars
Hopson, Janet L. "Battle at the Isle of Self," *Science 80,* March/April 1980.

Watch on the Self-Healing Earth
"*Amoco Cadiz:* A Lasting Disaster," *Science News,* Aug. 5, 1978.
Carter, Luther J. "*Amoco Cadiz* Incident Points Up the Elusive Goal of Tanker Safety," *Science,* May 5, 1978.
Schneider, Eric D. "Aftermath of the *Amoco Cadiz,*" *Oceans,* July 1978.

Tracking the Whirlwind
Allen, Everett S. *A Wind to Shake the World: The Story of the 1938 Hurricane.* Little, Brown, 1976.
Bixby, William. *Hurricanes.* David McKay Company, 1979.
Funk, B. "Swept Away: The Danger to Coastal Communities from Hurricanes," *New York Times Magazine,* Sept. 18, 1977.
Jennings, Gary. *Killer Storms: Hurricanes, Typhoons, & Tornadoes.* J. B. Lippincott Company, 1970.
Young, Louise B. *Earth's Aura.* Alfred A. Knopf, Incorporated, 1977.

Solving Crime with Science
Kind, Stuart and Overman, Michael. *Science Against Crime.* Doubleday and Company, 1972.
Kirk, Paul L. *Crime Investigation.* 2nd edition. John Wiley and Sons, 1974.
Waters, John F. *Crime Labs: The Science of Forensic Medicine.* Franklin Watts, 1979.

The Animal Navigators
Gould, James L. "Do Honeybees Know What They're Doing?" *Natural History,* June 1979.
Gould, James L. "The Evidence for Magnetic Field Sensitivity in Birds and Bees (Such As It Is)," *American Scientist,* May 1980.
Keeton, William T. "The Mystery of Pigeon Homing," *Scientific American,* May 1974.
"Lodestone Compass Inside Bacteria," *Science News,* April 28, 1979.
Schmidt-Koenig, Klaus and Keeton, William T. *Animal Migration, Navigation, and Homing.* Springer-Verlag, 1978.
Walcott, Charles; Gould, James L; and Kirschvink, Joseph L. "Pigeons Have Magnets," *Science,* Sept. 7, 1979.

Mending Shattered Minds

Arieti, Silvano. *Understanding and Helping the Schizophrenic: A Guide For Family and Friends.* Basic Books, 1974.

Kety, Seymour S. "Disorders of the Human Brain," *Scientific American,* September 1979.

O'Brien, Patrick. *The Disordered Mind: What We Know About Schizophrenia.* Prentice-Hall, 1978.

Snyder, Solomon H. *Madness and the Brain.* McGraw-Hill, 1974.

Keeping Nature's Diary

Alexander, Edward P. *Museums in Motion: An Introduction to the History and Functions of Museums.* American Association for State and Local History, 1979.

Burns, William. *Your Future in Museums.* Rosen, Richards Press, 1967.

Williams, Patricia M. *Museums of Natural History and the People Who Work in Them.* St. Martin's Press, 1973.

The Stuff Between the Stars

Chaisson, E. J. "Gaseous Nebulas," *Scientific American,* December 1978.

Heiles, C. "The Structure of the Interstellar Medium," *Scientific American,* January 1978.

Herbst, W. and Assousa, G. E. "Supernovas and Star Formation," *Scientific American,* August 1979.

Knacke, R. F. "Solid Particles in Space," *Sky and Telescope,* April 1979.

Loren, R. B. and Vrba, F. J. "Starmaking with Colliding Molecular Clouds," *Sky and Telescope,* June 1979.

Snow, T. P., Jr. "Ultraviolet Spectroscopy with Copernicus," *Sky and Telescope,* November 1977.

Digging for Black Gold

Marshall, Eliot. "OPEC Prices Make Heavy Oil Look Profitable," *Science,* June 22, 1979.

Maugh, Thomas H., II. "Tar Sands: A New Fuels Industry Takes Shape," *Science,* Feb. 17, 1978.

Reinterpreting Life's Blueprint

Crick, Francis H. C. "Split Genes and RNA Splicing," *Science,* April 20, 1979.

Kolata, Gina Bari. "Genes in Pieces," *Science,* Jan. 25, 1980.

Lewin, Roger. "Why Split Genes?" *New Scientist,* May 10, 1979.

Miller, Julie Ann. "Evolution: The Bottom Line," *Science News,* July 7, 1979.

Patrusky, Ben. "Split Genes: More Questions Than Answers," *Mosaic,* September/October 1979.

Science File

Science Year contributors report on the year's major developments in their respective fields. The articles in this section are arranged alphabetically by subject matter.

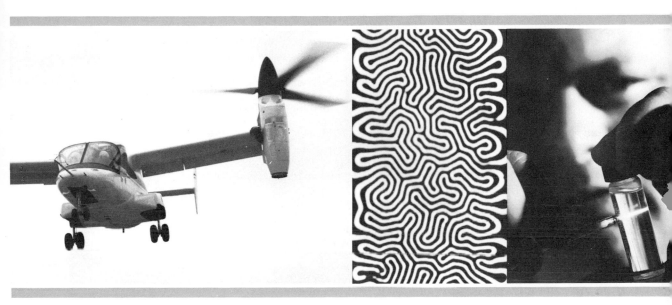

Agriculture

Scientists discovered new methods of dealing with plant pests in 1979 and 1980. Chemists William G. Williams, James D. Thacker, and John Bordner and entomologists George C. Kennedy and Robert T. Yamamoto at North Carolina State University in Raleigh reported in February 1980 that they had discovered a natural insecticide in the wild tomato, *Lycopersicon hirsutum f. glabratum.* The newly discovered substance, 2-tridecanone, is 74 times more abundant in the wild tomato than in the species of tomato most commonly cultivated, *Lycopersicon esculentum.*

The natural insecticide protects the wild tomato against a host of predatory insects, including fruit worms, pinworms, leaf miners, spider mites, and white flies. Because the wild tomato crosses readily with the domesticated species, it may be possible to produce offspring that combine the wild tomato's resistance to insects and the domestic strain's superior taste.

Plant pathologist Joseph Kuc of the University of Kentucky in Lexington reported in April 1980 that he had successfully vaccinated cucumbers against *Colletotrichum lagenarium,* the bacteria that spread cucumber anthracnose, a serious fungus disease. Kuc inoculated the first true leaves of cucumber seedlings with a weak concentration of the bacteria. He found that from 72 to 96 hours after inoculation, the plants had become resistant to the fungus-carrying bacteria and that the protection against those lasted up to five weeks.

War on weeds. A team of agricultural researchers announced in August 1979 that, for the first time, organisms that cause disease in plants are being developed for weed control. Fungi and bacteria can infect all plants and produce toxins, or poisons, that damage tissues. Lloyd A. Andres of the United States Department of Agriculture (USDA) Biological Control of Weeds Laboratory in Albany, Calif., reported that disease organisms that infect the northern joint vetch, *Aeschynomene virginica,* a weed that overruns the rice fields of Arkansas, can be produced in the laboratory and applied to these

The decorative East India neem tree provides more than shade. Its seeds contain a potent insect repellent that wards off the Japanese beetle, a voracious feeder that attacks more than 300 species of plants. Whole seeds are stored with grain to keep insects out. Powdered seeds, when mixed in an oil solution and sprayed on crops, provide up to two weeks' protection against beetle infestations.

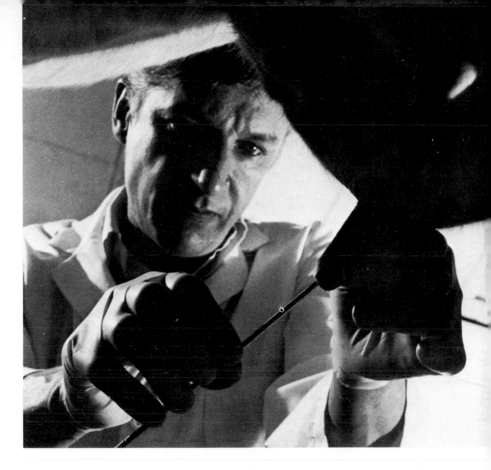

An animal physiologist uses a catheter to insert a small plastic loop into a cow's teat to prevent mastitis, a bacterial disease that affects milk production. The loop is a mild irritant and attracts white blood cells to the udder to destroy the bacteria that cause the mastitis.

Agriculture

Continued

weeds in the field. The disease affects only the weeds, not the rice.

Charles J. Arntzen, a USDA plant physiologist at the University of Illinois in Urbana-Champaign, and his associates reported in December 1979 that at least 10 weed species have become resistant to herbicides containing the chemical triazine. The triazines block photosynthesis as it takes place in the chloroplast, a small structure in plant cells. Arntzen found that photosynthesis was still taking place in the chloroplasts isolated from 10 triazine-treated weed species.

All of these resistant weeds are found in agricultural areas where triazines were used repeatedly and were not alternated with other nontriazine herbicides. Herbicide resistance has serious implications, because 85 per cent of the corn and soybean crops grown in the United States are treated with herbicides. Atrazine, a type of triazine, is the herbicide most widely used on corn, and a closely related compound called Sencor, a triazinone, is heavily used on soybean crops.

Growth-promoting bacteria, applied to soil and plants, emerged in 1980 as a practical approach to improved plant growth and pest control. Plant pathologists Trevor V. Suslow, Joseph W. Kloepper, and Milton N. Schroth of the University of California in Berkeley, and Thomas J. Burr of the Geneva (N.Y.) Experiment Station reported in December 1979 that the application of a species of bacteria, *rhizobacteria,* greatly increased the growth of potatoes, radishes, and sugar beets. Rhizobacteria live in the roots and stimulate the production of growth hormones in the plant.

The researchers soaked seeds of each plant in a liquid to which rhizobacteria had been added. The plants that grew from the treated seed were significantly larger than those not treated. For example, treated radishes harvested 35 days after planting were 60 to 144 per cent heavier than radishes the same age that were not treated. Crops with a short growing period showed the greatest gain. Because the treated plants were free of root diseases, the scientists

Grasshoppers, frozen to preserve spores that
transmit a fatal disease, are ground up, *above
left*. After the disease spores are isolated
from the residue, they are mixed with wheat
bran to create a natural insecticide which is
bagged, *above right*, to be deposited in fields
by a crop-dusting plane. Field grasshoppers
are later collected, *right*, to see if they
have eaten the bran and contracted the disease.

Agriculture

Continued

theorized that the bacteria may also provide protection by crowding harmful microorganisms out of the roots.

Plant hormone isolated. A team led by George Steffens, chief of the USDA Plant Hormone and Regulator Laboratory in Beltsville, Md., reported in February 1980 that they had isolated brassinolide, a new highly active and novel plant-growth regulator. The team collected 15 milligrams of brassinolide from 230 kilograms of pollen collected from the rape plant, a member of the cabbage family.

Potato seed treated with solutions of brassinolide produced 24 per cent more potatoes than untreated seed grown in the field. In the greenhouse, the researchers obtained the best growth by spraying the extract on seedlings.

Controlled animal reproduction. The development of a synthetic prostaglandin called Lutalyse climaxed 13 years of collaborative research by Michigan State University scientists and the Upjohn Company of Kalamazoo, Mich. The Michigan State team included Harold D. Hafs, Wayne C. Oxender, Ralph L. Fogwell, and David A. Morrow. Prostaglandins are natural substances found in almost all animal tissue, and scientists have only recently discovered how they can be used to bring about ovulation in farm animals.

Heifers or cows given two 25-milligram Lutalyse injections 11 days apart can be bred 80 hours after the second injection. Because the hormone allows the farmer to determine the breeding schedule, it is expected to provide great savings in time and labor by allowing many heifers to be bred at the same time, either naturally or by artificial insemination.

Exotic crops emerge. New varieties of safflower, in which the seed is only partially covered by a protective hull, were introduced by plant breeder Jerry Bergman at the Eastern Agricultural Research Center near Sidney, Mont., in December 1979. The deep-rooted and drought-resistant safflower plant produces a seed oil that commands a premium price because it is rich in polyunsaturated fatty acids and therefore low in cholesterol. Not only are the

Drawing by Booth; © 1979 The New Yorker Magazine, Inc.

"The United States Congress is urging all of us to produce more."

Agriculture

Continued

seeds of the new varieties easier to process, they also have 10 to 15 per cent more protein than those of other safflower varieties.

Test crops of hull-less seeded barley developed by plant breeders at the International Maize and Wheat Improvement Center in Mexico also yielded promising results in 1979. A barley called "Bichi" outyielded all other known varieties, surpassing even some varieties of high-yield grains, such as wheat and triticale. However, the new variety has one major disadvantage — because it is not protected by a hull, it is frequently crushed and broken during threshing.

Alternative energy sources. Agricultural engineer Harry H. Converse and chemical engineer Fang S. Lai of the U.S. Grain Marketing Research Laboratory in Manhattan, Kans., reported in March 1980 that they had devised a way to collect, store, and use solar heat to cut grain-drying time by 25 to 47 per cent. Converse and Lai's system collects heated air in a fiberglass solar collector and stores it in crushed lime-

stone rock next to the storage silos. A combination of air-heated by solar energy and unheated air is blown through ducts into the silos to dry moist grain that is stored there.

Abdul L. Kamal, food and agriculture horticulturist of the United Nations Food and Agriculture Organization's Center for Protected Vegetable Propagation in Kuwait announced in April 1980 that he had designed a solar still to purify irrigation water. Kamal placed a semicylindrical tunnel covered with clear ultraviolet-resistant plastic sheeting over an open water bed that was lined with black polyethylene plastic. Partially treated sewage or brackish wastewater was then channeled into the plastic-lined and covered bed.

The heat of the sunlight, absorbed by the black plastic, raised the temperature of the waste water and caused water vapor to condense on the inside surface of the clear plastic tunnel. This distilled water then streamed down the sides of the tunnel to irrigate seeds and seedlings planted in bands of soil along the edges.   [Sylvan H. Wittwer]

Anthropology

The fossil footprints of an early human dating to about 1.5 million years ago were found along the northeast shore of Lake Rudolf (Turkana) in Kenya in 1979. Geologists Anna K. Behrensmeyer and Leo F. LaPorte of the University of California, Santa Cruz, reported in November that they were studying fossil footprints of hippopotamuses, birds, and other animals when they saw the human prints.

The seven prints, all apparently made by the same person stepping in mud on the lake shore, are about 22 centimeters (9 inches) long and 8 to 9 centimeters (3 to 3.5 inches) wide. The scientists estimate that the person making the prints was about 152 centimeters (5 feet) tall and weighed 54 kilograms (120 pounds).

This would indicate that the person was larger than those who made the footprints in the Laetoli area of nearby Tanzania, as reported in 1978 by anthropologist Mary N. Leakey and her son Philip. The Tanzanian prints are much older, however, dating to at least 3.5 million years ago.

Physical anthropologists Michael H. Day and C. Magori of St. Thomas Medical School, London, and Mary Leakey reported in March 1980 on the unusual features of a cranium — a skull with the jaws missing — about 120,000 years old, found in the Laetoli area in 1976. The cranium combines modern features, such as roundness of the back of the skull, with more primitive features, such as a thick braincase and well-developed ridges over the brows.

The cranium, which was complete except for the cheekbones, belonged to an individual between 18 and 30 years old. The scientists say that the size of the cranium — larger than that of *Homo erectus,* such as Peking man, but smaller than that of early *Homo sapiens,* modern man — suggests that the species may have been a link between the two.

The Willandra Lakes area of Australia, the dry bed of Lake Mungo in particular, has produced the remains of about 50 individuals that have been carbon dated to 30,000 years ago. Anthropologist Alan G. Thorne of Australian National University in Canberra

Footprints of an early human who walked the earth about 1.5 million years ago were found in 1979 on the shores of Lake Rudolf in Kenya.

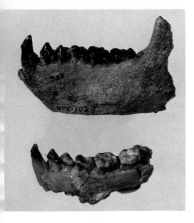

Fossil jawbones, *above,* helped inspire a sketch, *right,* of how an ancient tree-climbing ape that lived 30 million years ago in Egypt probably looked. *Aegyptopithecus zeuxis* is thought to be the direct ancestor of modern apes and humans.

Anthropology

Continued

studied the remains and reported in October 1979 that he found them quite different from today's Australian Aborigines and fossil Aborigines. The Willandra Lakes people were small and slight, with delicately formed skulls, rather flat faces, and small teeth. In many respects, they resembled a skull found in the Niah Cave in Borneo, dating from about the same period, rather than the robust Aborigines of a later period.

Thorne believes that the Willandra Lakes people came to Australia from Asia, perhaps from south China, before the Aborigines arrived. The Aborigines replaced the Willandra Lakes people or intermarried with them.

Hybrid ape. A "siabon," the offspring of a male gibbon (*Hylobates moloch*) and a female siamang (*Symphalangus syndactylus*) that mated at a zoo in Atlanta, Ga., may help scientists understand the evolution of these small apes. Psychologist Richard H. Myers of Georgia State University and psychiatrist David A. Shafer of Emory University School of Medicine, both in Atlan-

ta, reported in July 1979 that the gibbon and the siamang – once the same genus – separated into two lines because of changes in the number of their chromosomes. Chromosomes carry the genes that pass on the traits of the parent cell when it reproduces.

The siabon combines the physical features of both parents and has 47 chromosomes – 22 from the gibbon father and 25 from the siamang mother. A gibbon ordinarily has 44 chromosomes and a siamang has 50. Therefore, there is a greater difference in chromosomes between these two animals than there is between humans, with 46, and apes, with 48.

Scientists had long thought that two different animals evolved from one – as the gibbon and siamang did – because they were separated geographically. Yet gibbons and siamangs live in the same regions of Southeast Asia. They never mate in the wild, though the siabon birth shows that they could.

Evolution by chromosome changes in the gibbon and siamang suggests a new theory of how humans evolved.

Anthropology

Continued

Anthropologists have long thought that humans and apes evolved very gradually from a common ancestor. It may be, however, that somewhere on the evolutionary ladder a change in chromosome number initiated a rapid, drastic change.

Amino acid racemization, a chemical technique used to date early human remains, is now being applied to determine age at death. Physical anthropologist Patricia M. Masters and geochemist Jeffrey L. Bada of Scripps Institution of Oceanography in La Jolla, Calif., reported in August 1979 that they used the technique, based upon the fact that the proteins of all living organisms contain distinctive amino acids. The amino acids in most living tissues are renewed continuously, but those in eye lenses and teeth are not, so they can be used to set age.

The researchers tested a tooth from the remains of an Eskimo woman who died about 1,600 years ago. The body had remained frozen until now. Using the amino acid technique on the tooth, Masters and Bada set the woman's age

at death at 53 years, plus or minus five years. Traditional methods estimated her age at between 50 and 60, but required tests on an entire body.

A missing link. Scientists have now pieced together a comprehensive picture of an ape that lived 30 million years ago and may have been the ancestor of apes and man. Anthropologists Elwyn L. Simons and Richard Kay of Duke University in Durham, N.C., reported in February 1980 on their reconstruction of *Aegyptopithecus zeuxis* (connecting ape of Egypt).

Simons had found some bone fragments in Egypt's Al Fayyum area in the 1960s that he identified as belonging to an ancient ape. Now he has assembled fossils to establish that *Aegyptopithecus* weighed about 5.5 kilograms (12 pounds), had a long tail, and probably scampered from branch to branch on all fours. The males had large canine teeth that they probably used in fighting. Simons and Kay think that *Aegyptopithecus* is the immediate ancestor of *Dryopithecus,* which preceded apes and humans. [Charles F. Merbs]

Two Roads to Australia

A skull with a sloping forehead and broad jaw, *below right,* found near Cossack, Australia, may indicate that human beings came to Australia in two distinct migrations from Asia. The northern route from China, *below,* led many "down under." But the ancestors of robust Cossack man probably came via a southern route – from Java or other parts of Southeast Asia.

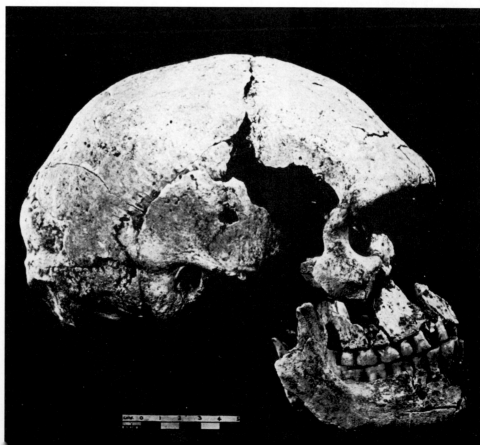

Archaeology

Old World. Ancient agriculture was an area of interest for archaeologists and anthropologists as well as historians in 1979 and 1980. Many farmworkers lived close to where they worked in ancient Greece and Italy, contrary to the original belief that they lived in cities and commuted to their farms.

Archaeologist Joseph C. Carter of the University of Texas in Austin reported preliminary conclusions in January 1980 on his team's study of the Greek colony of Metaponto in southern Italy. Carter's excavation of farmhouses and burial grounds indicated that people lived in this area continuously from the 600s to the 300s B.C.

The traditional argument against rural settlements in ancient Greece centered around the lack of suitable water supplies. But remains of a spring and reservoir at Pizzica near Metaponto, originally discovered in 1977, created considerable excitement among members of the international teams excavating the area.

The Metaponto area has also yielded evidence of industry. The Texas team found remains of four kilns used to make roof tiles, pottery, and clay plaques used as offerings to the gods.

Carter believes that Metaponto is not an isolated example of a rural settlement. He thinks that other such settlements will be found in rural areas that were part of ancient Greece.

Flowers and produce such as lettuce played an important role in the economy of Pompeii and nearby Herculaneum, cities in Italy destroyed by the volcanic eruption of Mount Vesuvius in A.D. 79. This information was published by archaeologist Wilhelmina F. Jashemski of the University of Maryland in *The Gardens of Pompeii, Herculaneum, and the Villas Destroyed by Vesuvius* (1979), a book based on her years of excavating and research at the site.

Jashemski found that flowers produced in the area were used to make perfume oil and also sold as cut flowers for garlands at banquets, funerals, and other ceremonial occasions. She studied fossils of plants and seeds, preserved under the lava, and also analyzed impressions in the soil made by

A building in Cayonu, Turkey, has been radiocarbon dated to about 7500 B.C., making it perhaps the oldest known building intended for public gatherings.

Archaeology

Continued

Postholes, *above,* at the Crickley Hill site in southern England outline a roundhouse that was part of a fortified settlement about 550 B.C. The postholes, pottery, and other artifacts suggest details of what the settlement looked like, *opposite page.*

plant roots to determine what kind of plants grew in the area.

Earliest public building. A forum, or meeting place, in Cayonu, Turkey, has been dated to about 7500 B.C. and may be the oldest known building designed for public gatherings. Anthropologists Robert Braidwood of the University of Chicago, Halet Cambel of Istanbul University in Turkey, and Wulf Schirmer of the Institute for Architectural History in Karlsruhe, West Germany, reported in March 1980 that they used radiocarbon dating to establish the age of the building, which was excavated in the 1960s. The scientists theorized that the large, one-room building was used as a church or meeting hall.

Nautical archaeology along Mediterranean Sea coasts has increased our knowledge of ancient ships and the cargoes that they carried. Archaeologist George F. Bass of the Institute of Nautical Archaeology in College Station, Tex., excavated a Hellenistic shipwreck off the island of Lipari, Italy, located at a depth of more than 50 meters (165 feet). The institute report-

ed in June 1979 that Bass used special equipment — consisting of a diving bell and a two-person submersible equipped with a video camera and recorder — to reach the wreck at that depth. The fact that Bass reached the wreck was an achievement in nautical archaeology; he planned further studies on its contents.

Counting on clay. Small clay tablets were used for counting about 5,500 years ago. An archaeologist, Denise Schmandt-Besserat, who studied hundreds of tokens found by various researchers at Middle Eastern sites, thinks that the tablets led to the start of writing. The small tablets of various shapes, found at many sites in Mesopotamia, Syria, Iran, and Turkey, were usually identified as "objects of uncertain purposes" or were dismissed in a sentence or two in archaeological reports as game markers or casual jewelry. But Schmandt-Besserat reported in June 1979 that the tokens were probably used in a system of recording by item and number that eventually led to the development of writing.

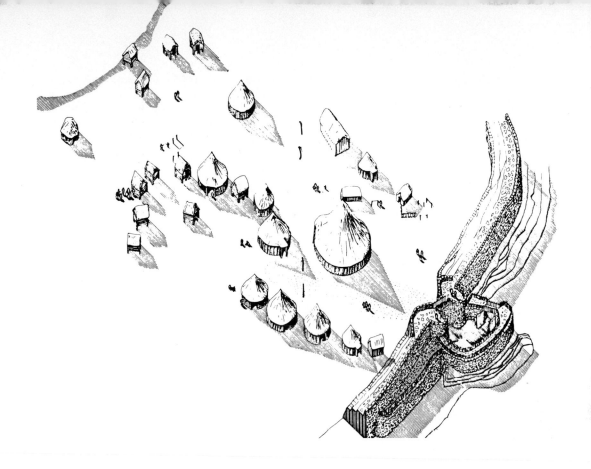

Archaeology

Continued

Some tokens date back as far as 10,000 years. Those early tokens were balls or cones used to record grain transactions. Packages of tokens were placed in hollow "envelopes" of clay, sealed, and then stamped with a symbol of the token on the outside. Schmandt-Besserat says these packages appear to represent more complex transactions in major trading centers.

The ancient peoples who used the ball tokens later abandoned them for flat tablets with symbols impressed on the surface representing items, such as animals, to be traded or taxed. The tokens and stamps were apparently used for record-keeping of all kinds in the Middle East. Schmandt-Besserat thinks that writing gradually developed through the practice of copying the pictorial symbols from the tokens. Schmandt-Besserat compared a number of tokens with symbols from early written languages and found that the shape of the token used to signify cattle, for example, resembles the symbol used for cattle by ancient Babylonians. [Ingrid E. M. Edlund]

New World. A colonial town, one of the oldest British towns in North America, has been unearthed unexpectedly on a plantation near Jamestown, Va. Archaeologist Ivor Noël-Hume of the Colonial Williamsburg Foundation reported in June 1979 on the excavations of Wolstenholme Town at Carter's Grove Plantation, 16 kilometers (10 miles) east of Jamestown. The town was established in 1619 by about 200 British colonists, but many of its inhabitants were massacred by Indians in 1622.

Noël-Hume and a team of archaeologists began an examination of a mansion at Carter's Grove Plantation in 1970 in an area that they thought dated to the 1700s. They were surprised to find that most of the broken pottery and other artifacts dated about 100 years earlier, to the 1600s.

Additional excavations in 1976 and 1977 revealed traces of Wolstenholme Town. The scientists located a number of graves, some of which they traced to people massacred in 1622. Based on patterns of postholes in the soil, they

235

Archaeology

Continued

identified a number of dwellings and a fort surrounded by a wooden fence or stockade. They also found armor—including several helmets—and weapons dating to the 1600s.

Remembering the Alamo. A human skull was found at the Alamo in San Antonio, Tex., a mission that became a fort in 1835. The skull was the first known skeletal remains from the historic battle there in 1836. Archaeologist Anne A. Fox and a research team from the University of Texas at San Antonio began excavations in April 1979 and continued in 1980 to search for traces of the battle. She also found pottery fragments and stone tools used by mission Indians when the Alamo was a Spanish mission in the 1700s.

The Fox team found a fortification trench dug by the defenders in the 1836 battle. The skull was found in the trench. In addition, the researchers unearthed the west wall of the Alamo compound, under a row of stores built in the 1880s. Musket balls and other materials from the battle were found near the wall.

El Mirador, Guatemala, may be the largest and earliest city in the New World. In July 1979, archaeologist Raymond Matheny of Brigham Young University announced preliminary results of his excavations at the site of El Mirador, about 480 kilometers (300 miles) north of Guatemala City. Matheny said that the structural remains of this Mayan city indicate that civilization reached its height there about A.D. 500. One aspect of the research focuses on how ancient peoples raised food crops in this jungle land and the implications this might have for present-day farming there.

Early life in Belize. The University of Texas at San Antonio issued a report in August 1979 on excavations at the site of Colha, Belize, in Central America. A team that I headed found evidence of the mass production of chipped stone tools—including axes, *adzes* (woodworking tools), and other implements—dating from as early as 300 B.C. We also found almost 100 workshops at the site, indicating that craftsmen in the area were highly specialized. Although

Archaeologist Stanley South, *below,* of the University of South Carolina and members of his team, *below right,* sort artifacts from Santa Elena, the lost capital of Spanish Florida in the 1500s. The researchers found the town on what is now Parris Island, S.C.

A stairway that was part of a two-story building is exposed in digging at El Mirador, Guatemala, the site of what may have been the largest and oldest Mayan city in Central America.

Archaeology

Continued

Mayan cities have been studied in detail, this kind of Mayan site has not been studied in depth until now.

About 48 kilometers (30 miles) north of Colha, archaeologist Billie L. Turner of Clark University in Worcester, Mass., investigated ancient farming practices in Pulltrouser Swamp. At a meeting in May 1980, he reported on the "ridged field" technique used in agriculture there about 300 B.C. This technique involved piling up ridges of dirt in swamps to claim otherwise unusable land. People in this area may have used many of the stone tools produced at Colha because apparently broken implements such as hoes and axes were repaired and "recycled" for jungle clearing and farming tasks.

Peruvian civilization appears to have begun as early as 1500 B.C. Archaeologist Terence Grieder of the University of Texas at Austin announced in March 1980 the result of studies of the ancient buried ruins of La Galgada in the Andean highlands. Grieder radiocarbon dated wood charcoal from the site and found the ruins traced back from 1500 B.C. to 2400 B.C. Buildings at La Galgada were made of stone, and the economy included cotton farming.

Preservation studies. Archaeologists Michael J. O'Brien and Robert E. Warren, members of the team working on the Cannon Reservoir Human Ecology Project, reported in March 1980 that as many as 1,500 archaeological sites, some of them 10,000 years old, may have been found in the area that would be covered by the Clarence Cannon Dam and Reservoir on Missouri's Salt River.

The Cannon project is one of the largest United States studies preceding the building of federally funded dams and reservoirs that would destroy important archaeological sites. O'Brien and Warren explained that the figure of 1,500 sites is an estimate obtained by excavating some smaller land areas, counting the sites, and multiplying the figures for the Salt River area as a whole. Sites already excavated include a log cabin of the 1800s and a hunting and fishing complex that may date to 6500 B.C. [Thomas R. Hester]

Astronomy

Planetary Astronomy. The National Aeronautics and Space Administration's (NASA) *Pioneer 11* spacecraft reached Saturn on Sept. 1, 1979, after a 6½-year journey from Earth. *Pioneer 11* sent back measurements that gave planetary astronomers a fascinating close-up look at the Saturn system. Among its primary discoveries were a magnetic field, a new component of the ring system, and evidence that helium may be separating from hydrogen in the interior of the planet.

Measurements showed that Saturn's magnetic field is about 600 times stronger than Earth's and about 30 times weaker than Jupiter's. In Earth and Jupiter, the magnetic axis is tilted at a large angle from the axis of rotation and off-center. However, Saturn's magnetic axis is aligned parallel to the planet's rotation axis, and very close to its geometric center.

Most astronomers had assumed that the angles of the magnetic axis on Earth and Jupiter were necessary in order to maintain magnetism in these planets. But the situation discovered on Saturn may require a new explanation of how planets generate magnetism.

Because of this peculiarity of Saturn's magnetic field, its satellites repeatedly sweep out the same narrow volumes of space throughout the magnetosphere — the zone of strong magnetic forces surrounding the planet — as they orbit the planet. As a result, these regions are almost entirely free of the positively charged particles found in the magnetosphere.

These observations led scientists to suspect there were more satellites around Saturn than had been observed. One object, called 1979S1, is clearly visible in *Pioneer* photos.

Pioneer photographed Saturn's ring system from a unique position with the Sun behind the planet. As a result, the pictures look like negatives — that is, the normally bright rings appear dark, while Cassini's division, the dark gap between the rings, is seen as a bright band. This indicates that the bright areas contain some light-absorbing particles, while the dark gaps, previously believed to be empty, contain some particles that scatter sunlight. The new view allowed scientists to estimate the thickness of the rings.

The clearest photo yet made of Saturn, its rings, and its satellite Titan was sent back to Earth on Aug. 29, 1979, by a *Pioneer* craft that was 2.5 million kilometers (1.5 million miles) from the planet.

The photographs also showed two new components of the ring system — an F ring and a new division between the A and F rings. A controversial D ring, which some astronomers believed they had detected from Earth-based observations, proved to be nonexistent.

Four members of the *Voyager* radio astronomy team reported in May 1980 that they had determined Saturn's rotation period — the length of time it takes to turn once around its axis. Michael Kaiser and Michael Desch of the Goddard Space Flight Center in Greenbelt, Md., and James Warwich and Jeffrey Pearce of Radiophysics, Incorporated, of Boulder, Colo., analyzed data obtained by the two *Voyager* spacecraft in January and February. They eliminated signals from the Sun, Jupiter, and other sources and determined that signals received every 10 hours 39.9 minutes originated at Saturn's north pole. The signals, from Saturn's rotating magnetic field, defined the planet's rotation rate.

A new look at Neptune was a treat for planetary astronomers. Neptune is difficult to photograph because, being so far from Earth, the angle it subtends is very small. The apparent diameter of Neptune is almost 1,000 times smaller than that of the Moon. Also, the planet usually appears blurred because its atmosphere changes so rapidly.

Bradford A. Smith, Harold J. Reitsema, and Stephen M. Larson of the University of Arizona's Lunar and Planetary Laboratory in Tucson reported in October 1979 that they had obtained the first clear images of Neptune. They took these unique photographs in infrared light with an extremely sensitive new camera that uses a solid-state electronic detector to take high-speed pictures. The photos show that Neptune has a broad, dark band across its equator and bright, cloudlike features to the north and south. While measurements were not exact enough to determine Neptune's rotation rate, the astronomers concluded that it must be no longer than 30 hours.

How Phobos was fractured. Phobos and Deimos, the two tiny satellites of Mars, appear remarkably different on *Viking* spacecraft photographs. Deimos is smoothly blanketed by a deep layer of fragmented material, while Phobos is

Astronomy

Continued

pockmarked with craters and a system of deep fractures that seem to permeate the satellite. In a February 1980 report, Stuart Weidenschilling of the Planetary Science Institute in Tucson clarified how Phobos was fractured and why the two satellites appear to be so different.

Planetary astronomers had proposed two explanations of how the fractures occurred. Some suggested a violent collision with another Mars-orbiting or interplanetary object that could have caused the fractures, as well as Phobos' largest crater, Stickney. Other astronomers thought that tidal forces broke up the body of the satellite as it slowly spiraled in toward Mars. Weidenschilling pointed out that a hybrid theory may provide the true answer.

It seems certain that after Mars captured Phobos and Deimos, gravitational tidal forces quickly synchronized the orbital spins — the time it takes to circle Mars — with their rotation rates. The tiny satellites also collided with other objects in orbit around Mars early in their history. These impacts weakened their interiors and threw clouds of fragmented debris into orbit around the satellites themselves. This debris was recaptured a few hundred years after each collision. It settled on each satellite's surface, covering it like a thick, smooth blanket. According to Weidenschilling, this is the state Deimos is in today.

Phobos, he believes, suffered such an unusual and violent collision when Stickney was formed that the satellite's rotation was temporarily, but substantially, changed from the synchronous rate as it traveled around Mars. The orbiting clouds of debris thrown up by that collision quickly settled back on Phobos or were captured by Mars. But the nonsynchronous spin that resulted from the collision created tidal stresses that altered the satellite's structure. Because Phobos was already weakened by the massive impact, the pull of these forces over millions of years cracked open its surface and created the fissures that are visible today.

This theory — combining the effects of gravity with a cataclysmic collision — explains the differences between the

The first scientifically accurate painting of Venus' surface is based on detailed radar data from the *Pioneer* orbiter. Penetrating the planet's thick clouds, it measured Ishtar Terra, a plateau as large as Australia that contains several rugged mountain ranges.

Astronomy
Continued

two satellites and the form and structure of the crater and fractures on Phobos. It also avoids the many inconsistencies that arise if either element of the explanation is used alone.

Planetary gases. The *Pioneer* spacecraft sent back measurements from Venus in the summer of 1979 showing that rare gases, such as argon and neon, are much more abundant there than on Earth and Mars. However, Venus' atmosphere has about the same amount of the common gases, such as nitrogen and carbon dioxide, as the combined amount found in Earth's atmosphere and locked up in rocks on the Earth's surface.

According to planetary astronomer James B. Pollack of NASA's Ames Research Center at Moffett Field, Calif., these measurements indicate that rare gases were incorporated into the material that formed these three planets under far different conditions than scientists previously believed. Most scientists had accepted the theory that temperatures in the cloud of dust and gas that made up the inner solar nebula from which these planets formed varied greatly at the time of each planet's birth. They believed this temperature difference was responsible for the planets' varying composition.

However, new measurements show that the temperature was similar, but that pressures were higher near Venus. Higher temperatures at the time Venus formed would have resulted in a smaller amount of rare gases sticking to the solid particles that formed the planet. Higher pressures permitted a larger amount to stick.

Pollack also compared the *Pioneer* measurements with similar measurements made by *Viking* on Mars and those made on Earth. His study showed that most of the present atmospheric gases originated in each planet's interior. Some scientists had believed these gases were created by the impact of comets. If that were true, all three planets would have similar amounts of the gases, because all had an equal chance of being hit by comets. The fact that Venus has more rare gases than the other two inner planets indicates that almost no atmospheric gases came from the impact made by comets hitting them.   [Michael J. S. Belton]

Stellar Astronomy. Astronomers surveyed interstellar gas bubbles, studied the pulsed radio signals from a new binary pulsar, and learned more about supernovae in 1979 and 1980.

Theoretical astrophysicists Peter S. Conti and Richard A. McCray of the Joint Institute of Laboratory Astrophysics in Boulder, Colo., in April 1980 reviewed the subject of stellar winds from O-type stars — young, hot, blue giants. These violent stellar winds — high-speed streams of escaping matter — are faster than the solar wind and carry away much more matter. The winds of O-type stars travel from 1,200 to 4,000 kilometers per second (kps) or 750 to 2,500 miles per second (mps). Individual stars can lose matter at a rate of up to one solar mass per 100,000 years. By comparison, the solar wind has a velocity of only 400 kps (250 mps), and carries off mass at a rate 1 billion times less.

Conti and McCray's report summed up work which has been going on for more than 12 years. It has established that the winds produce the unusual nebulae called interstellar bubbles. An O-type star's powerful wind blows away the interstellar gas surrounding the star, producing a low-density cavity, or bubble. The bubble is surrounded by a kind of shell of the denser gas that was swept out from the interior.

A striking example of this class of nebulae is the Rosette nebula in the constellation Monoceros, where the combined winds from a cluster of hot O-type stars have created an easily observed bubble. The accumulated gas around the cavity glows, excited by the ultraviolet light of the stars.

Astronomers have discovered a number of these bubbles on recent photographs made by telescopic cameras with special filters. They had previously believed some other interstellar bubbles, including the Rosette nebula, to be other types of objects, such as H II regions — clouds of ionized hydrogen — or rapidly expanding clouds of matter that are supernova remnants. See THE STUFF BETWEEN THE STARS.

Another binary pulsar. Four radio astronomers led by Richard N. Manchester of the Commonwealth Scientific and Industrial Research Organization in Epping, Australia, reported detecting a

The United Kingdom Infrared Telescope, high on Mauna Kea in the Hawaiian Islands, began measuring the infrared radiation from galaxies, interstellar clouds, and other objects in space in October 1979. With an aperture of 351 centimeters (138 inches), this infrared telescope is the world's largest.

Astronomy

Continued

second binary pulsar, PSR 0820+02, in February 1980. The first was reported in 1974.

If a massive star undergoes a supernova explosion but does not disintegrate completely, it leaves a condensed core, or remnant, which usually is a neutron star. If the neutron star has a powerful magnetic field and spins rapidly, it emits radio waves in concentrated beams, like a lighthouse beacon. Such an object is called a pulsar. Astronomers detected the first pulsar in 1967. Most stars are members of binary systems, but binary pulsars are rare.

In theory, binary star systems with a variety of orbital characteristics should be able to survive when one of their members explodes and finally becomes a pulsar. Unlike the first binary pulsar, in which the components revolve rapidly around each other, the parts of the newly detected system take about 1,700 days to orbit each other. In April 1980, a team of radio astronomers led by Joseph Taylor of the University of Massachusetts in Amherst reported that they discovered a third binary pulsar.

However, astronomers still wonder why so few of the more than 300 known pulsars are binaries.

Bare neutron star. Physicists Gordon P. Garmire of the California Institute of Technology in Pasadena and Ian Tuohy of the Australian National University in Canberra announced in January 1980 that they had discovered a new type of X-ray source. The object, found with the Einstein Observatory at the center of supernova remnant RCW103, is probably the first bare neutron star to be detected.

Until recently, astronomers have observed neutron stars that exist in two forms — as pulsars or as members of X-ray binary systems. In X-ray binaries, the observed X rays come from matter falling onto the neutron star, and not from the glow of an undisturbed surface.

Astronomers were eager to measure the surface radiation from a so-called bare neutron star that is not disturbed by matter transferred from a companion. They would be able to determine the star's temperature and learn about

A Solar Squeeze

"The sun is shrinking! The sun is shrinking!" Three teams of astronomers sounded that alarm in 1979. But unlike Chicken Little, who issued a somewhat similar report, they attracted scant public attention.

John A. Eddy of the Harvard-Smithsonian Center for Astrophysics in Cambridge, Mass., and Aram A. Boornazian of Boston reported in June that the sun seems to be growing smaller.

They studied more than 100 years of data and found that the sun's diameter has decreased 0.1 per cent per century. Because the solar diameter is about 1,392,000 kilometers (865,000 miles), the shrinkage amounts to more than 13 kilometers (8 miles) per year, or a decrease of 1.5 meters (5 feet) per hour.

Supporting evidence comes from an account of the eclipse of the sun viewed from Rome on April 9, 1567. The eclipse should have been almost total at Rome, but astronomer Christopher Clavius wrote that it was not.

Calculations based on today's measurements show that the moon was close enough in its orbit around the earth to have completely blocked out the sun. But because it failed to do so, we can infer that the sun may have been slightly larger in 1567 than it is today.

Sabatino Sofia of the Goddard Space Flight Center in Greenbelt, Md., in June 1979 reported less shrinkage, but later he and David W. Dunham studied the width of the total eclipse zone as it was determined at solar eclipses in 1715, 1976, and 1979. They deduced that the sun was about 640 kilometers (400 miles) smaller in 1976 and 1979 than it was in 1715.

News of the shrinking sun has aroused great interest among astronomers. But most are skeptical. Instead of running to tell the king, they are working to verify the findings and to determine what such solar changes could do to influence future climate trends on earth. [Stephen P. Maran]

Astronomy
Continued

its physical makeup. When Garmire and Tuohy studied the new X-ray source, they measured the star's temperature at 2.3 million°C, about 400 times hotter than the sun, making it possibly the hottest star ever measured.

Bizarre object SS433. Stellar spectroscopists led by David Crampton of the Dominion Astrophysical Observatory in Victoria, Canada, reported in August 1979 that SS433 is a binary star. The so-called bizarre star, discovered in 1978, produces emission lines that alternate between red shifts and blue shifts. This makes it appear to be moving away from and toward the earth simultaneously. The object is probably the remnant core of a supernova and may be a neutron star, a white dwarf star, or a black hole – a region in space from which not even light can escape.

Apparently, matter streaming off its large companion star flows toward SS433, and forms a thick disk around it. The visible light from SS433 comes from the hot gases of the disk, and not from either star in the binary system.

The strange emission lines apparently arise from two jets of matter that emerge from the center of the disk.

Unusual nebula. In a study of a much more distant object, supernova specialists Robert P. Kirshner and William P. Blair of the University of Michigan in Ann Arbor examined an unusual nebula in the galaxy NGC 4449, which is 16 million light-years – the distance light travels in a year – from the earth. Their report in February 1980 confirmed that there is a supernova remnant at this location, in addition to an H II region.

They could distinguish the two objects by studying the emission lines in their spectra with a spectrograph. Kirshner and Blair found that the supernova remnant produces detectable spectral lines only of oxygen as the supernova-ejected gas expands at about 3,500 kps (2,200 mps). Because oxygen, like all elements heavier than hydrogen and helium, must be produced by nuclear reactions in stars, they concluded that the exploding matter must have come from the massive supernova's core. [Stephen P. Maran]

Astronomy

Continued

High-Energy Astronomy produced a number of advances in 1979 and 1980, many of which were discussed at a January 1980 meeting of the American Astronomical Society in Cambridge, Mass. Featured at the meeting were the latest results gathered from the second High Energy Astronomy Observatory (HEAO-2), which is also known as the Einstein Observatory.

Astrophysicist Giuseppe Vaiana of Harvard University in Cambridge excited the assembled group with his report that X rays are emitted by practically all stars rather than just a few special classes of stars. Earlier results had shown that young, relatively hot and massive stars in spectral classes O and B emit as much energy in X rays alone as the sun emits across the entire radiation spectrum. Vaiana also found that normal, sunlike G, F, and K stars may be powerful X-ray sources, sometimes appearing as much as 500 times brighter than the sun to the Einstein Observatory telescope. Astronomers have also detected older and smaller M stars, previously thought to be quite dim, that actually outshine the sun in their X-ray emission.

These results have forced astrophysicists to take a new look at the standard models for stellar atmospheres and coronas, where the X-ray emissions originate. They had believed that energy from a star's interior reaches its surface and flows out through the atmosphere by means of convection, heating the corona to produce X rays. However, the detection of X-ray emission from the cooler M stars as well as from the very hot O and B stars means that this energy transfer must take place by some other means.

One possibility involves stellar magnetic fields and rotation. Astronomers have observed that some of the stars that shine brightly in X rays also spin relatively fast. This rapid rotation may generate magnetic fields, and the energy to heat the coronas may be carried out from a star's interior by magnetic waves traveling through the hot, highly ionized gas inside the star.

Neutron star formation has puzzled astrophysicists since the discovery of a

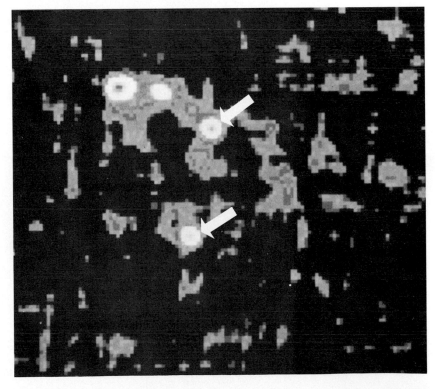

Two apparent sources (arrows) near the center of a radio map of quasar 0957+561 are believed to represent one quasar whose image is split by a gravitational lens. The lens is probably a huge intervening galaxy.

Astronomy

large number of pulsars, neutron stars that emit pulsed radio waves. A neutron star is a compact, superdense stellar remnant. A possible birthplace for a neutron star is the leftover core of a supernova, or exploded star.

David J. Helfand and his colleagues at Columbia University in New York City reported in January that they had made use of the Einstein Observatory to search for neutron stars in 10 supernova remnants, or nebulae. If these cores exist, they should be hot enough to radiate X rays, which would allow astronomers to detect the pointlike source of a neutron star inside the expanding supernova shell. Helfand's group found evidence for such a source only in the Crab Nebula and the Vela Nebula. The Crab Nebula resulted from a supernova explosion that was first reported in A.D. 1054. Knowing a nebula's age is important, because astronomers believe the remnants are hot enough to be detected for only a few thousand years.

No such cores have been detected in several other remnants for which accurate ages are known. This may be because neutron stars cool more rapidly than current theories suggest. Or neutron stars may result from supernova explosions less frequently than had been thought. The observations indicate that astronomers may have to consider revising their theories of how neutron stars are formed.

Extragalactic objects. Astronomers surveying very deep space have discovered several X-ray sources that are contributing to the well-known but little-understood background radiation that pervades the universe. Riccardo Giacconi and others at the Harvard-Smithsonian Center for Astrophysics reported in November 1979 that some of these sources are quasars, intense emitters of radio waves. Giacconi believes that most of the other unidentified sources are also quasars, which means that these objects are responsible for much of the radiation.

I analyzed additional X-ray data extending to fainter objects to compare the observations at the Harvard-Smithsonian Center with theories of

Fast-moving clumps of hot gas form the brightest areas in an Einstein Observatory X-ray photo of the supernova remnant in the constellation Cassiopeia. A fainter region expanding ahead of the glowing gas is the supernova's shock front.

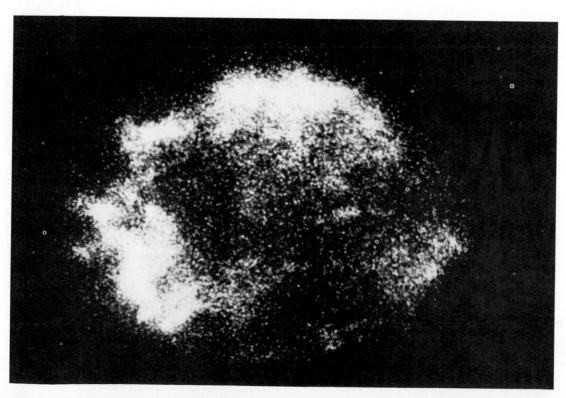

quasar evolution in January 1980. I concluded that apparently there were many more quasars earlier in the history of the universe than there are now.

These studies reflect on the continuing debate over whether the universe is open and ever-expanding or closed and fated to collapse. Both Giacconi's and my own observations show that the X-ray background is mainly due to a collection of individual sources, and is not a continuum of hot gas filling the otherwise empty space of the universe. Therefore, unless more material can be found in some currently unobserved form, the total cosmic mass is probably too small to allow gravity to ultimately reverse the outward motion that resulted from the big bang that scientists believe started the universe, and the universe will expand forever.

Meanwhile, astronomers working in a related area discovered new evidence that large amounts of dark, nonluminous matter exist in the great clusters of hundreds or thousands of galaxies bound together by gravity. Daniel Fabricant and Paul Gorenstein of the Harvard-Smithsonian Center reported in January that they had determined the mass of the giant galaxy M87 in the Virgo cluster.

According to their detailed measurements of the distribution of hot gas trapped around that galaxy, even more material is present than can be accounted for by either the visible stars or the X-ray-emitting gas. Therefore, they theorized that the extra material must be stars or gas of very low luminosity. Fabricant and Gorenstein concluded there is almost 10 times as much mass present as optical data indicated.

Spectroscopic studies reported in January by Claude R. Canizares of Massachusetts Institute of Technology in Cambridge and Stephen Holt of Goddard Space Flight Center in Greenbelt, Md., also provided information on this intracluster gas. These X-ray observations confirmed the presence of this material and are beginning to show how it is distributed. Unfortunately for those who prefer a closed universe, this mass has already been counted in computing the density of the universe, and the total falls short of the amount that is needed for a closed system.   [Stephen S. Murray]

Cosmology. Three cosmologists developed a new technique for measuring the distances to remote galaxies and made the surprising discovery that the universe may be only about half as old as scientists previously believed.

Marc Aaronson of the University of Arizona in Tucson, John P. Huchra of Harvard University in Cambridge, Mass., and Jeremy Mould of Kitt Peak National Observatory near Tucson reported in November 1979 that they had recomputed Hubble's constant, used to calculate the rate at which the universe is expanding, and estimated that only 9-billion years have elapsed since the big bang that scientists believe began the universe. Since 1952, most scientists had agreed that the universe probably began 13 billion to 18 billion years ago.

The distance measurements upon which the new determination is based depend on a special combination of radio and infrared measurements of spiral galaxies. Astronomers use radio observations that measure how fast a galaxy is rotating. They can also measure the galaxy's apparent brightness from infrared observations, which are unaffected by interstellar dust. Using nearby galaxies of known distance, they find that the rotation and apparent brightness are proportional. Thus, once rotation is measured, astronomers can infer the absolute brightness. Carrying out similar measurements for a more remote galaxy of unknown distance enables them to compare absolute and apparent brightnesses. Because brightness decreases with the square of the distance, comparing the two measurements gives the galaxy's true distance.

When Aaronson, Huchra, and Mould made these determinations for remote galaxies, they found the distances were much smaller than they expected. Combining the distances with the galaxies' velocities showed that the universe is expanding twice as fast — and, therefore, it is only half as old — as scientists once believed.

A gravitational lens. Observations of what appeared to be a distant pair of quasars that have identical red shifts shed new light on the remarkable system called 0957+561. The apparent binary quasar is either a true pair of quasars that are both identical and

Astronomy

Continued

adjacent — a thoroughly unexpected phenomenon — or it is an optical effect. The optical effect could be caused by the gravitational bending of light, due to the pull of some massive object in front of a quasar, that would make observers see two images of a single quasar. If it is an optical illusion, there must be an object in the foreground that acts as a gravitational lens to bend the light.

A team of scientists from the United States and Great Britain, led by astrophysicist Ray J. Weymann of the University of Arizona in Tucson, reported in October 1979 that they had found spectral absorption lines that helped solve the riddle. The red shift of the absorption lines — dark gaps in the spectrum caused by gas absorbing the radiation — in each quasar spectrum is slightly smaller than the red shift of the emission lines — bright spectral lines caused by gas adding to the radiation. But the absorption lines of the "two" quasars have equal red shifts. Thus, it is as if identical absorbing clouds of gas, mainly hydrogen, are located near

and in front of them. Because this is highly unlikely, it seemed more likely that only a single quasar and a single cloud exist, and that a gravitational lens makes us see two images.

Shortly after the Weymann group's report appeared, several other groups reported detecting an object that may be the lens. A team led by cosmologist James E. Gunn of Hale Observatories reported in November 1979 that the lens is a massive galaxy. The Gunn group observed it in a cluster of galaxies that appears between the quasar and the earth in a photograph. The picture was made with a red-sensitive electronic camera mounted on the 508-centimeter (200-inch) Hale telescope on Palomar Mountain.

Cosmological antimatter. Astrophysicist Robert L. Golden and his colleagues at New Mexico State University in Las Cruces reported in October 1979 that they had made the first direct measurement of interstellar antiprotons. Atomic physicists believe that for every particle of matter there exists a particle of antimatter identical in every

A supersensitive instrument that found the first tiny particles of antimatter in space was moved by a special crane, *below,* to the Palestine, Tex., launching site. There a huge helium balloon, *left,* carried it to an altitude of 37 kilometers (23 miles) where it detected a number of antiprotons.

Astronomy

Continued

way, but carrying an opposite electrical charge. For example, an antiproton is the negatively charged counterpart of a positively charged proton.

Before Golden's report, the existence of antimatter had been shown only in laboratory experiments. But his group theorized that antimatter should be produced in space when cosmic rays — atomic nuclei and subatomic particles traveling at high velocity — collide with atoms in the clouds of interstellar hydrogen. If protons and the nuclei of hydrogen atoms in the interstellar cloud smashed into each other, antiprotons would be created. Golden calculated that 4.4 antiprotons should be created for every 10,000 ordinary protons that exist.

Antimatter cannot be detected from earth because the atmosphere blocks it out, so the New Mexico group attached a 2,300-kilogram (5,000-pound) package of extremely sensitive instruments to a helium-filled balloon and sent it 37 kilometers (23 miles) into space. The results of the experiment, which was carried out on June 21 and 22, con-firmed the theory. The ratio of antiprotons to protons that the instruments detected was almost exactly what the astrophysicists had predicted.

The discovery that interstellar antimatter exists — and in amounts so disproportionate to the matter the universe is made of — has important implications for theories of the origin of the universe. For example, Steven Weinberg, winner of the Nobel prize for physics in 1979, argued that the universe might have been perfectly symmetrical at the instant of creation — that is, it might have been made of equal amounts of matter and antimatter. However, as the universe expanded, nuclear reactions may have destroyed most of the antimatter, leaving just enough excess matter to create everything that is now in the universe.

A far-reaching implication of Weinberg's theory is that protons should still decay, although very slowly. By examining a large enough mass of matter on earth, physicists are trying to detect the decay of even one proton, to verify this theory.   [Joseph Silk]

Biochemistry

Biochemical researchers in 1979 and 1980 made several related discoveries — a variation in the genetic code, a possible function for the "silent" regions in genes, and a new twist in the DNA molecule that will influence how scientists interpret the structure and function of genes.

Genes are segments of deoxyribonucleic acid (DNA) that contain the information the cell needs to manufacture proteins. The DNA molecule is composed of two strands of alternating sugar and phosphate molecules linked together by pairs of four types of nucleic acid bases — adenine (A), cytosine (D), guanine (G), and thymine (T).

The sequence of these bases in the DNA molecule determines the gene's information. That information is transcribed into molecules of ribonucleic acid (messenger RNA or mRNA). The cell subsequently uses a genetic code to translate the information into a protein. This code is written in units of three bases called codons, each of which calls for a particular amino acid to be added to the protein. Some codons act as a start or stop signal. Scientists completed deciphering the genetic code in the late 1960s. Since then they had assumed that codons designate the same proteins in all living organisms.

However, scientists examining mitochondrial genes and proteins in 1979 found some interesting and unexpected deviations in the code. Mitochondria are complex organelles (minute specialized structures) found in the cells of all higher organisms. They are often called the "powerhouses" of the cell because they contain the enzymes that act on nutrients to produce adenosine triphosphate (ATP), an energy-storing chemical. Although most of the components of mitochondria are made under the direction of genes in the nucleus, mitochondria contain a small amount of their own DNA that codes for a few mitochondrial proteins. They also contain genes for the RNAs that "read" the information in the mRNA.

Giuseppe Macino and Alexander Tzagoloff of Columbia University in New York City reported in August that they had determined the base sequences in mitochondrial genes for certain mitochondrial proteins and compared those sequences with the known sequences in nuclear genes for other proteins. They found that one mitochondrial protein had an amino acid, threonine, at a position where the nuclear genetic code would have dictated the insertion of another, leucine.

Research at Columbia and other laboratories showed that a codon, previously identified as a stop signal in bacterial cells, actually codes for the amino acid tryptophan in proteins of yeast and human mitochondria.

New insights into introns. Piotr Slonimski and his collaborators at France's National Center for Scientific Research reported in January 1980 on their studies of the gene for a yeast mitochondrial protein called cytochrome b. This gene has a complex structure with a coding sequence interrupted by four introns, segments of DNA that do not code for proteins.

The origin and role of introns have been a mystery since their discovery in genes from eucaryotes—cells with nuclei—in the late 1970s (see REINTERPRETING LIFE'S BLUEPRINT). Since then, scientists have determined base sequences of a number of introns from various genes in different organisms. Many scientists believed that the introns did not code for proteins because the introns contained the codon TGA, a stop signal.

However, Slonimski, Claude Jacq, and Jaga Lazowska proposed that certain introns do indeed code for specific proteins. They did this knowing, from earlier research, that mutations that blocked the formation of the mitochondrial cytochrome b were located in the introns, and that TGA might not be a stop signal in the mitochondrial version of the cytochrome b gene. They suggested that if the TGA codons in the first intron in the mitochondrial cytochrome b gene do not serve as a stop signal but instead code for tryptophan, other codons in the intron might code for other amino acids, and the entire intron might code for a protein.

Slonimski's team has proposed that the resulting protein might play a role

Drawing by Levin; © 1980 The New Yorker Magazine, Inc.

"Oh, nothing much. Just experimenting with some rabbits."

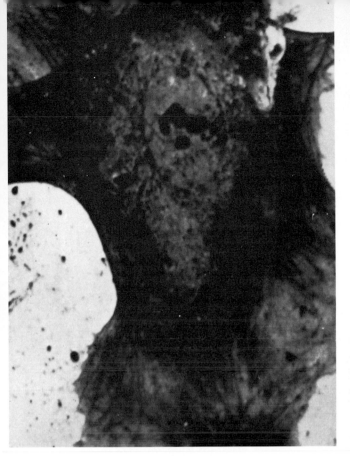
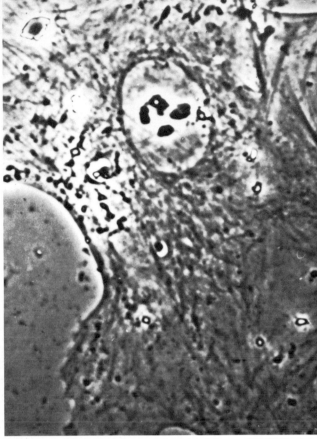

Biochemistry

Continued

The image of a connective cell from a chick embryo transmitted by an acoustic microscope, *above,* has almost as much detail as the image transmitted by an optical microscope, *above right,* at the same magnification (500 times). With the acoustic instrument, which registers the image from variations in sound waves, the specimen does not have to be killed and stained, but can be viewed live.

in processing that gene's RNA. The introns are cut out of the RNA before it leaves the cell nucleus as mRNA, so that only the coding sequences, or exons, remain.

The French scientists think that if the intron does indeed code for a protein, the resulting protein might play a role in splicing the exons together to form mRNA or to transport the mRNA across the nuclear membrane.

Slonimski theorizes that if TGA is found to code for tryptophan in organisms other than yeast, intron sequences may code for proteins as a general rule.

DNA takes a left turn. The model of DNA that James D. Watson and Francis H. C. Crick developed in 1953 is a double helix that twists to the right. In December 1979, researchers Alexander Rich, Andrew H. J. Wang, Gary J. Quigley, Francis J. Kolpak, James L. Crawford, Jacques H. van Boom, and Gijs van der Marel of the Massachusetts Institute of Technology (M.I.T.) in Cambridge proposed that an alternative structure can also exist. They reported that a synthetic DNA mole-

cule crystallizes as a left-handed double helix with a three-dimensional structure quite unlike that of the Watson-Crick model, known as B-DNA. The M.I.T. team called this new form Z-DNA, because its sugar-phosphate backbone follows a staggered zigzag course, unlike the smooth spiral structure of B-DNA. Another difference between the two forms is that Z-DNA is thinner and more extended than B-DNA. Also, Z-DNA contains 12 base pairs in every turn of the helix, whereas B-DNA has 10 pairs per turn.

Scientists do not yet know whether Z-DNA exists in natural DNA molecules. Some researchers suspect that there may be alternating stretches of B-DNA and Z-DNA within the DNA molecule, with the Z-DNA sequences in areas rich in G-C-base combinations. Many DNA molecules, particularly in some bacteria, contain a high percentage of G-C-base pairs.

Scientists also disagree about the purpose of Z-DNA. Z-DNA structures may enable certain enzymes or other proteins to attach to the DNA mole-

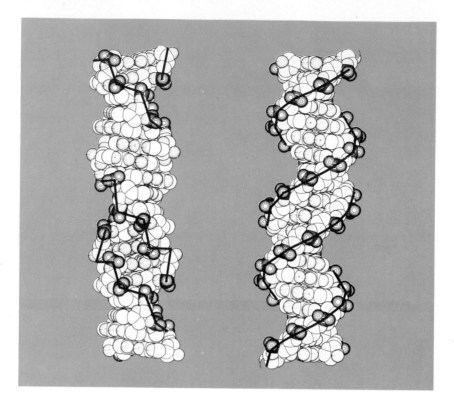

A synthetic molecule of DNA (left) was found to have a left-handed, zigzag, sugar-phosphate backbone in contrast to the right-handed, smooth spiral, sugar-phosphate backbone of the classic DNA molecule. If the left-handed structure exists in nature, it may provide a site for certain chemicals to attach to the DNA molecule, creating DNA mutations and possibly causing cancer.

Biochemistry

Continued

cule. Z-DNA sequences may also be a target site for certain chemicals that cause DNA mutations and possibly cause cancer.

Bacterial resistance. The increase in bacteria that are resistant to antibiotics continues to threaten the effectiveness of these drugs. Scientists exploring this problem in 1979 learned how one group of enzymes, the β-lactamases, which are found in many types of resistant bacteria, affect penicillin. Jeremy Knowles, Jed Fisher, Joel Belasco, and Sundeep Khosla of Harvard University in Cambridge, Mass., reported in September 1979 that they had analyzed the process by which the β-lactamases inactivate penicillin. Although scientists had known for some time that the enzymes catalyze the breakdown of penicillin, they did not know precisely how this occurred. Catalysts regulate, but are not used up in, a chemical reaction.

Knowles and his colleagues found that the β-lactamases are involved in one step of a multistep process. The β-lactamases catalyze a reaction in

which an intermediate enzyme is produced. When that intermediate is broken down in a subsequent reaction, the penicillin is inactivated. The team is using this knowledge to search for β-lactamase inhibitors.

Another research team of Harvard biochemists — Jack L. Strominger, R. Rogers Yocum, David Waxman, and James Rasmussen — suggested in June 1979 that β-lactamases may have evolved from the bacterial target enzyme with which penicillin combines to inhibit cell-wall synthesis.

Strominger and his colleagues found that the penicillin molecule attaches to the D-alanine carboxypeptidase protein at a position held by the amino acid serine. They noted that β-lactamases also have a serine in a similar position in the protein and that the amino acid sequence around the serine in the bacterial target enzyme is related to the amino acid sequences in the β-lactamases. These similarities suggest that resistance arose when the β-lactamases evolved from D-alanine carboxypeptidases. [Julian Davies]

Books of Science

Here are 24 outstanding new science books suitable for the general reader. They have been selected from books published in 1979 and 1980.

Artificial Intelligence. *Machines Who Think: A Personal Inquiry into the History and Prospects of Artificial Intelligence* by Pamela McCorduck presents the history of the development of machines that can be regarded by some standards as meeting criteria for intelligence. She also discusses the personalities of those who built the machines. (Freeman, 1979. 375 pp. $14.95)

Biology. *The Eighth Day of Creation: Makers of the Revolution in Biology* by Horace F. Judson uses numerous in-depth interviews with molecular biologists to present a history of the discovery of deoxyribonucleic acid (DNA) and discuss its meaning to science. He emphasizes the major personalities involved, their relationships with other scientists, and the significance of their discoveries. (Simon & Schuster, 1979. 686 pp. illus. $15.95)

Gaia: A New Look at Life on Earth by Jim E. Lovelock uses the myth of Gaia, the earth goddess of ancient Greece, to develop a theory of a self-regulating earth able to protect itself against pollution. The author argues that the earth holds the key to preservation of life. (Oxford University Press, 1979. 157 pp. illus. $11.95)

The Kindly Fruits of the Earth: Recollections of an Embryo Ecologist by G. Evelyn Hutchinson describes the author's experiences in learning biology 50 years ago. Hutchinson's education in England, research in Italy and South Africa, and later work at Yale University are blended with personal experiences in this engaging autobiography. (Yale University Press, 1979. 264 pp. illus. $18.50)

Cosmology. *The Cosmic Landscape: Voyages Back Along the Photon's Track* by Michael Rowan-Robinson takes a look at the electromagnetic spectrum from very high frequencies to very low frequencies. The author, a noted cosmologist, explains the importance of the parts of the spectrum that humans cannot see. (Oxford University Press, 1979. 149 pp. $12.95)

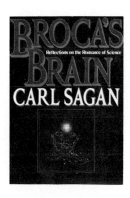

The Exploding Universe: Stars, Galaxies, and Black Holes by Nigel Henbest is a summary of current theories about the universe, enhanced by spectacular illustrations. Henbest includes a section on how life on earth fits into the universe. (Macmillan, 1979. 217 pp. illus. $19.95)

Energy. *Energy from Heaven and Earth* by Edward Teller is a wide-ranging discussion of the history of energy use and today's energy alternatives. Teller, an atomic scientist often called the "father of the hydrogen bomb," outlines choices that will have to be made in the near future. (Freeman, 1979. 322 pp. illus. $15)

A Golden Thread: 2,500 Years of Solar Architecture and Technology by Ken Butti and John Perlin tells how applications of solar energy affected the placement and construction of buildings in ancient Greece and Rome. The authors then relate how these early principles are rediscovered every time there is an energy crisis. (Cheshire, 1980. 291 pp. illus. $15.95)

Environment. *Progress for a Small Planet* by Barbara Ward reviews energy, population, and agricultural issues. Ward analyzes various options from the standpoints of the industrialized countries and the less developed countries and concludes with an assessment of the prospects for cooperation between the two groups. (Norton, 1979. 305 pp. illus. $13.95)

Geoscience. *The Earthquake Handbook* by Peter Verney contains information about earthquakes, including ancient and modern theories of their origin, suggested safeguards for those living in earthquake-prone regions, and the possibilities for prediction and eventual control. He includes extensive firsthand reports of major earthquakes around the world. (Paddington Press, 1979. 224 pp. illus. $10.95)

Ice Ages: Solving the Mystery by John Imbrie and Katherine Palmer Imbrie. The authors begin with a history of theories about glaciers. They then draw upon recent discoveries to describe what the ice ages were like, where they occurred, and when the next ice age might be due. (Enslow, 1979. 224 pp. illus. $12.95)

Natural History. *Archosauria: A New Look at the Old Dinosaur* by John McLoughlin summarizes modern interpretations of life in the Mesozoic Era, 65 million to 225 million years ago. The

Books of Science

Continued

book argues that dinosaurs were creatures capable of speed and agility, very unlike the slow-moving reptiles with which they are frequently classed. (Viking, 1979. 117 pp. illus. $10.95)

Bumblebee Economics by Bernd Heinrich examines how bumblebees generate and manage the tremendous amount of energy needed for hovering, foraging, and other activities. Heinrich shows how the bumblebee affects and is affected by its environment.(Harvard University Press, 1979. 245 pp. illus. $17.50)

Fox Family by Minoru Taketazu illustrates the seasonal patterns of foxes' lives through the year in a series of extraordinary photographs. A brief narrative and a descriptive caption follow the photographs. (Weatherhill, 1979. 139 pp. illus. $25)

Track of the Grizzly by Frank C. Craighead, Jr., is based on the findings of a long-term grizzly bear study conducted in Yellowstone National Park. The author describes the grizzly bears' social patterns, population changes, and territorial range, along with the personal feelings that he developed toward them. (Sierra Club, 1979. 261 pp. illus. $10.95)

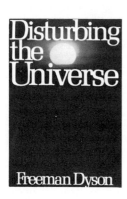

Philosophy of Science. *Advice to a Young Scientist* by Sir Peter B. Medawar, who shared the 1960 Nobel prize for physiology or medicine, discusses the fundamental issues of the practice of science for those contemplating such a career. Medawar discusses ethics, the limitations of science, and getting along with colleagues. (Harper & Row, 1979. 109 pp. $8.95)

Broca's Brain: Reflections on the Romance of Science by Carl Sagan pays tribute to three giants in the history of science — French surgeon and anthropologist Pierre Paul Broca, physicist Albert Einstein, and rocket inventor Robert H. Goddard. These 25 essays are intended to convey some of the "joys and social consequences of scientific endeavor." (Random House, 1979. 347 pp. $12.95)

Disturbing the Universe by Freeman Dyson is a largely autobiographical account of how scientists face the ethical problems of "war and peace, freedom and responsibility, hope and despair, as these are affected by science." Dyson, a physicist, includes his specu-

lations about the future of space travel and life in the universe. (Harper & Row, 1979. 283 pp. $12.95)

Mind and Nature: A Necessary Unity by Gregory Bateson is an essay on the basic patterns of order and disorder in the biological universe. Bateson says we need to understand the patterns to help us understand how all living creatures are interrelated. (Dutton, 1979. 238 pp. $11.95)

Physics. *The Forces of Nature* by P. C. W. Davies sets forth the concepts of subatomic physics with a minimum of mathematics. The author devotes special attention to explaining quantum theory, nuclear forces, and the bewildering array of elementary particles. (Cambridge University Press, 1979. 246 pp. illus. $29.50)

Light by Richard Morris tells how humans have developed increasingly sophisticated views of the nature of light, including how these views were applied in painting and in the development of photography. In his discussion of how light is regarded by modern physicists, he covers such topics as quantum theory, lasers, relativity, and black holes. (Bobbs-Merrill, 1979. 200 pp. illus. $10.95)

What Little I Remember by Otto R. Frisch is an autobiographical account of the physicist's life up to 1947. Frisch deftly draws profiles of other great physicists of the early 1900s, including Niels Bohr and Frisch's aunt and co-worker, Lise Meitner. He also explains how he coined the term *nuclear fission*. (Cambridge University Press, 1979. 227 pp. illus. $14.95)

Psychology. *Nim* by Herbert S. Terrace is an informal account of a four-year project to teach American Sign Language to a chimpanzee named Neam Chimpsky (nicknamed Nim). Terrace and his colleagues question previous research that concluded chimps can learn human language, including syntax. (Knopf, 1979. 384 pp. illus. $13.95)

Seeing: Illusion, Brain and Mind by John P. Frisby is an introduction to the psychology of perception. Frisby emphasizes illusion and what it tells us about the way in which the mind perceives and interprets the world. (Oxford University, 1979. 160 pp. illus. $16.95)   [William Goodrich Jones]

Botany

Research reported in 1979 began to present some solutions to a problem that had puzzled scientists for decades – determining the role of plant steroids. Steroids, and the closely related sterols, are compounds found in animals and plants. They often function as hormones in animals. A. J. Buchala and A. Schmid at the Institute of Plant Biology and Phytochemistry in Fribourg, Switzerland, reported in July 1979 that vitamin D and closely related chemicals derived from ergosterol, a sterol, actively promote the formation of roots on cuttings taken from various species, including two poplars and the common green bean.

The scientists divided cuttings from each species into four large groups. They soaked the stems of the first group in various solutions containing vitamin D compounds; the second group was immersed in a solution containing a synthetic auxin, a plant hormone known to promote root formation; the third group, in solutions containing both the auxin and the vitamin D compounds; and the fourth, in water.

They found that the cuttings soaked in the combination of auxin and vitamin D compounds developed many more roots than the cuttings in either the auxin or vitamin D solutions alone. Buchala and Schmid theorized that ergosterol might promote root formation in many plants.

Plant interferon. A team of scientists led by Ilan Sela at the Hebrew University in Jerusalem, Israel, reported in February 1980 that they had purified a substance similar to interferon – an antiviral animal protein – from plants. They recovered the substance from certain varieties of tobacco plants that were infected with viruses.

Plant interferon is similar in many ways to animal interferon. Both substances limit the multiplication of viruses and therefore prevent viral infections from spreading. Both are large, very potent protein molecules. Only four or five molecules per cell are necessary to protect a plant. Unlike animal interferon, which is only effective in the species that produced it, plant interferon from one species can prevent viral

The stately elm, *below,* can be cloned to produce offspring virtually identical to those of another tree of the same variety. However, when viewed through an electron microscope, (magnified 4,000 times) the leaf pores of two elm clones reveal differences in size and shape, *below right,* and *bottom right.*

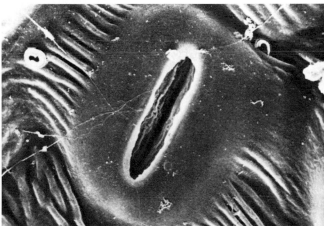

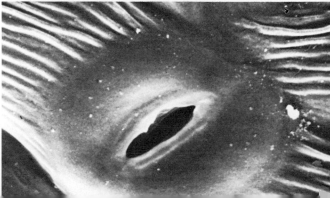

Botany

infections in a variety of plants, but not in animals.

Sela sees plant interferon as a potential solution to an important agricultural problem. Many plants that are grown from root, stem, or leaf cuttings, or by tissue cloning, rather than seeds, are infected by viruses passed along in plant cells from one crop to the next. If these cuttings were treated with interferon before planting, the new crops might be virus-free, at least at first.

Pepping-up photosynthesis. Horticulturalists Richard N. Arteca, B. W. Poovaiah, and Orrin E. Smith of Washington State University in Pullman reported in September 1979 that they had developed a method of increasing photosynthesis in plants grown outdoors. Photosynthesis is the process plants use to make carbohydrates from carbon dioxide (CO_2), water, and sunlight – releasing oxygen.

Scientists have known that photosynthesis can be accelerated in virtually every plant species by increasing CO_2 in the atmosphere around the plant. Although plant growers can pump extra CO_2 into greenhouses, no one has developed a practical way to increase atmospheric CO_2 in the field.

The Washington State researchers enriched the atmosphere around the roots, rather than the foliage, of potato plants with CO_2. To do this, they grew two groups of potato seedlings in a liquid nutrient. They then pumped a stream of gas composed of 45 per cent CO_2, 21 per cent oxygen, and 34 per cent nitrogen through the solution around the roots of one group for 12 daylight hours. The other group was not treated. Six weeks later, the researchers found that the treated group produced many more potatoes and that they weighed twice as much as those of the untreated group.

The researchers repeated the experiment, this time labeling the gas with radioactive carbon-14. After six weeks, they measured the radioactivity in the treated plants by pressing them against a sheet of X-ray film and then developing the film. They found that the labeled CO_2 had been transported from the roots to the stems and leaves. Apparently, CO_2 was fixed in the roots and later used to increase photosynthesis in the shoots.

The roots of several other vegetable species treated in the same way were damaged by the high concentrations of CO_2. Nevertheless, root applications of CO_2 can apparently help to increase potato yields, and growers might someday be able to supply CO_2 to potato roots in the field.

A team of plant physiologists, Kei-Ichiro Okabe, Geoffrey A. Codd, and William D. P. Stewart of the University of Dundee in Scotland reported in June 1979 on another approach to the photosynthesis problem.

The scientists were searching for a way to improve the rate of photosynthesis by inhibiting one function of the enzyme ribulose-bisphosphate carboxylase/oxygenase and thus freeing more of the enzyme to combine with CO_2. This enzyme can comprise from one-eighth to nearly one-half the protein in a leaf and is a catalyst in two cellular reactions. Catalysts are substances that regulate chemical reactions but are not used in them.

In one photosynthetic reaction, the enzyme combines briefly with a molecule of CO_2 and a sugar molecule containing five carbon atoms to produce two 3-carbon molecules. This reaction can take place with or without light. The enzyme can also combine with oxygen in photorespiration, resulting, after a complex series of reactions, in a release of CO_2.

As light levels increase, more oxygen is produced during one stage of photosynthesis. The extra oxygen competes with CO_2 for a place on the enzyme and thus reduces the formation of carbohydrates by as much as 50 per cent. This results in slower growth.

The British team decided to look for a substance that would block the enzyme's function in photorespiration while allowing it to function in photosynthesis. The researchers isolated the enzyme from a blue-green alga and tested several chemicals that affected its ability to combine with CO_2 and with oxygen. Most of the chemicals they tested – nitrates, nitrites, and ammonia compounds – inhibited both processes. However, one compound, hydroxylamine, considerably increased the enzyme's ability to combine with CO_2 and inhibited its ability to combine with oxygen.[Frank B. Salisbury]

Chemistry

Chemists Michael Grätzel, Pierre-Alain Brugger, and Andre M. Brun of Lausanne Federal Polytechnic Institute in Switzerland reported in March 1980 that they had used light to split water into hydrogen and oxygen. The only material consumed was water. Hydrogen is a useful fuel, so the experiment is a major step toward developing practical alternative energy sources.

The Swiss process uses fine particles of platinum and ruthenium oxide, and two catalysts — substances that cause chemical reactions while themselves remaining essentially unchanged. The catalysts were *tris*-(bipyridine)ruthenium(II) di-cation, a molecule of the metal ruthenium, and an organic bipyridine di-cation. The researchers placed these materials in water and exposed the mixture to sunlight.

First, the sunlight energized electrons of the ruthenium catalyst, causing them to jump to the organic catalyst. Both catalysts then reacted with the water. The molecules of the organic catalyst clumped together to form tiny spheres. When the spheres touched the platinum particles' surfaces, they gave up the electrons they had gained from the ruthenium catalyst and returned to their original state. Water molecules then absorbed these electrons, broke apart, and recombined into hydrogen molecules and hydroxide ions — molecules made of one oxygen atom and one hydrogen atom, with an electrical charge of −1.

Meanwhile, the ruthenium catalyst picked up electrons from the ruthenium oxide and returned to its original state. The ruthenium oxide then took electrons from water molecules, causing the water to form oxygen molecules and hydrogen ions — hydrogen atoms that have no electrons and have an electrical charge of +1. Finally, the hydrogen and oxygen molecules bubbled to the surface, the hydrogen ions combined rapidly with the hydroxide ions to form water, and the process began again.

A mixture of gases made up of hydrogen and oxygen molecules is stable, so a full-scale commercial production apparatus using the Swiss process would collect both kinds of molecules simulta-

A hair-thin glass fiber transmits laser light that makes chemicals in a liquid fluoresce, and then passes the data back to an instrument that analyzes it to determine the liquid's makeup. The equipment permits one instrument to analyze liquids at several remote locations up to 1.6 kilometers (1 mile) away.

neously. A refrigeration system could then separate the two elements by gradually lowering their temperature. First, the oxygen molecules would condense — form a liquid — and run off into a tank. Then the hydrogen would condense and be pumped into metal bottles for use as a liquid fuel.

Single-step silicon. Chemists Angel Sanjurjo and Leonard Nanis of SRI International in Menlo Park, Calif., reported a new one-step synthesis of high-purity silicon in August 1979. Silicon, a constituent of ordinary sand, is one of nature's most common elements, but the exceptionally high purity required in the silicon used in solar cells makes it very expensive. The SRI researchers claim that their process can lower the cost of silicon for solar cells by about 90 per cent.

The process uses the spontaneous, heat-producing reaction of sodium fluorosilicate with metallic sodium to produce silicon tetrafluoride. This compound then reacts with more metallic sodium to produce the silicon and sodium fluoride.

The silicon produced this way can be used in solar cells without further purification. In addition, aluminum producers can use the reaction's only by-product — sodium fluoride — to make cryolite, an important ingredient in the production of aluminum. Costs are further lowered by the use of sodium fluorosilicate as a starting material. This compound is obtained from an inexpensive waste product of the phosphate-fertilizer industry.

Chemical vision. Chemist Koji Nakanishi of Columbia University in New York City and biophysicist Barry Honig of the University of Illinois in Champaign-Urbana reported in November 1979 that the eye's sensitivity to light is caused by a molecule called 11-*cis*-retinal. This molecule combines chemically with negatively charged atoms in the amino acids of proteins on the retina of the eye.

The researchers found that the human eye has four visual proteins to which 11-*cis*-retinal can bind. Three of these proteins are involved in color vision and the fourth in black-and-

A Saucy Controversy

To the cook, Sauce Béarnaise is a sublime blend of butter, egg yolk, wine, shallots, herbs, and spices. To the chemist, it is an emulsion of oil and air in water. But, few things are more wretched than a failed Béarnaise — a study in broken emulsions with its rubbery clots adrift in an oily sea.

As a lipid biochemist at Boston University School of Medicine, I was intrigued by the failed Béarnaise. With my collaborator, Michael Bernstein, the head chef of a French restaurant, I set out to rescue a failed sauce.

Our mission was to transform a lumpy sauce into a smooth emulsion. Emulsions are one phase of matter dispersed and suspended in another phase. Stabilizing the emulsion requires a special type of molecule. In the case of Sauce Béarnaise, one part of the emulsifying molecule must line up with the aqueous phase — the wine, vinegar, and water — and another part with the oil phase — the clarified butter. The egg

yolk furnishes the crucial molecules, and stirring brings them in contact with both oil and water.

Sauce Béarnaise can be broken several ways. When we cooled the sauce below 20°C (78°F.), the butter crystallized. If we heated it above 80°C (176°F.), the egg coagulated. We also destroyed the sauce by adding oil too rapidly and by stirring too slowly.

After experimenting with a number of complicated procedures for restoring the sauce, we found that the time-honored cookbook method was the best — slowly pouring the broken sauce into another pan with a small amount of water at 40° to 50°C (104° to 122°F.) and stirring vigorously. Only the coagulated-egg sauce failed to respond.

Unfortunately, the rescued sauces lacked the lightness and delicate flavor of the originals. Why they did is unclear, perhaps because we are dealing with a chemical reaction that is not science, but art. [Donald M. Small]

white vision. One of the protein-retinal units absorbs red light, one absorbs green light, and one absorbs blue light. Mixtures of these colors provide all the other colors we see. Any animal that can see color has 11-*cis*-retinal, which is formed from vitamin A, but the number and positions of the negative charges in the retina vary.

The scientists proved their theory by depriving rats of vitamin A and then injecting them with a compound that is chemically similar to 11-*cis*-retinal. Radioactive atoms that the scientists had added to the injected compound showed that it occupied the same places in the four proteins as 11-*cis*-retinal. The rats became blind, but feeding them vitamin A restored their vision.

Metal electrides. Chemist James L. Dye of Michigan State University in East Lansing reported in December that he and his colleagues had created several unique chemical compounds called metal electrides. Ordinary chemical compounds are made of two chemical elements or groups of elements — the positively charged cation and the negative anion. In a metal electride, the anion is an electron.

To make his unique compounds, Dye uses a solution of liquid ammonia, an alkali metal such as lithium or potassium, and basket-shaped organic molecules called cryptands. The metal atoms move about freely until they enter the cryptands. Then the chemist evaporates the ammonia solvent. The electron remains on the outside of the cryptand and serves as the anion to the positive metal cation in the cryptand.

Metal electrides have interesting properties. For example, lithium electride acts like a metal and conducts electricity well at temperatures of about $-45°C$ ($-49°F$.). But its conductivity is poor at lower temperatures, like that of a nonmetal. Dye obtained electrides of lithium, potassium, and cesium. Attempts to make barium electrides failed when the ammonia solvent was removed. The electrides must be kept at temperatures below $-33°C$ ($-27°F$.) and protected from light and air in order to prevent the cryptand from breaking up.

Hydronium ion is almost flat. Chemists Gheorghe D. Mateescu and George M. Benedikt of Case Western Reserve University in Cleveland presented direct evidence in July 1979 for the geometrical arrangement of the hydronium ion, H_3O^+, which has one oxygen atom and three hydrogen atoms and carries an electrical charge of +1. The scientists used acidic water enriched with oxygen-17, an isotope of oxygen that can be studied by a technique called nuclear magnetic resonance (NMR). This technique is based on the ability of certain parts of molecules that are exposed to strong magnetic fields to absorb electromagnetic radiation vibrating at certain frequencies.

Scientists determine important parts of a molecule's structure by exposing it to such a field, sending radiation of various frequencies through it, and recording the frequencies of the radiation that it absorbs. An NMR study of hydronium ion at a temperature of $-15°C$ ($5°F$.) produced four signals — one for the oxygen atom and one for each combination of the oxygen atom with a hydrogen atom.

The four signals indicated that three hydrogens were bound to an oxygen and that these three hydrogens were in exactly equivalent positions around the oxygen. The chemists compared the hydronium-ion spectrum with that of ordinary water, which has a pyramid-shaped arrangement of two hydrogens and two pairs of electrons about the oxygen; and with the pyramid-shaped ammonium ion, which is made up of one nitrogen atom and four hydrogen atoms, and has an electrical charge of +1. They concluded that hydronium must be almost flat.

An asthma-related molecule was synthesized for the first time in February 1980 by an international team of chemists led by Elias J. Corey of Harvard University in Cambridge, Mass., and Bengt Samuelsson of the Karolinska Institute in Stockholm, Sweden. The researchers synthesized Leukotriene C, which may be involved in asthma attacks and anaphylaxis, or shock.

The compound was named the slow-reacting substance (SRS) of anaphylaxis more than 40 years ago. It consists of a 20-carbon fatty acid attached to three amino acids that form a water-soluble unit called a peptide. The fatty-acid portion is not water-soluble and resembles the potent body regulators called prostaglandins. Corey believes that SRS's structure allows it to replace prostaglandin in certain cell parts and thus interfere with prostaglandin function.

Corey and team members David A. Clark, Giichi Goto, Anthony Marfat, Charles Mioskowski, and K. Frank Austen first isolated natural SRS from lung tissue and then purified it. SRS occurs only in trillionths of a gram, so the purification was very difficult.

The synthesis started with the sugar ribose, whose structure is known in detail. The scientists synthesized Leukotriene C and many related compounds in several reaction steps, some of them carried out to best advantage at temperatures of $-90°C$ ($-130°F$.). At several stages of the synthesis, they sent samples to Samuelsson and his colleague Sven Hammerström for testing and further synthesis.

The Corey-Samuelsson SRS synthesis should allow significant amounts of the compound to be made available for the first time. Medical researchers will then be able to use radioactively labeled SRS to pinpoint the sites in the body where it acts. Chemists will be able to develop ways of measuring the amount of SRS in the body. Perhaps knowledge of SRS's structure will allow researchers to design compounds that will counteract its effects.

Interferon partly analyzed. There is lively scientific interest in interferons — complex molecules that form part of the body's natural defenses against virus infections. Interferon may prove effective in treating some types of cancer. However, research has been limited by the minute amounts of interferon available to scientists. For example, it takes 30,750 liters (65,000 pints) of blood to produce about 100 milligrams (0.003 ounce) of interferon.

Because it is difficult to obtain adequate amounts for analysis, interferon's chemical structure is not precisely known. Interferon is a glycoprotein — a protein with attached sugar molecules.

In a superb example of scientific cooperation, four teams of scientists announced in February 1980 that they had partially determined the amino acid sequences of the proteins of several types of interferons. Amino acids are the building blocks of proteins.

The key factor in the research was the development of a highly sensitive instrument, a spinning cup protein sequenator, by researchers Leroy E. Hood and Michael W. Hunkapiller of the California Institute of Technology (Caltech) in Pasadena. The sequenator can analyze interferon in microgram (millionths of a gram) quantities. It chemically removes the amino acids one at a time, then analyzes them automatically.

Collaborating with Hood and Hunkapiller in using the sequenator were chemists Christian B. Anfinsen, who shared the 1972 Nobel prize for chemistry, Pamela J. Bridgen, Mark E. Smith, and Kathryn C. Zoon of the National Institute of Arthritis, Metabolism, and Digestive Diseases in Bethesda, Md. The scientists determined the composition and sequence of 13 amino acids in the end portion of interferon from human lymphoblasts, a type of immature white blood cell.

Another research team consisting of E. Knight, Jr., B. D. Korant, and R. W. F. Hardy of E. I. du Pont de Nemours & Company in Wilmington, Del., used the sequenator to determine the 13 amino acids in interferon from human fibroblasts — cells that form scar tissue immediately after a skin injury. The sequence and composition of the amino acids were different from those found in interferon from human lymphoblasts.

The third team cooperating with the Caltech group worked on three types of mouse interferon having different molecular weights. Chemists Hideharu Taira, Robert J. Broeze, Bettadapura M. Jayaram, and Peter Lengyel of Yale University in New Haven, Conn., determined the sequence of the first 20 amino acids. Two of the mouse interferons, called types A and B, had the same amino acid sequences, but that of type C was quite different. However, the amino acid sequence of mouse type C interferon was found to be remarkably similar to that of human lymphoblast interferon. Of the first 20 amino acids, 13 are identical. But the sequence from types A and B bore only a slight resemblance to that of human fibroblast interferon, thus leaving for future research the problem of how different interferons evolve. [Lawrence Verbit]

Communications

Significant advances in fiber-optics communications were made in 1979 and 1980. Engineers at Siemens AG in Munich, West Germany, and at Bell Telephone Laboratories in Murray Hill, N.J., developed telephones that use thin glass (optical) fibers rather than wires to transmit signals.

In optical fiber communications, voice or data signals are sent through an optical fiber on a beam of light. The source of the beam may be a laser or a light-emitting diode (LED). Fiber-optics materials have been developed that will allow light to travel through several kilometers of cable with little weakening of the signal it carries.

The Siemens engineers announced in May 1979 that they had built a prototype of a radically new telephone that uses very few parts. All the energy needed to activate the earpiece and provide a ringing signal is contained in the light beam sent from a laser in the telephone company's central office.

To produce sound in the earpiece, the *modulated* (signal-carrying) light strikes a photoelectric element that converts the light into electrical signals. These, in turn, are fed to an electromagnetic earpiece that converts the electrical signals into sound.

Another photoelectric element in the receiver serves as the input for an electronically driven horn. This is the telephone's ringer, or alerting device. Light striking the element is converted into electrical pulses, which are used to produce an acoustic "ring."

The Siemens telephone set uses the power from the light beam to convert the user's voice directly to signals that are transmitted back to the central office. This is accomplished with an optical microphone that has a thin, partially mirrored membrane that vibrates in response to the sound of a voice. This permits the voice to modulate the light beam directly without intervening electrical translations.

Bell Laboratories engineers in early 1980 reported that they had devised a light detector and transmitter that would carry voice signals inside a telephone set solely on pulses of light traveling along a single hair-thin glass fi-

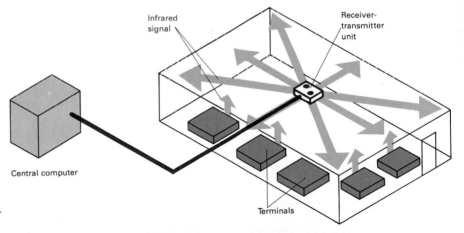

Infrared light-emitting diodes, *below right,* were developed by IBM to beam signals between computers. A receiver-transmitter on the ceiling, *above right,* relays data between the central computer and terminals in work areas, ending the need for bulky cables.

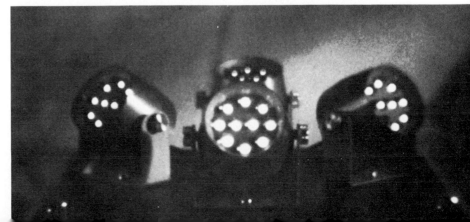

Communications

Continued

Panels of photovoltaic cells at the base of White Face Mountain at Lake Placid, N.Y., converted sunlight to electricity for phone and television links during 1980 Winter Olympic ski events.

ber. A photo detector inside the telephone modulates the incoming signal on one frequency, and another device sends outgoing signals on another frequency. This allows both the incoming and outgoing light signals to travel on one fiber. In conventional phones, electrical signals to and from the central office must travel on pairs of wires.

The infrared revolution. International Business Machines (IBM) Corporation scientists working at the IBM research laboratory in Zurich, Switzerland, reported in November 1979 that they had developed a scheme for infrared communication links between computers. Transmitting computer commands and data on infrared wavelengths would eliminate the need for bulky cables and wire connections between terminals and the central computer in an office or factory work area.

In the IBM scheme, each terminal is equipped with infrared LEDs that beam signals to a receiver-transmitter unit mounted on the ceiling. The unit then transmits the information to the central computer. The infrared light can either be beamed directly between the terminals and the service unit or be reflected throughout the room by a shield attached to the unit. Reflected light would be used for computers enclosed in cubicles and not in line of sight with the service unit.

The IBM scientists found that the infrared links were not affected by most forms of electrical interference. Not even arc welding, a source of electrical static and of considerable heat, disrupted experimental transmissions. The scientists had feared that heat might create problems, because most infrared wavelengths are sensed as heat. But those used in the computer system are in the near-infrared, close to the wavelengths of visible light.

Several manufacturers experimented during the year with this form of wireless transmission in products ranging from toys to telephones. Many European television makers switched from radar to infrared frequency signals for remote-control units. Several toy manufacturers in late 1979 introduced toy cars and trains that were operated by

Communications

Continued

A teletext weather forecast warning of tornadoes for the Salt Lake City area appears on an idle channel of a home TV set.

infrared remote control. Siemens in September unveiled a cordless telephone receiver that transmits voice signals on infrared wavelengths, allowing the user to walk around a room.

Teletext. During the year, broadcasters experimented with systems that transmit a variety of data to the home. For example, in Salt Lake City, Utah, in mid-1979, station KSL-TV began using the Ceefax system developed in Great Britain for teletext transmission.

Teletext uses the $\frac{1}{600}$-second interval before the electronic beam in the TV set begins to "paint" a new picture at the top of the screen to transmit information, which is stored in a microprocessor attached to the TV set. The viewer can then call up this information for display on the TV screen, using an idle channel. The Salt Lake City system carries 800 screen-size pages (the equivalent of 50 newspaper pages), providing information that ranges from advertising to airline schedules or detailed weather reports.

The same type of technology was used increasingly during the year to provide the nearly 2 million Americans suffering serious hearing deficiency with captions (subtitles) for television programs. The American Broadcasting Companies, Inc., and the National Broadcasting Company planned to caption five hours per week of prime-time television by the end of 1980. The Public Broadcasting Service planned for 10 hours per week.

Radio-navigation system LORAN-C neared completion in 1980, providing coverage for all regions along the U.S. Atlantic Coast. LORAN-C receivers costing as little as $3,000 were marketed in late 1979 for use aboard ships and even in automobiles. With such a receiver, navigators can determine their position within 0.3 kilometer ($\frac{1}{4}$ mile) by tuning to LORAN-C transmitters positioned along the East Coast. The navigator must know the positions of these transmitters and must tune his receiver to three of them to plot his position on a map. The position will be where three lines intersect, each showing the direction from the craft to a transmitter.   [E. Joseph Piel]

Drugs

Heroin addicts may find relief with a new drug therapy described in February 1980 by drug researchers Nancy K. Mello and Jack H. Mendelson of McLean Hospital in Belmont, Mass., and Harvard Medical School. Buprenorphine is a morphinelike substance that kills pain and produces mood effects similar to those of morphine. But chemically, it also interferes with the action of such opiate drugs.

Ten volunteer male heroin addicts, all of whom had failed to overcome their addiction by conventional methods, received daily injections of buprenorphine or a placebo. At the same time, they were all allowed to have heroin if they wanted it.

Those taking buprenorphine used very little of the heroin, while those given the placebo used almost all the heroin they were allowed. After buprenorphine was discontinued, the patients suffered none of the withdrawal symptoms caused by heroin and methadone, a heroin substitute used to treat addicts. Apparently, buprenorphine does not produce physical dependence.

Heroin addiction is a complex problem with many physical and psychological causes and these findings are preliminary. However, buprenorphine may prove to be a safe and effective part of a cure for heroin addiction when used in conjunction with other forms of therapy.

Weeding out side effects. The widely held notion that marijuana can soften the side effects of cancer-fighting drugs received scientific support in a March 1980 report by physicians John Laszlo and Virgil Lucas, Jr., of Duke University School of Medicine in Durham, N.C. Many cancer treatments depend on strong drug treatment to retard tumor growth and prolong life.

Unfortunately, such chemotherapy almost always induces nausea and vomiting. Frequently, the treatment seems worse than the disease itself. Although conventional antinausea drugs may prevent such side effects, they do not always work and sometimes have harmful side effects themselves. Thus, the search for more effective methods of preventing nausea and

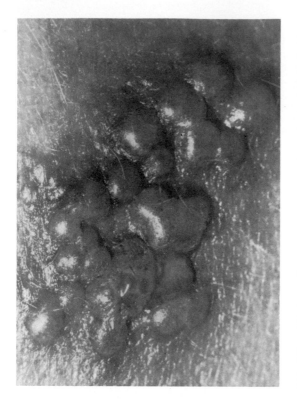
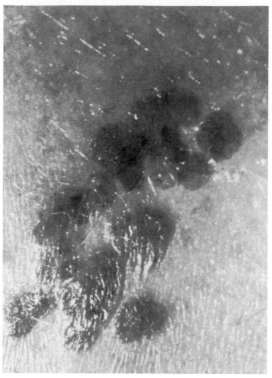

Drugs

Continued

Genital sores caused by herpes virus, *above,* are almost eliminated, *above right,* after four days of treatment with the experimental drug 2-deoxy-D-glucose. The viral infection, which accounts for about 13 per cent of all venereal disease, has resisted other drugs.

vomiting has intensified as the use of chemotherapy grows.

Laszlo and Lucas investigated the effects of delta-nine-tetrahydrocannabinol (THC), an active agent in marijuana, on patients receiving cancer chemotherapy. The potential usefulness of THC in controlling nausea and vomiting was suggested in the late 1960s by marijuana users undergoing cancer chemotherapy. These patients noted that using the drug substantially reduced their nausea and vomiting during chemotherapy. Subsequent studies tended to confirm this observation.

Laszlo and Lucas described the experience of 53 adult patients who were receiving cancer chemotherapy. All had experienced severe nausea and vomiting, uncontrollable by standard antinausea drugs, during previous cancer treatment. The doctors gave the patients THC in a single large dose before chemotherapy, but this almost always produced drowsiness or acute psychological reactions. Smaller, more frequent doses proved to be more acceptable to the patients. The THC was

dissolved in oil and given to the patient in capsule form.

Patients were observed and interviewed by the investigators, and notes on the progress of the therapy were kept to assess response to the treatment. Although 28 per cent failed to respond to the drug at all, 19 per cent were completely free of nausea and vomiting, and 53 per cent experienced a significant reduction of these symptoms. All the patients who responded to THC reported feeling the psychological effects of the drug, while most nonresponders failed to experience these effects. The observers found no long-term or delayed effects from THC.

In view of the drug's apparent benefit and its seeming lack of harmful effects, the researchers suggested that government regulations be modified to permit its therapeutic use. They also recommended further research to determine whether other related chemicals might have similar or superior medical properties.

Aspirin stand-off. The ability of aspirin to prevent heart attacks, particular-

Battling the Superbugs

Bacterial epidemics were once more widely feared than war because people were powerless against their attack. However, the development in the 1940s of several "wonder drugs" — penicillin, streptomycin, and sulfa drugs — provided physicians with potent weapons against bacteria. These drugs were joined by a host of other antibiotics, and it appeared in the 1950s that bacteria were no longer a major threat to human health.

In recent years, however, bacterial epidemics have returned, and the bacteria responsible for them have become resistant to the antibiotics normally used against them. A continuing cholera epidemic in Bangladesh, which broke out in the mid-1970s, has been attributed to the abrupt emergence of *Vibrio cholerae*, a bacteria that is resistant to the antibiotics tetracycline, ampicillin, kanamycin, streptomycin, and trimethoprim sulfamethoxazole. All of these antibiotics had previously been an effective treatment against cholera, but are now ineffective. Strains of two other potentially dangerous infections — pneumonia and gonorrhea — that had been treated successfully with penicillin since the 1950s are becoming resistant to this drug.

Although bacterial resistance has only recently become a major health problem, evidence that this would happen became apparent as early as 1952 during an outbreak of bacillary dysentery in Japan. This infection, caused by *Shigella* bacteria and normally treated with sulfonamide drugs, gradually began to withstand sulfa therapy, so physicians turned to other antibiotics to treat the disease. This worked for a while, but, one by one, strains of *Shigella* that were resistant to more than one drug began to appear. By 1967, 97 per cent of all *Shigella* strains studied in Japan were resistant to as many as four different antibiotics.

Scientists who examined them found that those multiple resistant *Shigella* contained resistance genes on plasmids, small circular pieces of deoxyribonucleic acid (DNA) that can be transferred from one bacterium to another.

These resistant bacteria can transfer resistance plasmids (R-plasmids) to nonresistant bacteria. The nonresistant bacteria pick up R-plasmids either by fusing with resistant bacteria and exchanging genetic material or, in a process known as transformation, by absorbing R-plasmids freed from bacteria that may have burst. R-plasmids can pick up any number of different antibiotic-resistant genes. The creation of these new resistance plasmids has been aided by the remarkable ability of resistance genes to move from one plasmid to another within a single bacterial cell (see BIOCHEMISTRY, *Science Year*, 1977).

Resistance genes code for various enzymes that act on specific antibiotics. These enzymes may destroy the antibiotic, or make it ineffective; change the bacterial cell so that the antibiotic cannot attach to it; modify a vital bacterial process, such as cell-wall building, that the action of the antibiotic had previously blocked.

By learning how these different resistance mechanisms work, biochemists have been able to design enzymes to inhibit them and new antibiotics that are not affected by them. Unfortunately, these new resistance inhibitors and antibiotics are only stopgap measures. Bacteria are likely to develop resistance to them, too. To really solve the problem, we must attack its cause — the extensive use of many types of antibiotics that provides a greater opportunity for R-plasmids to evolve and flourish, resulting in the development of bacteria with multiple resistance.

Approximately 10 million kilograms (22 million pounds) of antibiotics will be used in the United States in 1980. About half of these antibiotics will be used in human medicine; and the rest, at low concentrations, in agriculture to promote animal growth.

Although the United States has taken few steps to limit the use of antibiotics, many other countries have regulations that control antibiotic additives in animal feeds. As a result, the incidence of resistant bacteria in animals has declined to some extent in these countries.

Antibiotics are still a valuable weapon against human infections, but we must use them sparingly if we are to preserve their value. Otherwise, we might only enhance the ability of bacteria to develop new and stronger resistant forms.   [Julian Davies]

Drugs

Continued

A doctor inserts samples of body fluids from hospital patients into an automatic analyzer that can identify the different infections and the proper antibiotics.

ly in persons who have previously suffered a heart attack, remains in doubt. Studies published in 1980 produced conflicting data on the commonly used drug and its effects on the heart.

The largest study, the Aspirin Myocardial Infarction Study, conducted by the National Heart, Lung, and Blood Institute of Bethesda, Md., checked on more than 4,500 heart-attack patients for three years. During the study, half of the group took the equivalent of three aspirin tablets per day; the other half took a placebo.

About 8 per cent of the placebo group and 8.7 per cent of those who took aspirin died of heart attacks during the test period. Moreover, those who took aspirin suffered more gastrointestinal disturbances, which probably resulted from the chronic use of the drug. There were fewer nonfatal heart attacks, however, among those who took aspirin.

The other studies, including one in Great Britain and one in West Germany, gave some support to the theory that aspirin protects the heart from second heart attacks. Epidemiologist Peter C. Elwood of the Medical Research Council unit in Cardiff, Wales, reported 22 per cent fewer heart disease deaths among aspirin-taking patients in the first year after a heart attack.

Statistically, none of the studies gave the kind of clear-cut results that could guide physicians treating victims of first heart attacks. Meanwhile, the federal Food and Drug Administration (FDA) said in February 1980 that aspirin can reduce the risk of second strokes in men.

Cardiac arrhythmia, or irregular heartbeat, may be controlled by a group of drugs normally used to treat depression. Physicians Alexander H. Glassman and Elsa-Grace V. Giardina of New York City's Columbia-Presbyterian Medical Center reported in November 1979 that imipramine, one of a group of drugs called the tricyclic antidepressants, reduced arrhythmia in 11 depressed patients. Further tests are being conducted to determine how the drug affects the action of the heart.   [Edward G. Nash]

Ecology

Studies of two lakes reported in 1979 underscored the human impact on an ecosystem. One study was conducted in an isolated region and one in a densely populated area. Ecologists Jeffrey E. Richey and Robert C. Wissmar of the University of Washington carried out their study at isolated Findley Lake, a small soft-water lake in a heavily forested region of the Cascade Range, 65 kilometers (39 miles) east of Seattle. Few humans visit the lake or its watershed—the area that it drains.

Richey and Wissmar's ecosystem study of the lake emphasized two important nutrients for plant life—nitrogen and phosphorus. For a year, the ecologists made a series of measurements, taking water samples once a month during the winter and weekly during the spring and summer. They analyzed the levels of nitrogen and phosphorus in samples from streams flowing in and out of the lake, as well as in samples collected at 2.5-centimeter (1-inch) intervals from a central sampling station located over the lake's deepest point. The researchers also collected and sampled plant debris from the lake, snowpacks that fed the lake, and rain water.

Richey and Wissmar found that streams brought in the lake's major source of nutrients—plant debris, particularly fallen leaves—when the snowpack melted in the spring. These swollen streams are also the best sources of inorganic nitrogen and phosphorus, which may promote the growth of periphyton—complex colonies of algae, insect larvae, and tiny crustaceans.

Most of the nutrients pass through the lake because water moves through it rapidly, preventing a nutrient buildup that could support colonies of plankton, both *phytoplankton* (tiny plants) and *zooplankton* (tiny animals) that float on the surface of the water.

The researchers then compared this information to data collected from five other lakes similar in size to Findley. They found that the ratio of nitrogen to phosphorus flowing into Findley Lake was similar to the ratios of nitrogen to phosphorus flowing into the other lakes. This ratio remained the same in

Ecology
Continued

An oak and hickory
forest in North Carolina
was cut down with
minimal disturbance
to the forest floor,
below. As a result,
fast-growing plants,
bottom, including
softwoods, such as black
locust, *below right,*
covered the area before
wind and water could
erode the naked soil.

the material flowing out of Findley
Lake. However, in the other lakes, the
proportion of nitrogen flowing out was
higher, indicating that more phosphorus remained in the other lakes.

Richey and Wissmar also found that
the actual amounts of nitrogen and
phosphorus flowing through Findley
Lake were much greater than those
flowing through all the other lakes,
except Lake Wingra in Madison, Wis.,
which is highly eutrophic. Eutrophication is the accumulation of nutrients
that causes the excessive growth of
algae and depletes the oxygen in the
water, endangering fish and other life.
The percentage of these elements retained in Findley Lake was much
lower. The ecologists concluded that
Findley Lake's nutrient levels differed
from other lakes, probably because
water flows through it so rapidly.

Ecologists Robert L. Leonard, Louis
A. Keplan, John F. Elder, Robert N.
Coats, and Charles R. Goldman of the
University of California, Davis, report-
ed in September on their study of the
impact of human activities on Lake

Tahoe, a large lake on the California-
Nevada border. Because the lake is
used for fishing, boating, and water-
skiing, its water quality is important.

The Davis team studied nutrient
transport into Lake Tahoe from two of
its key watershed tributaries. They
sought detailed information on nutrient concentrations carried by the two
streams so that they could estimate
how nutrients contribute to the eutrophication of Lake Tahoe.

The ecologists established stations
throughout the watersheds drained by
each of the two streams to collect water
samples and measure the rate of water
flow. They measured the amount of
sediment, analyzed the nutrients, and
recorded the temperature of each water
sample. They found that the amount of
sediment in the samples and its nutrient content were generally lower when
the streams' flow rate was greater.

The researchers measured phosphorus, iron, zinc, and trace-metal levels as
well as nitrogen, because these elements pollute the lake and nourish
phytoplankton. One of the watersheds

A Woof in the Wool

A young komondor guards his flock.

What do the komondor and kuvasz, the maremma abruzzi and Anatolian shepherd, the shar planinetz and Great Pyrenees, have in common? All are big, woolly European dogs that guard big, woolly North American sheep.

United States livestock producers, faced with increasing coyote attacks, are learning what farmers in Europe and Asia have known for centuries—dogs can effectively protect their stock.

Guard dogs perform differently from herding dogs, such as border collies, which are bred to stalk and chase. Herding dogs work only with a shepherd, who controls their behavior. Guard dogs work alone.

Research biologists have set up several programs aimed at acquainting courageous dogs like the Hungarian komondor with the American way of (wild)life. At schools such as Hampshire College in Amherst, Mass., and government agricultural centers such as the United States Sheep Experiment Station in Dubois, Ida., dogs are being bred, trained, and put into the pasture with flocks of sheep and goats.

Guard dogs do not require much instruction. Raising the pups from birth in pens with their prospective charges seems to strengthen three necessary—and apparently inborn—traits. The dogs must be attentive to the flock, must not harm the flock, and must be aggressive toward predators.

Dogs like the komondor are characteristically wary of anything strange and are fearless in defense of their territory and property. Researchers are not sure if the dogs come to regard the sheep as other canines to be cared for, or if the flocks regard their protectors as "Supersheep." At any rate, strong bonds of identity and loyalty develop, hungry coyotes are intimidated, and dozens of sheep and goat producers in the United States and Canada have happily let their predator control "go to the dogs."   [Jeffrey S. Green]

Ecology

Continued

contributed up to 7 metric tons (6 short tons) of iron to Lake Tahoe in a single year. The scientists attributed the large annual flow of iron and other metals into the lake as evidence of watershed erosion caused by resort development and homebuilding, as well as by skiing and other recreational activities. This erosion also added enough nitrogen and phosphorus to the lake to stimulate the growth of algae and other forms of plankton, especially during spring.

The Davis ecologists concluded that eutrophication in Lake Tahoe is accelerating and that nitrogen concentrations would double in about 100 years if nitrogen continued to be added at the current rate. This increase would cause algae to spread over the entire lake, turning it a pea-green color. The algae would be most heavily concentrated along the shoreline, which would affect swimming, camping, and other shoreline activities.

Stream nutrition studies, like those of lake nutrition, require that scientists identify and analyze the most important factors nourishing life in the stream. Ecologists Ann G. Durbin, Scott W. Dixon, and Candace A. Oviatt of the University of Rhode Island reported in 1979 on the effects of the migration of spawning alewives on freshwater-stream ecosystems.

Ecologists have suspected that the carcasses of migratory fish are a significant source of nutrients to the lakes and streams where the fish spawn. On the East Coast, great numbers of alewives (*Alosa pseudoharengus*) migrate each year into large rivers, such as the St. John, the Connecticut, and the Potomac, and thousands of these fish also enter smaller brooks and streams.

Like salmon, alewives return from the sea to the streams in which they were born for spawning. Adult alewives do not feed in freshwater streams, but breed and die there.

To simulate natural stream conditions, the ecologists filled six concrete tanks, each measuring 7.6 x 2.4 x 0.55 meters (24 x 7 x 1.8 feet), with stream water, covering the bottoms of the tanks with a 5-centimeter (2-inch) layer of leaf litter. They stocked three of the

Ecology

A researcher at Oak Ridge National Laboratory in Tennessee takes a water sample from a research channel stocked with aquatic plants and animals. The simulated stream is part of a study on an ecosystem's ability to recover from pollution.

tanks with 20 mature alewives from the spawning migration and used three tanks as controls.

As stream plants grow, they convert carbohydrates to energy and release oxygen, some of which is consumed by alewives and other forms of animal life. The net release of oxygen is a measure of the system's respiration and growth.

The scientists calculated the respiration rate by determining hourly changes in oxygen levels in the water over a 24-hour period. They found that the respiration rates of the alewife tanks were about 2.5 times higher.

The scientists observed that 30 to 40 per cent of the alewives died in the first four weeks after stocking — a mortality rate similar to that in natural spawning runs. They did not remove the dead fish but allowed the carcasses to remain in the tanks. They concluded that the decomposing alewife carcasses, plus their eggs, sperm, and feces, provided additional nutrients that increased rates of growth and respiration.

The fish also had several short-term effects on the water. The researchers noted a two- to three-week temporary increase in ammonia and phosphate levels accompanied by an increase in phytoplankton growth in the fish tanks but not in the control tanks. Bacteria and other microorganisms in the leaf litter also increased shortly after the fish were added, and were sustained throughout the two-month spawning run. The growth rate of microorganisms was 2.5 times greater in the alewife tanks than in the controls.

The team concluded that the most important result of the alewife spawning migration may be its ability to provide nitrogen and phosphorus that increase the growth of periphyton and bacteria on the leaf surfaces. By increasing the growth of periphyton in the leaf litter, an alewife migration increases the number of small organisms that contribute to the overall food production of a lake. The increased numbers of bacteria speed up the breakdown of autumn leaves that choke many small streams and lakes in the spring, reducing the rate at which sediment is deposited in lakes.

Ecology

Continued

Ecologists Jackson R. Webster and Bernard C. Patten of the University of Georgia reported in the spring of 1979 on how the disturbance of watershed plant life influences stream ecosystems. This work studied two elements essential to life — potassium and calcium — in two streams. The watersheds of both streams were once hardwood forests that had been cut down. One watershed was replanted with grass and the other with white pine. The ecologists compared these studies with information collected from a stream with an unaltered hardwood forest watershed.

Webster and Patten found that the streams draining the altered watersheds processed nutrients less efficiently than the other stream. Organic and inorganic materials from these altered watersheds passed through the streams too rapidly to be broken down. These streams also had larger populations of crayfish and smaller populations of stream-dwelling insects. Because the hardwood trees had been replaced by grasses or pines, there was no autumn leaf fall to increase the amount of plant litter in the streams. Therefore, the litter available to insects that lay eggs in autumn was greatly reduced.

Crayfish, which do not depend on increased plant litter during the autumn, seemed better adapted to the more uniform year-round litter supply. Webster and Patten pointed to this population shift as an example of the tendency of animals that can survive in a variety of conditions to dominate altered ecosystems, and of those that thrive only in one set of conditions to dominate unaltered ecosystems.

Webster and Patten also found that changing the types of plants in the watersheds of the two streams had little effect on the amount of potassium and calcium in them, and that, aside from the predominance of crayfish, the streams in the altered watersheds differed only slightly from the stream in the unaltered watershed. They concluded that streams recover quickly after any watershed changes because of the rapid turnover of material and the ability of stream life to adapt to new conditions.   [Stanley I. Auerbach]

Electronics

New electrical circuits for synthesizing and recognizing the human voice highlighted developments in electronics in 1979 and 1980. Synthesis of speech is a complex process that requires a large amount of computer logic and memory to simulate the vocal tract and reproduce the voice in electronic form.

But systems that do this are becoming economically possible due to advances in large-scale integration (LSI). This manufacturing technique produces circuits containing tens of thousands of transistors on a silicon chip less than 0.6 centimeter (¼ inch) square. The new speech-synthesis circuits have found their way into electronic aids for the blind, spelling-instruction machines, and even toys and games.

In the latest use of a speech-synthesis chip, Texas Instruments, Incorporated (TI) of Dallas introduced a vocal language translator in May 1979. TI has applied its speech chip to a visual-display language translator — a battery-powered unit resembling a calculator that displays English words and their foreign equivalents. The result is a handheld device that not only translates and displays foreign words and phrases, but also speaks them in the foreign tongue. The TI translator has a 1,000-word vocabulary, of which 500 are pronounced as well as displayed.

The voice synthesizer relies on a technique called linear predictive coding to simulate the vocal tract from data stored in a read-only memory. Data compression methods used in the design limit the data rate to 1,200 bits per second. This results in low fidelity, but permits all of the translator's 1,000-word vocabulary to be in a 500,000-bit memory on just four chips.

Different techniques for synthesizing speech are used by Telesensory Systems, Incorporated, of Palo Alto, Calif., a firm that makes electronic products for the blind. Telesensory Systems announced a text-reading device in October 1979 with a vocabulary that can be programmed. The device is used in conjunction with an optical character-reading device that interprets letters and numbers on a page.

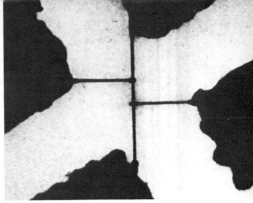

Concentrated area of bubble domains in a magnetic film, *left,* marks the path of a laser beam that reduced domain width from 16 to 7 micrometers, doubling the storage capacity. Another achievement in miniaturizing the world of electronics is experimental circuit elements, *above,* less than 200 atomic diameters thick — much smaller than human nerve fibers. The circuits are used in superconductivity tests.

Electronics

Continued

Words are produced in the text reader by stringing together phonemes, the basic elements of speech. This text-to-speech system produces as many as 200 English words a minute.

Voice recognition, the other side of the speech coin, is a much more difficult task to accomplish electronically. However, a relatively simple system was introduced by Dialog Systems, Incorporated, of New York City in June 1979. It is intended for applications where data must be entered into a computer over the phone by humans, primarily bank customers. The system has a vocabulary of 12 words — the 10 digits "zero" through "nine," plus "yes" and "no."

Despite its limited vocabulary, the device is complex because it is speaker-independent. It must work regardless of variations in a voice, such as accents or vocal pitch. The Dialog Systems device works by comparing the frequency content of a spoken word with a reference word that is derived statistically from 500 dialect samples of male and female speakers across the United States. This comparison takes only 30 microseconds.

An advance in speech recognition was announced by International Business Machines (IBM) Corporation's Thomas J. Watson Research Laboratory in Yorktown Heights, N.Y., in April 1980. The continuous speech-recognition group, under the direction of engineer Frederick Jelinek, programmed a computer to produce a printed output of sentences with up to 25 words. The sentences are constructed from a 1,000-word vocabulary. The experimental system has an accuracy of 91 per cent, and can handle continuous speech, spoken at a natural rate. But it is speaker-dependent, and slow. The computer must listen to the speaker for two hours to "learn" the voice.

Even after the system has learned to recognize a voice, it still takes about 200 times longer to recognize a sentence than to speak it. In other words, 100 minutes of computer time are necessary to transcribe only 30 seconds of speech. But IBM expects to develop an experimental dictation machine from

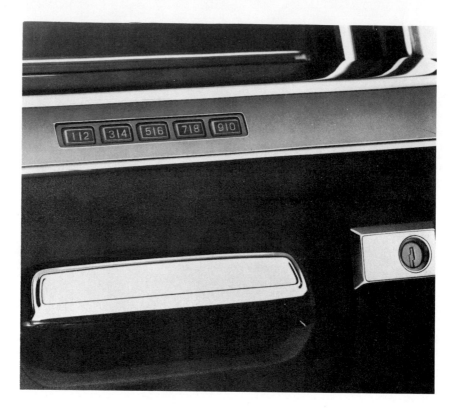

Electronic security in the parking lot is offered by a computer push-button system for automobile doors. Any sequence of numbers can be programmed that will lock and unlock the doors and trunk lid.

Electronics

Continued

this primitive prototype that can recognize 1,000 to 2,000 words and requires only 15 minutes of speaker-training time. A real-time system – where the printed output follows almost immediately after the spoken word – should be possible before the end of the 1980s.

A commercial version of this experimental system would probably use a speaker-activated video-display terminal on which the user could check the copy and correct it, perhaps with a light pen, before producing the printed letter or memo.

Radio frequency (rf) radiation may become a therapy to fight disease. Researchers at the Memorial Sloan Kettering Cancer Center in New York City discovered a way to use microwaves to treat certain cancers in 1979. Jal Ho Kim and his associates combined microwave radiation with ionizing-radiation therapy, such as X rays or cobalt rays, in treating malignant melanoma, a type of tumor known for its resistance to ionizing radiation.

Microwave radiation had previously been used to detect cancers. All human tissue emits microwave radiation whose frequency is proportional to the temperature of the tissue. Tumors are warmer than surrounding tissue. As early as 1974, Philip C. Myers and Alan H. Barrett of the Department of Physics at the Massachusetts Institute of Technology in Cambridge, Mass., detected tumors with 1.3 and 3.3 gigahertz microwaves in clinical tests.

Such a detection system uses a radiometer – a device that detects microwaves similar to the way a radio receiver detects them. The radiometer's antenna is a piece of rectangular wave guide or pipe that is pressed flush against the skin. The intensity of the microwave emission is compared with that of a temperature standard to provide an extremely accurate reading – within 0.1°C – of the thermal equivalent. This method is more accurate than infrared-measuring systems, such as thermography. Combining infrared with microwave detection results in a testing system that can pinpoint as many cancers as can X rays, but without the potential hazard.

Electronics

Continued

Microwaves, as well as other radio frequencies, fight cancer with a technique called hyperthermia, or fever therapy. This therapy has been used for a long time in the form of hot baths and other direct heat treatments. It is based on the simple technique of heating a body to a temperature that normal cells can withstand but cancer cells cannot.

Rf hyperthermia has advantages over other heating methods because it permits good temperature control and because its effect can be localized to the area of the tumors. Moreover, it can be used in many cases where ionizing-radiation therapy, with its frequent side effects ranging from nausea to hair loss, cannot. Sometimes it is even more effective than the ionizing radiation in killing or reducing tumors.

Kim treated two groups of cancer patients—one with the combined therapies and the other with ionizing radiation alone. The second group acted as an experimental control.

Kim heated the patients' tumorous tissues with 27.12 megahertz microwaves to a minimum of 42.4°C. After holding the tissue at this temperature for 30 minutes, he began the ionizing-radiation therapy. Six months after this combined therapy, 16 of 18 tumors in nine patients had "completely responded," but only 1 of 8 tumors treated with radiation alone had responded.

The $117,000 units combine a microprocessor-controlled rf system with cathode-ray-tube displays and a paper printout of experimental data. The rf system ranges in frequency from 10 to 2,500 megahertz, making it possible for the researcher to control the depth of the rf penetration, and thus the depth of the heating. Lower frequencies penetrate more deeply; the higher ones are restricted to areas near the surface of the body.

To monitor the temperature in a tumor, the medical researcher implants a thermistor, a device whose electrical resistance changes with change in temperature. The signal from this thermistor is fed to the microprocessor, which regulates the temperature to within 0.1°C.   [Raymond P. Capece]

Energy

Scientists in the energy field experimented in 1979 and 1980 with ways to make better use of coal. About 75 per cent of the energy consumed in the United States during 1979 was provided by petroleum and natural gas, while less than 20 per cent came from coal. Yet coal is the most abundant resource in the United States while petroleum and natural gas are the least abundant. So a major objective of the U.S. program to become energy independent is to produce clean fuels from coal.

To accomplish this objective, two innovative coal-gasification programs —underground coal gasification and solar coal gasification— were initiated by scientists of the Lawrence Livermore National Laboratory (LLNL) in California, in 1979. In addition, one of the largest and most advanced plants for converting coal into synthetic oil was dedicated in February 1980.

It's a gas. Coal is gasified in a reaction with steam or carbon dioxide at high temperatures. The high temperature is normally provided by burning part of the coal with either air or pure oxygen. An LLNL team conducted an experiment in underground coal gasification at Hoe Creek, Wyoming, between August and November 1979.

The experimenters burned almost 3,630 metric tons (4,000 short tons) of coal underground to produce about 5.6 million cubic meters (200 million cubic feet) of gas. The gas consisted of methane, hydrogen, and carbon monoxide. This mixture is suitable for heating homes and generating electricity or for use in various industrial processes.

The scientists ignited the underground coal by lowering an electrical igniter 61 meters (200 feet) into the coal seam. During the first seven days of the experiment, high-pressure air was pumped underground to aid combustion. This produced a gas mixture with a heating value of 115 British Thermal Units per standard cubic foot (B.T.U./scf), approximately 11 per cent that of natural gas. (Standard cubic foot refers to gas volume at sea-level pressure and room temperature.)

Subsequently, a rich mixture of pure oxygen and steam was used to feed the

271

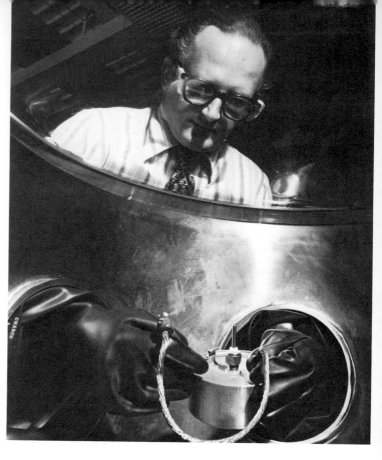

A General Motors technician checks lightweight zinc-nickel oxide batteries, *above,* being repeatedly charged and discharged by automatic testing units to determine if they will last long enough for use in an electric car. Another car-battery candidate, a lithium-iron sulfide battery, *right,* is opened inside a glove box to prevent its chemicals from reacting with moisture and oxygen in the air.

Energy

Continued

flame. With this technique, the heating value of the gas was increased to 218 B.T.U./scf. The scientists considered the initial tests of the coal gasification concept successful. They planned additional tests for 1981 at a site with a thick coal seam covered by dry clay stone or sandstone, which will produce higher-quality gas.

A series of solar coal-gasification experiments were conducted during the fall of 1979 by a team of LLNL scientists led by chemical engineer David W. Gregg, inventor of the solar coal-gasification process.

The advantage of the solar process is that the heat required for the chemical reaction is supplied by solar energy. In this system, the coal is not burned, and so the amount of gas produced per ton of coal is greatly increased. In addition, expensive pure oxygen is not required.

For his experiment, Gregg used the 30,000-watt solar furnace at White Sands Missile Range in New Mexico. In the solar furnace, an array of 356 mirrors automatically track and reflect the sun onto a fixed-focus mirror. The mirror focused the "captured" sunlight onto a 13-centimeter (5-inch)-diameter spot on a window in a chamber, and the concentrated beam heated the coal inside the chamber. Gregg and his team added steam to react with the coal, producing gas with a heating value of 300 B.T.U./scf.

A coal-liquefaction pilot plant based on the Exxon Corporation's Donor Solvent Process was dedicated in Baytown, Tex., in February 1980. In this process, coal reacts with hydrogen at temperatures of 427° to 482°C (800° to 880°F.) and pressures between 105 and 175 kilograms per square centimeter (1,500 and 2,500 pounds per square inch). Under these conditions, the densely packed molecular structure of coal breaks down, allowing hydrogen atoms to attach to the molecules. The coal begins to liquefy as the amount of hydrogen increases. The hydrogen is supplied by a liquid solvent in the presence of a catalyst, a chemical agent that regulates the reaction. The solvent is added to a liquefaction vessel, where it "donates" hydrogen to the coal.

Energy

At full operation, the plant can process up to 227 million metric tons (250-million short tons) of coal to produce more than 600 barrels of synthetic oil per day. The oil can be used directly as boiler fuel or can be upgraded to gasoline. The pilot plant will operate for about 2½ years and the technical data collected will be used to design commercial plants for the late 1980s.

The world's largest wind turbine generator went into operation in July 1979 at Boone, N.C. The Blue Ridge Electric Membership Corporation operates the wind turbine for the U.S. Department of Energy (DOE). The Boone turbine has a propeller-type rotor 61 meters (200 feet) in diameter mounted on a tower 43 meters (140 feet) above ground. An automatic control system monitors wind direction so that the rotor is always aligned with the wind.

The turbine is designed to operate at a constant 35 revolutions per minute (rpm) in wind speeds between 18 and 56 kilometers per hour (kph) or 11 and 35 miles per hour (mph). If the wind speed is less than 18 kph or greater than 56 kph, the rotor blades are automatically adjusted to shut down the system. At wind speeds between 40 and 56 kph (25 and 35 mph), the wind-turbine generator can produce 2 megawatts of electricity. This is the amount of electricity used by 500 homes.

But in April 1980, the DOE restricted the operation of the Boone wind-turbine generator because it was creating a low-frequency sound. Although the sound frequency is below the range of human hearing, Boone residents complained of an irritating "swish-swish" noise. The DOE planned first to decrease the speed of the rotor from 35 to 23 rpm. If this does not eliminate the noise, then the steel rotor blades will be replaced by fiberglass blades.

A cluster of three 2.5-megawatt wind turbines were under construction in 1980 in a windy gorge of the Columbia River in the state of Washington. The rotors, 91.5 meters (300 feet) in diameter and mounted atop a 61-meter (200-foot) tower, will rotate when the wind speed reaches 16 kph (10 mph) and will supply enough electricity for 2,000

The largest magnet for a magnetohydrodynamic electric-power generator is prepared for testing at a U.S. Air Force engineering center in Tennessee. The magnet will generate current in ionized combustion gases from fossil fuels.

homes. These tests are being conducted to determine whether wind-turbine generators can provide reliable electrical generation over an extended period of time at a cost competitive with coal and nuclear power.

Electric car. DOE introduced an advanced four-passenger, subcompact experimental car in June 1979. Electric Test Vehicle One (ETV-1) has a range of about 113 kilometers (70 miles) in stop-and-go traffic and more than 185 kilometers (115 miles) at a constant speed of 56 kph (35 mph). General Electric Company, the prime contractor for the project, developed the electrical drive system. Chrysler Corporation was responsible for styling, body construction, and vehicle testing, while Globe Union, Incorporated, designed and built the high-energy batteries that power the vehicle.

The car has 18 lead-acid batteries and its own battery charger. The batteries can be charged in 10 hours using a wall outlet. They can be recharged an estimated 500 times. According to the DOE, the ETV-1 was designed to be mass-produced for about $6,400 (in 1979 dollars) by 1985.

Better bulbs. General Electric announced in July 1979 the development of the halarc bulb, a radically new gaseous-discharge light bulb for home use. General Electric plans to market a two-way halarc bulb in 1981 to replace the standard three-way incandescent bulb. The halarc bulb provides the same amount of light as an incandescent bulb, which produces light as a result of electrical resistance in a wire filament. But the halarc bulb uses only one-third as much electricity as the incandescent one. In addition, the new bulbs are expected to last at least five times longer than incandescent bulbs.

The halarc bulb is a miniature version of the metal halide lamps used in parking lots and sports stadiums. Since the halarc bulb takes 30 seconds to heat up fully, it contains two incandescent filaments for the initial lighting. However, these are shut off when the bulb is in full operation. The octagon-shaped bulb is designed to fit standard incandescent sockets. [Marian Visich, Jr.]

Environment

The disposal of synthetic chemicals in the United States continued to present the most pressing environmental problems of 1979 and 1980. Much of the waste from manufacturing and chemical production processes cannot be degraded naturally and has begun to appear in ground water used for drinking-water supplies near waste-disposal sites. Substantial numbers of these compounds are known or suspected *carcinogens* (cancer-causing substances) or have other toxic effects.

On May 21, 1980, President Jimmy Carter declared the Love Canal waste-disposal site in Niagara Falls, N.Y., a federal emergency area. His action came after medical tests revealed that some residents of the area had suffered chromosomal damage, a condition that is often linked with cancer and birth defects. The Enviromental Protection Agency (EPA) disavowed the study on May 27 because it was not done under properly controlled conditions.

The Hooker Chemicals and Plastics Corporation had buried thousands of barrels of toxic materials at this site between 1947 and 1953, covered them with a clay cap a few meters deep, and sold the land to the city of Niagara Falls. Homes and a school were later built on the site. In 1976, heavy rains forced some of these toxic materials to the surface and area residents began to report increased health problems.

In the emergency declaration, the United States government allotted up to $5 million to evacuate 710 families from the Love Canal area and provide temporary housing for them. These relocation charges would be added to the $124.5-million damage suit that the U.S. Department of Justice had filed against Hooker on Dec. 20, 1979. The suit, the largest environmental damage award ever sought by the U.S. government, asks compensation for the effects of dumping at Love Canal and three other Niagara Falls sites.

Unfortunately, such careless disposal practices have proved to be the rule, rather than the exception, throughout the United States. By Jan. 31, 1980, the EPA had identified 4,598 spots as potentially hazardous waste-disposal sites.

Environment

Continued

Great balls of fire shoot into the sky over Elizabeth, N.J., *below,* as drums of toxic and volatile chemicals explode in a warehouse in April. Water brought the blaze under control, *below right,* but rising smoke and fumes blanketed a 24 kilometer (15-mile) area.

Through a survey of the 53 largest chemical companies, a House of Representatives commerce subcommittee determined in 1979 that 700 million metric tons of chemical wastes have been dumped in 3,383 sites since 1950.

J. Gustave Speth, chairman of the Council on Environmental Quality, believes that ground-water contamination by toxic chemicals is a matter of special concern. Unlike air quality and surface-water quality, which are holding constant or improving, ground-water quality is decreasing, and regulations for its control are seriously inadequate. The EPA reported on April 25, 1980, that an assessment of 8,000 surface chemical-storage sites revealed that 30 per cent are potential sources of ground-water pollution. Wells in Grey, Me.; Hartford, Conn.; and Lincoln, R.I., were found to contain compounds which are suspected carcinogens.

Justice Department officials announced in April 1980 that they would begin taking action against corporate polluters. They planned to bring 100 suits in 1980, at least half of which involve sites as severely contaminated as Love Canal. In addition to financial-damage awards and cleanup costs, the Justice Department has begun to seek criminal penalties.

The EPA finally issued regulations instituting a system to track hazardous wastes as they move from the producer to the disposal site. The first regulations were announced on Feb. 19, 1980, more than two years after they were due under the terms of the Resource Conservation and Recovery Act (RCRA) of 1976. Other regulations set labeling and transportation requirements and defined operating standards for disposal sites. The EPA estimates that 90 per cent of the 57 million tons of waste produced annually in the United States are disposed of improperly. If producers meet the new RCRA standards, their current disposal costs of between $1.50 and $5 per ton will rise to about $50 per ton.

However, the availability of legal dump sites may be a more serious obstacle to proper waste disposal than the tenfold increase in disposal costs.

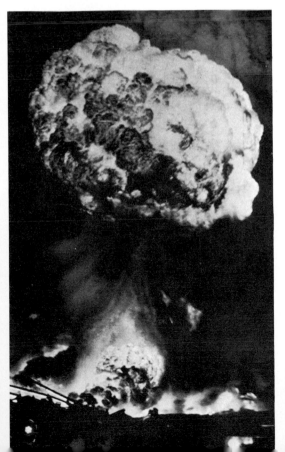

Rain Today? It Can Be Deadly

A scientist examines plants exposed to acid rain in a rainmaker room at Oak Ridge National Laboratory in Tennessee.

"Acid rain is literally the rain of death." This grim description by Canada's Environment Minister John Roberts underlies a concern shared with the United States Environmental Protection Agency (EPA) and with environmental officials in all the industrialized nations of the world. Although this pollution problem has received widespread public attention only since 1979, deposits of acid from the atmosphere have been increasing since the Industrial Revolution in the 1800s.

Acid rain — or acid snow — results from sulfates and nitrates in the atmosphere that change to sulfuric and nitric acids and combine with raindrops or snowflakes. Although sulfates and nitrates can enter the atmosphere from natural sources, their dramatic increase in recent years is caused by the ever-growing combustion of fossil fuels in automobiles, furnaces, and power plants. Some oils and coals are contaminated with significant amounts of sulfur, which forms sulfur dioxide when the fuel is burned. In addition, burning fossil fuels converts atmospheric nitrogen to nitrogen oxides. Further oxidation forms sulfates and nitrates. These can fall in dry form. Or the sulfates and nitrates can combine with ice or water droplets in clouds, making the precipitation highly acidic.

Scientists specify acidity in pH units, a measurement of hydrogen ion concentration. The pH scale runs from 14 (highly basic) to 0 (highly acidic). Pure water would be at the neutral midpoint, pH7. A drop in one pH number equals a tenfold increase in acidity.

Most rain water is normally slightly acidic because carbonic acid, created from carbon dioxide in the atmosphere, lowers the pH of "pure" rain to about 5.6. But by 1955, precipitation averaging below pH4.5 was falling in the New England states, Ohio, Pennsylvania, West Virginia, and New York. Since then, the area affected by acid rain has expanded to include most of the continental United States east of the Mississippi River. Precipitation between pH3 and pH4 is now observed routinely in New England.

Acid rain is seriously disturbing the ecology of many lakes when the surrounding soils and rocks cannot neutralize the acid. Some lakes in the affected areas have become 100 times more acidic than they were 40 years ago. Fish can no longer survive in more than 100 lakes in the Adirondack Mountains of New York, and fish in 40,000 Canadian lakes are endangered. The acid also interferes with the food chain in lakes by slowing bacterial decomposition of natural organic materials such as leaves. Increasing acidity in drinking water from the lakes may subject people to lead poisoning by corroding lead water pipes.

In the United States, the EPA and many citizens' environmental groups have assigned a high priority to the acid rain problem in response to the government's approach to the current energy shortage. President Jimmy Carter's plan to make the United States less dependent on foreign oil calls for the mandatory conversion of power plants from oil- or natural gas-burning to coal-burning operations. The plan is expected to increase acid rainfall by 10 to 15 per cent in the United States.

The EPA requires that new coal-burning power plants use flue-gas desulfurization units, or scrubbers, to remove 70 to 90 per cent of the sulfur from their emissions. But old plants, especially in the Midwest, are not covered by the regulations, and they may continue to operate for 20 to 30 years.

Another problem is the height of smokestacks. For example, the U.S. Clean Air Act requires sulfur dioxide control only when a plant's emissions exceed air-pollution standards in its immediate vicinity. Thus, utilities are encouraged to use tall stacks. The sulfur oxides and nitrogen oxides are sent high into the air where the wind can carry them long distances. This converts a national problem into an international problem, setting state against state, and government against government. Canada and the United States have held inconclusive talks on acid rain. Although some pollutants from Canada reach the United States, the flow is mostly the other way.

Proposed solutions to the acid rain problem are costly and controversial. But acid rain may be an irreversible threat to the world environment. It presents industrialized nations with a clear test of their dedication to environmental quality.   [Harold R. Ward]

Environment

Continued

Because of such well-known pollution cases as the Love Canal site, local communities are understandably unwilling to tolerate chemical waste dumps within their boundaries. By May 1980, there were no longer any legal chemical landfills in the entire New England area. Because of local resistance, federal intervention may be necessary to designate certain sites for hazardous-waste-disposal facilities. In the meantime, the incentive for illegal disposal grows even stronger.

Oil spills in ocean waters reached record proportions in 1979 for the third consecutive year. One spill alone surpassed the 260,000 tons spilled in all of 1978. This spill of 292,000 tons of oil resulted when two supertankers, *Aegean Captain* and *Atlantic Empress* collided on July 19, 1979, in the Caribbean. Tanker accidents in the first nine months of 1979 accounted for a total of 513,000 metric tons of spilled oil.

Tanker spills were overshadowed, however, by the world's largest oil spill in the Campeche Bay in the Gulf of Mexico. Ixtoc 1, a well drilled by Pemex, the Mexican national company, blew out on June 3, 1979, and discharged more than 556,000 tons of crude oil before it was finally capped on March 24, 1980.

Mexican and American technicians made several unsuccessful attempts to cap the well. Attempts to fill the well with canvas plugs and to cover the leak with a giant steel cone-shaped oil-collection "sombrero" reduced, but did not halt, the oil flow. However, relief wells lessened the oil pressure in the main well sufficiently to allow technicians to pump three plugs of liquid cement down the well shaft to seal it.

Technicians also tried to limit the spread of the oil slick and skim the oil off the water but strong ocean currents spread the oil in spite of their efforts. However, surface fires burned away large amounts of the oil, and detergents dispersed slicks that approached the Mexican shore. Some oil hit Texas beaches in August, but a change in winter currents kept most of the oil in the water to the south. The National Oceanic and Atmospheric Administration initiated studies due to be reported in September 1980 of the overall ecological effects of the spill. See WATCH ON THE SELF-HEALING EARTH.

Greenhouse effect. The President's Committee on Health and Environmental Effects of Increased Coal Utilization in 1979 identified two major global environmental problems. One is acid precipitation and the other is the increased emissions of carbon dioxide (CO_2) and the resulting effect on world climate (see Close-Up). George M. McDonald, author of a National Academy of Sciences (NAS) study released in July, identified the problem as "one of the most critical that will face mankind in the next decade."

The study predicts that the continued use of fossil fuels at the current rate will have produced an atmosphere by 2005 in which concentrations of CO_2 in the atmosphere are twice as high as they were in the 1700s.

Atmospheric CO_2 absorbs infrared radiation and reflects it back to warm the earth in a greenhouse effect. The higher concentration of CO_2 will increase average world temperatures by 1° to 2° C and is expected to have the greatest effects at the poles. According to such forecasts, polar icecaps would then melt and raise the sea level, inundating many coastal cities. These changes would shift agriculturally productive areas close to the poles, benefiting some countries and harming others.

However, the greenhouse effect may be slightly offset by the aftereffects of the eruption of Mt. St. Helens in Washington that began on May 18, 1980. Some observers predicted that volcanic particles discharged into the atmosphere might temporarily lower temperatures around the world.

Unfortunately, technological advances will probably not reduce CO_2 emissions because "clean" burning, which increases the efficiency of fossil fuels and reduces other pollutants, also increases CO_2 production. The only practical way to control CO_2 emissions is to reduce consumption of fossil fuels, either by conserving energy or by using such alternative sources as solar and wind energy. [Harold R. Ward]

Genetics

Certain genes can jump, or change location, on chromosomes. Geneticists Edward Strobel, Pamela Dunsmuir, and Gerald M. Rubin of Harvard Medical School reported this discovery in June 1979.

Chromosomes are tiny threadlike objects in the cell nucleus that carry the genes, the bearers of hereditary information. Each chromosome has about 1,000 genes lined up end to end, and most genes do not change their position on the chromosome. But the "jumping genes" are frequently found in different positions. Strobel, Dunsmuir, and Rubin discovered that different but normal strains of fruit flies have two genes, called copia and 297, at different locations on their chromosomes.

These genes were first discovered in fruit flies in 1976 by Rubin, then at Stanford University in California, and his associates, David Finnegan and David S. Hogness. But at that time the scientists had no idea the genes could move. The researchers singled them out because they possessed another strange characteristic.

Most genes occur only once in each sperm or egg cell, but copia and 297 fruit fly genes — and nearly 20 others — occur many times. For example, in a laboratory fruit fly strain developed from specimens originally collected at a fruit market in Roseburg, Ore., in 1925, copia is present in each sperm or egg cell 28 times and 297 is present 21 times. The unusual genes are called "dispersed repeated gene families."

The Harvard researchers used *in situ* (in place) hybridization, a technique invented in the late 1960s at Yale University by geneticists Mary Lou Pardue and Joseph G. Gall. In situ hybridization takes advantage of giant chromosomes found only in certain glands of immature fruit flies. When cells from these glands are mixed with a special stain and looked at through the microscope, the giant chromosomes — identical to normal fruit fly chromosomes except in size — are found to have dark-staining bands across them. Each of these dark bands corresponds to a single gene and thus gives the position of that gene.

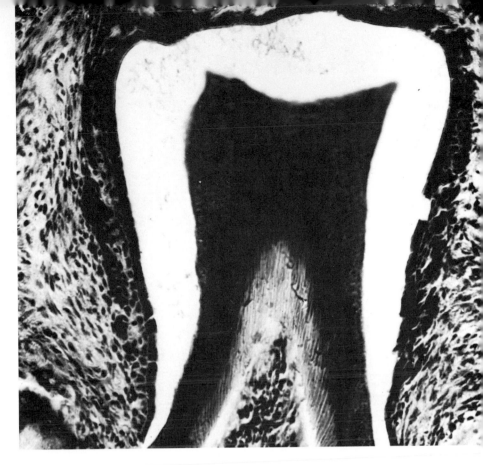

A tooth, which grew from tissue taken from a chicken embryo and implanted in a mouse, resembles the teeth of reptiles, the ancestors of birds. This suggests that birds' tooth-making genes were suppressed, not lost, as birds evolved.

Genetics

Continued

Pardue and Gall found a method to pair up deoxyribonucleic acid (DNA) — the chemical that makes up all genes — of a fruit fly gene with the corresponding band in the chromosome. The scientists dip a glass slide holding the stained chromosomes into a solution containing radioactive DNA. The DNA attaches itself to its corresponding chromosome band on the glass slide.

When the slide is covered with photographic film, the radioactivity darkens the film over the chromosome band, much as light would cause the film to darken. Under the microscope, all the chromosome bands are still visible, but there is a group of black spots over the chromosome band that paired up with the radioactive DNA. These spots mark the position of the gene being studied.

Strobel, Dunsmuir, and Rubin used in situ hybridization of DNA to find the positions of the copia and 297 genes on the chromosomes of several strains of fruit flies. All fruit flies have four chromosomes — the X chromosome, which determines sex, and chromosomes 2, 3, and 4.

The researchers examined the position of the copia genes in the Oregon strain and found 28 copies of the gene — 2 on the X chromosome, 11 on chromosome 2, 15 on chromosome 3, and none on chromosome 4. Then they examined the copia genes in a strain called Canton, which had originally been collected near Canton, Ohio, in the 1920s. To their surprise, they found that the Canton strain has only 18 copies of the copia gene — none on the X chromosome, 12 on chromosome 2, 6 on chromosome 3, and none on chromosome 4. In fact, every strain that they examined had a different number of copia genes, ranging from 18 to 43.

The investigators were even more surprised to find that the copia genes occupied different positions on the chromosomes in each strain. Of four strains examined, only one copia gene, on chromosome 2, was in the same position in all four strains. Nor were these unexpected results unique to the copia gene. The number of copies of the

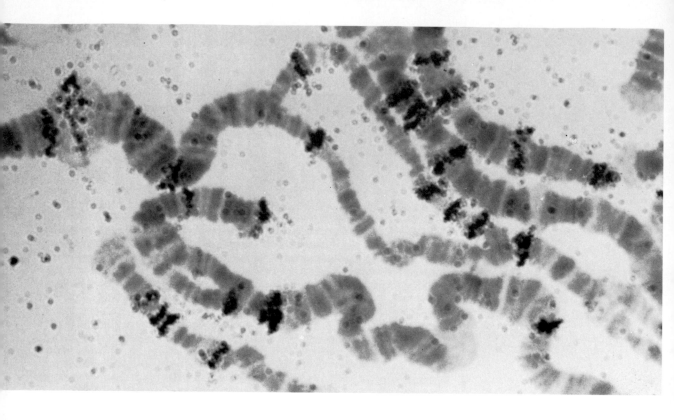

Genetics

Continued

Dark, radioactive hot spots mark the locations of the repeating 412 gene on the banded chromosomes of a hybrid strain of fruit flies. Unlike other genes, the newly discovered 412 may be found in different locations on the chromosomes of different strains of fruit flies.

297 genes in the four strains ranged from 20 to 30, and only four of these genes were found at the same chromosomal position in all four strains.

At first, the researchers did not know how much importance to attach to their finding. After all, the strains had been originally collected in such widely separated parts of the world as North America, Japan, and Sweden. The differences could have merely represented genetic drift — random changes due, in this case, to geographic separation.

However, further studies revealed differences among individual fruit flies from the same strain. Among seven individuals from the Oregon strain, for example, the number of copia genes ranged from 25 to 32, and the researchers found many differences in the chromosomal position of the copia genes. Copia genes can therefore increase or decrease in number, even within a single strain of flies. They can also change their position on the chromosomes from one individual to another.

Because they can change their number and position, these jumping genes represent a distinctive new class of genes in higher organisms. No one yet knows what function they perform or whether similar kinds of genes occur in other organisms, such as mice or human beings.

Some DNA veers left. A new form for the DNA molecule was described by a number of X-ray crystallographers in December 1979. Since its discovery in the 1950s, the DNA molecule has been visualized as a double helix, a two-stranded, ladderlike series of atoms that twists to the right. Studies by Struther Arnott of Purdue University in West Lafayette, Ind.; Alexander Rich of Massachusetts Institute of Technology in Cambridge, Mass.; and others, reveal that some DNA molecules twist to the left. Moreover, they do so in a more disorderly, zigzag fashion than do the right-handed molecules of DNA.

The scientists do not know how common this DNA type is, but they believe that some features of its structure may be important in gene regulation. See BIOCHEMISTRY. [Daniel L. Hartl]

Geoscience

Geochemistry. Studies of rocks from Greenland in 1979 and 1980 have shed some new light on the earth's early geochemical history and how the earth's oxygen-rich atmosphere was created. These studies have led geochemists to believe that about 3.8 billion years ago — only about 700 million years after the formation of the solar system — there was an abundance of primitive life forms, such as bacteria, on earth.

In fact, these primitive life forms accounted for approximately as much organic matter on the earth then as there is today. These organisms were able to manufacture carbohydrates by photosynthesis, chemical reactions in which plants use sunlight to make food from inorganic compounds, such as carbon dioxide and water.

Geoscientists have gained insight into the natural relationship between the waste products of photosynthesis and the evolution of life by studying ancient rocks found at Isua, Greenland, in the narrow band of ice-free land between the sea and the glacial icecap. Scientists have determined through radioactive dating that these rocks are the oldest known rocks on earth, about 3.8 billion years old.

The Isua rocks include iron ores that have bands, or layers, of minerals rich in oxidized iron. Geochemists generally agree that such iron formations occur only when that metal combines with oxygen gas.

Yet oxygen gas did not begin to accumulate in the atmosphere until about 2 billion years ago. Breathing oxygen, a chief characteristic of higher plants and animals, became possible only after the time that the earth's atmosphere contained a significant amount of oxygen.

Chemist Manfred Schidlowski, now at the University of California, Los Angeles, and his colleagues at the Max Planck Institute for Chemistry in Mainz, West Germany, discussed the oxygen question in two 1979 papers on the chemistry of the ancient Isua rocks. They showed that these oldest iron ores are similar in some ways to more recent rocks of the same general kind, but different in other ways. The differences provided clues to the formation of the atmosphere and the evolution of life.

Schidlowski and his co-workers studied carbon isotopes — atoms of carbon having the same atomic number but different atomic weights — in the Isua rocks. They measured the heavy isotope carbon-13 in relation to the more abundant light isotope carbon-12. The chemical properties of these substances are similar, but not identical.

Organic carbon produced by plant photosynthesis tends to have less carbon-13 than does the inorganic carbon of carbon dioxide found in the atmosphere or carbon combined with calcium in carbonate rocks, such as limestone. The scientists used this difference to compare the ancient rocks to those formed more recently. They found that the proportion of organic carbon to inorganic carbon in the 3.8-billion-year-old rocks was similar to that found in modern sediments. Thus, the researchers concluded that there must have been an abundance of primitive life forms producing gaseous oxygen through photosynthesis. However, they speculate that this oxygen may have immediately reacted with various minerals, such as iron, to form oxides, leaving no oxygen gas to accumulate in the atmosphere.

This conclusion fits well with the results of a study of heavy and light sulfur isotopes in the Isua rocks, which showed a major geochemical difference between the oldest and the more recent rocks. In this study, published in 1979 by chemist Jan Monster of McMaster University in Hamilton, Canada, in collaboration with five co-workers, there were large variations in the proportions of light and heavy sulfur isotopes in more recently formed iron ores. But the Isua rocks show very little of this difference in sulfur isotopes.

Laboratory studies showed that such large variation between heavy and light sulfur isotopes in rocks is caused by sulfate respiration by certain bacteria that obtain their energy from processing such chemicals. Because the Isua rocks do not vary much in light and heavy sulfur isotopes, Monster concluded that the process of oxidizing carbohydrates from sulfates had not yet evolved in a major way 3.8 billion years ago. However, ancient rocks from other areas showed that sulfate respiration was widespread at a somewhat later

Geoscience

Continued

time, about 2.7 billion years ago — still more than 700 million years before oxygen-breathing life forms evolved.

Together, these studies present a picture of the evolving history of the earth. They show that even as early as 3.8 billion years ago, there not only were organisms using photosynthesis to manufacture carbohydrates, but also bacteria that produced carbohydrates and sulfate by chemically processing carbon dioxide and hydrogen sulfide produced in volcanoes.

These waste products of photosynthesis began to build up as time went on, in a sense polluting the environment. The soluble sulfate accumulated in the seas, and by 2.7 billion years ago there was enough of it to aid organisms that had evolved chemical mechanisms for using it to oxidize carbohydrates similar to the way we use oxygen from the atmosphere to oxidize the food we eat. But when this use of sulfate began to be important, the atmosphere still contained little oxygen because there were many minerals to combine with this highly reactive gas. Finally, about 2 billion years ago, these rocks were oxidized enough for excess oxygen to accumulate in the atmosphere. Only then could higher forms of life evolve that, like ourselves, breathe oxygen.

Early oceans. In another investigation of the Isua rocks, geochemist Peter Appel of the Max Planck Institute of Chemistry reported in February 1980 on the rocks' low concentration of potassium relative to the chemically similar element sodium, compared with that in younger rocks of the same type. Iron ores deposited during the last 600 million years contain about eight times as much potassium as sodium, and most ores contain at least somewhat more potassium than sodium. By contrast, the Isua rocks were found to contain only about one-third as much potassium as sodium.

Scientists do not fully understand why there is less potassium than sodium in these rocks, but they think it says something important about the ancient environment in which the Isua rocks were formed. They know that ordinarily there is about 8 times as much

Geologist Gary A. Nowlan scrapes manganese deposits from a boulder in a stream in central Maine. Manganese, a valuable mineral, is usually found in nodules, or lumps, on the ocean floor, but nodules also occur in ponds and streams that form transition areas between freshwater streams and stagnant waters.

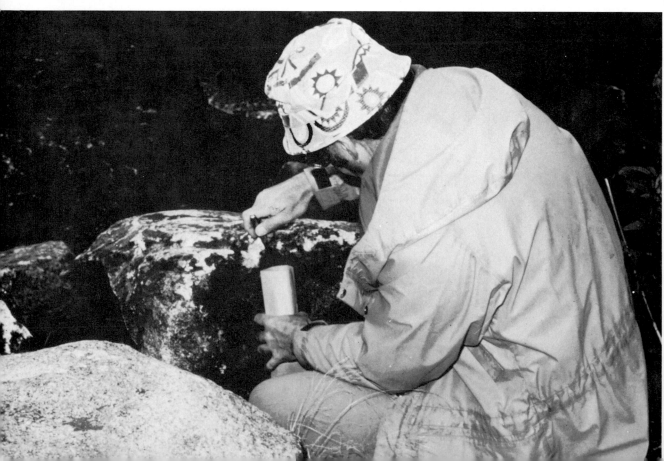

Geoscience
Continued

potassium as sodium in oceanic sediments, but the seawater that deposits these substances contains three times as much sodium as potassium. Sodium remains in solution, which is why seawater contains a high concentration of sodium chloride, or common salt. On the other hand, potassium clings to the surface of aluminum-rich clay particles that make up part of the oceanic sediments, and is not retained in seawater. However, the scientist noted that the Isua rocks have an unusually low concentration of aluminum.

Appel suggests that both the low ratio of potassium to sodium and the low aluminum concentrations indicate that continental land masses above sea level — the source of aluminum-rich clay particles today — were not yet present when the Isua rocks were formed. This theory suggests that there were large quantities of water on the earth's surface soon after its formation, and that the large elevated continents that we know today developed much later.

Earth scientists continue to investigate old rocks, such as those at Isua, and plan to compare them with ancient moon rocks and meteorites. These old rocks may unlock the secrets of the earth's earliest history.

Modern rock relics. Geochemist Lina Echeverria of the Carnegie Institution of Washington, D.C., reported in March 1980 that she had found komatiite, a magnesium-rich volcanic rock less than 60 million years old, on Gorgona Island off Colombia. Earth scientists formerly thought that all komatiites were at least 2.7 billion years old. They also presumed that komatiite flowed to the surface of the primitive earth in liquid form as a unique consequence of the high temperature of the earth at that time.

Komatiite was abundant in ancient lava flows and has an extremely high melting point. Although Echeverria's discovery indicates that the ancient environment was not unique, the abundance of this type of lava in ancient rocks suggests that the early earth was very hot. The discovery also provides earth scientists with the opportunity to study fresh and unaltered samples of komatiite, in contrast to the ancient rock samples that are in badly deteriorated condition. [George W. Wetherill]

Geology. Much research was reported in 1979 and 1980 on plate tectonics, documenting the way in which plates of the earth's lithosphere move slowly against one another. Progress was reported in understanding subduction, the sinking of one plate below another.

Earth scientists have generally viewed subduction as though the overriding plate is stationary and the subducting plate slides down an incline beneath the overriding plate into a slot in the mantle. New evidence points to subduction as the vertical sinking of one plate beneath an advancing, overriding plate. In the new view, trenches and other boundaries between plates are not fixed in the deep mantle, but themselves move with lithospheric plate movements.

One type of evidence for this direct sinking comes from the collision in progress of two plates over a third south of the Philippines. In a 1979 book on plate movements published by the U.S. Geological Survey (USGS), I described the movement of the Sangihe island arc on the west toward the Halmahera island arc advancing from the east. These island arcs are chains of volcanic islands formed above sinking lithospheric plates. Each arc is on the advancing edge of a plate, and the plates are moving toward each other.

The Molucca Sea Plate between the two island arcs is sinking beneath both island arcs and has bent into a broad "A" shape. As the Sangihe and Halmahera plates advanced toward each other, the Molucca Sea Plate sank on both sides, and the other two advancing plates overrode it.

The new ocean basins — regions of spreading sea floor — that open up behind island arcs also provide evidence of subducting plates sinking. As an island arc advances over a sinking lithosphere plate, new sea floor is created by spreading behind the advancing arc. In extreme cases, the advancing island arc takes on the shape of a giant U, and the subducting plate is bent into the shape of a giant spoon. I reported that the Banda Island arc of Indonesia formed a basin in this way, as did the Caribbean arc between North and South America, and the Scotia Arc between South America and Antarctica. These and other features of plate

Pits and grooves in a grain of augite, a mineral found in many rocks, are a result of weathering, in contrast to the smoothing effect expected. The pits and grooves appear, under the keen eye of a scanning electron microscope, to follow the mineral's crystal structure. (Magnified 6,350 times.)

geometry indicate the sinking is vertical, or nearly so.

Mathematical analysis also suggests that subduction is mainly a process of vertical sinking. Geoscientists Raphael Freund, Dan Kosloff, and Alan Matthews of the Hebrew University in Jerusalem, Israel, reported in 1979 on their calculations of the physical and geometric characteristics of subducting slabs and associated features. They deduced that a sinking plate breaks into many blocks. In the old view of subduction, a plate slides down at an angle in one piece.

Another report provides new data on the way that island arcs migrate and open oceanic "marginal basins" behind them, forming small oceans. An example is the Sea of Japan, which was formed as the islands that make up Japan pulled away from Asia. Geophysicist Donna Jurdy of Princeton University in New Jersey reported in November 1979 that western Pacific marginal basins opened in the direction from which the main Pacific Plate met the island chain. When the Pacific Plate changed direction, the basins shifted their directions of spreading. This too is best explained by subduction by vertical sinking.

Earthquakes occur deep in the mantle as the subducting lithosphere slowly sinks. Seismologist Frank Richter of the University of Chicago reported in November 1979 on his new study of earthquakes in the Tonga-Kermadec subduction system of the southwest Pacific Ocean. He found that quakes are most common in the area at depths of 500 to 700 kilometers (310 to 435 miles) and that none occur beneath a depth of 700 kilometers.

Richter theorizes that the composition of the earth's mantle changes at 700 kilometers. Pieces of the sinking slab can go no farther, so they accumulate at this depth. The slabs do not melt in the hot mantle because they have already lost all of their easily melted material at shallow depth.

Undersea plateaus. Earth scientists are gradually solving many of the puzzles presented by the broad submarine plateaus that rise from the deep ocean. Some are topped by large or small islands. Some of these plateaus are submerged pieces of continents. A new

Geoscience

Continued

study sheds light on the history of the Seychelles Plateau in the western Indian Ocean — long known to consist of ancient continental granite.

Geophysicists Ian Norton and John G. Sclater of Massachusetts Institute of Technology reported in November 1979 that the Seychelles Plateau was originally part of western India, as India moved to the northeast away from Africa. The plateau split from India 65 million years ago and was left behind as the Indian subcontinent continued moving to the northeast. India has since moved 2,000 kilometers (1,250 miles) away from the plateau.

Norton and Sclater made a series of detailed reconstructions of the Indian Ocean area at different geologic times to develop their explanation. They started with the supercontinent called Gondwanaland, which existed in the Indian Ocean area until about 200-million years ago and then began to break up into many pieces. Some are still land masses, others are under water. The Seychelles Plateau is one of the pieces, as is India.

Other oceanic plateaus are formed where new ocean floor is created by magma, or molten rock, flowing up where two large plates are moving apart. The Iceland Plateau in the North Atlantic Ocean is an example of this kind of plateau. The igneous rocks in its crust are three to five times thicker than those of ordinary oceanic crust, so the top of the plateau is high. The voluminous igneous rocks indicate an unusual amount of melting in the mantle beneath it. Scientists do not know yet what caused such melting.

Recent research indicates that the Ontong Java-Manihiki Plateau in the western Pacific — the largest known submerged oceanic plateau — was also formed along a spreading center in the sea floor. Ontong Java-Manihiki, northeast of New Guinea, is about 2,000 kilometers (1,250 miles) in diameter.

Geophysicists Donald M. Hussong, L. K. Wipperman, and Loren W. Kroenke of the University of Hawaii reported in October 1979 on their seismic studies of the Ontong Java-Manihiki Plateau. They found that the

Geologists lower a seismic boomer, *below right,* into the North Sea to study rock layers below the ocean floor. The boomer and a sonar that records the ocean floor profile may help explain the origin of the pockmarks found in this area, *below.*

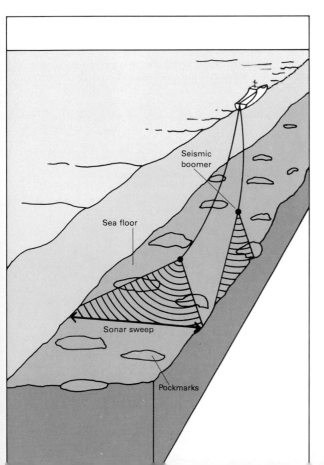

Geoscience

Continued

Technicians check seismic group recorder readings in a van that serves as a traveling computer center for crews exploring for oil. The portable unit assures that data from soundings for oil and gas deposits is complete before the crew leaves the exploration site.

earth's crust under the plateau is about 35 kilometers (22 miles) thick, about five times thicker than most oceanic crust, probably because of excessive melting of the mantle. Seismic waves travel through this thick crust in the same way that they travel through normal thin oceanic crust. This shows that the plateau is not a piece of continent. The crust of the plateau is about 120 million years old, but oceanic crust of the same age in most other areas is of normal thickness.

Other plateaus, like the Kerguelen Plateau of the southern Indian Ocean, remain mysterious. Most geologists assume that the Kerguelen is an oceanic plateau like Iceland and Ontong Java-Manihiki. However, in the 1979 USGS report on plates, I offered data to support the interpretation that the Kerguelen Plateau is a continental fragment, like the Seychelles.

If the Kerguelen is an oceanic plateau, then the usual reconstructions giving the positions of India and Antarctica within Gondwanaland cannot be correct. These reconstructions allow no space for the Kerguelen Plateau.

The Kerguelen Islands atop the Kerguelen Plateau show no exposed basement rock, to show directly whether the plateau is oceanic or continental. The islands consist of geologically young igneous rocks of types which could form on either oceanic or continental crust. Seismic data on these rocks are incomplete or ambiguous.

However, tree fossils on the Kerguelen Islands provide strong support of the idea that the plateau was a continental fragment. Although no trees grow on these cold, desolate islands today, forests consisting of southern bush and conifers characteristically found in the Southern Hemisphere existed there millions of years ago.

Botanists have shown that seeds of living beech and conifers related to these fossils cannot cross broad expanses of water; the trees grow only on land masses that were once connected. The living trees closely related to the fossil trees on the Kerguelen Islands are found growing on continents and islands that were once part of Gondwanaland. Presumably, the Kerguelen Plateau was once also part of that ancient land mass. [Warren Hamilton]

Geophysics. Geophysicists reported in March 1980 that a major study of the Pacific Ocean floor uncovered the hottest water that flows from the earth. The water was found by a team of scientists studying the rocks and the nature of the processes that shaped them on the floor of the Pacific at a depth of 2.5 kilometers (1.5 miles), along the axis of the East Pacific Rise. The site is about 300 kilometers (186 miles) due south of Cape San Lucas at the tip of Baja California Sur, Mexico.

The team of more than 20 scientists from the United States, France, and Mexico was led by geophysicists Frank N. Speiss and Ken C. McDonald of the University of California's Scripps Institution of Oceanography. Their project, the Rivera Submersible Experiment (RISE), was designed to study this ocean-floor area, where new rocks are formed by underwater volcanism.

The expedition used the *Alvin*, a three-person research submarine, and *Angus*, an underwater sled, carrying a camera and a device for detecting water temperature, towed by the research ship *Melville*. Data from *Angus* was used to pinpoint important areas to be studied in detail by *Alvin*.

Plate tectonics theory holds that the earth's crust is made up of about 20 giant plates that move against one another. Much research has been done on critical boundary areas between the plates, such as the East Pacific Rise. The East Pacific Rise extends south to meet the Chile ridge and, farther south, the ridge that separates the Antarctic and Pacific plates. Measuring the ages of the rock on both sides of the East Pacific Rise indicated that magma, or molten rock, is being thrust up into the ridge so that the Pacific Plate to the west and Rivera Plate to the east are forced away from the ridge at a rate of 6 centimeters (2.4 inches) per year.

Earth scientists have long known that heat flow from the earth's interior along such ridges is about five to 20 times the oceanic average. In 1976, oceanographer Robert D. Ballard discovered hot springs of 20°C (68°F.) water flowing through vents in the ocean's crust along the Galapagos Rift Valley, about 3,000 kilometers (1,864 miles) southeast of the RISE area. By contrast, the pitch-black waters on the

ocean floor are usually a cool 2°C (35.6°F.). Scientists began to wonder if similar vents might be found along other plate boundaries.

During the RISE expedition, the *Angus* explored a zone of the East Pacific Rise about 40 kilometers (25 miles) long and 6 kilometers (3.7 miles) wide. The scientists observed a number of narrow vents expelling clear hot 20°C water just as in the Galapagos Rift area. These hot springs support an exotic population of giant tube worms, clams, limpets, and crabs.

The RISE scientists discovered the very hot water in an extremely narrow zone — 100 to 200 meters (328 to 656 feet) wide and about 6 kilometers long. There, in an area of young basaltic lavas, they found 25 superhot jets carrying black particles at temperatures of up to 380°C (716°F.). The high pressure on the ocean floor allows the water to remain in liquid form, rather than turning to steam at these high temperatures. The particles in the water appear to consist of minerals that do not dissolve in normal ocean water.

Unlike the 20°C "hot spring" waters that come from cracks in rocks, the 380°C water comes out of black structures shaped like chimneys. The chimneys, as well as the mounds that form the chimney bases and the black particles, are made of metal sulfides.

The *Alvin* scientists took gravity measurements on the ocean floor that indicated less pull from gravity than would be there if the rocks beneath were solid. This suggests that a chamber of magma, which is less dense than its surroundings, exists within the ocean floor, possibly only 550 meters (1,800 feet) below the floor. This chamber of molten rock apparently is the water-heating source. Seawater may be drawn down through the crust, flow near the magma, become superheated, and then be expelled as very hot springs along the ridge.

Stress levels. A controversy has occurred among geophysicists over how much stress the oceanic lithosphere, or earth's crust, can withstand. Geophysicists have long thought that a key to understanding the strength of the lithosphere is its apparent ability to support massive volcanic islands. A volcanic island forms when a plume of molten

A device to monitor earthquakes, *above,* was installed on Mt. St. Helens' west slope in April — in time to monitor a major volcanic eruption in May that blew away the upper part of the mountain's northern slope, *top.*

Geoscience

Continued

The first fossil carnivorous dinosaur egg was found near Choteau, Mont. The pebble-surfaced egg was unearthed in July 1979.

material pierces the oceanic plates. Continued plate motion over a plume, or hot spot, produces a line of islands. Prominent examples of such islands are the Hawaiian chain, which extends northwest from the island of Hawaii.

Geophysicists Anthony B. Watts and James R. Cochran of Columbia University and Marcia McNutt of the U.S. Geological Survey (USGS) reported in July 1979 on their analysis of the surface features of the oceanic lithosphere. They analyzed information from a radar system on the Geodynamics Experimental Ocean Satellite 3 (GEOS 3), sent into orbit in 1975 by the U.S. National Aeronautics and Space Administration, and found that the oceanic lithosphere is about 30 kilometers (19 miles) thick. They also estimated that the lithosphere is as elastic as steel in its response to the stresses imposed by the weight of the oceanic islands.

This analysis presents some severe problems to geoscientists. Using data from the Watts team, geophysicists Donald W. Turcotte of Cornell University in Ithaca, N.Y., and Thomas C. Hanks of USGS reported in 1978 and 1979 on broad rises, usually 200 to 500 meters (656 to 1,640 feet) high, produced on the seaward side of most oceanic trenches by the buckling of the lithosphere where the edge of one plate is being subducted, or forced down, into the mantle at the point where it meets another plate.

Turcotte calculated that such buckling would produce extremely great shear stress, usually resulting in part of a plate breaking off, with a pressure ranging up to several thousand bars. (One bar equals approximately one atmospheric pressure.)

If these high shear stresses occur, they must be relieved by an earthquake that breaks the plate. However, geophysicists William Stauder of St. Louis University, Hiroo Kanamori of the California Institute of Technology, and Peter H. Molnar of Massachusetts Institute of Technology reported in 1979 and 1980 that the amount of stress released in major earthquakes is only 200 bars at most. Such earthquakes occur when the lithosphere breaks and descends into the mantle along faults that may extend for hundreds of kilometers.   [Thomas J. Ahrens]

Paleontology. Geoscientists offered new explanations in 1979 for an old mystery – why so many animal and plant species died at the same time, at the end of the Cretaceous Period, 65 million years ago. About 70 per cent of the species living at that time perished, including dinosaurs.

Arctic Ocean theory. Oceanographer Stefan Gartner and meteorologist James P. McGuirk of Texas A&M University in College Station reported in December 1979 on a theory they call the "Cretaceous extinction scenario." They suggested that an overflow of the Arctic Ocean resulted in mass destruction of life. Parts of the theory were published earlier by Gartner and John Keany of the Phillips Petroleum Company in Bartlesville, Okla.

The scientists proposed that the Arctic Ocean was landlocked and full of fresh cold water near the end of the Cretaceous Period. Plate tectonics, the theory that the earth's crust is made up of giant plates that move against one another, holds that Norway and Greenland were one land mass during the Cretaceous Period but broke apart suddenly and dramatically. The fresh water in the Arctic was then flushed out and floated over all the world's oceans, forming a cold layer of water tens of meters thick that was low in salinity.

Many plants and animals living near the surface of the oceans died because they could not adapt to the sudden change to less salty, colder water. Marine animals that lived in deeper layers and on the ocean bottom also died because the layer of Arctic water did not mix with saltier water below. This prevented oxygen from being carried down by the ocean currents that normally circulate it. The most active animals, such as ammonites – shelled animals – were most affected.

Land animals also died out, because the massive change in the earth's oceans triggered changes in climate. The cool water lowered air temperatures and reduced evaporation. Climate over all the continents became cooler and drier. Land animals had to adjust quickly to the new climate to survive. Many, like the dinosaurs, did not do so and became extinct.

Gartner and Keany developed their theory in an attempt to explain obser-

288

Geoscience

Continued

vations they made on three core samples of deep-sea sediment taken from the North Sea floor. They found that the fossils of Cretaceous plankton — tiny plants and animals that live near the ocean surface — disappear from the sediment at a certain level and are replaced at the next level by new species. This definite change should mark the Cretaceous Period mass extinction and therefore the boundary between the Cretaceous Period and the Tertiary Period, the next geological period in the earth's history.

However, Gartner and Keany were surprised to find that the Cretaceous species reappear in a layer a few meters above the Tertiary species. The Cretaceous species are present in the next 55 meters (185 feet) and then disappear once again, this time for good. The Tertiary species that were sandwiched between the two layers of Cretaceous species then reappear.

To explain this strange layering, Gartner and Keany theorized that the Tertiary species evolved in a land-locked Arctic Ocean during the late Cretaceous Period. It may be that the Arctic Ocean was isolated then by a combination of low sea level and slightly different continental arrangement. The first movement of Tertiary species into the North Sea might have occurred when Greenland began moving away from Norway.

The North Sea nearby got an early flood of fresh, cold Arctic water, which killed off the warm-water, high-salinity species there and replaced them with Arctic species. The amount of water entering the North Sea may have been small, because the samples show that the Cretaceous species quickly returned. However, after the final break occurred between Norway and Greenland, the Cretaceous species died and never reappeared.

The extinctions on land probably occurred almost simultaneously with the marine extinctions. Gartner and McGuirk theorize that the Arctic water lowered the oceans' surface temperature by an average of 10°C (18°F.), which cooled the atmosphere and reduced evaporation. Precipitation on

Fossil skeletons of two *Teleoceras* rhinoceroses found in a volcanic ash bed in Nebraska contained fossils of grasses they ate just before they died. This proves that the rhino of 26 million years ago was a plant eater.

A Tale of
Two Heads

A complete dinosaur was not a museum staple in the middle 1870s, when paleontology – the study of old life – was still a young science. Most specimens then were single bones or disordered bits of skeletons in museums.

Suddenly, in the spring of 1877, dinosaurs stampeded into the public consciousness. Newspapers in Boston, New York City, and Philadelphia carried startling reports from tiny frontier towns in Colorado and Wyoming of the discovery of giant skeletons in rocks more than 130 million years old. Not mere isolated bones, but nearly complete specimens were shipped via Union Pacific Railroad boxcars to museums in the East. The most spectacular of these finds were the immense sauropod dinosaurs, named *Brontosaurus, Barosaurus, Camarasaurus,* and *Diplodocus,* that measured almost 30 meters (100 feet) from head to tail.

Dinosaur paleontology became a prestigious science in America. In the "bone rush" to the West, scientists scrambled to get good skeletons, and two formidable rivals clashed – O.

Charles Marsh of Yale University and Edward Drinker Cope of the Philadelphia Academy of Natural Sciences.

The first naturalist to describe and name a new genus of organism achieves a kind of immortality – the name he or she gives it remains the only legal scientific term for the genus, and the scientist's name and the date of description are appended to it. For example, we still list one of the sauropods as "*Barosaurus* – Marsh, 1890."

Marsh and Cope fought to be first in the nomenclatural race, and fired off new names as soon as each box of fossils was unpacked. They described many genera from fragments because complete skeletons might take several years to excavate. Both scientists sometimes gave names to genera already described. For instance, Marsh's *Morosaurus* turned out to be the same genus as Cope's *Camarasaurus;* and Marsh's *Atlantosaurus, Apatosaurus,* and *Brontosaurus* referred to different specimens of the same animal.

The name *Brontosaurus* became fixed in the popular scientific press

A paleontological patchwork, the wrong-headed, false-faced *Brontosaurus* stands in a museum hall, *above.* After a century with the head of the snub-nosed *Camarasaurus, right* (right), it now has a delicate, long-snouted head like its reconstructed cousin, *Diplodocus* (left).

because Marsh based the genus on a superb skeleton from Como Bluff in Wyoming. Pictures of the skeleton were soon found in most geology texts. However, the original skeleton lacked a head and, in his competitive eagerness, Marsh may have lost his own head. He committed a capital offense for a paleontologist and faked a skull to fit the skeleton from cranial fragments found in Canon City, Colo.

Marsh's would-be *Brontosaurus* skull resembled that of *Camarasaurus,* and it soon became customary to think of *Brontosaurus* as related to that sauropod. So when *Brontosaurus* skeletons were mounted in a number of museums in the early 1900s, models of a large camarasaur skull topped them off.

However, the scientists who dug these skeletons out of the rocks pointed out a curious pattern: big camarasaur-like skulls were never found near brontosaur skeletons. But at least once, a very large *Diplodocus*-like head was found with a brontosaur skeleton. The two skull types are quite different: *Camarasaurus* has a boxlike skull with large spoon-shaped teeth while *Diplodocus* has an elegantly tapered snout with narrow, closely set teeth.

John S. McIntosh of Wesleyan University in Middletown, Conn., a theoretical physicist and a brontosaur bloodhound, began to put the pieces together in the 1950s. As he examined old quarry records and studied the individual specimens, McIntosh became convinced that the correct *Brontosaurus* skull had been found in several quarries as early as 1878. McIntosh delayed his final judgment until he published a 1978 paper with paleontologist David Berman of the Carnegie Institute's Museum of Natural History in Pittsburgh. The evidence they presented was conclusive.

Whenever skull remains were found closely associated with brontosaurs, the skulls were unmistakably like those of *Diplodocus.* Furthermore, as the shrewd Chicago paleontologist Elmer S. Riggs noted in 1904, *Brontosaurus* was a heavy-set version of *Diplodocus* in all aspects of spinal and limb anatomy. The case was solved. Museums began to make the switch in 1979 and, after 100 years, the brontosaur has its rightful head. [Robert T. Bakker]

land also dropped, possibly by 50 per cent or more. The continental climate changed to cool and dry; severe seasonal droughts were then likely. Animals such as dinosaurs could not adjust to the sudden and severe changes.

Rainfall theory. Another recent theory on the extinctions of the Cretaceous Period also focuses on dinosaurs, but blames their sudden extinction on increased rainfall. Three West German geologists, Heinrich K. Erben of the Institute of Paleontology in Bonn and J. Hoefs and K. H. Wedepohl of the Geochemical Institute in Göttingen, reported in November 1979 that increased rainfall near the end of the Cretaceous Period stimulated plant growth, thus enlarging the food supply for vegetarian dinosaurs. With more food, the dinosaurs had more young, leading to overcrowding and to stress.

The geologists believe that, because of stress, the female dinosaurs developed hormonal imbalances — estrogen shortages — causing them to lay eggs with shells that were too thin. The embryos inside the eggs were crushed, or they died from dehydration. The dinosaur population was suddenly and rapidly reduced, and eventually they became extinct.

Erben, Hoefs, and Wedepohl based their theory on a study of fossil eggshells from the giant sauropod species *Hyselosaurus priscus,* found in southern France and Spain. They measured oxygen isotopes and strontium in the shells and found evidence that the climate became humid toward the end of the Cretaceous Period. This implies increased rainfall, which naturally led to increased plant growth.

The scientists also used a scanning electron microscope to study the structure and thickness of eggshells found in sediments that date to the last few million years of the Cretaceous Period.

Just before the Tertiary Period began, about 90 per cent of the shells were abnormally thin. Erben, Hoefs, and Wedepohl said that the embryos in these thin shells died before hatching because the insides of the fossil shells do not show reabsorption craters. Such craters normally appear in a reptile egg as some of the shell's calcium carbonate dissolves to help form the embryo's bones. [Ida Thompson]

Immunology

Researchers reported in May 1979 that a substance in blood plasma can convert T lymphocytes, a strain of white blood cells, into killer cells capable of destroying cancer cells in mice. T lymphocytes normally mobilize other white blood cells against foreign substances or tumor cells but do not attack these agents directly. T lymphocytes are produced in the body's bone marrow and must pass through the thymus, a gland in the base of the neck, to become active.

A team of immunologists including Amnol Altman, Jose M. Cardenas, Thomas E. Bechtold, and David H. Katz of the Scripps Clinic and Research Foundation in La Jolla, Calif., discovered this converting function in a blood plasma substance called allogenic effect factor (AEF). Katz discovered AEF in 1974 and showed that it helped stimulate the formation of antibodies by B lymphocytes, another type of white blood cell.

Altman and his group prepared AEF using Katz's method. They irradiated one strain of mice to prevent them from producing any white blood cells that would participate in the subsequent reaction. They then inoculated these mice with thymus cells taken from the same strain of mouse. They also inoculated the mice with a mixture of T and B lymphocytes from the spleens of a second strain of mice that had been irradiated to prevent the lymphocytes from reproducing. These lymphocytes reacted with the thymus cells in the first strain of mouse.

A week later, the scientists removed the spleens from these mice and isolated the thymus cells that had collected in the spleens. They put the thymus cells in a test tube containing lymphocytes from the second strain of mice. The reaction that occurred between the two types of cells produced AEF within 24 hours.

The scientists then added AEF to a culture of T lymphocytes taken from the first strain of mouse and tumor cells. The T lymphocytes destroyed the tumor cells. However, T lymphocytes added to a culture without AEF could not kill the tumor cells.

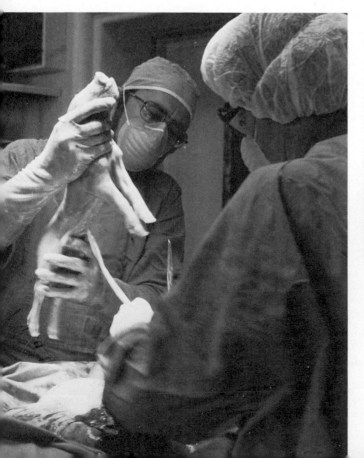

A piglet, delivered by Caesarean section to prevent contamination in the birth canal, is exposed to room air just long enough for veterinarians to sever the umbilical cord, *left*. After an antiseptic bath, it joins its siblings in a sterile isolator, *above*. The germ-free pigs will live in isolation as test subjects for immunological research.

Immunology

In addition, Altman's team found that AEF-stimulated cells killed normal cells from the original strain of mouse. The scientists theorized that AEF may play some role in triggering autoimmune diseases in which white blood cells attack the body's own cells.

Another tumor-cell killer, a white blood cell called a macrophage, was investigated by Theresa L. Gerrard, Jose J. Terz, and Alan M. Kaplan of the Medical College of Virginia. The researchers reported in April 1980 that the ability of macrophages to kill tumor cells is inhibited by a substance found in the blood plasma of cancer patients.

The team added macrophages from healthy volunteers to cultures of three different types of tumor cells and found that the macrophages killed the tumor cells. They then added macrophages from cancer patients to cultures of the same three kinds of tumor cells. The cancer patients' macrophages also effectively destroyed the tumor cells.

However, when the scientists added plasma from the cancer patients' blood to both groups of cultures, neither group of macrophages killed the tumor cells. In contrast, plasma from healthy volunteers had no effect on the killing ability of either type of macrophage. The scientists concluded that the cancer patients could not rid themselves of the tumors because their macrophages were inhibited by some factor in the blood plasma. If scientists can isolate and identify the inhibiting substance, they may be able to remove or neutralize it and free the macrophages to perform their natural function.

Malaria research reported in December 1979 involved the body's response to the disease. Malaria is caused by *Plasmodium,* a parasite transmitted by the *Anopheles* mosquito.

Immunologists Anil N. Jayawardena, Charles A. Janeway, Jr., and John D. Kemp of Yale University in New Haven, Conn., studied the effects of *Plasmodium* infestations on mice that have only limited ability to produce a type of antibody classified as IgM.

The researchers inoculated normal mice and IgM-deficient mice with *Plasmodium* and took blood samples from both groups periodically. They found that the parasite remained in the red blood cells of the IgM-deficient mice much longer than in the normal mice. However, when the deficient mice finally began to produce IgM antibodies, the infection subsided.

The Yale group concluded that the IgM antibodies might help to control malaria by attacking the parasite-ridden red blood cells. They speculated that the parasites cause changes in the blood cell membrane that label the cell as "foreign" and attract the antibodies.

MS link. Studies reported in October 1979 linked certain white blood cells, called T_G lymphocytes, and the crippling disease, multiple sclerosis (MS). MS results when the protective myelin sheaths that cover nerve cells in the brain and spinal cord are destroyed.

Immunologists John R. Huddlestone and Michael B. A. Oldstone of Scripps pursued the possibility that a defect in the immune system might be destroying the myelin sheaths. The scientists knew from earlier research that the cerebral spinal fluid of MS patients contains a high level of antibodies produced by B lymphocytes and that these antibodies may play some role in the disease. They also knew that T_G lymphocytes suppress this antibody production. They wanted to find out whether the excess antibodies in MS victims were due to a defect in the production of T_G lymphocytes.

To study T_G lymphocytes, the Scripps researchers took blood samples from 25 MS patients and a control group of healthy volunteers. They gathered the samples from the MS patients at regular intervals, noting whether the sample was drawn when the patient was suffering an acute attack of the disease or when the disease was in remission. They recorded T_G levels in the MS samples and compared them to T_G levels in control group samples.

Huddlestone and Oldstone found that the levels of T_G cells in MS patients during remission were significantly higher than those in the control group. They concluded that the B cell antibodies decreased in the presence of high T_G levels, but flourished when there were few T_G cells to suppress them. They now hope to determine whether low T_G levels precede the onset of acute MS attacks and why levels of T_G cells fluctuate dramatically in MS patients.   [Beverly Merz]

Medicine

Dentistry. A more sensitive method of measuring bone loss in alveolar, or jaw, bone that is caused by chronic periodontal disease was reported in April 1980. Researchers Michael L. Kaplan, Marjorie K. Jeffcoat, and I, of the Harvard School of Dental Medicine in Boston, injected a radioactive chemical into the bloodstream of dogs to detect changes in alveolar bone.

Currently, dental specialists measure bone loss by comparing bone levels in X rays of the patient's jaw taken at least one year apart. However, they can only detect bone density losses greater than 30 per cent. More subtle bone changes cannot be recognized.

In the dog studies, we found that the alveolar bone of animals with periodontal disease takes up the radioactive chemical technetium-99m-tin diphosphate more readily than does the bone of disease-free animals. We also used X rays to correlate the amount of radioactive material uptake in the bone around various teeth with the rate of bone loss around these teeth over the next two years. The new method can thus predict rate of bone loss, something X rays alone cannot do.

In our latest studies, we found that the alveolar bone absorbed less of the radioactive chemical after the disease was treated with the antibiotic tetracycline. These findings indicate that the new method can determine the status of alveolar bone destruction much sooner than X rays can. Further tests, including trials on human subjects, are needed to fully evaluate the technique.

Pocketing the tetracycline. Dental researcher Jeffrey M. Gordon of the Forsyth Dental Center and the Harvard School of Dental Medicine in Boston in April 1980 reported one reason why tetracycline may be effective in treating periodontal disease. Gordon gave the drug to volunteers and measured at various time intervals the amount of tetracycline in their bloodstream and the amount present in fluid in the crevices between their gums and teeth, where pockets of infection form in periodontal disease. He found two to 10 times more tetracycline in the fluid in the crevices than there was in the bloodstream, suggesting that the drug concentrated selectively in the crevice fluid.   [Paul Goldhaber]

Cross sections of teeth from rats fed a high-sugar diet show heavy decay, *top,* only two weeks after infection by a common strain of mouth bacteria; less decay, *middle,* from bacteria that produce less acid; and no decay, *bottom,* in teeth exposed to a harmless substance.

Internal Medicine. Red blood cells may hold the key that will allow doctors to distinguish between different kinds of hypertension, or high blood pressure, according to an April 1980 report by physiologist Ricardo P. Garay and his associates at Necker Hospital in Paris. Although hypertension is a common medical problem, important questions about its causes remain unanswered.

High blood pressure can be caused by a variety of physiological or biochemical problems. So it is especially important to distinguish between patients with essential hypertension, which is not caused by any known pre-existing condition, and those with secondary hypertension, caused by something else, such as kidney disease. Patients suffering secondary hypertension may be cured by one treatment, while victims of essential hypertension require lifelong drug therapy.

The French researchers studied normal and hypertensive patients. They knew that there was a higher concentration of sodium in the red blood cells of patients with essential hypertension than in the red cells of normal persons, and they isolated red cells from both groups of patients. These cells were suspended in a solution that loaded them to capacity with sodium (Na) and depleted them of potassium (K).

The test cells were then placed in another solution with known amounts of Na and K. The researchers measured the movement of Na out of the cells and K into the cells as the cells attempted to establish their normal balance of the two salts. These measurements provide a ratio of Na to K that is a measure of how efficiently cells transport salts.

They found that patients with essential hypertension had a considerably lower Na:K ratio than patients with secondary hypertension. Furthermore, the cells of normal persons and secondary hypertensives had almost identical ratios. The results strongly suggest that the cells of patients with essential hypertension are not operating as efficiently as the cells of other persons. These cells cannot maintain the high concentration of K and low concentration of Na that normal cells can. Moreover, it is possible that essential hyper-

Bionic Blood

Blood's most important function is to carry the oxygen from the air we breathe to the cells in our bodies. If our cells do not receive oxygen for about seven minutes, we will die. So it is surprising that an animal can survive for several hours after all of its blood is removed and replaced by a milky liquid made in the laboratory.

Even more surprising is the successful use of this substance as a replacement for natural blood during surgery on human beings. And the key ingredients of this life-saving artificial blood turn out to be fluorocarbons, which were first produced as part of the atomic bomb project during World War II.

The development of artificial blood began in our laboratory at the Children's Hospital Research Foundation in Cincinnati, Ohio, one day in 1966. Fluorocarbons had been known to be good carriers of oxygen. They dissolve oxygen just as water dissolves sugar. On a hunch, I pumped oxygen into a beaker containing a fluorocarbon liquid and then immersed a mouse in the liquid. The mouse breathed the liquid for hours and survived. My experiment showed that this particular liquid fluorocarbon carried enough oxygen to sustain life, was not poisonous, and did not damage the lungs. I immediately recognized liquid fluorocarbon's potential as an artificial blood. However, this chemical had a fundamental drawback: It did not mix well with natural blood.

In addition to carrying oxygen to our cells, natural blood supplies them with nutrients and hormones, and carries waste products from them. It also contains substances that fight disease germs and cause clotting if a blood vessel is damaged. Fluorocarbons alone can only supply oxygen to cells and carry carbon dioxide away from them. So artificial blood alone cannot completely substitute for natural blood.

During 1966 and 1967, hematologist Henry A. Sloviter of the University of Pennsylvania in Philadelphia, nutritionist Robert P. Geyer of Harvard Medical School in Cambridge, Mass., and I developed fluorocarbon emulsions — mixtures of liquids that do not dissolve in one another.

These emulsions, suspended in water, formed a substance that mixed well with natural blood when infused into experimental animals. The fluorocarbon particles, 100 times smaller than red blood cells and thousands of times more numerous, were removed naturally from the animals' blood over a period of two to three days. Natural body systems deposited them in the liver and spleen. But the fluorocarbons stayed there for years — which may be too long for the substances to remain safely in the human body.

This was the first major problem we encountered. But our laboratory in Cincinnati and the laboratory of physician and chemist Ryoichi Naito at the Green Cross Corporation in Osaka, Japan, solved this problem by 1973. We found that a fluorocarbon called perfluorinated decalin worked well as artificial blood and was exhaled by the lungs and passed through the skin.

Then a second problem arose — the decalin did not make a stable emulsion. Particles gradually increased in size in the bloodstream until the artificial blood would not circulate well. However, Naito found that the size of the particles could be stabilized by adding another fluorocarbon to the emulsion. Japanese surgeons began testing this substance in April 1979.

The artificial blood is made of fluorocarbon particles held in an emulsion with lecithin, a substance found in egg yolks. It also contains salts that keep the heart beating. However, the emulsion must be stored frozen, and only half of the chemicals leave the body in about 65 days.

Scientists in our laboratory are now making and testing new fluorocarbons, trying to develop an artificial blood that requires no refrigeration and will leave the body within a few days. The artificial blood we hope to produce could be stored for years at room temperature, sterilized, and given to people of all blood types. In addition, this artificial blood's ability to dissolve three times as much oxygen as natural blood does and its fine particle size might enable it to carry large amounts of oxygen to tissues that are temporarily deprived, such as heart muscle after a heart attack or brain tissue after a stroke. We are close to such a product now, only 14 years after we tried our simple experiment with a mouse and a beaker. [Leland C. Clark, Jr.]

An experimental insulin pump, worn on the waist, automatically monitors the blood-sugar levels and injects insulin as needed during the active day of a diabetic boy.

Medicine

Continued

tension, since it has no other known cause, may be genetically determined.

If these preliminary data are confirmed in further studies, it may be possible to use the red cell Na:K flux as a blood test to identify persons who are predisposed to hypertension from birth, and secondary hypertensives, who have a correctable, and perhaps unknown, underlying cause of their condition.

Diabetic pregnancy. A new self-help program that promises to limit the risks of pregnancy in diabetic women and improve the chances of their infants' survival was described in November 1979 by medical researcher Ian Peacock of University Hospital in Nottingham, England. Because of metabolic complications due to glucose, or blood sugar, imbalances, pregnancy has always been a hazard both to the diabetic mother and the fetus. Over the past 30 years, better medical treatment, including methods of controlling glucose levels, has reduced the infant death rate from 30 to 5 per cent.

Peacock and his associates allowed 25 diabetic women aged 17 to 41 to monitor their own blood sugar levels throughout pregnancy and adjust their own diet and insulin intake to maintain proper levels. Twenty-four of the pregnant diabetics were taking insulin to control their diabetes; the twenty-fifth controlled the disease by dieting.

The women were taught to measure their own blood glucose by pricking their fingers, draining off a drop of blood, and placing it on a chemically treated test strip. The strip was then placed in a portable meter that provides a fairly accurate reading of the glucose concentration by measuring the chemical reaction of the blood with the test strip. They tested themselves before meals, one and two hours after meals, at bedtime, and sometimes at 3 A.M., throughout pregnancy. Doctors performed *amniocentesis* (examination of fetal cells from the fluid surrounding the fetus) at the 37th or 38th week of pregnancy to see whether the fetus was mature enough for delivery. If it was, they induced labor.

The 25 patients made a total of 4,247 blood glucose measurements. The aver-

Medicine

Continued

age level was remarkably good. Although a few patients reported episodes of too much or too little blood glucose, the women generally remained in excellent health. Following three final weeks in the hospital, the 25 mothers were delivered of live babies.

This new technique permits the patient herself to control accurately at home both food consumption and insulin administration for the best blood glucose levels. This has been possible in the past only by putting pregnant diabetics in the hospital.

Bone food. The simplest and safest way to prevent osteoporosis – the thinning or weakening of bone that comes with aging – is to dramatically increase the amount of calcium in the diet. This conclusion was reported by internist Robert P. Heaney and his associates at Creighton University in Omaha, Nebr., in February 1980.

Broken bones are an increasing problem for elderly people in the United States. Each year, 190,000 persons, most of them in late middle age or older, suffer broken hips. Perhaps as many as 17 per cent of these individuals die from the ensuing complications and many others are incapacitated.

Vertebral fractures are also common among the aged. In such "crush fractures," the vertebrae simply collapse under the strain of carrying the body upright. The result is pain, loss of height, and, frequently, deformity.

Both vertebral and hip fractures are most likely to occur in persons who have underlying osteoporosis. In this common condition, large amounts of the calcium-containing structural protein responsible for the strength of bone are lost. Under these circumstances, bones can be broken in minor accidents that would not fracture healthy bone.

Heaney reported that about 25 per cent of white American women have suffered one or more fractures by age 65. Women are more prone to severe osteoporosis than men, partly because women's bones are lighter and more likely to lose mass. Menopause also accelerates the rate of bone loss.

Heaney suggests, and other researchers have confirmed, that the hormone estrogen, whose secretion decreases after menopause, protects bone from the effects of parathyroid hor-

mone, which draws calcium from bone to maintain proper levels in the blood. Estrogen treatment prevents osteoporosis, but such hormone treatment is associated with an increased risk of uterine cancer.

Other agents, designed to reduce bone loss or increase the synthesis of new bone, have been effective. Calcitonin, fluoride, and vitamin D-like substances, for example, have all been used with some success. But researchers are still trying to identify the chemical mechanisms of osteoporosis.

In the meantime, Heaney recommends that older persons – particularly women – increase their calcium intake. Before menopause, about 800 milligrams (mg) of calcium per day maintains the proper calcium balance, but postmenopausal women seem to need roughly 1,500 mg – the amount of calcium contained in about 1.1 liters (1½ quarts) of milk – every day. Other foods, such as sardines and green leafy vegetables, are also suitable sources of the mineral.

While the focus of research has primarily been on women, men are not immune. All adults should maintain an adequate calcium intake to minimize the risk of developing osteoporosis.

Interim report on interferon. Medical researchers met in San Diego, Calif., in May 1980 to discuss their studies of interferon, a substance produced in the body that fights viruses and appears to have some effect on cancer. Their reports indicated that much more research is needed to determine the value of the so-called miracle chemical. See THE ELUSIVE PROMISE OF INTERFERON, *Science Year,* 1980.

Interferon is produced by white blood cells in response to viral infections and tumor cells. The substance appears to enhance the capacity of certain white cells, called lymphocytes, to destroy tumor cells and invading viruses. In a series of experiments, immunologist Barry R. Bloom of the Albert Einstein College of Medicine in New York City demonstrated that interferon seems to activate "natural-killer" cells.

Natural-killer cells have long been thought to be part of the body's immune system. Scientists theorize that the appearance of a malignant cell in

Moving, flashing light patterns in a hospital test chamber send nerve impulses from a patient's eye to the brain and thence to the eye muscles. Abnormal eye-muscle responses may indicate such nerve disorders as multiple sclerosis, myasthenia gravis, or Huntington's disease in the patient.

Medicine

Continued

A thin electrode snakes around its guide, a thicker fiber-optic probe, through the bladder and ureter into a kidney. There, the electrode produces a high-voltage spark, creating an electrical shock wave that breaks up a kidney stone.

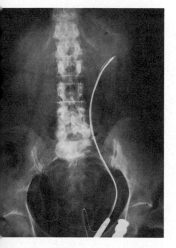

the body normally arouses the killer cells, which destroy the cancerous cell. Interferon not only helps recruit these defensive cells but also magnifies their destructive power. There is even some evidence that these cells may actually produce interferon.

A major difficulty with interferon research is that supplies of the substance are limited and expensive. Interferon must be extracted from human cells, in which it exists in very small quantities. Physician Sol Shepartz of the National Cancer Institute (NCI) in Bethesda, Md., estimates that half of the NCI's $10-million interferon budget for 1980 will be spent on supplies of the drug—enough to treat only 450 patients in clinical tests.

Preliminary studies seem to show that interferon has some effect on cancer. However, the results are not as encouraging as some had hoped.

In one such study, physician Elliott F. Osserman and his associates at Columbia University's School of Medicine in New York City reported that four out of 14 patients with multiple myeloma, a bone cancer, showed significant improvement after interferon treatment. However, statistics from other studies indicate that 11 out of the 14 would have improved with conventional chemotherapy.

Some studies indicate that interferon may act more effectively as a preventive measure than as a treatment, especially against viruses. In June 1979, physician Sarah H. Cheeseman and her associates at Massachusetts General Hospital, Harvard School of Medicine in Boston, and other institutions described the treatment of kidney-transplant patients with interferon for six weeks before transplantation. The researchers reported a significant reduction in the incidence of cytomegalovirus infection, a common complication after kidney transplants. Other studies have shown that interferon helps prevent infections caused by herpes simplex and Epstein-Barr viruses.

While clinical research continues on interferon's ability to fight cancer and viral infections, other researchers are trying to synthesize the substance and reduce its cost, or find drugs that stimulate the human body to make more of it. [Michael H. Alderman]

Surgery. A 33-year-old Maryland woman in September 1979 became the first person ever to receive an artificial spine. In a grueling 19-hour operation, Charles C. Edwards, chief of orthopedic surgery at the University of Maryland Hospital in Baltimore, and his assistants, Mukund Dibolkar and James Murphy, implanted the metal and plastic prosthesis, or artificial part. Edwards had removed a section of the patient's spine, including three full vertebrae and two half-vertebrae, along with a massive spinal tumor, in July.

The spinal column is a complex structure of bone, muscle, and tendon that supports the upper body and protects the nerves of the spinal cord. In the past, surgical work on the spine has been severely limited by the spinal column's complexity.

In order to remove the spinal tumor, Edwards had to remove the vertebrae. In effect, this disconnected the patient's ribcage from her pelvis. Without the surgical implant, the patient was doomed to spend the rest of her life in a horizontal position, strapped to a special bed called a Stryker frame. However, the spinal cord was left intact, so doctors hoped that the prosthesis would enable her at least to sit up and move about in a wheelchair.

The device consists of several metal rods connected to the separated vertebrae to provide support, protection for the cord, and resistance to various pressures that the spine receives. A cylinderlike metal device was also attached between the vertebrae above and below the gap. This cylinder was packed with bone grafts, which were to provide long-term support as they grew. Edwards designed the 17-part structure from X-ray measurements made before the operation.

Unfortunately, the patient died of other problems in early 1980 before this revolutionary treatment could be adequately evaluated. However, the spinal prosthesis is the first step toward surgical treatment not only of spinal tumors but also of severe spinal injuries that have in the past resulted in permanent crippling of the patient.

Much of the stability and strength of the spine comes from the combination of the vertebrae and the strong back muscles attached to them. Edwards'

Medicine

Continued

device had to function without muscles, because they were removed with the tumor. In spinal injury cases, however, the muscles would still be present. More sophisticated devices will undoubtedly follow now that the critical first step has been taken.

Toehold. Two Swedish pediatric surgeons have used a toe muscle to create a sphincter muscle to open and close defective urinary bladders in children. H. Jan W. Gierup and Lars Hakelius of Uppsala University Hospital in Uppsala discussed their surgical technique in May 1979.

Some children born with congenital abnormalities of the lower urinary tract cannot control their bladder. Severe emotional difficulties often result as they grow beyond the diaper stage. The traditional surgical approach has been to make an artificial bladder that delivers urine to a bag fitted to an opening in the abdominal wall. The new procedure, using the muscle that extends the big toe, brings hope that some of these children can now achieve normal urinary function.

The technique requires that the nerve to the toe muscle be cut two weeks before the muscle is transplanted to the bladder outlet. The nerve atrophies so that new nerves from the tissue around the bladder can grow along the toe nerve pathways into the muscle after transplantation, enabling it to contract. The muscle is then placed around the bladder outlet and begins to function as a sphincter as new nerves grow into it, contracting to hold urine in the patient's bladder, and then relaxing to allow urination.

The Swedish surgeons have restored bladder control to the two children on whom they operated. They stress that the method requires a normal nerve supply to the tissues around the bladder outlet. If these nerves are not present, the toe muscle cannot receive the necessary new nerve supply to function like a normal urinary sphincter muscle.

A beam in the eye. A miniaturized carbon dioxide (CO_2) laser instrument that may help to prevent blindness was described in November 1979. It is being designed by ophthalmologist

The first artificial spine is a complex array of rods mounted to bridge a gap in the spinal column between the ribcage and pelvis. It was designed to support the upper body, protect the spinal cord, and allow some flexibility in movement.

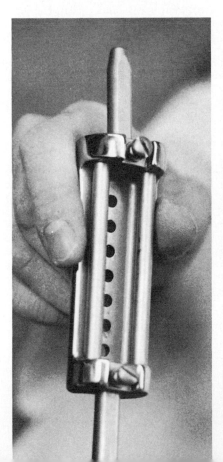

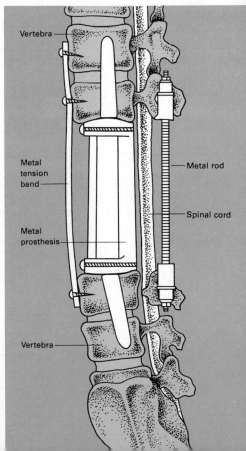

Vertebra

Metal tension band

Metal prosthesis

Metal rod

Spinal cord

Vertebra

Medicine
Continued

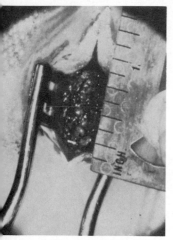

An incision only 2.54 centimeters (1 inch) in length along the spine is needed to treat a slipped disk in a microsurgical technique. The procedure limits blood loss and permits faster recovery than traditional operations.

David B. Karlin of the New York Hospital-Cornell Medical Center in New York City and laser researchers C. Kumar N. Patel and Obert R. Wood of Bell Telephone Laboratories in Murray Hill, N.J. Using the laser instrument, the ophthalmic surgeon can probe the eye to treat detached retinas and diabetic retinopathy, the leading cause of blindness in patients over 40. Diabetic retinopathy is a result of long-term diabetes. In the disease, abnormal blood vessels form in the retina and may bleed into the vitreous humor, the clear jellylike substance in the center of the eyeball. This can cause the vitreous humor to become cloudy, leading to blindness. Removal of the bloodfilled vitreous humor and associated scar tissue will sometimes restore vision, but the miniaturized mechanical cutters used to perform this surgery can damage delicate eye tissue.

The new CO_2 laser probe allows the surgeon to cut into the eye by evaporating the eye tissue. The probe simultaneously coagulates the blood vessels with the laser beam and thus prevents any extensive bleeding.

The laser probe's precision also allows surgeons to cut out eye tumors without removing the entire eye. Although argon and ruby lasers have been used extensively in treating eye diseases, the new CO_2 laser is especially suited to vitreous surgery because of its shallow penetration. The instrument effectively treats the tissue at the focus of the beam, but spares the vital surrounding eye structures.

Replantation comes of age. Surgeons successfully replanted the severed legs of a New York City man in June 1979 in the first known double-leg replantation operation. The surgery climaxed a series of dramatic operations in the United States and emphasized the growing importance and increasing success of limb replantation surgery.

The first successful limb replantation in the United States occurred in 1962, when a Massachusetts boy's arm was rejoined to his body. But such operations were rare until 1973, when the U. S. medical community became aware of advances made in China.

The Chinese had moved far ahead of the rest of the world, replanting hundreds of severed fingers, arms, legs, and feet with impressive success. They took a different approach to replantation, in that they repaired everything—blood vessels, tendons, and nerves—during the initial operation. Western surgeons generally repaired only the blood vessels in the first operation. The Chinese had also demonstrated that amputated parts could survive up to 24 hours if kept cool. The Chinese approach was eagerly adopted by surgeons in the United States. See SURGERY IN MINIATURE, *Science Year,* 1977.

Surgeon Harry J. Buncke, Jr., of San Mateo, Calif., estimates that by 1979 some 500 to 1,000 replantations occurred each year in the United States. Surgical teams report a success rate of from 70 to 90 per cent. However, this optimistic figure refers to survival, which simply means that blood circulation has been successfully re-established. In 1979 and 1980, surgeons began to evaluate functional survival — how much of the limb's normal function is restored. Restoring function depends on the rejoining of the severed nerves, which is still the most difficult part of this surgery.

Restoring function is a long process that often takes more than a year. This rehabilitation is such an important aspect of replantation surgery that patients are often selected only if they are considered capable of cooperating in the long and arduous program of exercise and retraining that is needed.

Improvement in surgical techniques and a greater number of experienced surgeons play a part in the recent increase in the number of replantations. In addition, replantation teams are ready to work around the clock throughout the United States. But also, the public has become aware of what can be done. People who observe an accident are alert to the need to retrieve and cool amputated parts.

Because of these factors, replantation can now be considered almost a routine procedure. Certainly, patients who have had this surgery are pleased with the results even when the function of the reattached part remains limited. Many have shown remarkable ingenuity and courage in coping with the functional disability. At best, they consider their own limb superior to an artificial one. [Frank E. Gump]

Meteorology

Meteorologists continued to make progress on a wide range of problems in 1979 and 1980. Some improvements resulted from developing new instruments and making better observations. Others came about in response to the increasing demand for more accurate long-range weather and climate forecasts in connection with energy use and agricultural projects.

An emerging United States energy policy favoring increased use of coal and synthetic fuels instead of oil and natural gas heightened meteorologists' concern about the build-up of carbon dioxide (CO_2) in the atmosphere. This would cause undesirable changes in the earth's climate. A National Academy of Sciences study group, chaired by meteorologist Jule G. Charney of Massachusetts Institute of Technology in Cambridge, examined that problem in July 1979.

Since systematic measurements were begun in 1958, the CO_2 concentration in the atmosphere has risen by about 20 parts per million (ppm) to 334 ppm in 1979. Charney's group reported that the effect of this atmospheric CO_2 on climate depends upon a complicated sequence of physical processes involving radiation, atmospheric moisture, and surface reflectivity.

From an analysis of the transfer of infrared radiation in the atmosphere, a radiation physicist, Vedrabhadran Ramanathan of the National Center for Atmospheric Research in Boulder, Colo., and planetary scientists Ming-Shih Lian and Robert D. Cess of the Laboratory for Planetary Atmospheres Research at State University of New York in Stony Brook drew some interesting conclusions. They showed in August 1979 that in the absence of certain climatic feedback processes triggered by the radiative warming, doubling the atmospheric CO_2 would cause heating. This heating, in turn, would raise the earth's atmospheric temperature by about 1°C.

However, Charney pointed out that surface temperature increases significantly in the presence of these feedback processes. For example, when the atmosphere is warmed by the direct radi-

A computer-generated map of rainfall in England during a disastrous August 1979 storm is based on radar data. Dark gray areas on the map represent heaviest rainfall. Such maps will make it possible to track approaching storms and accurately predict rain six hours before it falls.

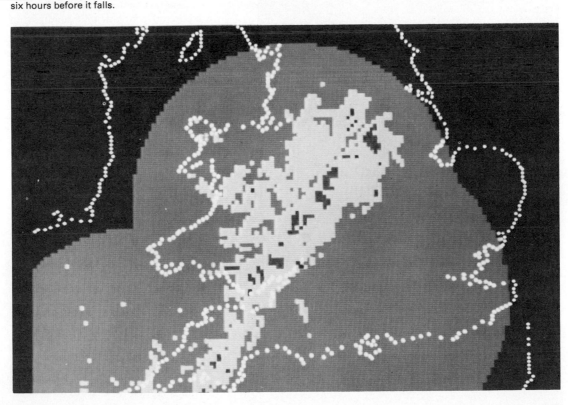

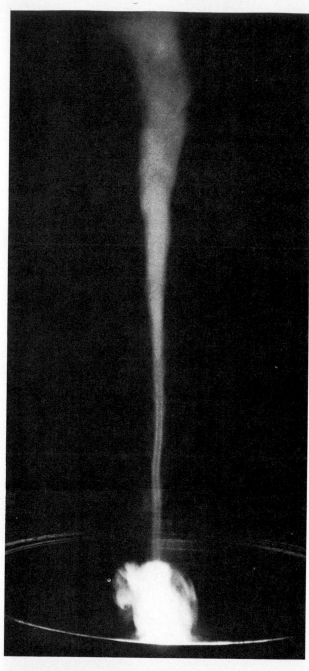

A tornado simulator at Purdue University creates a miniature twister 92 centimeters (36 inches) high for storm research. A fan sucks air from below into the chamber, which revolves to create the whirling vortex.

ative absorption of CO_2, it holds more water vapor. This increases infrared absorption, and additional warming of 1°C to 2°C therefore occurs as a result of this increase.

The research also showed that a further increase of the overall warming to about 3°C for doubled CO_2 could be expected from the feedback between the surface temperature and the decreasing reflectivity of melting snow and ice, which increases the earth's absorption of solar radiation.

In a related experiment, the investigators sought to learn why clouds have only a small effect on the temperature rise accompanying CO_2 increase. They found that the clouds' reflection of solar radiation, which leads to cooling, and their net absorption of infrared radiation, which leads to warming, tend to cancel each other. The former dominates when low and mid-level clouds increase, while the latter dominates when high clouds increase. Thus, if more clouds formed at all levels as a result of increased CO_2, as seems to occur, there would be little effect on the temperature.

A general circulation model (GCM) is a computer program that simulates in detail the three-dimensional behavior of the earth's atmosphere as it changes over time. Research meteorologists use GCMs to study hypothetical situations in an effort to better understand the real world. Syukuro Manabe and Richard T. Wetherald of the National Oceanic and Atmospheric Administration's (NOAA) Geophysical Fluid Dynamics Laboratory in Princeton, N.J., reported in January 1980 that they had confirmed earlier results obtained with such a model.

They hypothesized a swamplike ocean in a world without seasons and with a specific distribution of land and ocean, where doubled CO_2 causes an average atmospheric warming of 3°C. They found that the warming in such a world would reach as much as 8°C in the lower atmospheric levels at high latitudes. They also found that rainfall and evaporation would increase at nearly all latitudes.

However, the normal mid-latitude rain belt would shift toward the poles and soil moisture would decrease in normally agricultural regions. If such

A powerful sound generator produces intense audio pulses and analyzes their echoes to measure the speed and direction of winds and the heights at which temperature inversion layers form. The device is designed to help understand and forecast smog.

Meteorology

Continued

changes actually occurred, the consequences to farmers would be drastic.

Manabe and Ronald J. Stouffer, also a research meteorologist at NOAA's Princeton laboratory, reported an important extension of this work. When they considered the effects of the changing seasons, along with a shallow and static mixed layer of ocean water — approximately the top 50 meters (164 feet) of water — in actual geography, the average warming accompanying a doubling of CO_2 was lowered to about 2°C. This new calculation showed that it would take about 15 years before the mixed layer — and hence the overlying atmosphere — cooled off enough to remain in balance.

This work showed that the CO_2 induced warming in high latitudes would occur only in the winter months, especially in the Northern Hemisphere. It also suggested that Arctic Ocean ice would disappear each summer if the atmospheric CO_2 were to reach four times its present concentration.

New support for some of these research efforts came from the U.S. De-

partment of Energy (DOE) through the Carbon Dioxide Effects Research and Assessment Program. In April 1980, Roger C. Dahlman and Thomas Gross, research administrators of the DOE program in Washington, D.C.; Lester Machta and William P. Elliott, administrative research scientists with NOAA's Environmental Research Laboratories in Washington, D.C.; and Michael C. MacCracken, a research meteorologist at the University of California's Lawrence Livermore Laboratory and a DOE consultant, reviewed progress on the CO_2 problem. They reported that, in addition to devising new GCMs and continuing research on the carbon cycle's action, meteorologists opened 15 new CO_2-monitoring stations during 1979, expanding the worldwide network from 10 to 25 sites.

The long-term role of the biomass — surface vegetation, such as forests, and organic matter in the soil — in the earth's carbon budget is widely recognized. However, the report emphasized that no one knows whether the biomass is acting as a source or a sink (removal mechanism) for atmospheric CO_2. Similarly, the rate at which the oceans can remove CO_2 from the atmosphere depends on the solubility of CO_2 in surface ocean waters and, in turn, on surface waters mixing with deeper ocean waters.

The scientists also noted that the oceans' ability to absorb CO_2 decreases as water temperature and CO_2 concentration increase. The warmer surface waters of the world's oceans are now saturated with CO_2, and researchers believe they are the reservoir into which about half of the man-made CO_2 has passed. The great size of this potential CO_2 reservoir makes the oceans' behavior critically important.

Global Weather Experiment. During May and June of 1979, researchers observed the earth's atmosphere and oceans more intensely than ever before. Research meteorologist Rex J. Fleming of NOAA summarized the results of the second Special Observing Period (SOP-II) of the Global Weather Experiment in November 1979. Activities during this period, which was part of the Global Atmospheric Research Program (GARP), included about 39,000 daily surface observations from land stations, 3,000 daily surface observations from ocean stations, 2,800 daily upper-air observations from both land and ocean stations, and 4,900 daily aircraft reports. In addition, the system of five geostationary satellites positioned over the equator and operated by the European Space Agency, Japan, and the United States provided more than 130,000 measurements of cloud motion during SOP-II.

The U.S. polar-orbiting satellites NOAA-5 and TIROS-N made nearly 1 million measurements of sea-surface temperature. NOAA-6 was launched on June 27 to provide additional atmospheric soundings and reports from remote sensing platforms.

SOP-II also included the especially successful Southern Hemisphere Drifting Buoy Program. Eight nations launched 243 buoys that transmitted until July 31, 1979, providing measurements of pressure and temperature at the sea surface. [W. Lawrence Gates]

Microbiology

A team of molecular biologists in April 1980 reported the first successful transplant of a gene into a living animal. Previously, scientists had succeeded in inserting genetic material that functions only in cells in cultures.

Martin J. Cline, Howard Stang, Karen Mercola, Larry Morse, Ruth Ruprecht, Jeffrey Browne, and Winston Salser of the University of California, Los Angeles, worked with a gene for resistance to methotrexate (MTX), a toxic drug used in cancer therapy. They inserted the MTX-resistance gene into bone marrow cells of mice who had no resistance to the drug. MTX works by inhibiting an enzyme, dihydrofolate reductase (DHFR), that stimulates cell division and promotes tumor growth. If bone marrow cells could be made resistant to MTX, the drug could inhibit tumor growth in other parts of the body, but bone marrow cells could grow normally.

To transplant the gene, the scientists first extracted bone marrow cells from nonresistant mice and transferred the cells to a special culture with deoxyribonucleic acid (DNA) extracted from cells of resistant mice. The nonresistant cells absorbed the DNA. These cells, which could be identified by distinctive surface molecules, were removed from the culture by centrifuge and mixed with equal numbers of untreated marrow cells taken from nonresistant mice.

This cell mixture was injected into the bone marrow of another group of mice that had been radiated so that they could no longer produce their own bone marrow cells. The injected cells —those from nonresistant mice and those with the transplanted resistance gene—divided and eventually constituted most of the mice's marrow cells.

The scientists then divided the mice into two groups and treated one group with MTX. The other group served as a control. The scientists assumed that if the resistance gene had been successfully transplanted, the cells carrying that gene would produce DHFR. In the mice treated with MTX, the cells with the transplanted resistance gene should have an advantage over the cells without resistance genes. The scientists

Microbiology

Continued

expected these mice to have more resistant than nonresistant cells.

The research group took blood samples from the mice and found that cells with the resistance gene comprised 68 per cent of the cells in the treated group and 35 per cent in the control group 71 days after inoculation. The cells with the resistance genes had become predominant in MTX-treated mice.

In another check on the results, Cline and his team tested the levels of DHFR produced in the spleens of another group of MTX-treated mice and of a control group of untreated mice. They found that the DHFR levels in the treated mice were two to four times higher than those in the controls. They concluded that the cells with the transplanted resistance gene were predominant only in MTX-treated mice.

Although the procedure might work to confer drug resistance on human cells, it does not necessarily open the way for other types of gene transplants. Cline suggested that the technique worked with the MTX-resistance gene only because the gene gave its cell an advantage during MTX treatment. Other cells were killed by MTX, allowing the resistant cells to multiply.

Other desirable genes, such as the gene for a normal oxygen-carrying protein, β-globin, which is defective in victims of sickle-cell anemia, would not confer any immediate survival advantage on bone marrow cells. However, Cline thinks it might be possible to link these kinds of genes to resistance genes. For example, a β-globin gene could be linked to an MTX-resistance gene and transplanted in bone marrow cells. In a sickle-cell patient inoculated with these cells and then treated with MTX, the MTX-resistance cells—carrying the β-globin gene—would multiply.

Fungal herbicides were reported in September 1979 to be an effective alternative to chemical herbicides for some crops. Plant pathologists Clyde D. Boyette and George E. Templeton of the University of Arkansas in Fayetteville and R. J. Smith of the U.S. Department of Agriculture in Stuttgart, Ark., tested two fungi against weeds in rice and soybean fields. One fungus infects the

Square bacteria with light gas vacuoles, *right* (magnified 2,400 times), belong to a newly discovered species whose unique shape is determined by the structure of the cell wall rather than by internal pressure. Other new-found bacteria, *far right* (magnified 2,000 times), which can convert sugars to alcohol at very high temperatures, are a potential energy source.

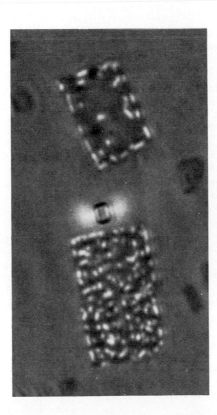

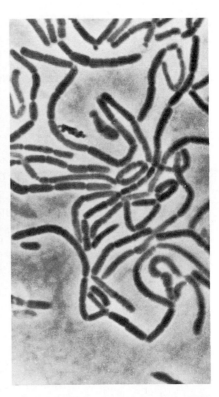

Microbiology
Continued

winged water primrose, the other infects the northern jointvetch, related weeds with similar growth patterns.

The Arkansas researchers collected fungus-ridden weeds, ground them up, and centrifuged fungus spores from the residue. They used these spores to develop large fungal cultures in commercial fermenters and gathered large stocks of long-lived spores from these cultures. They then harvested spores and mixed them with water to make a solution that was sprayed on the fields.

Over a three-year period, the scientists recorded 90 per cent fewer weeds in the treated fields than in untreated control fields. They concluded that the fungal controls were as effective as the chemical herbicides previously used. The fungi infected only one variety or closely related varieties of plants and caused no apparent harm to animals.

Generations of virus. Research reported in January 1980 raised the possibility that a virus causing serious developmental defects in humans may be passed on from one generation to the next. Immunologists Francis J. Dutko, Alan R. Brautigam, and Michael B. A. Oldstone of Scripps Clinic and Research Foundation in La Jolla, Calif., made this discovery while studying the cytomegalovirus (CMV) in mice.

The Scripps scientists infected mice with CMV at birth and took cell samples from the animals at regular intervals. One week after infection, they found that each cell in the ovaries of the female mice and in the testes of the male mice contained copies of CMV DNA. The amount of CMV DNA in these reproductive tissues declined as the mice grew older, but all the mice still had detectable amounts as adults, indicating that the virus might lie dormant in the reproductive organs.

Their findings suggest diagnostic difficulties if the virus behaves the same way in humans. Because physicians have assumed that CMV is transmitted from the mother as the baby passes through the birth canal, they test for the active virus in newborn infants. But tests cannot detect an inactive virus transmitted to the fetus in the uterus. [R. S. Hanson and M. J. Albert]

Neuroscience

Brain tissue from fetal, or unborn, rats, implanted in brain-damaged adult rats, markedly improved the functions of the damaged area, researchers announced in June and November 1979. Working independently, neuroscientists Mark J. Perlow and his associates at the National Institute for Mental Health in Bethesda, Md., the University of Colorado Medical School in Denver, and the Karolinska Institute in Stockholm, Sweden, and Anders Björklund and his associates at the University of Lund in Sweden studied rats whose brains had been chemically damaged.

The damage badly disturbed the rats' physical movements and significantly reduced their levels of dopamine, an important neurochemical transmitter of information between brain cells. The researchers grafted pieces of brain tissue taken from the *substantia nigra,* a part of the fetal brain that is a major source of dopamine, to the appropriate parts of the damaged brains of adult rats.

In most cases, the transplanted material began to grow and function, and make contact with other parts of the brain. Most important, the rats' muscular control markedly improved.

The Lund researchers and other scientists had previously shown that brain cells and pieces can survive and function after being implanted in the brains of other animals. However, the 1979 reports were the first to indicate that an implant from the brain of one animal to another improved disturbed behavior in the receiving animal. Parkinson's disease, a disorder of the human nervous system that reduces muscular control, is caused by a disruption of the dopamine supply. Researchers hope that further studies of this kind may lead to cures for Parkinson's and perhaps other such human diseases.

Color-coded cells. Single brain cells "perceive" color in the same way humans report seeing color. In April 1980, neuroanatomist Semir M. Zeki of University College in London published the results of his research on the electrical activity that rhesus monkey brain cells produced when the animals perceived color.

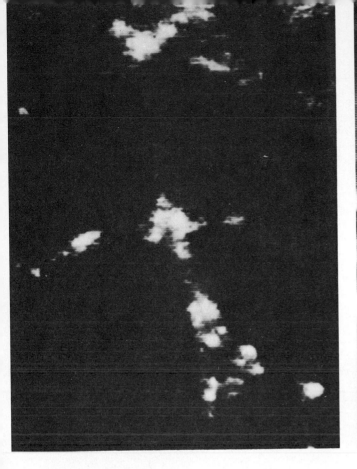

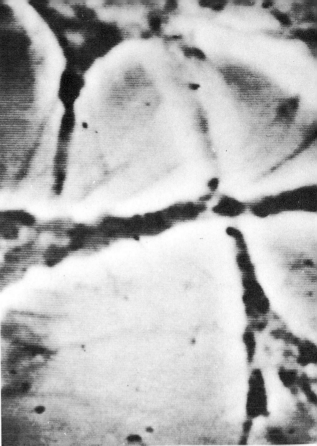

Neuroscience

Continued

Molecules of enkephalin treated with a fluorescing chemical can be seen in brain cells in a fluorescent microgram, *above*. Comparison with a normal microgram of the same cells, *above right*, shows that enkephalin, a natural pain-killing substance found in the brain, concentrates where nerve cells interconnect.

The studies stem in part from the work of scientist Edwin H. Land, who invented the Polaroid Land Camera. Land proposed the "retinex theory" of color vision, which states that the amount of red, green, or blue light on an object does not determine what color we see. Land used collages of colored papers, which he named Mondrian displays after Piet Mondrian, a Dutch painter. When Land changed either the amount or the color of the light that was falling on a Mondrian display, observers reported that the colors of the individual papers remained essentially unchanged.

Zeki showed Mondrian displays to rhesus monkeys and recorded individual brain cell responses. He used a painless technique to insert an electrode into single cells in a monkey's cortex — the outer layer of the brain — and found cells that responded selectively to differently colored papers when the monkey looked at them. When Zeki changed the color of the light shining on the Mondrian displays, the response of each cell was unchanged — just as the human perception of the colors of the papers was unchanged with changing illumination in Land's experiments. The work provides new insights into the basic mechanisms of sensory processing.

Nature needs nurture. Two independent studies published in October 1979 demonstrated that differences in rearing conditions can cause basic structural changes in brain cells during development. Neuroscientists Mary K. Floeter and William T. Greenough of the University of Illinois in Urbana-Champaign raised 16 monkeys from birth to 6 months in one of three situations: in isolation; with some social exposure; or in a seminatural colony with much energetic physical activity.

After sacrificing the monkeys, the researchers dissected Purkinje nerve cells from the cerebellums of the animals. The cerebellum is the structure at the back of the brain that is involved in the control of motor activity. The branches extending from some Purkinje cells of monkeys raised in the active environment developed in a more complex way than those from monkeys kept in restricted environments.

Neuroanatomists Joseph J. Pysh and Gary M. Weiss of Northwestern University Medical School in Chicago did similar studies on baby mice. They raised one group of six mice in a large cage where the mice exercised actively in a variety of devices — ladders, tunnels, and running wheels. They even trained the mice to swim and climb. The other group of five litter mates were kept in a small cage and moved only enough to eat and drink.

When the mice were 35 days old, they were sacrificed and their cerebellums examined. Again, the researchers found that Purkinje cells from the active animals had larger branches with more spines than did those of the inactive animals.

The implication that early environmental stimulation and physical exercise has an important effect on brain cell development in two mammalian species — monkeys and mice — may well have direct bearing on methods of rearing human infants.

Fruit fly larvae can learn to discriminate between specific odors, according to neuroscientists William G. Quinn and Efraim O. Aceves-Piña of Princeton University in New Jersey. In their 1979 experiments, the researchers placed about 100 of the tiny larvae in a dish and gave them 30-second pulses of two different odors known to attract fruit fly larvae. The larvae received electrical shocks with the first odor, none with the second. After three trials, the larvae were exposed again to the odors. A significant number moved away from the odor that had been paired with the shock and toward the nonshocking one, indicating that they remembered the bad experience.

The larvae forget more quickly than adult flies. All trace of memory of the shock was gone in 30 minutes while adults "trained" in the same type of experiment retained some learned behavior for as long as six hours. Neuroscientists can use this extremely simple brain as a tool for studying the fundamental cellular processes involved in learning.   [George Adelman]

Nutrition

The relationship between diet and such diseases as atherosclerosis and cancer was questioned in a May 1980 report issued by the Food and Nutrition Board of the National Research Council (NRC). The board, a group of scientists that sets the Recommended Dietary Allowances (RDAs) for essential nutrients, commented on dietary influences on obesity, diabetes, and hypertension, or high blood pressure.

A major finding — that a link between dietary intake of cholesterol and the development of atherosclerosis has not been proved — raised a storm of controversy in nutritional circles. Atherosclerosis is the accumulation of fatty deposits in arteries that restrict blood flow and lead to heart disease and stroke. It is the most common cause of death in the United States. Many nutritionists believe that a diet high in cholesterol promotes atherosclerosis by increasing blood levels of the fatty substance.

Basing their report on studies of how low cholesterol diets affect the incidence of heart disease, the American

Heart Association and a U.S. Senate committee recommended in 1977 that U.S. adults reduce their cholesterol intake from an average of 450 milligrams (mg) per day to 300 mg per day. They also advised a total reduction of diet fats from 40 to 30 per cent of total caloric intake. Reviewing the same evidence in December 1979, the American Society of Clinical Nutrition found persuasive evidence that dietary cholesterol was linked to atherosclerosis.

The NRC board was unimpressed with the diet studies, particularly with regard to cholesterol, saying that they showed only marginal reductions in heart disease. The NRC board recommended that the fat content of the diet, including cholesterol, be adjusted to the individual's requirements. It saw no reason to reduce the intake of fats in infants, adolescent boys, pregnant teen-agers, and adults who do heavy manual labor. Less active persons were advised to adjust their intake as needed to maintain proper weight.

The American Medical Association and industry groups such as the

Nutrition

Continued

National Dairy Council and the National Livestock and Meat Board supported the NRC recommendation. But other groups, notably the American Heart Association, continued to advocate a lowering of dietary cholesterol. The Department of Agriculture and the Department of Health and Human Services also declined to alter their anticholesterol stands. Many nutritionists criticized the makeup of the NRC board, pointing out that there were no cardiologists or epidemiologists—scientists who study disease patterns in populations—in the group.

The board also examined possible connections between diet and several forms of cancer, the second leading cause of death in the United States. Past studies have shown that obesity is associated with breast cancer, the most common cancer in women, and cancer of the uterus. Colon cancer has been linked with high-fat, low-fiber diets.

The NRC board found little evidence that specifically implicated any major nutrient as a cause of cancer. But it admitted that overall caloric intake—either too high or too low—might be related to some cancers.

Since the 1920s, great progress has been made in treating nutritional deficiency diseases such as scurvy, rickets, pellagra, goiter, and general malnutrition. The addition of certain vitamins, minerals, and proteins to the diet practically eradicated these disorders. However, Americans have developed a new spectrum of nutritional diseases—the diseases of overconsumption. While diet may not be their only cause, it nonetheless may be a decisive factor, and one that can be affected by intelligent diet planning.

Obesity, or overweight, is really a form of malnutrition—the most common form in the Western world, according to the board. It is clearly related to the overconsumption of food. The body simply takes in more food than can be expended as energy, so fat is stored in the body. Lack of physical activity may also be an important factor. The NRC board recommended a proper balance of diet and exercise as the best way to combat obesity.

Closely related to obesity is the adult-onset type of diabetes mellitus. This disorder occurs most frequently in people who are overweight. In adult-onset diabetes, body cells do not respond properly to insulin, which removes sugar from the blood. Adult-onset diabetes can usually be regulated by diet and exercise.

High blood pressure is a common cause of disability and death in the United States. Much high blood pressure is now thought to be associated with a diet high in salt. Most high blood pressure occurs in persons who have a high-salt diet, and it can readily be induced in experimental animals by feeding them a high-salt diet. The disease is treated by a low-salt diet and proper medication.

The average American consumes about 10 grams (0.35 ounce) of salt per day — more than 20 times the daily nutritional requirement of 250 to 500 mg. The board believes that the average American's salt intake is excessive and could be reduced to 3 grams (0.1 ounce) per day with no harm to most

people and perhaps some benefit to the 15 to 20 per cent of the population who risk developing hypertension. See MEDICINE (Internal Medicine).

Except with reference to obesity, the report did not discuss the consumption of alcohol. However, about 8 per cent of the total calories in the U.S. diet come from alcoholic beverages. Furthermore, alcohol has been decisively associated with several degenerative diseases, including cirrhosis of the liver, now among the 10 leading causes of death in the United States.

In its conclusions, the NRC board warned against excessive fears about our present diet and excessive hopes for different diets, especially with regard to avoiding disease. It emphasized that individuals vary in metabolism and in their susceptibility to disease, and stressed the responsibility of each individual to select a nutritionally adequate and varied diet. Good food, it said, "should not be regarded as a poison, a medicine, or a talisman [magic charm]. It should be eaten and enjoyed." [Edward G. Nash]

Oceanography

Marine scientists in 1979 and 1980 reported new findings on the intricate links between marine organisms and their environment, the effects of pollutants and wastes on marine life, and the origins of the sea floor and ocean water. They also developed new tools for exploring the evolution of ocean basins.

Oceanographer Stefan Gartner and meteorologist James P. McGuirk of Texas A&M University in College Station reported in December 1979 that ocean-induced climate change might explain the abrupt extinction of dinosaurs 65 million years ago. The scientists theorized that a combination of crustal-plate movement and retreating shallow seas may have isolated the Arctic Ocean from other oceans about 90 million years ago. Excess rainfall and runoff then flushed out the salt water, making the Arctic Ocean either a fresh or *brackish* (slightly salty) body of water.

About 65 million years ago, this water recirculated, sharply reducing the ocean's surface salinity and lowering its surface temperature. Such a

change would make the climate much cooler and drier and alter the distribution of plants and animals. This change is documented in the fossil record.

Gartner and McGuirk suggested that a prolonged drought lasting about 10 years could have abruptly wiped out the large animals, including the dinosaurs, while the smaller reptiles and mammals survived. Dinosaurs were adapted to a moderate climate with a constant year-round food supply. They probably never learned to cope with seasonal variations in food supply by migrating. Consequently, most dinosaurs died when food or water ran out in their territory.

Wastes and marine life. Efforts to determine the effects of waste materials on marine life emphasized the intricate ties between organisms and their environment. Scientists reported in January 1980 that they had completed an eight-year study of the effects of pollutants on communities of marine organisms. They used large plastic bags suspended in the waters of Patricia Bay, Vancouver Island, Canada, to test the

Oceanography

effects of pollution in the Controlled Ecosystem Pollution Experiment (CEPEX).

Marine zoologist George D. Grice of Woods Hole Oceanographic Institution in Massachusetts summarized the results of CEPEX and related experiments. He determined that laboratory studies on a single species provide limited and sometimes misleading results. For example, bacteria and phytoplankton reacted almost the same in the bags as in the laboratory. However, lower doses of pollutants affected zooplankton in the bags than in the laboratory.

Grice also reported that smaller organisms are more vulnerable to pollutants than larger ones, and the young are more sensitive than adults. How fast a population of organisms recovers after exposure to pollution depends on its reproductive speed. For example, bacteria are affected first by pollutants, but there are so many types and they adapt and breed so fast that the bacteria population as a whole recovers rapidly. Zooplankton, which have fewer species, smaller populations, and longer reproductive spans, recover more slowly. See WATCH ON THE SELF-HEALING EARTH.

A richer harbor. Environmentalists usually try to prevent factories from dumping their by-products into local water sources. However, rich nutrients from fish-processing wastes and treated sewage, mixed in the water by local winds and currents, helped to revitalize Los Angeles Harbor, scientists reported in 1979. The area, virtually devoid of life in 1971, had become the richest soft-bottom marine area in southern California by 1974. But efforts begun in 1977 to further improve the harbor waters backfired.

Marine biologists Dorothy F. Soule and Mikihiki Oguri of the University of Southern California, Los Angeles, reported in April on their biological analysis of the harbor from 1977 to 1979. They showed that the harbor's population of fish, bacteria, and bottom-dwelling organisms declined sharply after secondary waste treatment on fish-cannery and sewage wastes began in 1977. The number of birds that eat these animals also declined.

The more stringent disposal standards disrupted a highly productive food web nurtured by the availability of nutrient-rich wastes. Soule and Oguri suggested that releasing controlled levels of cannery and sewage wastes into the harbor without secondary treatment would improve the nutrient balance and biological productivity.

Male whale songs. Marine scientists maintained their fascination with the great ocean mammals. Peter Tyack of Rockefeller University in New York City continued to analyze the songs of the humpback whale, and reported in January 1980 that it is the male humpbacks who sing during the breeding season. He speculated that their songs might play a role in mating much like that played by birdsong in signaling species identity, sex, location, and readiness to mate.

Katherine Payne of the New York Zoological Society also reported in January that humpback songs recorded near Bermuda from 1959 to 1980 revealed most of the whales sing a similar song on any given date, but that the song continually changes over time. The song is almost totally replaced over a four-year period. Although the changes are extensive, all the humpback whales use the current version of the song.

Galapagos Rift revisited. Marine organisms such as the clams, mussels, worms, and crabs that live near volcanically heated hydrothermal vents 2½ kilometers (1½ miles) beneath the sea surface thrive on bacteria that produce carbon dioxide. Before scientists using the submersible *Alvin* detected these vents, they believed that such animals fed on the small fraction of food that was converted to particulate matter by photosynthesis in the sunlit upper levels of the ocean and then fell to the great depths. However, it is now clear that organisms in the hydrothermal vent communities do not depend on nutrients based on photosynthesis.

Oceanographers David M. Karl of the University of Hawaii in Honolulu and Carl O. Wirsen and Holgar W. Jannasch of Woods Hole Oceanographic Institution reported in March 1980 that new studies made at the Galapagos Rift in the Pacific Ocean confirmed data that scientists on *Alvin* collected in 1977 (see LIFE WHERE THE EARTH IS RENEWED, *Science Year*, 1979). The

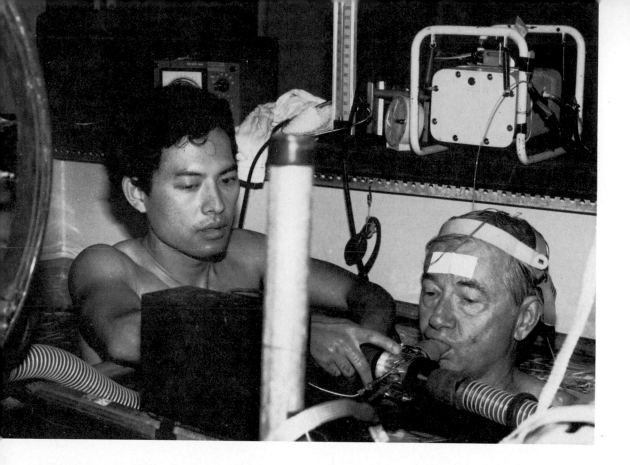

Oceanography

Continued

A volunteer is monitored for heartbeat and breathing rate as he pedals a bicycle while submerged in a tank of water. Such tests determine stress effects on humans who live and work under water.

new studies show that the biological communities in these vents rely on bacterial chemosynthesis. The scientists reported that the organisms feed on bacteria that they filter from the water or scrape off rock surfaces.

Hot springs on the RISE. Fred N. Spiess of Scripps Institution of Oceanography in La Jolla, Calif., reported in March 1980 that the scientists in the Rivera Submersible Experiments (RISE) program were continuing to study the creation of new ocean crust. The RISE site is about 1,045 kilometers (650 miles) north of the Galapagos Rift on the East Pacific Rise crest. The Pacific and Rivera plates, which make up part of the ocean floor, are separating there at the rapid rate of about 60 millimeters (2.4 inches) per year.

Using remote-controlled cameras and direct observations from *Alvin,* RISE team members determined that a zone of recent volcanic activity about 1,000 meters (3,300 feet) wide stretches along the axis of the East Pacific Rise. They saw 25 active hydrothermal vents along a 7-kilometer (4-mile) strip that

ranged from 200 to 300 meters (650 to 980 feet) wide.

Some vents released clear water at temperatures of 5°C to 20°C (41°F. to 68°F.) and showed flow rates of only centimeters per second and marine life similar to that on the Galapagos Rift. The oceanographers named other vents "black smokers" because they spewed water containing dark particulate matter at rates estimated at hundreds of centimeters per second, and temperatures estimated at up to 380°C (716°F.). Based on observations at the Galapagos Rift and the East Pacific Rise, the RISE team concluded that vent communities are widespread.

Marine chemists John Edmond of Massachusetts Institute of Technology in Cambridge and Harmon Craig of Scripps Institution of Oceanography retraced Spiess's route in *Alvin* and visited the East Pacific Rise site in November 1979. Using improved temperature probes, they determined that the water from the hottest vents was a uniform 350°C (662°F.). Preliminary analysis showed that the vent water

Oceanography
Continued

contained fairly high concentrations of helium, methane, hydrogen sulfide, and dissolved metals and silica, but lacked typical sea-water chemicals such as magnesium and sulfate. Copper and lead were also found near the vents.

Oceanographers estimate that ocean water filters through the deep basaltic rock of the seabed once every 8 million to 10 million years. Analysis of waters returned to the ocean through vents like those along the Galapagos Rift and the East Pacific Rise will improve scientists' understanding of the role this process plays in controlling ocean chemistry. See GEOPHYSICS.

Deep-sea drilling. Geologists on the drilling ship *Glomar Challenger* used several new instruments to extend the depth from which they could extract sea-floor cores. In August 1979, they used a recently developed hydraulic piston corer to take samples of sediment from the floor of the Caribbean Sea and eastern Pacific Ocean. The device enabled them to compile a detailed, continuous magnetic and biological record of the past 8 million years. Knowledge of both the magnetic and fossil changes is necessary for accurate dating. Earlier drilling and coring devices had scrambled the soft upper layers of sea-floor sediment and made it impossible to trace the sedimentary record in fine detail.

A second innovation, a specialized imaging device lowered into a drill hole midway between Ecuador and the Galapagos Islands, gave scientists their first look at the inside of a drill hole. The device, originally designed for oil-well inspection, scanned the walls of a hole drilled through about 260 meters (850 feet) of sediment and 75 meters (245 feet) of basalt that lay 3.2 kilometers (2 miles) below the ocean surface.

Using these images, the scientists put together a 2.7-meter (9-foot) mosaic showing the horizontal layering of the sediment and the lower, more complex fissures, cracks, and cavities within the sea-floor rock. This picture confirmed the theory that the ocean bottom results from eruptions of lava along mid-ocean ridges, and that such rock is porous. [Feenan D. Jennings]

Physics

Atomic and Molecular Physics. Two physicists at the University of Amsterdam in the Netherlands announced in January 1980 that they had maintained hydrogen gas in its atomic form for 10 minutes. Ordinary hydrogen gas is in the form of molecules made up of two hydrogen atoms (H_2). Atomic hydrogen gas is easy to produce in the laboratory by passing H_2 through a space that has an electrical current flowing through it. But until the Amsterdam experiment, all the atoms formed in this manner recombined into H_2 within a fraction of a second.

Isaac F. Silvera and J. T. M. Walraven kept the atoms from recombining by orienting the directions in which their single electrons orbited their single-proton nuclei and by maintaining that orientation. Physicists call these directions spin-up and spin-down. A spin-up hydrogen atom will form a hydrogen molecule only with a spin-down atom.

First, the scientists formed a beam of hydrogen atoms by passing molecular hydrogen through an electrical discharge. Then they pumped a vapor of superfluid helium—a liquid that flows without resistance—at a temperature of about 2.19°C (3.94°F.) above absolute zero (−273.15°C or −459.67°F.) into the beam, pumping hydrogen atoms into an open cylinder a few centimeters long. A powerful magnet surrounding the cylinder repelled spin-down atoms but allowed spin-up atoms to enter the cylinder.

The magnetic field maintained the spin directions of the atoms that moved about inside the cylinder. But the scientists' early attempts failed because many atoms collided with the cylinder wall with such impact that they turned upside down and quickly combined with spin-up atoms to form H_2.

Silvera and Walraven then coated the wall with a moving layer of superfluid helium to soften the impacts. The coating reduced the number of spin reversals so that nearly all of the atoms "stayed single" for 10 minutes.

Light push. Scientists led by physicist Ronald F. Stebbings of Rice University in Houston discovered in the spring of

$$\int_a^b f(x)\,dx + \int \sum_{i-1}^{rn} \Delta_{\gamma}$$

"This is the part I always hate."

Physics

Continued

1979 that radiation at room temperature raised the energy level of an atom in its Rydberg state. In a Rydberg atom, a negatively charged outer electron orbits so far from the positively charged nucleus that the electrical attraction between them is very weak.

The distance of an electron's orbit from the nucleus depends upon the electron's energy level — the greater the energy, the higher the orbit. An electron can jump to a higher orbit if it absorbs a sufficient amount of energy, called a quantum, from a photon — a particle of electromagnetic radiation. Physicists describe the atom's energy level by a numeral called the principal quantum number, n. Most atomic physicists experiment with atoms that have principal quantum numbers of 1 through 5 and outermost orbits about one angstrom (one hundred-millionth of a centimeter) in radius.

However in Rydberg atoms, n is as large as 100 or more, and the radius of the outermost orbit ranges to hundreds of angstroms. At such large distances, the electron is bound to its nucleus so weakly that it requires a quantum of only a few thousandths of an electron volt to jump from one orbit to the next, and only a few hundredths of an electron volt to escape the grip of the nucleus and leave the atom. By contrast, the outermost electron of the least energetic atom of xenon — the element that the Rice investigators used — must absorb 12 electron volts to escape.

The Rice physicists used a laser to irradiate xenon atoms, raising them to an n of 23. Nine-millionths of a second after the laser irradiation, the scientists turned on a rapidly increasing electrical field and recorded the voltage at which the electrons were removed. Had all of the irradiated atoms remained in the $n = 23$ state, the physicists would have detected electrons removed at only one voltage.

Instead, Stebbings' group found electrons removed at several·dozen voltages — those required to remove electrons from atoms in the $n = 23$, 24, 25, 26, and higher states. The researchers concluded that some atoms had absorbed room-temperature radiation that raised them to these higher states during the laser irradiation and before exposure to the electrical field.

Light measurement. Five scientists reported in September 1979 that they had made the first direct measurement of a visible laser light's frequency – the rate at which the photons that make up the light vibrate as they travel through space. This is the highest frequency measurement on record.

The scientists measured this frequency by comparing it with the frequency that defines the second – 9,192,631,770 cycles per second (hertz), a vibration rate of photons given off by cesium atoms. The laser frequency was about 520 trillion hertz (terahertz) – 56,571 times as great.

Kenneth M. Evenson, Donald A. Jennings, and F. Russell Peterson of the National Bureau of Standards (NBS) in Boulder, Colo., began with a klystron – a tube that produces high-frequency waves – calibrated against the cesium vibration. They compared the klystron's frequency with that of a klystron that produced higher-frequency waves, then repeated the procedure with a series of klystrons that produced waves of successively higher frequency. They reached the limit of this technique at a frequency of 0.89076055 terahertz, near the highest frequency that a klystron can produce.

But this frequency was close to that of a hydrogen cyanide laser, so the scientists calibrated such a laser to the last klystron. They then used a series of lasers and klystrons to tie the cesium frequency to the frequency of a near-infrared helium-neon laser – about 260 terahertz. This last step brought the derived frequency to half that of the visible laser light, but their technique could take them no further because they were near the limits of the devices that combine klystron and laser signals to produce higher frequencies.

Meanwhile, physicists Kenneth M. Baird and Gary R. Hanes of Canada's National Research Council in Ottawa had developed a laser that could produce waves whose frequency was exactly twice that of the near-infrared laser. The NBS scientists took their helium-neon laser to Ottawa and produced and measured radiation at about 520 terahertz.   [Karl G. Kessler]

Elementary Particles. Physicists obtained the first concrete evidence for the existence of particles called gluons in 1979 and 1980. Theoretical physicists developed gluon theories in the 1970s to explain the makeup of protons, neutrons, and other related particles.

According to these theories, these are not elementary particles, as was formerly believed. They are like miniature atoms, but 100,000 times smaller than atoms, and composed of still smaller subunits called quarks. Gluons hold quarks together by transmitting energy from one quark to another. Until June 1979, however, there was no direct indication that gluons really exist. See THE COLORFUL WORLD OF THE ATOM.

The evidence appeared in data taken at the German Electron Synchrotron Laboratory (DESY) near Hamburg, West Germany. It was obtained with the aid of the PETRA particle accelerator that began operating there in 1978. PETRA consists of two intersecting rings of strong electromagnets. One ring contains a beam of electrons and the other a beam of positrons – the antiparticles of electrons, which are like electrons except that they have a positive charge. The beams move in opposite directions and collide head-on where the rings intersect.

In such encounters, the particles and antiparticles annihilate one another, and their combined energy – as high as 36 billion electron volts (GeV) at PETRA – is converted into a burst of electromagnetic energy. This energy then turns into matter in the form of a particle and an antiparticle – usually a quark and an antiquark – traveling in opposite directions.

Quarks are never found alone, however. As long as collision energy is available, some of it will be used to manufacture more quarks and antiquarks in a process known as fragmentation. The quarks and antiquarks will combine in two jets of particles moving in opposite directions. Most of these particles are quarks linked to antiquarks in particles called mesons. The mesons are unstable, but they last long enough to be observed by particle detectors, so physicists can reconstruct the quark and antiquark motions.

However, part of the energy occasionally turns into a gluon, which also

315

fragments, producing a third jet of mesons. Physicists know that the third jet cannot be a quark or antiquark jet, because such jets form in pairs. And since only quarks and gluons can form jets, the very existence of an odd number of jets is strong evidence for the presence of a gluon.

Physicists using an assembly of particle detectors called TASSO reported the first clear examples of three-jet events in June 1979. Experiments at PETRA detectors named JADE and MARK-J had confirmed these findings by the end of the summer of 1979.

Missing partner. One PETRA discovery was somewhat disappointing, however. A search for new, heavier forms of quarks failed. So far, experimenters have found five kinds of quarks, called up (u), down (d), strange (s), charmed (c), and bottom or beauty (b). Physicists believe that there must be an even number of kinds of quarks. But the b quark, discovered in 1977 at the Fermi National Accelerator Laboratory (Fermilab) in Batavia, Ill., still has no partner. PETRA can provide more than enough energy to produce a quark four times as heavy as the b quark, so the failure proves that the proposed sixth quark, already named the top or truth (t) quark, must be at least that heavy.

The b quark has become the object of detailed study at the Cornell Electron Storage Ring (CESR), a 14-GeV electron-positron machine at Cornell University in Ithaca, N.Y., which began operation in October 1979. Although CESR is much less powerful than PETRA, it is ideal for studying b quarks, which are produced in combination with their antiquarks at energies slightly higher than 10 GeV. Electron-positron colliding-beam accelerators work best near their maximum energy, so 10 GeV is awkwardly low for the 36-GeV PETRA.

Exciting find. Two groups at CESR have been studying the upsilon particle, a b quark combined with a b antiquark. They confirmed the existence of two excited upsilon particles whose quarks and antiquarks move more rapidly than the quarks and antiquarks of normal upsilons. Physicists analyze the energy differences among the various versions of the upsilon to measure the force that binds the quark to its antiquark. These differences also provide a clue as to how this force depends on the distance between the quark and the antiquark.

Neutrino transformation. Frederick Reines and two other researchers from the University of California at Irvine revealed evidence in April 1980 that neutrinos may have some small amount of mass. Neutrino mass had previously proved too small to measure, so physicists were not certain that neutrinos had any mass.

Neutrinos have always been the most elusive subatomic particles. They are immune to most of the basic forces of nature, so they can pass right through the earth with only a small chance of hitting anything. There are three types of neutrino called electron, muon, and tau neutrinos for the particles that they can be transformed into after one of their rare collisions with a nucleus.

Physicists have long known that if neutrinos have some mass, and if the masses of the three types are not the same, then neutrinos of each type would be able to change into one of the other types. The Irvine researchers now think they have seen evidence of this kind of transformation.

The researchers used neutrinos produced by the decay of radioactive fission products at the Savannah River nuclear reactor of E. I. du Pont de Nemours & Company in South Carolina. They put a neutrino detector 11 meters (35 feet) from the reactor's core. The detector produced two kinds of signals — one that registered any type of neutrino and one that registered only electron neutrinos.

The signal indicating any type of neutrino indicated the presence of more than twice as many neutrinos as the one that registered electron neutrinos. This suggests that more than half of the electron neutrinos produced in the reactor might have changed into other types during their 11-meter flight to the neutrino detector.

If this result is confirmed, it could solve the long-standing mystery of the missing solar neutrinos. Raymond Davis of Brookhaven National Laboratory has for many years been observing neutrinos from the sun, using an electron-neutrino detector. He finds

Physics

Continued

A 110-wheel truck-trailer needed three weeks in 1979 to move a magnet weighing 97 metric tons (107 short tons) from its old home at Argonne National Laboratory near Chicago to the new PEP elementary particle research ring at Stanford Linear Accelerator Center in California.

only about one-third as many neutrinos as expected, considering the rate at which the sun emits energy. In their long flight from the sun, electron neutrinos would have more than enough time to transform into an equal mixture of the three types.

More beams. Now that PETRA has given European scientists their first taste of leadership in particle physics, they have launched two new projects to retain it. Both will be built at the multinational European Organization for Nuclear Research (CERN) near Geneva, Switzerland.

The first project, scheduled for completion in 1981, will provide CERN's present 400-GeV proton accelerator with a countercirculating beam of antiprotons. Because antiprotons are difficult to produce, head-on collisions will be fairly rare. But when they do occur, CERN will set a new record for energy of colliding particles. Fermilab plans to duplicate this arrangement with its proton accelerator, which eventually will be twice as powerful as CERN's. But the modified equipment will

not be ready until several years after the CERN project.

CERN's large electron-positron ring (LEP) project is even more ambitious. A 30-kilometer (19-mile) circular tunnel would contain countercirculating beams of electrons and positrons. The 12 nations that support CERN have approved LEP design studies but are not yet committed to the project.

U.S. projects. The future of U.S. particle physics is in some doubt. Brookhaven National Laboratory on Long Island, N.Y., has run into technical difficulties in its attempt to build ISABELLE, an accelerator that would produce head-on collisions of protons with protons at a combined energy of 400 GeV. Fermilab is moving ahead with plans to double the energy of its single-beam accelerator to 1,000 GeV, however, which will ensure leadership in this form of research. Construction was completed in April 1980 on an accelerator called PEP at the Stanford Linear Accelerator Center (SLAC) in Palo Alto, Calif. PEP is very nearly a twin of PETRA.   [Robert H. March]

Nuclear Physics. Physicists at the Massachusetts Institute of Technology (M.I.T.) in Cambridge announced in March 1980 that they had measured the distribution of protons in deformed nuclei. Scientists had determined the proton distribution in nondeformed, spherical nuclei by deflecting electrons from them. They deflected the electrons off nuclei that were in their ground state, their state of lowest energy, without transferring energy to the nuclei. They then measured the electrons' angular deflection and calculated the distribution of the protons. During the 1970s, researchers determined proton distributions within an accuracy of several per cent.

The M.I.T. physicists experimented with the much more complex deformed nuclei. These are nuclei of atoms with a total of neutrons and protons between 155 and 185 and greater than 225. The nuclei resemble a rotating football. Such a rotating nucleus can increase its energy state by taking on quanta, or packages, of angular momentum. The nucleus has a complete band of rota-

tional states, each corresponding to a certain amount of angular momentum. The key to determining the shape of the nucleus experimentally is to excite nuclei from the ground state to each of these rotationally excited states. To excite the nucleus to a specific rotational state, electrons must lose a precise amount of energy. Detectors measure the angles of deflection of these electrons so the shape can be calculated.

But previous experimenters could not obtain accurate results from this technique, because all machines that produce electron beams pose a serious problem. These machines, called electron accelerators, produce a beam of electrons with nearly uniform energy. But the range of difference in electron energies is larger than the energy loss to be measured. Thus, a high-energy electron that lost energy to the nucleus it struck might still be more energetic than a low-energy electron that did not lose any energy. The detector would not be able to distinguish between the two. However, the energy loss spectrometer built at the Bates Linear Ac-

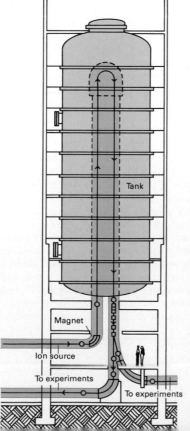

A new tandem Van de Graaff accelerator at Oak Ridge National Laboratory in Tennessee energizes heavy ions to 25 million electron volts as it pulls them up a 30-meter (98-foot) tank. It then repels them to the base, where magnets guide them to experiments.

celerator in Middleton, Mass., in 1975 made experiments with deformed nuclei feasible. The electron beam from the accelerator is spread out across the piece of material containing the nucleus to be struck so that the electrons strike the nuclei with energies that vary precisely with the location of their points of impact. The spectrometer magnet focuses a high-energy electron that loses a certain amount of energy at one edge of this target and a low-energy electron losing exactly the same amount of energy at the other edge on precisely the same point in the electron detector. As a result, the M.I.T. experimenters were able to make an extensive set of measurements over a five-year period on a variety of deformed nuclei.

Star collapse. Hans A. Bethe of Cornell University in Ithaca, N.Y., winner of the 1967 Nobel prize for physics, and Gerald E. Brown of State University of New York at Stony Brook in July 1979 published a theory of the nuclear physics governing the gravitational collapse of stars. Stars that are about 10 times as massive as the sun live about 10 million years. During that time, energy produced by nuclear fusion provides an outward pressure that prevents the star from collapsing because of the tremendous inward gravitational force. But fusion reactions occur only when light nuclei combine to form heavier products that have a greater total binding energy. Thus, the sequence of fusion reactions begins with hydrogen nuclei combining to form helium. The sequence ends with the production of iron nuclei, which are the most strongly bound of all nuclei.

When all the light nuclei in a star have undergone reactions leading to the formation of iron, there is no longer any energy source to counteract the gravitational force. Within about one second, the star collapses to the density of matter within a nucleus — 10^{14} (one hundred million million) times the density of water, or the density that would occur if all the matter in the earth were packed into a sphere with a radius as long as a football field.

The dynamics of stellar collapse is completely governed by the variation of pressure with density and temperature. The theory of Bethe and Brown explains the relationship of pressure, density, and temperature at densities from roughly one hundred-thousandth of nuclear density up to several times nuclear density. At stellar densities, the most significant component of matter is electrons. By the Pauli exclusion principle, developed by Austrian physicist Wolfgang Pauli in 1925, electrons must occupy different quantum states so increasing the density of electrons in a large container by decreasing the container's volume will force the electrons into successively higher energy states. Thus, both energy and pressure increase with density. As the density increases, electrons eventually become so energetic that they combine with protons to form neutrons and neutrinos. This produces new forms of nuclei containing a much larger ratio of neutrons to protons than in ordinary matter. Neutrinos travel at the speed of light and interact so weakly with other particles that collisions are highly improbable at stellar density. The neutrinos escape easily. However, at roughly one hundredth of nuclear density, the neutrinos become trapped inside the collapsing star.

A major question answered by the Bethe-Brown theory is the stellar density at which nucleons — protons and neutrons — cease to be bound in nuclei where they contribute relatively little pressure. At a certain density, the nucleons form a uniform gas that contributes much more pressure. During stellar collapse, nucleons remain in nuclei until the stellar matter becomes as dense as the nuclei. All nuclei then merge into a uniform gas.

The conclusion of the theory is that collapsing stellar matter does not decelerate until it becomes as dense as nuclear matter. At this density, a uniform nucleon gas forms, increasing the pressure substantially. This increased pressure reverses the collapse when the star's core reaches about three times nuclear density, forming a shock wave that travels outward. In stars of the appropriate mass, the shock wave blasts off the star's outer layer, forming a supernova. The material remaining in the core of the star, which is at nuclear density, forms a neutron star that has a mass approximately equal to that of the sun.   [John W. Negele]

Plasma Physics. Physicist Thomas C. Simonen and his research group at Lawrence Livermore National Laboratory (LLNL) in California verified experimentally the basic theoretical properties of the tandem mirror concept (TMC) of plasma confinement in November 1979. Plasma is a gas made up of ions – atoms stripped of their electrons – and free electrons. This experiment is a major step in the effort to heat and confine a plasma so that it generates more energy than is required to produce it. Success will lead to energy generation by nuclear fusion.

Heating a dense plasma to successively higher temperatures eventually makes the nuclei fuse and emit energy. But to be commercially practical as a source of electrical power, a plasma reactor must heat the plasma to about 100 million°C. At the same time, the fuel density (expressed in ions per cubic centimeter) times the period the plasma is confined (in seconds) must be greater than 10^{14} (100 trillion). No one has yet achieved this combination.

Because such a gas is too hot for ordinary containers, theoreticians in 1949 conceived of confining the plasma with magnetic mirrors. A strong magnetic field at the end of a cylindrical reactor would form a magnetic bottle that would confine the plasma along the cylinder's axis. M. S. Ioffe and his colleagues at the Kurchatov Institute in Moscow verified experimentally in 1962 that a magnetic field increasing outward in all directions from the bottle's center would prevent the plasma from leaking through the bottle's sides. However, a slow but persistent leakage along magnetic lines of force that pass out through the ends of the bottle prevented earlier magnetic mirror devices from achieving the desired fuel density and confinement time.

In 1977, Livermore physicists T. Kenneth Fowler and B. Grant Logan proposed the TMC. Each end of the bottle would have a positive electrostatic mirror to repel positively charged ions – the plasma's nuclei – and a negatively charged electrostatic mirror to trap the electrons.

Simonen and his colleagues enhanced the confinement abilities of a simple single magnetic mirror by a factor of almost eight by using two magnetic mirrors and an electrostatic mirror at each end. The researchers observed no additional losses through the sides, even though the magnetic field did not increase uniformly from the center.

However, the plasma has equal numbers of positive and negative particles, so each electrostatic mirror trapped only half of the particles at its end of the bottle. But David E. Baldwin of LLNL and Logan improved on the original TMC idea in 1979. They suggested using three magnetic mirrors and two electrostatic mirrors at each end.

Simonen's results and their close agreement with theory led the United States Department of Energy to authorize construction of an advanced machine called the Large Mirror Fusion Test Facility (MFTF) at LLNL. The MFTF will test the TMC on a plasma that has ion temperatures of about 174 million°C and a density-confinement time product of 50 trillion. The device will cost $220 million and will be completed in 1985.

Radio frequency heating. Physicist Joel C. Hosea and his colleagues at the Princeton Large Torus (PLT) at Princeton University's Plasma Physics Laboratory in New Jersey finished the first phase of experiments that will develop radio frequency (RF) heating for tokamaks, doughnut-shaped fusion reactors. A device similar to a television station's transmitter produces powerful radio waves that vibrate at 42 million cycles per second. A copper pipe guides the waves to the tokamak and antennae aim them at the plasma.

The radio waves will heat the plasma if their frequency equals the plasma ions' cyclotron frequency – the rate at which the ions circulate around the doughnut-shaped magnetic field. Cyclotron frequency depends upon the strength of the magnetic field and the ions' mass. During the PLT experiment, 600 kilowatts of RF power heated plasmas from 580,000°C to 23.2-million°C. This RF technique is being extended to higher power to determine its usefulness in heating tokamak or mirror magnet reactors.

The plasma ring of a commercially successful tokamak reactor would have to carry a large current – typically 3 million amperes – to remain confined

This current would have to last about two hours. But such a current has lasted for only one second in experimental tokamaks. A promising proposal for producing a steady current in the plasma ring involves using RF waves to push plasma electrons around the ring, thereby creating a current. This principle is similar to a surfboard being pushed by a wave.

Clean plasma. Princeton physicists led by Kees Bol began operating a machine called the Poloidal Divertor Experiment (PDX) in February 1980. Specially shaped magnetic fields in the PDX create a cleansing action on hot, confined plasma, which can become contaminated with impurities by rubbing against a metal-lined vessel. The PDX magnetically peels away the plasma's dirty outer skin, leaving a clean, hot plasma core. In early tests, the PDX worked as expected.

Inertial confinement. Also under development are machines that will fuse nuclei by radially compressing a fuel pellet of the hydrogen isotopes deuterium and tritium to densities of about 10^{25} (10 trillion trillion) nuclei per cubic centimeter. The fuel's inertia will provide a long enough confinement time – about one ten-billionth of a second – before the pellet expands. Intense electron or ion beams or intense light from lasers will strike the pellet surface, causing the surface to vaporize and crunch the pellet inward in much the same way as burning fuel creates gases that propel a rocket.

This rocket effect is most efficient when the external heating energy is deposited in a very thin layer at the pellet surface. Ion beams are best in this regard, but intense ion beams have not been available. Therefore, inertia-confinement experiments have been conducted only with laser beams. However, physicists Gerald Yonas, Glenn Kuswa, and other scientists at Sandia Laboratories in Albuquerque, N. Mex., developed a powerful ion beam of about 1 trillion watts (1 terawatt) per square centimeter in May 1980.

The researchers estimate that 50 terawatts per square centimeter will be needed to make the fusion system produce as much energy as it consumes. Sandia plans to build such a system by 1985.   [Dale M. Meade]

Solid-State Physics. Dennis Jerome of the University of Paris-South in Orsay, France, announced in March 1980 the first observation of superconductivity, the flow of electricity without resistance, in an organic material that can be synthesized, or put together, in the laboratory. Certain chemical elements such as lead, mercury, and tin become superconductive when cooled to temperatures near absolute zero – $-273.15°C$ or $-459.67°F$. But Jerome's material, a complex crystal known as $(TMTSF)_2PF_6$, contains none of these. Instead, its superconductivity stems from the arrangement of its atoms.

The crystal contains flat layers of two five-sided groups of three carbon atoms and two selenium atoms, all interconnected. Layers of phosphorous and fluorine atoms lie between these layers and parallel to their planes. Current flows perpendicular to these planes.

Jerome and his colleagues experimented with extremely pure crystals of $(TMTSF)_2PF_6$ from Klaus Beckgaard of the H. C. Oersted Institute in Copenhagen, Denmark. They connected electrodes to a crystal and increased the pressure on it to 12,400 kilograms per square centimeter (176,000 pounds per square inch). They then sent an electrical current through the crystal and measured the crystal's electrical resistance. The researchers repeated this procedure as they lowered the temperature. $(TMTSF)_2PF_6$ became superconducting at approximately 1°C (1.8°F.) above absolute zero.

The scientists then measured the material's resistance at atmospheric pressure – 1.03 kilograms per square centimeter (14.7 pounds per square inch) – as they lowered the temperature. Resistance decreased as the temperature was lowered to 18°C (32°F.) above absolute zero, then increased as the temperature was lowered further.

The physicists believe that resistance increased in this manner at atmospheric pressure because lowering the temperature made all of the TMTSF layers form pairs. For example, the second layer from the bottom moved slightly toward the bottom layer and formed a pair with it. The third layer moved upward, forming a pair with the fourth layer, which moved downward, and so on throughout the crystal. This pairing

Secrets
of a Dark
Cover-Up

Solar radiation makes a black robe hotter than a white robe. But the black-robed Bedouin's skin is no hotter than that of the one wearing white, because the temperature is the same under both robes. The air currents under the black robe apparently carry away more heat.

Your summer-school biology teacher has just scheduled the annual field trip to the nearby desert to study cactuses. The school will provide tents, food, and plenty of water, and the school nurse will go along to make sure that nobody suffers any ill effects from the heat. The teacher cites Nurse Henderson as an example of how to dress for the desert. She always wears a white uniform.

But maybe that is not such good advice. According to scientists from Tel Aviv University in Israel and Harvard University in Cambridge, Mass., black robes may provide just as good protection against the heat of the desert as white robes. The scientists, who reported their discovery in January 1980, found this surprising. One of the most obvious ways to minimize the sun's heating effect is to wear white clothes, which reflect most of the sun's radiation before it reaches the body.

Deserts pose two serious problems for the people who live there — heat and lack of water. These problems are related because people keep cool by evaporating water — that is, by perspiring.

Each gram of water that evaporates from the body carries away about 580 calories of heat. But perspiration draws on the body's water reserves. Water lost as perspiration must be replaced by drinking or by eating moist food.

The loss of more than 10 per cent of body weight through perspiration can cause serious illness or even death. Desert people must adapt to the scarcity of water by conserving their water reserves. They must minimize the amount of body water they lose through perspiration by keeping the amount of heat surrounding the body as low as possible.

So Tel Aviv zoologists Amiram Shkolnik and Arieh Borut and Harvard zoologist Virginia Finch and I wondered why the Bedouin nomads who live in the Negev-Sinai Desert wear black robes rather than white ones.

In an attempt to learn something about desert survival from the Bedouins, we bought black Bedouin robes and tailored similar white robes out of the same material. Then we put tiny wire temperature detectors into

Surface
47°C

Skin
33°C

Air
space
38°C

Air
38°C

Surface
41°C

Skin
33°C

Air
space
38°C

Air
38°C

the robes, laid them out in the sun, and measured the radiant heat that the robes absorbed. Tests in the laboratory and in the desert showed that the black robes picked up 89 per cent of the heat from the sun's radiation and reflected only 11 per cent. The white robes picked up only 35 per cent and reflected 65 per cent.

But the white robe's advantage vanished when a person wore the robe. Despite the black robe's much greater heat gain at its surface, the person wearing it gained no more heat than when wearing a white robe. The black robe's surface temperature was 47°C (117°F.), much higher than the white robe's 41°C (106°F.). Yet a detector wound in a loop and taped inside the robes showed that the temperature of the air space between both robes and the person's skin was the same. It was almost identical to that of the air outside the robe. So the sun's radiation did not affect the temperature of the air under the robe.

We concluded that cooler outside air was entering the air space beneath the black robe and replacing the warm air. Either the robe's billowing action as it flapped in the breeze caused the air movement, or there was a chimney effect — warm air rising and passing out through the loosely woven fabric. The airflow would be greater beneath the black robe than beneath the white robe, because the air next to the black robe's inner surface would rise more quickly than the air under the white robe. This greater airflow might make black robes more comfortable, just as hot, moving air in front of a fan is more comfortable than still air of the same temperature. So the Bedouins are no worse off for wearing black robes in the desert, and they may be better off.

The Bedouins are not the only desert dwellers who favor a black covering. The goats that they herd have black hair. We did not study the goats, but other researchers have shown that white hair on cattle and white feathers on pigeons let in a greater amount of harsh ultraviolet radiation than do black hair or black feathers. So it is obvious, even to a goat, that wearing black in the desert can be comfortable.

Perhaps something in a gray, Nurse Henderson?   [C. Richard Taylor]

increased the distance between the electrons on facing paired layers and therefore inhibited current flow. The resistance of a crystal under high pressure does not increase at low temperatures because increasing the pressure reduces the distances between layers and therefore between the electrons of adjacent layers. Under this pressure, the layers maintain equal distances, allowing superconductivity to develop.

Scientists hope to alter the makeup of $(TMTSF)_2PF_6$ to make it superconducting at atmospheric pressure and at considerably greater temperatures. Such a material would be of great value in ordinary devices that must conduct large amounts of electricity at practical temperatures — for example, power cables that transmit electrical energy over great distances.

Imprisoning isotopes. Two physicists, Lynn A. Boatner and Gary W. Bealle of Oak Ridge National Laboratory in Tennessee, announced in November 1979 that they had synthesized crystals similar to the mineral monazite, in which materials such as uranium can be stored for billions of years. This development may provide a safe way to dispose of the radioactive waste produced by nuclear power reactors.

Fuel rods used in reactors produce dangerous radioactive isotopes, for example, neptunium-237, plutonium-239, americium-241, and curium-246 that emit alpha particles and have half-lives ranging from 500 to 2 million years. The Oak Ridge scientists grew synthetic monazite that incorporated several such isotopes into its crystal structure. At a temperature of 200°C (392°F.) and a pressure of 17.6 kilograms per square centimeter (250 pounds per square inch), they found that both water and brine dissolved these isotopes 16 to 300 times more slowly than they dissolved borosilicate glass, which the French now use to embed radioactive wastes.

Dirty current. Nicholas J. Giordano, W. Gilson, and Daniel E. Prober of Yale University in New Haven, Conn., reported in September that long, thin wires made from dirty metals — those with a large number of defects or impurities — conduct electricity differently from normal metals at low temperatures. A relatively pure metal's

A new crystal analyzer's pencil-thin crystal holder is aligned with the cylindrical neutron source behind the ring at right and the neutron detector inside the frame at left. The analyzer, at Argonne National Laboratory near Chicago, will record energy losses and flight times of neutrons that bounce off a crystal so that the scientists can determine the crystal's structure.

Physics

Continued

electrical resistance increases proportionally as the metal's length increases. For example, if an ordinary copper wire's length is doubled, its resistance is doubled. But physicist David J. Thouless of Birmingham University in England had predicted in September 1977 that, below a certain temperature, an ultrathin dirty wire's resistance would increase rapidly with an increase in length.

The Yale scientists' experiments on wires made up of 60 per cent gold and 40 per cent palladium appear to confirm Thouless' idea. The wires were made triangular in cross section, as small as 25 nanometers in diameter and 0.1 millimeter long. (A nanometer is one-billionth of a meter.) The researchers gradually lowered the temperature to 1°C (1.8°F.) above absolute zero as they measured the wires' resistance. They found that lowering the temperature increased the resistance as Thouless had predicted.

These experiments are the first to demonstrate an effect known as electron localization in metals. Flowing electrons that make up an electrical current follow a narrow path as they move from atom to atom in a thin wire. A dirty wire has an irregular path and the electrons of many of the wire's atoms are held in restricted regions, and are therefore unable to act as flowing electrons. Current cannot flow along this kind of path, but it would move easily through pure metal whose atoms are arranged in orderly accessible rows.

But heat makes the atoms in any material move constantly — the higher the temperature, the greater the motion. This thermal motion in a dirty wire moves electrons from one restricted region to another, allowing them to participate in the current. But thermal motion vanishes at extremely low temperatures, so resistance increases as Thouless predicted. Future experiments with different kinds of metals and smaller diameter wires may give researchers a much deeper understanding of how current flows so that they can develop more efficient electrical materials.   [Raymond Orbach]

Psychology

A lively controversy was renewed in 1979 and 1980 concerning the ability of apes to use language. Psychologist Herbert S. Terrace of Columbia University in New York City reported in November 1979 on his team's work with Neam Chimpsky (Nim), a female chimp.

Nim's full name resembles that of linguist A. Noam Chomsky of the Massachusetts Institute of Technology, who argued in the 1960s that language abilities are unique to humans. Psychologists interested in learning and behavior in animals regarded Chomsky's assertions as a challenge, and some claim that they have taught apes to use a language — for example, American Sign Language (ASL).

Terrace and his associates, however, concluded that apes cannot combine symbols to create new meanings. They agree that apes can learn the sign-language names of objects in order to receive rewards such as food, but say that apes cannot reliably combine signs into grammatically correct sentences — the distinctive aspect of human language, according to Chomsky.

Nim was raised from the age of 2 weeks in a homelike environment by humans who acted as parents and teachers. They taught Nim to use ASL, and by the time she was 4 years old, she used well over 100 signs. Terrace and his colleagues concentrated on Nim's ability to combine signs into meaningful groupings. Nim developed more than 2,700 combinations of signs in two- and three-word groupings, and her most common two-word signs — "play me," "me Nim," and "tickle me" — were similar to two-word sentences used by very young children.

However, as Nim moved on to three- and four-word combinations, her language became less similar to that of humans. Her most common four-word sequence, "eat drink eat drink," was repetitious and not grammatical. Other combinations — "eat grape eat Nim," "grape eat me Nim," and "grape eat Nim eat" — were random variations that showed little sense of language order. As human children grow, they increase the length and complexity of their sentences, adding new thoughts or

Nim the chimpanzee uses American Sign Language to say (top row, left to right, bottom row, left to right) "me," "hug," "cat," whereupon she is handed the unhappy cat. Careful studies of the sequence of Nim's signs indicate a lack of sentence structure and refute other research that suggests chimps can be taught language.

qualifying previous ones in some logical order. Nim failed to do this.

Terrace's findings contradicted research done in the late 1960s by psychologists R. Allen Gardner and Beatrice R. Gardner of the University of Nevada, Reno. The Gardners began teaching ASL to a chimp named Washoe in 1966, using signs to get around the animal's inability to pronounce human language sounds. They reported that Washoe eventually learned hundreds of signs for different objects and occasionally put together creative combinations of signs. For example, Washoe labeled a duck as a "water bird." See TALKING WITH CHIMPANZEES, *Science Year,* 1974.

The Gardners said that "water bird" and other signs demonstrated the creative use of language – which Chomsky emphasized as uniquely human. Many psychologists were excited by the Gardners' report and concluded that Chomsky might be wrong in claiming that language is uniquely human.

Terrace and his co-workers agree that chimps could learn to label objects with words, but they pointed to another major insight of Chomsky's: that ability to form sentences is the most distinctive of human language abilities.

In addition to concluding that Nim could not form sentences, Terrace – on the basis of his videotapes of Nim's signing and a film of Washoe's signing – questioned whether Washoe had actually displayed human language abilities. Children learning ASL almost never interrupt their parents' signing, because this disrupts communication. However, the videotapes showed that 70 per cent of the time that Nim signed, she interrupted humans. Videotapes also showed that Nim often imitated signs made by the humans, and this accounted for many of her "sentences."

Artificial food coloring may contribute to hyperactivity in some children. Psychologists Marcel Kinsbourne of the University of Toronto, Canada, and James M. Swanson of the Hospital for Sick Children in Toronto in March 1980 reported on their tests of the additive-free "Feingold diet" for hyperactive children. The diet, first proposed by physician Benjamin F. Feingold in his book *Why Your Child Is Hyperactive* (1975), initially met with skepticism in scientific circles. Early clinical trials showed little evidence that artificial food coloring and other additives made children hyperactive. Kinsbourne and Swanson attribute these results to the low doses of food coloring used in the early trials.

Kinsbourne and Swanson studied 40 children referred to a clinic as hyperactive. The children were separated into two groups based on their response to stimulant drugs. One group of children displayed the classic hyperactive symptoms – short attention span, irritability, and difficulties in learning. Their behavior improved after they took stimulants such as caffeine. This paradoxical improvement did not appear in the other group, children who had serious behavior problems but who did not fit the classic medical definition of hyperactivity.

When they gave capsules containing food coloring to hyperactive children, Kinsbourne and Swanson found a clear effect. Almost immediately after the children took a large dose of food coloring, they showed lower than normal ability to learn in a simple memory task. The nonhyperactive children showed no such reaction to food coloring. Hyperactive children given a capsule that looked like the food-coloring capsule – but contained only sugar – showed no such reaction.

Bernard Weiss of the University of Rochester and seven co-workers reported a study in March 1980 that supports the Kinsbourne and Swanson study. The Rochester scientists kept 22 children on the Feingold diet. None of the children had been previously diagnosed as hyperactive. On most days, each child received a soft drink with either one of two natural colors – caramel and cranberry. Occasionally, a child received artificial colors – a blend of seven chemicals approved as artificial food coloring. The two drinks looked and tasted the same, and neither the child nor the observers knew which drink was given to a child on a particular day.

During the 77-day test period, only one of the 22 children showed an unmistakable reaction to the artificial coloring. Five of the six times she drank the artificially colored pop, this child responded with an increased incidence

Psychology

Continued

of whining, throwing and breaking things, and "acting as if driven by a motor." Another child showed similar reactions, but only on three occasions. The other 20 children apparently were not affected by the food coloring.

The impressionable mind. Psychologists have uncovered more evidence for subliminal perception—the ability to receive and use information from the environment without being aware that this is happening. William R. Kunst-Wilson and Robert B. Zajonc of the University of Michigan reported research on this topic in February 1980.

Scientists have known for more than 20 years that increased familiarity with a stimulus such as a piece of music makes the composition more pleasant and attractive. But they had assumed this heightened pleasure was caused by increased experience and by conscious appreciation of the stimulus.

Kunst-Wilson and Zajonc showed that a preference for particular patterns develops even when the subjects do not realize they have seen the patterns before. The scientists, using a camera projector with a special viewing tunnel leading to a screen, showed their subjects a series of irregular geometric shapes for about one-thousandth of a second each. At that speed, none of the shapes could be seen clearly. Then the subjects looked at pairs consisting of one of the shapes they had seen and a shape they had not seen before.

The subjects were asked to indicate which shape they liked better and which shape they had seen previously. They could not tell which of the two shapes they had seen before; when forced to guess, they were wrong as often as they were right. But when the subjects were asked which shape they liked better, they usually picked the shape they had seen earlier.

Kunst-Wilson and Zajonc say that this finding means people can develop a preference for something without even realizing they have encountered it before. This implies, for example, that background music in department stores and elevators may shape our likes and dislikes more strongly than we realize. [Russell A. Dewey]

Public Health

Many nonsmokers have long felt that tobacco smoke is irritating and obnoxious. They now have reason to fear that chronic exposure may cause permanent damage to their lungs, according to a March 1980 report by physicians James R. White and Herman F. Froeb, specialists in sports medicine at the University of California, San Diego.

The two doctors evaluated more than 5,000 participants in a "Physical Fitness Profile" course sponsored by the university. Subjects were categorized according to the degree of their exposure to cigarette smoke. At one end of the scale were those rarely exposed to smoke at home or at work. At the opposite extreme were those who had smoked and inhaled 40 cigarettes a day for at least 20 years. Then the researchers tested subjects selected from each group and matched according to age and sex for lung function by measuring the air flow of their exhalation. None of the subjects had active heart or lung disease or other illnesses.

The tests revealed an increasing loss of small-airway lung function from the least to the most exposed groups. The small airways are the subdivisions of the bronchial tube that carries air into and out of the lungs. Even "passive smokers"—those nonsmokers who had worked for 20 years in an enclosed area that customarily contained tobacco smoke—were affected.

An important discovery in this study was the observation that the small-airway loss of function was about equal in passive smokers, smokers who did not inhale, and those who smoked less than 10 cigarettes per day. This small-airway breakdown appears to be a first stage of progressive lung disease. It is another hazard to be added to the short-term hazard of exposure to carbon monoxide experienced by people who are in the vicinity of smokers.

Traveler's diarrhea may become a less frequent scourge of tourists and business travelers. Internist Herbert L. DuPont and his co-workers at the University of Texas Medical School in Houston and at the Norwich-Eaton Pharmaceutical Division of Morton-Norwich Products, Incorporated, in

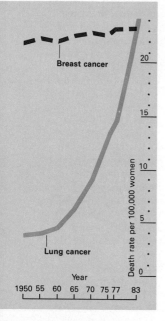

Hazardous curve
After a dramatic 30-year rise, lung cancer may soon overtake breast cancer as the most lethal cancer in women. The rise closely parallels the increase in cigarette smoking among women.

Chicago, reported in January 1980 on their tests on an antidiarrheal compound called subsalicylate bismuth.

In recent years, scientists have learned that a single bacterium, enterotoxigenic *Escherichia coli* (ETEC), causes about half the reported cases of traveler's diarrhea by producing an intestinal poison, or enterotoxin. Antibiotics can prevent the disease by killing the bacteria, but antibiotics sometimes have undesirable side effects. DuPont's research has centered on subsalicylate bismuth, which is not an antibiotic. It protects by blocking the effects of the enterotoxins produced by the *E. coli*.

The University of Texas investigators studied the effect of daily doses of subsalicylate bismuth by treating half of a group of 128 United States students taking summer classes in Guadalajara, Mexico, with the test compound and half with a placebo, an inactive substance. During a 21-day period, 40 members of the control group given the placebo contracted diarrhea compared with only 14 of the treated group — a highly significant difference. The treated students did not develop constipation, a potential side effect. Protection began a few days after treatment started and lasted through the study.

The researchers had previously demonstrated that subsalicylate bismuth effectively controlled established diarrhea in patients with ETEC infection. Their laboratory studies also showed that subsalicylate bismuth appeared to keep the poison from attaching to the intestine's mucous membranes. This prevented excessive amounts of fluid from accumulating in the intestines, which causes the diarrhea and cramps. The compound may also hinder the colonization of *E. coli* in the intestines.

Whooping cough, or pertussis, a viral disease primarily affecting children, has been nearly eliminated by a vaccine introduced in the 1930s and 1940s and a vaccination program that continues today. However, scientists in the United States and elsewhere have recently begun to question the wisdom of continued universal vaccination. Concerns about the hazards of the

Drawing by Ed Arno; © 1979 The New Yorker Magazine, Inc.

Public Health

Continued

vaccine and its costs, as well as the decreasing incidence of the disease, have led some to propose that the use of pertussis vaccine be curtailed.

Public health researcher Jeffrey P. Kaplan and his associates at the Center for Disease Control in Atlanta, Ga., and the Harvard Schools of Public Health and Medicine provided statistical evidence in an October 1979 report that justifies continuing a mandatory U.S. vaccination program. Using existing data, the investigators estimated the risks, benefits, and costs of pertussis vaccination.

Among vaccine complications, they classified seizures as a major effect, and fever, soreness at the vaccination site, and illness lasting up to 48 hours as minor effects. Severe reactions affect as many as 1 in 3,100 persons vaccinated, and 1 person in 34,000 may have repeated convulsions and contract meningitis, an inflammation of the brain and spinal cord. Minor reactions seem to affect 8 out of 10 vaccinated persons at least once during the four-dose immunization schedule.

Against these statistics, the researchers weighed the benefit from prevented cases of pertussis. Data from Massachusetts suggested that the rate of cases fell from more than 100 in 100,000 to less than 1 in 100,000 after the vaccine was introduced. With a vaccination program, researchers estimated that the number of potential cases among 1 million children falls from 6,745 to 95, the number of severe cases — with pneumonia, seizures, encephalitis, and long-term defects — falls from 231 to 9, and deaths decline from 7.6 to 0.3. In addition, permanent disability cases decline from 8.4 to 3.7 persons in 1 million, a substantial benefit.

If the pertussis vaccination program were continued, it would cost $700,000 per 1 million children. If the program were ended, the cost of the disease would be an estimated $1.8 million. Therefore, in view of the apparent rarity of serious complications, the ease and low cost of vaccination, and the protection from the disease, the researchers recommended continuing the program.   [Michael H. Alderman]

Space Exploration

Space exploration activity in 1979 and 1980 ranged from the applied technology of orbiting space stations and satellites to the basic science of planetary probes. As the United States struggled toward launching the first reusable space shuttle, the European Space Agency (ESA) sent aloft its first heavy launch rocket, the three-stage *Ariane*. Russian cosmonauts again set a new endurance record in orbit aboard the *Salyut 6* space station, and U.S. craft made new discoveries about Jupiter and Saturn.

Shuttle delay. Development of the U.S. space shuttle continued to run behind schedule because of difficulties with the craft's main engines and heat shield. The National Aeronautics and Space Administration (NASA) had originally scheduled the craft to make its first orbital flight in March 1979. In April 1980, NASA Administrator Robert A. Frosch predicted that a launch was likely about mid-February 1981.

Meanwhile, Orbiter 101, the *Enterprise,* was taken apart in the summer of 1979 and flown to the Rockwell International Corporation's factory in California, where it will be used for spare parts. *Enterprise* made the first flight tests at Edwards Air Force Base in California's Mojave Desert in 1977. It was ferried to the Kennedy Space Center in Florida early in 1979, where it was used to test procedures for attaching the external liquid-fuel tank and strap-on solid-fuel rocket boosters to the shuttle.

Orbiter 102, *Columbia,* the craft destined to make the first shuttle flight, reposed in its Kennedy Space Center hangar. Valve and pump failures plagued its high-pressure hydrogen-oxygen engines, and new problems in attaching a heat shield to the shuttle raised doubts about safety.

The shield consists largely of 31,000 ceramic tiles 15 and 20 centimeters (6 and 8 inches) square. Most of the tiles are shaped to fit the form of the craft. The shield must protect the shuttle from temperatures of up to 1370°C (2500°F.) generated during re-entry into the atmosphere. Tests showed the tile material was an efficient heat insu-

Triumphant but weak after a record-breaking stay in the weightless conditions of orbit, cosmonauts Valery Ryumin (left) and Vladimir Lyakhov settle back in special carriages to answer an interviewer's questions.

lator, but the method of bonding the tiles to the aluminum skin of the orbiter was unsatisfactory. About 100 tiles fell off *Columbia* during preparation for its piggyback trip atop a Boeing 747 jet from California to Florida in March 1979.

NASA and Rockwell International then launched a yearlong process of testing each tile individually and replacing those that were improperly bonded. NASA officials and Rockwell engineers hoped to complete the installation of a safe heat shield by the end of July 1980.

In other respects, *Columbia*'s progress was more encouraging. The three-engine liquid-propulsion system that powers the shuttle was certified for flight after tests at a NASA facility in Mississippi in March. The solid-rocket boosters, which fire at launch along with the shuttle's main engines, completed their flight-certification tests in Utah in February.

During December 1979 and January 1980, the prime and backup astronaut crews put *Columbia* through a grueling series of flight rehearsals, testing flight controls and related systems. The engineers and astronauts who took part in the tests were pleased with the results. "It's an exciting machine," said astronaut John W. Young, who will command the first manned orbital flight. "You need a computer to fly it, though. Human reactions are not fast enough." *Columbia* will be flown by four computers, with a fifth in reserve.

More Russian records. Cosmonauts Vladimir Lyakhov and Valery Ryumin set a new orbital-endurance record of 175 days and 36 minutes. Launched on Feb. 25, 1979, they landed on August 19. Although they were weakened by the prolonged weightlessness, both were reported in good condition as a result of two hours of daily exercise.

Ryumin returned to *Salyut 6* on April 9, 1980, along with rookie cosmonaut Leonid Popov. The Russian space agency did not say whether they planned to set yet another record. The space station had been resupplied with food and other provisions in March by an unmanned space freighter.

European rocket. ESA scored a major breakthrough in heavy rocket development with the successful launch

on Dec. 24, 1979, of *Ariane* from facilities in French Guiana. The ESA rocket is designed to put a satellite 35,800 kilometers (22,300 miles) above the equator where the satellite's orbit will keep it seemingly motionless over the same spot on earth.

Even though *Ariane* is not reusable, its charges for satellite launches will be reduced to about the same as those of the shuttle. *Ariane* will thus compete with the U.S. space shuttle for communications satellite launches for other countries and private corporations. *Ariane*'s launch site in French Guiana, near the equator, allows for savings in rocket energy needed for such missions.

***Skylab* fell.** Worldwide suspense accompanied the plunge of the U.S. *Skylab* space station on July 11, 1979. No one had been able to predict where *Skylab* might come down. On its final orbits, NASA engineers maneuvered the craft in an attempt to keep it from crashing in densely populated areas. The drama ended after residents of Perth on the southwest coast of Australia reported seeing a fiery shower of debris. After the big space station reentered earth's atmosphere, it disintegrated above the Indian Ocean just off the Australian coast. Thousands of *Skylab* metal and plastic shards sprayed over hundreds of kilometers of Australian wilderness, but there were no reports of damage.

The *Skylab* crisis occurred because the space station began dropping from its original orbit four years earlier than NASA had calculated. This loss of altitude resulted from unusually high solar activity that heated the upper atmosphere, causing it to rise to the altitude of the orbiting *Skylab*. The friction of atmospheric gases exerted drag on the station, slowing its orbital speed and causing it to drop.

Planetary probes. The U.S. space probe *Voyager 2* flew past Jupiter in July 1979 and sent back a set of high-resolution photographs. They revealed a 14th and 15th Jovian moon, a previously undetected ring around Jupiter, and volcanic eruptions on Io, one of Jupiter's largest moons. The *Voyager* data also showed that three other large moons, Europa, Ganymede, and Callisto, appear to have water ice on their surfaces. See JOURNEYS TO JUPITER.

Ariane, the European Space Agency's first rocket capable of carrying a satellite to orbit, rose from its launch pad in French Guiana on December 24.

Space Exploration
Continued

In September 1979, *Pioneer 11* approached Saturn, providing scientists with their first close-up view of this planet. The craft discovered an additional moon of Saturn and uncovered evidence of up to three more.

The spacecraft passed within 1,500 kilometers (930 miles) of a small, previously unknown body while crossing the plane of Saturn's outer ring. Scientists estimated that the object, dubbed "Pioneer Rock," was about 100 to 300 kilometers (62 to 186 miles) in diameter. *Pioneer 11* data also disclosed two previously undetected rings around Saturn and indicated that most of the ring material was ice. See ASTRONOMY (Planetary Astronomy).

In July, *Pioneer 10,* which in 1973 was the first craft to fly by Jupiter, passed the orbit of Uranus and headed out of the solar system into interstellar space — where *Pioneer 11* will eventually follow.

Satellite launches. On Sept. 20, 1979, a third High Energy Astronomy Observatory (HEAO-3) was launched. Like the other HEAO satellites, it will gather X-ray observations from deep space. Other U.S. launches included *Magsat,* sent aloft on October 9 to monitor changes in the earth's magnetic field, and the Solar Maximum Mission Observatory satellite, which was launched on Feb. 14, 1980. *Solar Max* carried instruments to measure the intensity of radiation from the sun during the 1980 and 1981 period of maximum sunspot activity. This is also the first satellite equipped with special latches so that it can be retrieved by a future space shuttle. NASA's tentative 1980 schedule called for nine launches, down from a high of 20 in 1978.

Space funding. The NASA budget proposed for fiscal year 1981 (Oct. 1, 1980, to Sept. 30, 1981) by President Jimmy Carter provided $5.7 billion, of which $1.9 billion was slated for the space shuttle. However, no funds were provided for new planetary probes. Carter also cut out funds for the solar-electric propulsion system, or ion engine, NASA planned to develop for sending a craft to intercept Halley's Comet in 1986. [Richard S. Lewis]

Transportation

Engineers seeking alternative energy sources for transportation have been trying to develop an efficient battery for electric cars. Engineers Wally E. Rippel and Dean B. Edwards of the Jet Propulsion Laboratory (JPL) at the California Institute of Technology in Pasadena reported in January 1980 that they made an improvement in the lead-acid battery that may do the trick. Industry had ignored the lead-acid battery because there seemed to be no way to decrease its weight. But the new design relies on modern materials that lighten the battery while making it twice as powerful and durable.

A battery stores its energy in chemical form which it converts to electrical energy when called upon to power the various devices in the automobile. A conventional lead-acid battery has three to six cells, each containing two sets of positive and negative lead electrodes in the form of rectangular plates. Openings in the negative plates are filled with pure lead; openings in the positive plates are filled with lead dioxide. Surrounding the plates is an electrolyte — a chemical compound that can conduct electrical current — of sulfuric acid and water. Chemical reactions that occur between the lead and the acid-water compound produce the required electricity.

The new design, based on a concept called bipolar construction, cuts weight by replacing the various forms of lead in the traditional battery with plates made of electrically conductive graphite fibers molded into lightweight sheets of polyethylene plastic. And because these plates are so thin, as many as 60 cells can be packed into the same volume as the three to six cells of a conventional battery.

Rippel and Edwards claim that a series of their batteries — in a 545-kilogram (1,200-pound) pack — can provide enough power for a 1,360-kilogram (3,000-pound) car to accelerate from 0 to 97 kilometers per hour (kph) or 60 miles per hour (mph) in 12 seconds. The car can cruise at 88 kph (55 mph) for up to 240 kilometers (150 miles) before recharging. Also, the battery can be recharged about three times

Transportation

Continued

The Bell XV-15 Tilt Rotor vertical take-off and landing (VTOL) aircraft converts from a vertical helicopter, *above,* to a horizontal airplane, *above right.* The craft has twice the range and cruising speed of standard helicopters.

faster than the eight hours it takes to recharge conventional batteries.

In June, Gulf & Western Industries announced that it had developed a battery using graphite plates with a zinc-chloride electrolyte. The electrolyte must be chilled to hold the energy, so the system requires refrigeration. But, the battery can be recharged almost indefinitely and delivers full power even at a relatively low charge.

More common composites. Materials such as the graphite fibers used in the new lead-acid battery are tough, lightweight mixtures called advanced composites. Made up of elements like boron or graphite and a resin, usually epoxy, the materials are being used in 1980 designs of cars and aircraft to replace heavier and more costly metals.

Parts made of advanced composites weigh up to 40 per cent less than similar aluminum parts and are stronger. Graphite fiber, the most popular advanced composite, is composed of stretched and heated polyester yarn woven into a fabric that is impregnated with a resin. Aircraft manufacturers,

for example, create a desired part, such as a wing cover or landing-gear door, by piling the fabric on a mold and curing it in a pressure oven for several hours until it turns into a material that looks like smooth black fiberglass.

Is it antipollution or procombustion? Clarence M. Ditlow, director of the consumer-oriented Center for Auto Safety in Washington, D.C., called on the National Highway Traffic Safety Administration in November 1979 to restudy the potential safety hazards of catalytic converters. These devices, which burn pollutants before they can be released into the air, have been installed on most cars made in the United States since 1975, as well as on many cars made in other countries.

A catalytic converter's internal temperature reaches about 870°C (1600°F.) and its surface temperature averages 535°C (1000°F.). When a car fitted with a converter is parked over flammable material, such as dry leaves, the heat retained can ignite such material even after the automobile engine has been turned off. [Marsha F. Goldsmith]

Zoology

At what periods in their lives do army ants wage their battles? The question was answered by Howard Topoff and John Mirenda, researchers in the Animal Behavior-Biopsychology Program at Hunter College, City University of New York, who reported in March 1980 on the nomadic behavior of army ants.

The investigators set up Tube City, a system of wooden nest and food boxes and plastic tubular runways, at the American Museum of Natural History in New York City, with which they are also affiliated. They wanted to determine whether the migratory army ant, *Neivamyrmex nigrescens,* begins its nomadic plundering and looting of other ants' nests – in search of the insects it eats – when larvae are developing or when food reserves are low.

The researchers regulated the quantity of food available and observed the migration of ant colonies in Tube City. They allowed a colony to bivouac, or set up camp, in one of three nest boxes outfitted with soil, rocks, and logs. Because the ants are nocturnal, the researchers opened the door from the

nest box into the system of tubes each night at 9 P.M. The "soldiers" could then forage on food supplies placed about 21 meters (69 feet) from the nest.

For more than two weeks, Topoff and Mirenda tested four colonies, providing two colonies with only 0.5 gram (0.017 ounce) of booty, or food, and two colonies with 6 grams (0.2 ounce) of food. The researchers reported that the underfed colonies emigrated from their nest more often than the overfed colonies – on 62 per cent of test days compared with 28 per cent of test days. Emigration involved the mass movement of the entire colony – including the larvae, which are carried by adult ants – to another nest box 32 meters (105 feet) from the first.

The results suggest that lack of food stimulates emigration. Because the larvae eat most of the food brought back to the camp by adults, it seems probable that the presence of developing larvae stimulates emigration, especially when there is not enough food. However, there are other factors as well. The researchers found that even over-

Migrating adult army ants carry larvae on their backs as they seek new food sources.

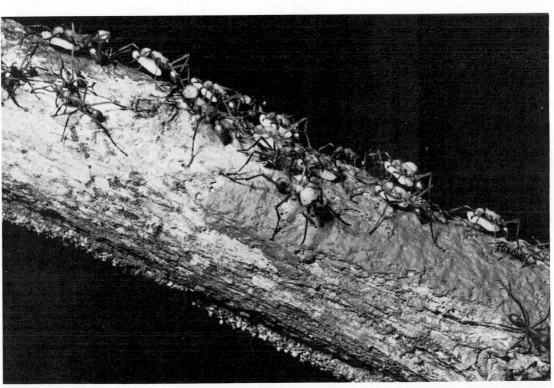

Drawing by Dedini; ©1979 The New Yorker Magazine, Inc.

Zoology

Continued

fed colonies eventually emigrated and left large amounts of uneaten food. Topoff and Mirenda concluded that the larvae may secrete substances that arouse adult ants and cause them to begin their migration.

Good vibrations. Male and female water striders, *Gerris remigis*, look exactly alike to observers as they stalk over the surface of North American streams on their long thin legs. Zoologist R. Stimson Wilcox of the Department of Biological Sciences at the State University of New York in Binghamton reported in June 1979 that he had discovered how water striders discriminate between the sexes.

Wilcox had found in previous studies that male water striders shake their legs to produce high-frequency vibrations of 80 to 90 waves per second or low-frequency vibrations of 3 to 10 waves per second. These vibrations travel on the surface of the water. Females produce only the low-frequency waves.

During the mating season, Wilcox discovered, male striders attract females by emitting high-frequency vibrations. When a male is approached by another water strider, the first male sends out the high-frequency vibration. If the second male also sends high-frequency signals, the pair separate. But if the second male for some reason does not signal, the first male pounces on it, intending to mate. In that case, both males seem to realize their error. Each insect immediately signals high-frequency vibrations, and they separate. From these studies, Wilcox theorized that surface wave signals were the only way water striders could tell males from females at a distance.

To test his hypothesis, Wilcox fitted both males and females with rubber masks so that they could detect no visual sexual clues, if any existed. He made the masks by painting the head of a dead water strider with black silicone rubber. After the rubber had hardened, the zoologist stripped the mask from the dead insect and slipped it over the head of an experimental subject.

Next, he equipped the females to produce the typically male high-frequency vibrations. He attached a

The infant siabon with its siamang foster mother, *below,* is the product of a love affair between its real siamang mother and a male gibbon, *right.*
A siamang ape has 50 chromosomes in its cells; a gibbon has 44. The siabon, which has 47 chromosomes, is the first known hybrid of parents so different genetically.

tiny magnet to one of each female's legs and installed a signal-transmitting coil of wire around the small aquarium in which he conducted the tests.

When Wilcox transmitted recordings of the male insect's vibrations through the coil, the magnet on a female's leg vibrated so that the male high-frequency sound waves traveled on the surface of the water. This technique enabled Wilcox either to allow a female to transmit typical female signals or typical male signals.

Wilcox repeatedly put one male and one female in the aquarium. When a male got within 2.5 centimeters (1 inch) of a female, Wilcox transmitted a typical male vibration through the female's magnet, and the interested male left immediately. When Wilcox sent no signals through the coil, the female transmitted her usual signal and the approaching male grasped the female to mate with her.

Wilcox concluded that the sound wave signals identify the sexes among water striders. Sexual odors are not involved because females were not identified by the masked males.

Vision cannot be very important either, because masked males rejected or accepted females solely on the basis of signals transmitted along the surface of the water. Wilcox suggested that surface vibrations may also be important for signaling territoriality, defense of food, and identification among various species of water striders.

Thief in the web. Tropical spiders of the genus *Argyrodes* do not construct their own webs. They steal prey caught and packaged by other spiders. Zoologist Fritz Vollrath, studying at the Smithsonian Tropical Research Institute in Balboa, Panama, reported in September 1979 on the thieving spiders' technique.

A spider's web is obviously a dangerous place to forage for food. Therefore, the *Argyrodes* attaches fine threads to the snares of its "host," an orb-weaving spider. The *Argyrodes* then runs the threads to its own resting place, about 20 to 30 centimeters (8 to 12 inches) outside the host's capture area.

Vollrath's close observation and his photography revealed that the *Argyrodes* initiated its own "attack" after the host spider had wrapped up the prey, usually a fly or cricket caught in its web. By recording the vibrations produced when the host spider captured and wrapped its prey, and playing these back to the *Argyrodes,* Vollrath found that the thief simply "listens in" to the host spider's activities.

When vibrations caused by prey-wrapping cease, the thief crawls onto the web, locates the prey, and eats it. The thief runs little risk of being caught because the host spider's senses are not acute enough to detect its presence. The *Argyrodes* does not waste its time venturing onto the web if it senses only capturing, but not wrapping, vibrations. It seems to know that the prey escaped or was too small to wrap.

It's a wise father . . . How nature ensures that the giant water bug, *Abedus herberti,* tends its own offspring was reported by entomologist Robert L. Smith of the University of Arizona in Tucson in September 1979. In many kinds of egg-laying animals, males care for and protect the eggs of females with which they have mated. The male benefits only if the young that hatch from these eggs have his genes. Because females of many species, including the water bug, mate with several males, the male runs a risk of having to raise another male's offspring. This problem led to Smith's investigation.

In the laboratory, Smith supervised matings of 24 nonstriped females with 24 males, both nonstriped and striped. The female water bug lays its eggs on the male's back and he carries them until they hatch. If a male carried eggs that hatched into nymphs identical to himself, Smith knew that male was the father. A series of trials showed that a male water bug mates with a female several times before permitting her to deposit eggs on his back. Smith found that these repeated encounters ensure that the eggs the female then lays will be fertilized by her most recent mate — the prospective father.

Fall of the monarchs. During 1977 and 1978, three researchers studied the wintering sites of monarch butterflies in Mexico and reported their results in May 1979. Millions of butterflies collect in mountainous regions there, turning the green foliage into a blanket of orange, black, and white. Zoologist William H. Calvert and be-haviorist Lincoln P. Brower of Amherst College in Massachusetts and wildlife biologist Lee E. Hedrick of Humboldt State University in Arcata, Calif., observed extraordinarily heavy mortality in the colonies during the wintering season and wanted to find out why so many butterflies died.

When Calvert, Brower, and Hedrick began their study of five Mexican monarch colonies covering 0.2 to 2 hectares (0.5 to 5 acres) in February 1977, the forest floor was thickly carpeted in places with as many as 776 butterflies per square meter. More than 4 million butterflies died in one season in the colonies they studied. Many of the dead butterflies they collected for analysis were not intact. Body parts, such as wings or abdomen, were missing.

The scientists observed the areas where the monarchs wintered with binoculars and took photographs. These showed that three species of birds — Scott's orioles, black-backed orioles, and blackheaded grosbeaks — flying in flocks of about 25, preyed heavily on roosting monarchs. The birds carefully stripped open the butterflies' abdomens and fed on the inner parts.

The birds' voracious appetite for monarchs surprised the researchers because scientists have long known that at least some monarchs contain bitter-tasting, and even poisonous, cardiac glycosides. The monarchs acquire these substances when they are larvae from eating plants such as milkweed. Closer examination showed that the birds had learned how to thwart the chemical defense system of the monarchs by rejecting the butterflies in which they tasted poison. Also, they fed primarily on the insides of the monarchs' abdomens or on their flight muscles, which have a lower concentration of cardiac glycoside than the outer parts of the monarchs' abdomen.

Because birds mainly attack the butterflies on the edges of colonies, small groups of monarchs suffered the highest rate of mortality — a larger proportion of butterflies are on the edges of a small colony. Although some butterflies will always be eaten, colonies with extremely high population densities are safer on the whole, because more butterflies can avoid the edges and cluster toward the center.   [William J. Bell]

Science You Can Use

In areas selected for their current interest, *Science Year* presents information that the reader as a consumer can use in making decisions—from buying products to choosing appropriate medical care.

Balanced Meals for Your Family Pet

The average American family of four is actually a family of five — two adults, two children, and one pet. And that extra mouth is a force to be reckoned with. The 48.8 million dogs and 39-million cats in the United States consume an estimated 4.2 million metric tons of food each year. The annual bill for this food is almost $3.3 billion — or $14.50 per American.

If you are a pet owner, your pet food bill is undoubtedly a lot closer to $58.00 — the average pet food bill per family — and you have probably wondered if you were getting your money's worth . . . or if you should be spending even more to give your pet what it needs. In either case, you have probably wondered exactly what your pet does need.

The nutritional requirements of cats and dogs were once somewhat different than they are now. Early dogs and cats were hunters who instinctively satisfied their nutritional needs, and, because their nutritional needs, and, because

hunting required so much energy, they needed more calories. As some animals were domesticated over the centuries, many of them lost the ability to catch food in the wild.

Size, more than any other factor, determines how much food an animal needs. A full-grown dog of one species may weigh up to 100 times more than an adult of another species. But although a Chihuahua may weigh 0.89 kilogram (2.2 pounds) and a St. Bernard 90 kilograms (200 pounds), the St. Bernard does not need 100 times as many calories as the Chihuahua. Animals expend energy in proportion to the surface areas of their bodies, and not in proportion to their body weight. Since the surface area of a St. Bernard is about 15 times that of a Chihuahua, the large dog needs only 15 times as many calories as its tiny cousin.

Actually, dogs and cats are very much like humans in their nutritional requirements. Like us, they require

A pet owner provides one of the highlights in her dog's day — its dinner. However, pets depend on their meals for more than taste pleasure. They need the balanced blend of nutrients that good pet foods provide.

more than 50 nutrients. Unlike us omnivores who eat both meat and vegetables, dogs and cats are considered carnivorous because of their physical characteristics. Their ancestors usually caught and ate small animals. However, the digestive tracts of that prey usually contained vegetable matter, which the predators absorbed. In fact, domestic cats and dogs today can survive on certain plant materials supplemented with vitamins and minerals.

Dogs and cats seem to need a slightly different mix of vitamins and minerals than their owners need. In dogs, a lower than normal calcium intake may cause rickets, a softening of the bones; too much vitamin D can produce harmful calcium deposits in the heart or lungs; and too little arginine, an amino acid, can result in muscle tremors and drooling.

A deficiency of vitamin E in cats can result in steatitis, a degeneration of muscles and nerves, and lack of the amino acid, taurine, can lead to blindness. For these reasons, cats may not thrive on commercial dog food, although dogs can do well on a diet solely of cat food.

Human food or table scraps, which may seem like a royal diet for a pet, may actually rob the animal of the very nutrients it needs to survive or provide an oversupply of starch and fat that can do more harm than good. In any case, it is not possible for the pet owner to determine the balance of nutrients in this kind of food.

Commercial pet foods provide the nutrients in balanced ratios. The three types of food — dry, moist, and canned — are similar except for water content, and perhaps the sources of nutrients. Canned foods may contain meat by-products that are considered unsuitable for human consumption, such as meat from animals that have died of injuries or disease that does not affect the tissues. Canned dog and cat food

Pet food labels provide a wealth of nutritional information. Both the dry food (left) and the canned food (right) fulfill the National Research Council's daily nutritional requirements for healthy dogs (center). The only difference is in moisture content: it is 75 per cent of the canned food; 10 per cent of the dry food.

COMPLETE AND BALANCED NUTRITION FOR YOUR
Nutrient Content of Wayne Dog Food**
Compared to the Requirements Established by N

Nutrients	NRC*	Wayne Dog Food**	Required For:
Protein, %	20.00	25.00	growth & tissue repa
Fat, %	4.50	8.00	energy & hair coat
Linoleic Acid, %	0.90	2.00	skin & hair coat
Calcium, %	1.00	2.10	bones & teeth
Phosphorus, %	0.80	1.40	bones & teeth
Potassium, %	0.50	0.55	regulate body fluids
Salt, %	1.00	1.10	regulate body fluids
Magnesium, %	0.036	0.18	bones & teeth
Iron, mg/kg	54.00	220.00	blood
Copper, mg/kg	6.50	13.00	blood & hair coat
Manganese, mg/kg	4.50	80.00	bones & maintenan
Zinc, mg/kg	45.00***	140.00	growth & skin
Iodine, mg/kg	1.39	1.40	thyroid
Selenium, mg/kg	0.10***	0.10	growth & maintenan
Vitamin A, IU/kg	4500.00	11500.00	eyes & skin
Vitamin D, IU/kg	450.00	3800.00	bones & teeth
Vitamin E, IU/kg	45.00	50.00	reproduction & grov
Vitamin B12, mg/kg	0.02***	0.02	growth & blood
Folic Acid, mg/kg	0.16	0.90	blood & growth
Thiamine, mg/kg	0.90	4.70	appetite & nerves
Riboflavin, mg/kg	2.00	4.10	body functions, hai
Pyridoxine, mg/kg	0.90	7.00	blood & protein util
Pantothenic Acid, mg/kg	9.00	11.50	growth
Niacin, mg/kg	10.30	42.80	skin, nerves & ener
Choline, mg/kg	1100.00	1300.00	liver & growth
Biotin, mg/kg	0.09***	0.13	skin

Nutritional Requirements for Dogs

	Type of Diet	
	Dry	Canned
Per cent Moisture	10	75
Per cent Dry matter	90	25
Nutrients (in per cent)		
Protein	20.0	5.5
Fat	4.5	1.25
Linoleic Acid	0.9	0.25
Minerals		
Calcium	1.0	0.3
Phosphorus	0.8	0.22
Potassium	0.5	0.2
Sodium chloride	1.0	0.3
Magnesium	0.036	0.010
(mg./kilogram)		
Iron	54	15
Copper	6.5	1.8
Zinc	90	24
Iodine	1.39	0.39
Vitamins (International Units)		
A	4,500	1,250
B	450	125
E	45	12.5
(mg./kilogram)		
Thiamine	0.9	0.25
Riboflavin	2.0	0.5
Pantothenic acid	9.0	2.5
Niacin	10.3	2.8
Pyridoxine	0.9	0.25
Folic acid	0.16	0.04
Vitamin B12	0.02	0.006
Choline	1,100	300

contains plant proteins, carbohydrates, vitamins, minerals, and 75 per cent moisture. Most dry foods are made from meat, fish, bone meal, plant proteins, grains, vitamins, and minerals.

The popularity of moist foods can be attributed to a tendency to assign human characteristics to animals. Designed with the look and texture of the juicy meats that humans prefer, these foods must be preserved with agents that prevent bacteria and fungi. They must also be packaged in moisture-proof wrappings to keep them from drying out.

Whatever their form, pet foods are cooked to increase their digestibility and control bacteria. Moist and dry foods are prepared in an extruder that compresses and cooks the food under extremely high pressures and temperatures. As these foods leave the extruder's high pressure, they expand, filled with air, in the same way popcorn explodes. If the extruded food is destined to be sold as "dry," it will be dried in huge ovens until its water content is less than 10 per cent. If it is to be sold as a "moist" pet food, preservatives will be added.

Each package of pet food sold in the United States has a label that contains a great amount of information. Most pet food manufacturers use the term "complete and balanced." This means that the product has either been tested for the specific use for which it was designed, or meets nutritional standards set by the National Research Council. This is your assurance that the food supplies everything your pet needs, except water. The label also includes a complete list of ingredients, product weight, a guarantee that the ingredients in the package are indeed those listed, feeding directions, and data about the product's adequacy in meeting your pet's nutritional needs.

The name of the type of food can itself be a great source of information,

although it may have to be decoded. If a pet food is labeled "Beef Flavor Feast," it means that it contains only enough beef flavor to provide a beef taste by a "recognizable test method"; "Beef Dinner" must have at least 25 per cent beef or beef by-products; while "Beef," or a similar one-word title, means that the food contains at least 95 per cent of that ingredient. "All Beef" or "100 Per Cent Beef" means that the can contains only beef.

Several dog foods are designed to be fed to dogs in different age groups or conditions. There are puppy foods, foods for growth, maintenance, and foods for workers. There is some justification for each of these, since rations with extra milk coatings may taste better to young puppies; extra fat is a source of energy for hard-working dogs; and a low-fat diet may prevent inactive dogs from becoming obese. However, most of the good commercial dog foods can be fed to healthy dogs throughout their lives.

The pet food industry also furnishes a choice of snacks. However, these treats, and the snacks and table scraps commonly fed to supplement a pet's diet can create a finicky eater.

Commercially produced pet snacks, like moist foods, were a response not only to owner's projections of their pets' tastes, but also to research on those tastes. All animals prefer moist foods. Dogs prefer cheese to many other flavors because cheeses contain organic acids and fats.

Whatever commercial food your pet seems to prefer, or you choose to feed it, you can be assured that it was prepared only after extensive research. We know more about the nutritional requirements of cats and dogs than about the dietary needs of human beings. And there is evidence that most pets in the United States are, in reality, being fed better than many of the nation's children.   [James E. Corbin]

Helping the Hearth
to Heat the Home

Glass doors and vents built into a fireplace permit a fire to be seen and felt without wasting room heat. The attractive brickwork and mantel conceal a complex mechanical system that controls the flow of air into and out of the room.

Until a couple of centuries ago, the fireplace, which was invented during the Middle Ages, was the most common device with which people heated their homes. As population increased, wood became harder to get and the fireplace had to be replaced. The wood-burning stove, developed in the late 1700s, operated more efficiently. Then came coal stoves in the mid-1800s, and furnaces that burned oil and gas in the early 1900s. Electric heat was introduced in the mid-1900s.

Even so, there are some 22 million wood-burning fireplaces in the United States today. Displaced as a heat source, the fireplace flourishes as a source of pleasure. Today, however, energy-conscious Americans would like to improve fireplace efficiency so that their fireplaces can contribute a significant amount of heat to their homes.

In an ordinary fireplace, wood burns in a metal grate that holds it above the brick floor. Heat from the burning wood flows into the room by radiation and convection.

Radiation transmits heat through the air in invisible waves of infrared light. Air does not absorb much of this light. Instead, the radiation travels until it meets an object that does absorb it, such as skin or clothing.

Convection transfers heat to the room through the circulation of warmed air. Because it is lighter, warm air near the fire rises in front of the fireplace and spreads out across the ceiling. Colder air near the floor replaces the warm air and is, in turn, heated by the fire and rises to the ceiling. The warm air gradually cools, sinks toward the floor, and is reheated by the fire as the cycle continues.

However, warm air in the room is much more likely to be drawn into the fire than to rise to the ceiling of the room. As a result, the ordinary fireplace heats a room very inefficiently. Most studies indicate that less than 10

per cent of the heat that comes from the burning wood stays in the house.

A typical fireplace fire sends enough air up the chimney to empty an average room every few minutes. Air from other rooms will replace it, but eventually air must be drawn into the house through leaks around doors and windows. The house's regular heating system then wastes energy heating this cold air before the air even gets to the fireplace. To make matters worse, after the fire is out, the hot bricks in the fireplace and chimney may continue to heat air and send it up the chimney.

A fireplace fire also loses efficiency because much of its radiation does not go into the room. A fire radiates in all directions. Some radiation heats the floor and walls of the fireplace. Some goes up the chimney, and some heats the cooler logs on the fire's outer layers.

Manufacturers have responded to homeowners' wishes for more efficient fireplaces by producing devices de-

signed to correct these defects. I have tested a number of them.

The simplest of these new developments are modified grates that hold the logs so that more of their glowing surfaces face the room, thus increasing the amount of radiation that enters the room. One such device holds the logs in a vertical semicircle around the flame, like a C with its opening facing the room. These arrangements increase efficiency to 20 to 30 per cent. The grates cost less than $100.

An inexpensive fireplace door that is closed only when the fire goes out prevents heated bricks from drawing warm air from the room. Another way to control the air supply is to put glass doors over the fireplace entrance. This lets cool air in through adjustable holes under the doors and warm air out into the room through a space above the doors. It also lets you see the fire.

Other devices aid heat transfer by convection. Most of these have metal

A simple metal reflector shield, *left,* fits into the back of a fireplace. Heat headed up the chimney reflects off the curved surface into the room. An angular grate, *below,* permits the logs to be stacked to expose more of their burning surfaces to the room.

tubes wrapped around or under the grate. Electric fans blow air from the room through the tubes, which heat the air, then direct it back into the room. Such devices cost from $100 to $200, but they increase fireplace efficiency to about 40 per cent.

More complex devices bring in air from other sources. One guides air from the outside ash door of an outside-wall fireplace through tubes to the front of the fire. Another air-supplying device lets in cold air from a crawl space beneath the fireplace and also serves as a grate. This type of device is my preference among those I tested. It sells for about $40 and can increase fireplace efficiency by more than 300 per cent.

The most complex and most expensive device I tested was a combination alternate-air supplier and convection aid. Glass doors close off the fire from the room. The grate is made of a group of parallel U-shaped tubes set up so that the "bottom" of the U faces the back of the fireplace. One end of the tubes is exposed to the room through an opening below the doors and the other end through a similar opening above the doors.

Air from the room enters the tubes through the lower opening, travels back through the grate portion of the tubes where the fire heats it, then rises and finally returns to the room through the upper opening. This device, which can be used with or without a fan, is more than 50 per cent efficient — that is, it delivers to the room more than 50 per cent of the heat from the burning wood. This is as efficient as a good wood-burning stove. However, the device costs about $700.

Clearly, simple and inexpensive accessories that will dramatically increase the efficiency of any fireplace are available. Perhaps this means that the fireplace will again play a role in heating your home. [James S. Trefil]

A fireplace grate, *below,* has hollow arms that draw cool air from behind the fireplace to the front of the grate beneath its log-retaining posts. A fan-driven device, *right,* draws cool air from the room through metal tubes. After it is heated, the air is blown back into the room through the louvered opening at right.

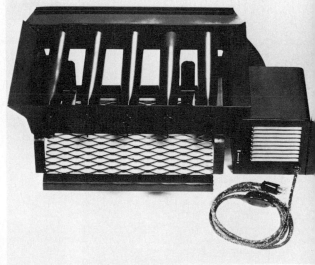

Give Your Skin a Sporting Chance

The athletic life is prone to a host of foot problems, such as, *left to right,* athlete's foot, a fungal infection; infectious dermatitis, an allergic reaction to low-grade infections; contact dermatitis, an allergic reaction to the sponge and rubber lining in tennis shoes; and friction blisters.

Millions of former television addicts have left their easy chairs for the nearest tennis court, bowling alley, or hiking trail in recent years. Jogging, biking, and racquetball have become national obsessions.

Such athletic activity has been the perfect prescription for a nation that had grown soft as spectators. Physical activity promotes good health and encourages good nutrition.

However, a few medical problems have accompanied the sporting boom. Among them are skin troubles. Fortunately, you can easily prevent or treat many of these.

A common skin problem related to all outdoor activity—jogging, swimming, and even skiing—is sun damage. Sunburn is caused by overexposure to the sun. Painful, reddened, swollen skin, often followed by blistering and peeling, results from ignoring the dangers of too much sun. Gradually increasing your exposure to allow your skin to become accustomed to the sun and using sunscreening creams or lotions that block harmful radiation are the best preventive measures. Sunscreens containing para-aminobenzoic acid (PABA) are the most effective.

If you should become sunburned, try a simple home remedy — repeated soaking in a cool bath to which you have added a pint of milk or a cup of oatmeal. Lubricating creams and over-the-counter preparations containing hydrocortisone will also help.

Severe sunburn blistering can be dangerous and should be treated by a physician. If you are taking a medication, such as tetracycline, it may have a side effect — increasing your skin's sensitivity to the sun.

Chafing, caused by friction and perspiration in areas where skin rubs against skin, is also a frequent problem. The raw skin that results can be very painful. You can use petrolatum and talcum powder as effective preventives.

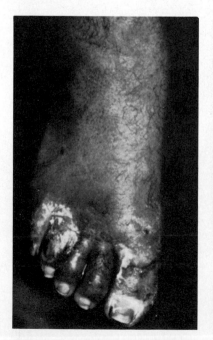
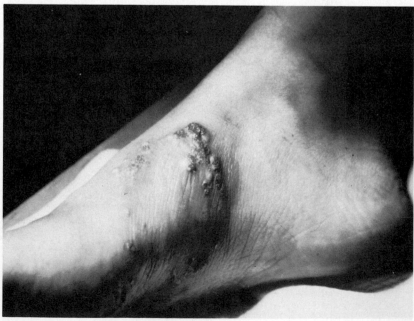

Blisters are fluid-filled skin sacs caused by excessive rubbing of the skin — especially on the feet and hands — over a short period of time. Properly fitting and properly broken-in footwear, such as jogging or tennis shoes, and the use of adhesive tape and felt padding, or moleskin, on blister-prone areas will almost always prevent blisters. Once they are formed, however, you should leave blisters alone until they dry up and disappear.

Skin infections are a common athletic hazard. You can pick up bacteria on any cut or scrape. These infections, called impetigo, produce open sores with cloudy fluid, topped by honey-colored crusts or scabs. Frequent cleansing, antiseptics, and antibiotics — when prescribed by a physician — are the usual treatments. Careful use of towels and washcloths helps prevent impetigo's spread.

Chronic skin infections known as "jock itch" and athlete's foot are caused by fungi that are common in locker rooms and other sports-related areas. They thrive in the warm, moist climate created by perspiration in skin creases in the groin and between the toes. They produce scaly, cracked, and itchy skin in the affected areas. Soft, absorbent cotton underclothing and socks help prevent these afflictions. There are antifungal creams, powders, and sprays to treat them.

Perhaps the most troublesome skin problems for some people arise when activity or equipment aggravates a pre-existing skin condition. The irritation of sweat and friction, for example, can aggravate dermatitis, a skin inflammation. And special equipment, such as the chin straps on cycling helmets, can provoke acne pimples or cysts.

Exercise and sports are wholesome elements of our life style. Being careful to prevent and treat skin problems will make the vigorous life all the more rewarding.   [Lawrence J. Bass]

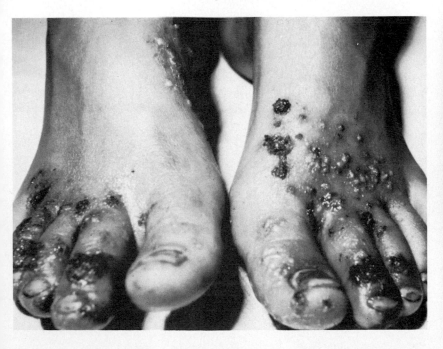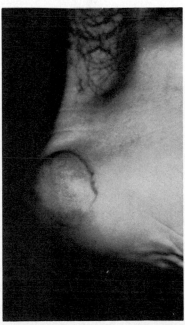

A Candid Look at Cameras and Films

When Mathew B. Brady photographed the battlefields and army camps of the American Civil War, he needed a horse and wagon to haul his cameras and equipment. Today's roving photographer has it better. Cameras are light, compact, and easy to use. Films are fast, clean, and sharp. But the modern amateur photographer does have a problem. There are now hundreds of cameras and dozens of films to choose from — so many, in fact, that making a choice can seem an all but impossible task to a beginner.

Choosing a camera and the correct film is easier if you analyze your photographic needs and desires, then match them against your budget and the equipment available.

If you simply want pictures, without a lot of effort or expense, you have two basic choices: the instant-picture type, such as the Polaroid camera and the Kodak Instant camera; or the modern version of the old box camera, such as the Kodak Instamatic and Pocket Instamatic series.

Which type is better for you? The instant cameras have the obvious advantage of giving you pictures almost instantaneously. If you miss a shot, you know it immediately and can reshoot. On the other hand, Instamatic pictures must be processed at a studio. But, unlike instant cameras, they take a variety of film types — all in convenient cartridge form. You can make color slides, color prints, or black-and-whites. And the smallest of these cameras, the supercompact 110 cartridge camera, is literally pocket-sized.

The simplest of these two camera types, such as the Polaroid One Step or the Kodak Trimlite Instamatic 18, let you point and shoot without focusing. In fact, focusing is impossible. The lens is fixed and any subject at least 150 centimeters (5 feet) away will be acceptably sharp. Cameras in this class usually sell for under $30.

Match a Camera to Your Needs

Instant-developing camera
- Easy to operate
- Most models are inexpensive
- Fixed lens and fixed focus
- Easy-loading film pack
- Pictures develop within minutes
- No negative, so extra prints are not easy to obtain
- Film available only in color
- Expensive film, but no developing costs

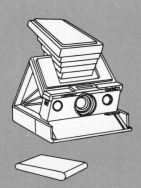

110 camera and film
- Easy to operate
- Easy-loading film cartridge
- Has generally the same types of features as the 126 models
- Smallest, most compact camera; fits easily in pocket or purse

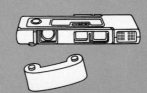

126 camera and film
- Easy to operate
- Most models are inexpensive
- Most have fixed lens and fixed or limited focus
- Easy-loading film cartridge
- Film available in black-and-white or color
- Color film for slides or prints
- Prints are made from negative

35mm camera and film
- Models range from fully automatic to those in which all settings are adjusted by hand
- Most are relatively expensive
- Many allow interchangeable lenses
- Film winds on spools and is relatively inexpensive
- Greatest variety of film, including fast film
- Produces best-quality pictures

A step up from these very basic cameras are those with a lens you can focus. These cameras will give you sharper pictures and the ability to shoot close-ups to within 90 centimeters (3 feet) of the subject. Focusing systems vary from camera to camera. Some require you to guess the distance and set it on a scale. Others allow you to focus only in limited steps, such as near, midrange, or distant.

Range-finder focusing is best in this camera class. To use it, you focus until two halves of a split image merge in the viewfinder. The system is accurate, and a double image in the finder reminds you to focus. Cameras in this class run from about $60 to more than $100, with the range-finders on the higher side.

If you are willing to spend more for better equipment, it pays to shift your attention to the 35-millimeter (mm) range-finder cameras, which have higher-quality components than do pocket cameras and produce better-quality pictures. A wide variety of film for these cameras is available. The cameras offer good value in the $100 to $200 range.

If you are seriously interested in photography as an art, you will probably want a 35-mm single-lens reflex (SLR), named for its viewing system. Unlike the less expensive cameras, it has interchangeable lenses that range from extreme wide angles to long-range telephoto and zoom lenses with variable focal lengths.

There are dozens of SLRs to choose from, ranging upward in price from $150. They fall into four broad classes:
▪ Fully automatic compacts, such as the Olympus OM-10, Nikon EM, Pentax ME and MV, and Canon AV-1. These set the exposure automatically and are good for beginners.
▪ Auto-manual SLRs, including the Olympus OM-2 and Nikon FE. These cameras are also automatic, but they can be operated manually to give you more control over tricky exposure situations and special effects. Cameras in this class are suitable for both amateurs and professionals.
▪ Manually metered cameras. These are easy to use, but they do not operate as fast as the automatics.
▪ Cameras without an exposure meter. These are best suited to advanced photographers who can use a separate light meter to determine the best exposure.

When you have selected your camera, what kind of film should you use? Instant and Instamatic cameras give you little choice, but you can make more selections with your 35-mm.

Most people use color film and most prefer prints to slides because prints are easier to enjoy and share with others. On the other hand, slides provide better and brighter color. Black-and-white film is used mainly by professionals and advanced amateurs.

No matter whether you choose black-and-white or color film, a few fundamental rules apply. The higher a film's American Standards Association (ASA) number, the faster it is. Fast films, ASA 400 or above, allow you to shoot in dim light without a flash and to use fast shutter speeds to freeze action, or small f-stops (lens openings) for sharpness. Fast films are not as sharp as slower films, ASA 64 and below, and they produce coarser-grained images. However, today's films are so good that even the high-speed types are considered all-purpose films. But there is no need to stick with a single film. Experiment until you find one you like.

Unfortunately, few of us can afford to experiment with cameras, so it is important to shop wisely for your camera. There is no point in buying one beyond your means, needs, or skills, but it can be just as bad to buy a camera so simple that you outgrow it. A well-chosen camera will give you much service and pleasure.   [A. J. Hand]

Shopping for the Super Sound

Suppose that after listening to a new high-fidelity outfit at your friend's house you decide that you want to buy your own stereo system. So you visit a local hi-fi store, and are confronted by row after row of radios, turntables, amplifiers, speakers, and tape decks. It is hard to tell the difference between the various brands and models that look almost identical but bear vastly different price tags. The specifications are not much help either: "35-watt receiver plus two 3-way speakers; frequency response of 20-20,000 Hz with not more than 0.02 per cent THD; Dolbyized cassette tape deck; belt-drive turntable; wow and flutter 0.05 per cent; hinged dust cover." Except for the dust cover, such information means little to most people.

To avoid walking out of the stereo store with a system inappropriate for your needs, it will pay to take time to examine those needs and learn how to select equipment to match them.

First of all, consider your taste in music — is it rock, jazz, symphonic, or chamber music, or easy-listening? If you are an expert in symphonic listening, you will want more sensitive equipment than someone who just wants background music for hours at a time. Also consider the room in which you plan to use the equipment and the distance to your nearest neighbor. If you have a small room or neighbors close by, you will not be able to use all the power available in the more expensive sets. You must also consider how well you can hear. Many young persons exposed to loud music have lost the ability to hear high notes.

So let us look at one hi-fi component at a time as we relate your listening needs to the technical terms. We can begin with the amplifier, which controls the flow of electrical power to the loudspeaker. The greater the power, the louder the sound. Electrical power is measured in watts, and a typical

A high-fidelity music store contains a bewildering array of components to choose from.

amplifier is rated at 35 watts. This amplifier will actually provide slightly less than 35 watts, because some power is lost inside it.

You must relate the power to the characteristics of your room, your listening habits, and the efficiency of your loudspeakers. Sound bounces around a room that has few pieces of furniture and many smooth surfaces – such as a tile floor, exposed windows, and painted walls and ceilings. You could get by with a relatively low-powered sound system in such a room. But if you add furniture, carpet the floor, install draperies, hang textured wallpaper and pictures, and put acoustic tiles on the ceiling, your room will absorb much more sound, so your power requirement will increase.

You can tell whether 35 watts is too much power or too little by remembering that greater power produces louder sound. Sound is measured in decibels (db). The lowest db level audible to people with excellent hearing is 0 db. A whisper is 20 db and a power lawn mower roars at 96 db. If you wish to hear a recording of a symphony orchestra as you would hear it in the audience, you need a little more than 80 db. A good average loudspeaker will provide about 80 db from 1 watt of power. Eight watts will produce 89 db, and 35 watts will provide about 95 db – enough to rattle your chandelier. A 35-watt unit playing at full blast in your yard would annoy neighbors about 60 meters (200 feet) away.

The next item to consider is frequency response – the range of frequencies, or rates of vibration, of the sounds that a component produces. The greater the frequency, the higher the pitch. The lowest pitch on a piano has a frequency of 27 vibrations per second, or hertz (Hz), and the highest, about 4,200 Hz. Newborn babies can hear sounds whose frequencies range from 20 to 20,000 Hz, but recent tests indicate that half of the college freshmen in the United States may have impaired hearing, mostly at high frequencies.

So is there any point in buying more sensitive equipment if you cannot hear single-tone sounds above 16,000 Hz? It could be worthwhile, because your ears may respond subtly to frequencies above 16,000 Hz. The sounds of orchestral instruments combine to produce vibrations that affect our perceptions of the audible tones, though they are above our hearing range.

All the subtleties of sound must be delivered through speakers. The simplest and least expensive speaker has one vibrating unit that produces the entire range of frequencies. A two-way speaker – two speakers in one housing – produces richer tones by splitting the range in two. It has a large horn called a woofer for the lower notes and a small horn called a tweeter for the upper ones. A three-way speaker, the most expensive type generally available, produces even better tones because it has a third unit, called a squawker, for the middle frequencies. As you listen, think about whether the richer tones of the more expensive speakers will enhance your enjoyment of the music enough to make the speakers worth the extra money.

In examining FM radios, or tuners, check the Total Harmonic Distortion (THD), the measure of a radio's ability to reproduce the original blend of a musical instrument's fundamental tones and its overtones, the related, higher-pitched notes that sound when the fundamental tones are played. A THD of 0.5 per cent is acceptable and anything less than 0.1 per cent is more than anybody but the most ardent hi-fi hobbyist needs.

A radio's sensitivity is important if you live far from the FM transmitter. It is measured in microvolts. A sensitivity of 2 microvolts or less is good. If you live in a metropolitan area, you will be more interested in selectivity, the ability to tune in an FM station whose frequency is close to nearby stations. A selectivity of 70 db or higher is fine.

Record players, or turntables, are available in a wide variety of options. A belt-drive turntable, for example, is driven by a thin, plastic belt from the motor pulley, while a direct drive is turned by rollers. Which should you buy? That depends on the turntable's wow and flutter rating, a measure of its ability to turn at constant speed. When the turntable changes speed slightly, frequency of the sound changes, producing an audible wow sound or flutter. This kind of distortion is expressed in percentages. Unless your hearing is exceptional, you will not discern any change in frequency less than 0.06 per cent, so this figure is sufficient for a good turntable.

Tracking force, which keeps the needle in the record groove, will eventually wear down records, so the lower this force, the better. But if you are holding a dance in the living room, you will want to increase the force to prevent the needle from skipping. Most turntables have an adjustable tracking force.

Another option to consider is a semi-automatic turntable, which holds only one record at a time, rather than a stack of records that might scratch each other. If you are sensitive to such scratches and carefully put the record back in its jacket after each playing, and if you do not mind changing each record when it ends, get the single-play turntable. But if you leave records lying around, you might as well use an automatic record changer. With this, you can have continuous music for hours. When buying a turntable or record changer, be sure that the output is matched to the amplifier system so that the record player will produce good volume at moderate amplifier settings.

Many stores offer packaged combinations of speakers, turntable, tuner, and amplifier. Should you buy a combination or the individual components? Study the combination's components as if you were going to buy them separately, then decide.

Suppose you want to complete your outfit with a tape player, or tape deck. What kind should you buy? Reel-to-reel decks make tape editing and splicing easy, so they are best for elaborate home recording. If you are just going to play prerecorded tapes or record an occasional FM or AM radio program, buy the cheaper and more convenient 8-track or cassette deck.

Prerecorded cassettes produce a faint hiss in the background. But you can get tapes that do not produce a hiss when played on a special deck called a Dolbyized deck, named after its inventor, United States physicist Ray Dolby. Should you buy one? Try out an ordinary deck and a Dolbyized deck with the equipment that you own or plan to buy, then decide whether the improvement is worth the money.

If you are planning to spend a great deal on the latest and best equipment, you should consider two developments that are nearly ready for the market place. One of these is the metal-particle tape, which can produce the purest sounds, especially at higher frequencies and higher volumes. This kind of tape requires special tape decks.

The other development, the digital record, may revolutionize the basic stereophonic sound unit. A digital record carries sound as a series of 0s and 1s represented by laser-burned pits in its grooves. The record looks like an ordinary long-playing record, but it has more than 100 times as many grooves. It is played by focusing a weak laser beam on the grooves. The special turntable rotates the record at 450 revolutions per minute. This provides 2½ hours of continuous play on each side, and there is never any wear on the record.   [E. Joseph Piel]

Breast Cancer: The Options in Treatment

A diagnosis of breast cancer, number-one cancer killer of females in the United States, is sure to inspire fear, horror, and disbelief in the potential patient. In the past, she faced the trauma of living with the aftermath of disfiguring—even somewhat crippling—surgery. But if you, a member of your family, or a friend are among the 100,000 U.S. women who get breast cancer every year, you should know there is now a range of treatment options available.

Gone are the days when the breast cancer patient automatically faced a radical mastectomy. Gone are the days when a woman had no choice in her own treatment.

Cancer, or malignancy, occurs when body cells multiply at an abnormally fast rate and begin invading and destroying surrounding tissue. In the breast, cancer usually appears in the fat tissue and can spread later to the underlying muscles of the chest wall and to the lymph glands in the armpit area. Lymph glands help protect the body against infection. Surgeons have long preferred the radical mastectomy because they wanted to prevent the cancer from spreading to these areas.

Not all women are equally threatened by breast cancer. The disease is rare among women under age 35 and most frequent among those over 50. Those who have had cancer in one breast face an increased risk of developing cancer in the other, as do those whose mothers, sisters, or aunts have had the disease.

All women should be alert for warning signs. The most frequent sign is a lump or thickening in the breast. Other signs include swelling, dimpling, puckering of the nipple or breast tissue, and discharge or bleeding from the nipple. There is rarely pain and tenderness, at least in the early stages.

Early detection is the key to surviving the disease. The 10-year survival

Getting Advice About Breast Cancer

For more information about breast cancer, write to the National Cancer Institute, Bethesda, Md., 20205, for *The Breast Cancer Digest.* You can also call your local unit of the American Cancer Society or the toll-free telephone number of the Cancer Information Services, listed here by state.

Alabama
800-638-6694

Alaska
1-800-638-6070

Arizona
800-638-6694

Arkansas
800-638-6694

California
(For area codes 213, 714, 805)
1-800-252-9066
(All other area codes)
800-638-6694

Colorado
1-800-332-1850

Connecticut
1-800-922-0824

Delaware
1-800-523-3586

District of Columbia
(202) 232-2833

Florida
1-800-432-5953

Georgia
800-638-6694

Hawaii
(Oahu) 536-0111
(Neighbor Islands)
Enterprise 6702

Idaho
800-638-6694

Illinois
800-972-0586

Indiana
800-638-6694

Iowa
800-638-6694

Kansas
800-638-6694

Kentucky
800-432-9321

Louisiana
800-638-6694

Maine
1-800-225-7034

Maryland
800-492-1444

Massachusetts
1-800-952-7420

Michigan
800-638-6694

Minnesota
1-800-582-5262

Mississippi
800-638-6694

Missouri
800-638-6694

Montana
1-800-525-0231

Nebraska
800-638-6694

Nevada
800-638-6694

New Hampshire
1-800-225-7034

New Jersey
800-523-3586

New Mexico
1-800-525-0231

New York State
1-800-462-7255
New York City
212-794-7982

North Carolina
1-800-672-0943

North Dakota
800-638-6694

Ohio
800-282-6522

Oklahoma
800-638-6694

Oregon
800-638-6694

Pennsylvania
1-800-822-3963

Rhode Island
800-638-6694

South Carolina
800-638-6694

South Dakota
800-638-6694

Tennessee
800-638-6694

Texas
1-800-392-2040

Utah
800-638-6694

Vermont
1-800-225-7034

Virginia
800-638-6694

Washington State
1-800-552-7212

West Virginia
800-638-6694

Wisconsin
1-800-362-8038

Wyoming
1-800-525-0231

rate for breast cancer victims can run as high as 85 per cent — if the condition is discovered and treated early. And patients themselves discover an estimated 95 per cent of breast cancers. Every woman should therefore learn the proper self-examination technique and examine her breasts every month. If you discover a lump or other unusual change, see a physician immediately.

The doctor will examine you and probably order further tests, such as X rays; thermography, which measures temperature differences in the breast to identify the warmer-than-normal tumor tissue; or ultrasound, which uses high-frequency sound waves to create a picture of the breast tissue.

A lump does not necessarily mean breast cancer, however. Nearly 80 per cent of all breast tumors are not malignant. Nevertheless, the physician, after confirming that there is a lump, will probably perform a biopsy — the surgical removal of tissue for analysis.

For years, the standard procedure was to keep the woman on the operating table while the tissue sample was analyzed. If the tissue was malignant, the surgeon would immediately remove the breast. But a June 1979 report by the National Cancer Institute (NCI) officially recommended that the biopsy and the surgery be separated into two steps. This gives the patient the opportunity to make some decisions.

If the tests show breast cancer, ask the doctor to spell out the treatment options. If the doctor is reluctant to discuss alternatives to radical mastectomy, or to discuss those you suggest, you may want to seek a second opinion.

The treatment depends on such factors as how far the disease has advanced, the type of tumor, and where the tumor is located. In general, the earlier breast cancer is diagnosed, the less severe the treatment.

The least disfiguring surgical procedure is lumpectomy. Only the cancerous tumor and a small amount of surrounding tissue are removed, leaving intact the exterior of the breast. This procedure is highly controversial and appropriate only when cancer is detected very early.

Subcutaneous mastectomy is also controversial among some surgeons. The inner tissue is removed, but the skin of the breast, including the nipple, is left untouched.

In the simple mastectomy, the entire breast is removed, but the lymph nodes and underlying muscles of the chest wall are left in place.

The modified radical mastectomy is now the most widely performed breast surgery and is recommended by the NCI for women with small tumors. The breast and the lymph nodes are removed, but not the chest muscles. Studies have shown this technique to be as effective as the radical mastectomy, and it is less disfiguring.

In the radical mastectomy, the breast is removed along with the surrounding muscles, the lymph nodes, and sometimes part of the ribcage. By 1976, only about 25 per cent of breast cancer patients underwent this type of surgery — for very advanced cases.

The doctor will often recommend drugs, radiation therapy, or hormone treatment as a follow-up to surgery. Here, too, you should ask questions about risks and benefits.

The new variety of treatments and breast-reconstruction techniques have made the outlook for breast cancer patients brighter now. But deciding on a treatment that will leave as few physical and psychological scars as possible — while granting the greatest chance for survival — requires information. If you need advice, contact your local unit of the American Cancer Society or the National Cancer Institute, or call the Cancer Information Service in your area. Help is literally yours free for the asking.   [Patricia Skalka]

World Book Supplement

Revised articles on subjects in
science and technology reprinted
from the 1980 edition of the
World Book Encyclopedia.

TEETH

TEETH are hard, bonelike structures in the upper and lower jaws of human beings and many kinds of animals. They are the hardest parts of the body.

People use their teeth chiefly to chew food. Chewing is the first step in the process of *digestion*. Digestion begins as the teeth chop and grind chunks of food into smaller pieces. As the teeth chew the food, it is mixed with *saliva*, a liquid produced in the mouth. The food becomes a moist pulp, which is easy to swallow. The food is further broken down in the stomach and the small intestine, where it is absorbed by the blood. The blood carries the digested food to all parts of the body. Without teeth, people could not eat foods that must be chewed. They could only swallow soft foods and liquids.

Teeth also play an important part in speech. The teeth and tongue are used together to form many sounds that make up words. To produce the *th* sound, for example, the tip of the tongue is placed against the upper front teeth. A person who lacks these teeth may be unable to make the sound.

Teeth also help support the muscles around the mouth and so contribute to a person's appearance. People who have lost their teeth lack this support. Unless they wear artificial teeth, they may have deep, saggy lines around the mouth.

Like human beings, most animals use their teeth to chew food. They also use their teeth to obtain food. Many animals that eat plants tear off the leaves or stalks of the plants with their teeth. Most meat-eating animals use their teeth to seize and kill prey.

This article chiefly discusses human teeth. The last section of the article describes the differences in the teeth of various kinds of animals.

Kinds of Teeth

Human beings grow two sets of teeth: (1) deciduous teeth and (2) permanent teeth. The individual deciduous teeth appear and fall out gradually early in life. They are replaced, one by one, by the permanent teeth. See the table *Ages at Which Teeth Appear* for the times the various kinds of deciduous and permanent teeth generally appear.

Deciduous and permanent teeth have the same basic structure. Each tooth has a *crown* and one or more *roots*. The crown is the part of the tooth that can be seen in the mouth. The root or roots are covered by the gums. The roots hold the tooth in a socket in the jawbone.

Deciduous Teeth are also called *baby teeth, milk teeth,* or *primary teeth*. They start to form about 7½ months before a baby is born. They begin as oval or round swellings called *buds*, which gradually develop into teeth. When a baby is born, parts of all the deciduous teeth are present deep within the jaws. As the teeth grow, they push through the gums. This process is called *eruption* or *teething*. Babies begin to teethe at about 6 to 9 months of age. Most children have all their deciduous teeth by about 2 years of age.

John P. Wortel, the contributor of this article, is Assistant Professor of General and Oral Pathology at Loyola University School of Dentistry.

There are 20 deciduous teeth, 10 in each jaw. They consist of three kinds of teeth: (1) incisors, (2) canines, and (3) molars. Each jaw has 4 incisors, 2 canines, and 4 molars. The incisors and canines are used to bite into food, and the molars to grind food. The positions of these teeth in the mouth are shown in the illustration *Kinds of Teeth*.

The deciduous teeth help the permanent teeth erupt in their normal positions. Most of the permanent teeth form near the roots of the deciduous teeth. When a child is about 3 years old, the roots of various deciduous teeth begin to dissolve slowly. By the time a permanent tooth is ready to erupt, the root of the deciduous tooth has completely dissolved. The crown of the tooth then becomes loose and falls out.

Permanent Teeth, like deciduous teeth, begin to develop before birth. But most of their growth occurs after birth. The permanent teeth begin to erupt after the deciduous teeth start to fall out.

The first permanent teeth appear when a child is about 6 or 7 years old. Between the ages of 6 and 12, a child has some permanent and some deciduous teeth in the mouth. The last permanent teeth erupt when a person is 17 to 21 years old.

There are 32 permanent teeth, 16 in each jaw. They are larger than the deciduous teeth and consist of four kinds of teeth. The four kinds are (1) incisors, (2) canines, (3) premolars, and (4) molars. Each jaw has 4 incisors, 2 canines, 4 premolars, and 6 molars. The following discussion describes the four kinds of permanent teeth. Their positions in the mouth are shown in the illustration *Kinds of Teeth*.

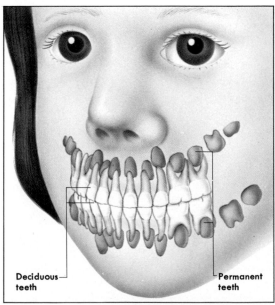

Deciduous teeth

Permanent teeth

WORLD BOOK diagram by Charles Wellek

The Teeth of a Child. By the time a child is about 4 years old, most of the permanent teeth have formed within the jaws near the roots of the deciduous teeth. The deciduous teeth, all of which have erupted by about age 2, will gradually fall out and be replaced, one by one, by the permanent teeth.

Kinds of Teeth

The illustrations below show the kinds of deciduous and permanent teeth and their positions in the mouth. There are 20 deciduous teeth, 10 in the upper jaw and 10 in the lower jaw. There are 32 permanent teeth, 16 in each jaw.

WORLD BOOK diagrams by Charles Wellek

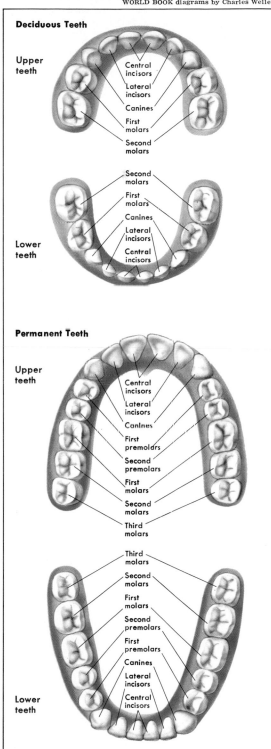

Deciduous Teeth

Upper teeth
- Central incisors
- Lateral incisors
- Canines
- First molars
- Second molars

Lower teeth
- Second molars
- First molars
- Canines
- Lateral incisors
- Central incisors

Permanent Teeth

Upper teeth
- Central incisors
- Lateral incisors
- Canines
- First premolars
- Second premolars
- First molars
- Second molars
- Third molars

Lower teeth
- Third molars
- Second molars
- First molars
- Second premolars
- First premolars
- Canines
- Lateral incisors
- Central incisors

Ages at Which Teeth Appear*

Deciduous Teeth:	Lower Teeth	Upper Teeth
Central incisors	6 months	7 months
Lateral incisors	7 months	9 months
Canines	16 months	18 months
First molars	12 months	14 months
Second molars	20 months	24 months

Permanent Teeth:	Lower Teeth	Upper Teeth
Central incisors	6-7 years	7-8 years
Lateral incisors	7-8 years	8-9 years
Canines	9-10 years	11-12 years
First premolars	10-12 years	10-11 years
Second premolars	11-12 years	10-12 years
First molars	6-7 years	6-7 years
Second molars	11-13 years	12-13 years
Third molars	17-21 years	17-21 years

*The ages given are approximate. In many cases, individual teeth may erupt at an earlier or later age.

Incisors are the chief biting teeth. They have a sharp, straight cutting edge. In most cases, incisors have one root. The central incisors of the lower jaw are the smallest permanent teeth.

Canines are used with the incisors to bite into food. They are also used to tear off pieces of food. The name for these teeth comes from another word for *dog*—that is, *canine*. The canine teeth resemble a dog's fangs. They have a sharp, pointed edge and one root. Canines are also called *cuspids* or *dogteeth*. The upper canines are sometimes known as *eyeteeth*.

Premolars are used to crush and grind food. They have a broad, lumpy top instead of a sharp biting edge. The small surface lumps are called *cusps*. The cusps enable the teeth to mash pieces of food.

Premolars are sometimes called *bicuspids* because, in most cases, they have two cusps. The prefix *bi* means *two*. The first upper premolars normally have two roots. The other premolars have one root. The premolars erupt in the place of the deciduous molars.

Molars, like premolars, grind food. They are shaped much like premolars but are larger. The various molars normally have three to five cusps and two or three roots.

The permanent molars do not form beneath any of the deciduous teeth. They develop as the jaws grow, which makes space for them. Some adults lack one or more of the third molars, which are commonly called *wisdom teeth*. In many cases, the jaws do not grow large enough to provide space for the wisdom teeth. As a result, the wisdom teeth may become *impacted*—that is, wedged between the jawbone and another tooth. The wisdom teeth must then be removed.

Parts of a Tooth

A tooth consists of four kinds of tissues. They are (1) pulp, (2) dentin, (3) enamel, and (4) cementum. Connective tissue surrounds the root of the tooth. This tissue, called the *periodontal ligament*, holds the root in the socket in the jaw.

Pulp is the innermost layer of a tooth. It consists of connective tissue, blood vessels, and nerves. The blood vessels nourish the tooth. The nerves transmit sensations of pain to the brain.

The pulp has two parts, the *pulp chamber* and the *root canal*. The pulp chamber lies in the crown of the tooth. The root canal lies in the root of the tooth. Blood vessels and nerves enter the root canal through a small hole that is located at the tip of the root. They extend then through the root canal and run on into the pulp chamber.

Dentin is a hard, yellow substance that surrounds the pulp. It makes up most of a tooth. Dentin is harder than bone. It consists mainly of mineral salts and water but also has some living cells.

Enamel overlies the dentin in the crown of the tooth. It forms the outermost covering of the crown. Enamel is the hardest tissue in the body. It enables a tooth to withstand the pressure placed on it during chewing. Enamel consists of mineral salts and a small amount of water. Enamel is white but it is also transparent. The yellow color of the dentin shows through the enamel, and as a result, most teeth appear slightly yellowish.

As a person grows older, small amounts of enamel begin to wear away. This process, called *attrition*, results from the use of the teeth over a long period. As the enamel wears away, the dentin becomes exposed. The teeth may then become increasingly sensitive to hot and cold liquids.

Cementum overlies the dentin in the root of the tooth. In most cases, the cementum and enamel meet where the root ends and the crown begins. Cementum is about as hard as bone. Like dentin and enamel, it consists mainly of mineral salts and water.

Periodontal Ligament consists of small fibers. These fibers extend through the cementum and into the bony socket, which is called the *alveolus*. Besides anchoring the tooth in the alveolus, the periodontal ligament serves as a shock absorber during chewing.

Most cases of tooth decay and gum disease could be prevented if people took proper care of their teeth and gums. Proper care requires (1) a good diet, (2) cleaning the teeth after eating, and (3) dental checkups.

A Good Diet. Dentists advise people to eat well-balanced meals. Such meals include a variety of foods and provide the *nutrients* (nourishing substances) needed by the teeth and gums. Nutrition experts divide foods into groups to make it easier for people to plan well-balanced meals. According to one system, foods are classified into four groups. Another system lists seven groups. The article NUTRITION describes these groups.

Dentists also urge people to eat fewer sugary foods because these foods contribute to tooth decay. Bacteria in the mouth digest sugar and produce an acid as a result. The acid dissolves tooth enamel, forming a cavity.

Foods that have a large amount of sugar include candies, pastries, most breakfast cereals, and sweetened canned fruits. Many people eat sugary foods as snacks. In place of sugary foods, dentists advise people to snack on such foods as fresh fruits and vegetables, cheeses, and nuts. They also recommend that people drink milk or unsweetened fruit and vegetable juices instead of soft drinks and other sugar-sweetened beverages.

Dentists further recommend that children drink water that contains chemical compounds called *fluorides*. Fluorides are absorbed by the enamel as the teeth grow. They help the teeth resist the acid that forms cavities. Some communities have a water supply that naturally contains fluorides. Many other communities add fluorides to the water supply. However, some people oppose *fluoridation* (the addition of fluorides to water supplies). See FLUORIDATION.

Parts of a Tooth

The *crown,* or visible part of a molar tooth, includes projections called *cusps.* The *root* extends into the bone of the jaw. A tissue called *dentin* makes up most of the tooth. A layer of *enamel* covers the dentin of the crown, and *cementum* overlies the dentin of the root. Within the dentin lies the *pulp,* including the *pulp chamber* and the *root canal,* through which blood vessels and nerves enter the tooth. The *periodontal ligament* surrounds the root and holds the tooth in its socket.

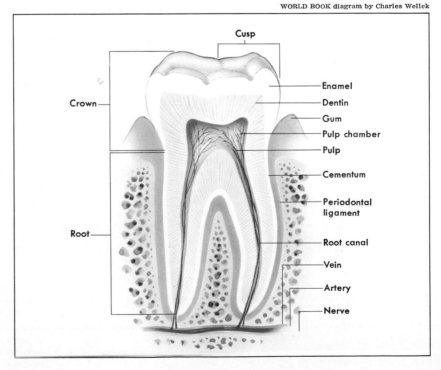

WORLD BOOK diagram by Charles Wellek

Cusp — Enamel — Dentin — Gum — Pulp chamber — Pulp — Cementum — Periodontal ligament — Root canal — Vein — Artery — Nerve — Crown — Root

Fluorides may be applied directly to a child's teeth during a dental checkup. In some cases, dentists prescribe a fluoride substance that children can apply at home. Most dentists also advise children to brush their teeth with a toothpaste that contains fluorides.

Cleaning the Teeth. Dentists advise people to clean their teeth by brushing after every meal and by using *dental floss* once a day. Dental floss is a thin thread that comes in a roll. It is used to clean the areas between teeth and under the gum line. Brushing and flossing remove trapped food particles and *plaque* from the teeth. Plaque is a sticky film that consists of saliva, food particles, and bacteria. The bacteria digest certain foods, particularly sugars, and form an enamel-dissolving acid.

To brush the teeth, you should use a small, soft toothbrush and a toothpaste that contains fluorides. There are several methods of brushing. You should use the one recommended by your dentist. One commonly recommended method is to place the brush against the teeth at a slight angle, with the bristles pointed toward the gums. Brush the upper teeth with a downward, sweeping motion. Brush the lower teeth with an upward, sweeping motion. Clean both the outside and the inside surfaces of the teeth in this way. Use a scrubbing motion to clean the biting surfaces of the premolars and molars. Lastly, brush the tongue to remove food particles and bacteria, which contribute to bad mouth odors. Then rinse the mouth thoroughly. Rinsing with water is just as effective as rinsing with mouthwash.

To floss the teeth, cut a piece of floss about 18 inches (46 centimeters) long from the roll. Wrap one end of the floss around each middle finger. Using the index fingers and thumbs, gently guide the floss between two teeth. Then pull the floss up and down, cleaning the sides of both teeth and the areas around the gum line. Repeat this procedure on all the teeth.

Some people use *disclosing tablets* to determine if any areas of the teeth remain unclean after brushing and flossing. Disclosing tablets contain a red or purple dye. When you chew a tablet, the dye sticks to any unclean areas of the teeth. You can then rebrush and refloss these spots. You can obtain disclosing tablets from your dentist.

Dental Checkups. Dentists advise people to have a dental checkup at least once a year. Children should start going to a dentist after all their deciduous teeth have erupted. Dentists can recognize and treat diseases of the teeth and gums at an early stage, before the diseases cause serious damage. Dentists also provide services that help prevent diseases of the teeth and gums. Many dentists employ a licensed *dental hygienist* to help them in their work.

During a checkup, the dentist looks at the teeth, gums, and other tissues inside the mouth for signs of diseases. The dentist—or the dental hygienist—also X-rays the teeth. X rays can show the location of dental decay that cannot be seen. They also show any abnormal conditions of the jawbones and other tissues that support the teeth. After reviewing the X rays, the dentist may decide to fill cavities or plan other treat-

How to Brush Your Teeth Use a small, soft toothbrush and a toothpaste that contains fluorides. Place the brush against the teeth at a slight angle, with the bristles pointed toward the gums. The illustrations below show one of the brushing methods commonly recommended by dentists.

WORLD BOOK diagrams by Charles Wellek

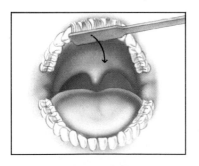

Outside Surfaces of Upper Teeth. Use a downward, sweeping motion.

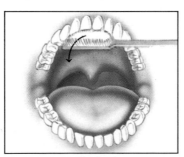

Inside Surfaces of Upper Teeth. Use a downward, sweeping motion.

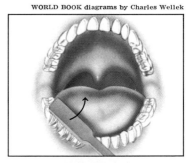

Outside Surfaces of Lower Teeth. Use an upward, sweeping motion.

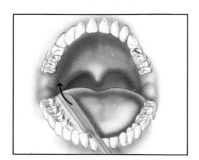

Inside Surfaces of Lower Teeth. Use an upward, sweeping motion.

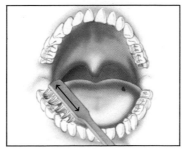

Biting Surfaces of Premolars and Molars. Scrub back and forth.

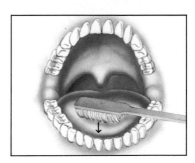

The Tongue. Brush to remove food particles and bacteria.

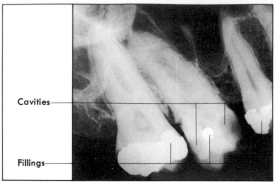

Cavities

Fillings

Patrick D. Toto

An X Ray of the Teeth shows the location of cavities and fillings. Cavities appear as dark spots on the teeth. Fillings show up as distinct white areas.

ment. The dentist or hygienist then cleans the teeth to remove plaque and *calculus*, a hard, yellowish substance formed by the buildup of plaque. Calculus is also called *tartar*. After the teeth have been cleaned, a fluoride substance is applied to help the teeth resist decay. Generally, only children and teen-agers receive applications of fluorides. Lastly, the dentist or hygienist may instruct the patient on how to brush and floss the teeth properly.

Diseases and Defects of the Teeth

Dental decay, also called *caries*, is the most common disease of the teeth. Most people under the age of 35 who lose their teeth do so because of dental decay. A defect in the position of the teeth, called *malocclusion*, is also a common problem among young people. Diseases of the gums and alveolus, called *periodontal diseases*, are the chief dental problem of people over the age of 35. A less common but very severe disease is *oral cancer*, which kills about 8,000 people in the United States each year. The following discussion describes the causes and treatment of (1) dental decay, (2) malocclusion, (3) periodontal diseases, and (4) oral cancer.

Dental Decay is a complex process that involves plaque, bacteria, and food. Saliva produces an invisible film on the teeth. Bacteria and food particles stick to this film, forming plaque. The bacteria digest the *carbohydrates* (sugars and starches) in food and produce an acid. The acid dissolves enamel, causing a cavity. If the cavity is not treated, the decay will progress through the enamel and into the dentin. When the decay reaches the pulp, a toothache results.

The *occlusal* (biting) surfaces of the premolars and molars tend to decay easily because they have many small pits, which trap food. On the other hand, the surfaces of the incisors and canines are smooth. These surfaces do not trap food and so do not decay as easily.

Dentists have several methods of treating dental decay, depending on the severity. The most common methods include (1) filling a cavity, (2) performing root canal therapy, (3) crowning a tooth, and (4) removing and replacing teeth. Before beginning any of these procedures, the dentist usually injects an *anesthetic* (pain-killing drug) into the gums near the nerves of the tooth.

Filling a Cavity. To fill a cavity, the dentist first re-

moves the decayed and soft parts of the tooth, using small hand instruments or an electric drill. The dentist then makes tiny undercuts or ledges in the hole with a high-speed drill. These undercuts help hold the filling, which is not adhesive.

In most cases, dentists fill cavities with *silver amalgam* or gold. Silver amalgam consists of silver and a small amount of copper and tin. To fill the front teeth, dentists sometimes use a plasticlike material that closely resembles the color of natural teeth. But this material is not as hard as silver amalgam or gold, and so it is seldom used to fill the back teeth.

The filling is packed into the hole and allowed to harden slightly. The dentist then carves the filling to restore the original shape of the tooth.

Performing Root Canal Therapy. Root canal therapy is the removal of the pulp of a tooth. It is performed if the pulp has become infected. When decay extends into the pulp, a small sac of pus, called an *abscess*, may form. An abscess can be extremely painful. If it is not treated, infection may spread to other parts of the body.

To perform root canal therapy, the dentist first anesthetizes the area and then drills a hole into the crown of the tooth. The dentist uses small files to reach through the hole and clean out the pulp. After removing the pulp, the dentist fills the empty space, usually with a rubberlike substance called *gutta-percha*. Sometimes,

Filling a Cavity

These illustrations show how a dentist fills a cavity. The dentist usually begins by injecting a drug called an *anesthetic* into the gums near the tooth. The anesthetic prevents the patient from feeling the pain that drilling might produce.

WORLD BOOK diagrams by Charles Wellek

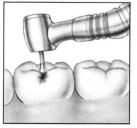

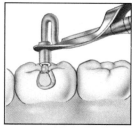

Drilling. The dentist uses a drill to remove decayed and soft parts of the tooth and to form undercuts or ledges that will help hold the filling.

Filling. An instrument is used to place filling material into the hole. Silver amalgam, made from silver, copper, and tin, is a commonly used filling.

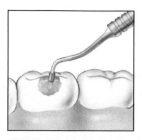

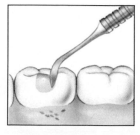

Packing. Using another instrument, the dentist firmly packs the filling into the hole. The filling is then allowed to harden slightly.

Shaping. The dentist carefully carves the filling to restore the original shape of the tooth. Finally, the dentist smooths down any rough edges.

the hole in the crown of the tooth is then filled. But in the majority of cases, the tooth must be fitted with an artificial crown.

Crowning a Tooth. Crowns are toothlike caps that may be made of metal, porcelain, or plastic. They are used when the natural crown of a tooth is so badly damaged that it does not have enough healthy tissue to hold a filling.

To crown a tooth, the dentist first anesthetizes the area and then prepares the natural crown by grinding it down slightly. Next, the dentist covers the prepared tooth and the teeth next to it with a jellylike material. After this material hardens, it is removed from the patient's mouth and serves as an *impression* (mold). The dentist also makes an impression of the teeth in the opposite jaw that press against the prepared tooth and the teeth next to it. The impressions are used to make a plaster reproduction of the prepared tooth and other teeth. Dental technicians then produce a crown, using the plaster reproduction as a model. They must make sure that the crown not only fits the prepared tooth but also fits in place with the other teeth.

Meanwhile, a temporary crown is placed on the tooth. When the permanent crown is ready, the dentist removes the temporary crown and cements the permanent one onto the tooth.

Crowning a Tooth

A crown is a toothlike cap made of metal, porcelain, or plastic, which is cemented onto a damaged tooth. It is used when a damaged crown does not have enough healthy tissue to hold a filling.

WORLD BOOK diagrams by Charles Wellek

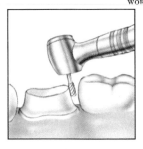

Preparing the Tooth. The dentist uses a drill to remove damaged parts of the tooth and to shape the tooth so that a crown will fit over it.

Making a Mold. The teeth are covered with a gel that forms a mold. Plaster teeth made in this mold serve as models for making the crown.

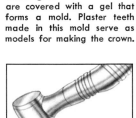

Cementing the Crown. The crown must fit the prepared tooth and also fit in place with the teeth next to it and those in the opposite jaw.

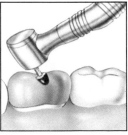

Final Fitting. The dentist may use a small grinding stone to make minor adjustments in the crown so that it will fit properly.

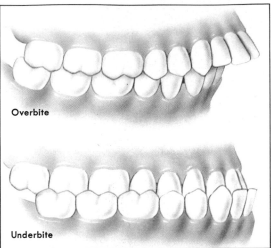

WORLD BOOK diagrams by Charles Wellek

Malocclusion is the failure of the upper and lower teeth to meet properly when a person bites. There are two main kinds of malocclusion, *overbite* and *underbite*. In overbite, the upper front teeth stick out farther than normal over the lower ones. In underbite, the lower front teeth extend in front of the upper ones.

Removing and Replacing Teeth. In severe cases of dental decay, a dentist may remove one or more teeth and replace them with artificial ones. But artificial teeth do not function as well as natural teeth. Dentists therefore remove teeth only if no other method of treatment is considered possible.

To remove a tooth, a dentist first anesthetizes the area. The dentist uses an instrument that resembles a pliers to grip the crown of the tooth and loosen the root from the socket. Both the crown and the root are then removed. After the gums heal, the patient can be fitted with an artificial tooth.

Artificial teeth are made from impressions taken of the patient's mouth. In most cases, the teeth are made of plastic. The most common types of artificial teeth are *bridges*, *partial dentures*, and *full dentures*. Bridges are permanently fixed in the mouth, but partial dentures and full dentures are removable. Bridges are used when only a few teeth are missing. They consist of one or more artificial teeth with a metal or porcelain crown on each side. The crowns fit over the adjoining natural teeth, which must be prepared to hold the crowns. Partial dentures are also used to replace only a few missing teeth. A partial denture has metal clasps that hook around nearby teeth and hold the denture in place. Full dentures are used when all the teeth of one or both jaws are missing. In a full denture, the artificial teeth are attached to a plastic base that fits over the ridge left after the teeth have been removed. In the upper jaw, the plastic base also covers the roof of the mouth.

Malocclusion is the failure of the teeth in the upper and lower jaws to meet properly when a person bites. Normally, the upper front teeth should slightly overlap the lower front teeth. There are two main types of malocclusion, *overbite* and *underbite*. In overbite, the upper front teeth stick out too far over the lower front teeth. This defect is commonly called *buck teeth*. In underbite,

WORLD BOOK diagrams by Charles Wellek

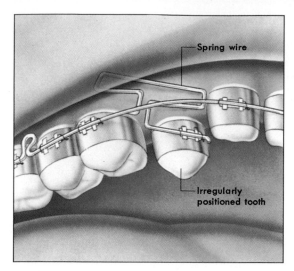

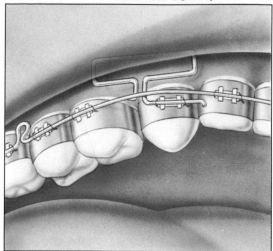

the lower front teeth extend in front of the upper ones. Many people have the correct *occlusion* (bite), but their teeth are crowded.

Malocclusion has various causes. In some cases, a deciduous tooth falls out before a permanent tooth is ready to erupt. The nearby teeth then gradually move into the open space and prevent the permanent tooth from erupting in the correct position. In other cases, the permanent teeth are too large for the jaw and crowd one another. The edges of some teeth may then overlap, or one tooth may grow above another. In still other cases, the jaws do not grow properly.

Malocclusion prevents the teeth from functioning normally when a person chews food. It also may affect the way a person speaks. In addition, malocclusion contributes to the development of dental decay and periodontal diseases, partly because irregularly positioned teeth are hard to clean.

Most cases of malocclusion can be corrected with *orthodontic bands*, commonly called *braces*. Braces consist of metal bands that are placed around each tooth and connected by wires. The wires are tightened periodically to force the teeth to move into the correct position. But the teeth must be moved slowly, and so the treatment may take a year or more. In some cases, one or more teeth must be removed to allow enough space for the others to move into a normal position.

Periodontal Diseases are caused chiefly by the buildup of plaque and calculus between the gums and teeth. The plaque and calculus irritate the gums, causing them to become inflamed. In time, the jawbones may become infected. The best way to prevent plaque from building up under the gum line is by flossing daily. The gums can also become irritated by habitually breathing through the mouth, smoking or chewing tobacco, brushing improperly, or wearing ill-fitting dentures. In addition, irregularly positioned teeth can irritate the gums. There are three main kinds of periodontal diseases: (1) gingivitis, (2) periodontitis, and (3) Vincent's infection.

Gingivitis is an inflammation of the *gingivae* (gums). The gingivae become red and swollen and bleed easily when brushed or prodded. Dentists treat gingivitis by cleaning the teeth and gums to remove plaque and calculus. They also instruct patients on how to brush and floss the teeth and on how to massage the gums. If gingivitis is not treated, it can lead to periodontitis.

Periodontitis, also called *pyorrhea*, is a severe infection of the gingivae, alveolus, and other tissues that support the teeth. The infection gradually destroys the bony walls of the sockets, and the teeth become loose. Periodontitis is difficult to cure. Treatment may involve surgical removal of the damaged tissues and repair of the remaining healthy tissues. Sometimes, loose teeth can be *splinted* (attached) to nearby teeth that are still

Periodontal Diseases

The illustrations below show two kinds of periodontal diseases. In *gingivitis*, calculus builds up between gums and teeth, causing the gums to become inflamed. Gingivitis may lead to *periodontitis*, an infection that gradually destroys the bony socket.

WORLD BOOK diagrams by Charles Wellek

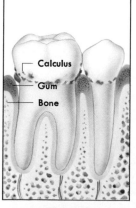

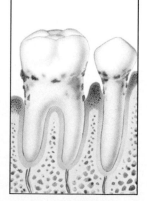

Gingivitis   **Periodontitis**

firm. But in many cases, the loose teeth must be removed and replaced by artificial ones.

Vincent's Infection, also called *trench mouth*, is a painful infection of the gingivae. The gums become red and swollen and bleed easily. The mouth has an extremely bad odor, and the victim may develop a fever. To treat Vincent's infection, a dentist cleans the teeth and gums thoroughly and instructs the patient on mouth care. In most cases, the dentist also prescribes antibiotics to combat the infection.

Oral Cancer is a disease that destroys the tissues of the mouth and may spread to other parts of the body. Scientists do not know for certain what causes oral cancer. But many factors can contribute to its development. For example, people who smoke or chew tobacco, drink excessive amounts of alcoholic beverages, or wear ill-fitting dentures increase the risk of developing oral cancer.

Oral cancer may be painless and unnoticeable in its early stages. The first symptom may be a small sore in the mouth that does not heal. To test for cancer, a dentist removes some tissue from the sore. The tissue is examined under a microscope to determine if it is cancerous. Oral cancer may be treated with drugs, radiation, or surgery.

Teeth of Animals

Many kinds of animals have teeth. However, birds, toads, turtles, and some types of insects and whales do not have teeth.

Cats, dogs, and most other mammals have *heterodont teeth*—that is, they have at least two types of teeth, which have different uses. For example, they may have incisors for biting into food and molars for crushing or grinding food.

The teeth of various kinds of mammals differ in shape and size, depending chiefly on what the animals eat. For example, plant-eating mammals, such as elephants, giraffes, and sheep, have unusually broad, flat molars. They use the molars to chew and mash plants. Meat-eating mammals, such as lions, tigers, and wolves, have long, pointed canines. They use the canines to rip and tear the bodies of their prey.

Some mammals have teeth that grow continuously. The tusks of elephants are actually incisors that have become very long. The tusks have an open pulp, which enables them to keep growing. Beavers, rats, and other rodents also have teeth that grow continuously. But most of the growth is worn down by continual use of the teeth, and so the teeth do not lengthen greatly.

Unlike most mammals, many fish and most reptiles have *homodont teeth*—that is, all their teeth are about the same size and shape and have only one use. In general, animals that have homodont teeth use their teeth to catch prey. Fish and reptiles lose and replace their teeth continuously.

Snakes have teeth that curve back toward the throat. Snakes swallow their prey whole and use their teeth to

TEETH

Some Animal Teeth Animal teeth vary in size and shape. Most mammals have *heterodont teeth*, which consist of two or more types: incisors and canines for biting and tearing food, and molars for crushing it. Most reptiles and many fish have *homodont teeth*, a single type that generally is used to catch prey.

WORLD BOOK diagrams by Patricia J. Wynne

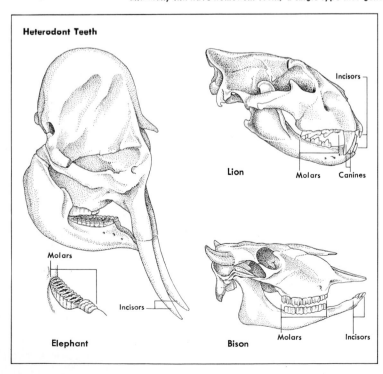

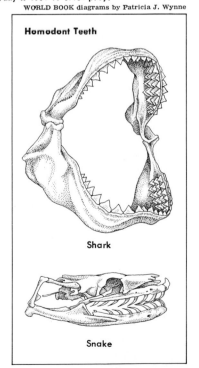

pull the prey back into the throat. In poisonous snakes, certain teeth have a canal or a groove, through which poison can be ejected. The poison comes from glands in the roof of the mouth.   JOHN P. WORTEL

Related Articles in WORLD BOOK include:

HUMAN TEETH

Abscess	Mouth
Dental Hygiene	Orthodontics
Dentistry	Periodontitis
Digestion (From Mouth	Races, Human (picture:
to Stomach)	The Upper Front Teeth)
Fluoridation	Saliva
Fluorine	Toothpaste and Toothpowder
Mastication	Trench Mouth

ANIMAL TEETH

Animal (Jaws and	Insect (Mouth Parts)
Teeth)	Lion (The Body of a Lion)
Beaver (Teeth)	Mammal (What Mammals Eat)
Cat (Teeth)	Rodent
Dog (Mouth)	Ruminant
Elephant (The Tusks	Shark (Teeth and Scales)
and Teeth)	Snake (Skeleton)
Fish (Digestive System)	Whale (picture: Toothed
Horse (Teeth)	Whales)

Outline

I. Kinds of Teeth
   A. Deciduous Teeth   B. Permanent Teeth

II. Parts of a Tooth
   A. Pulp   D. Cementum
   B. Dentin   E. Periodontal Ligament
   C. Enamel

III. Care of the Teeth and Gums
   A. A Good Diet
   B. Cleaning the Teeth
   C. Dental Checkups

IV. Diseases and Defects of the Teeth
   A. Dental Decay   C. Periodontal Diseases
   B. Malocclusion   D. Oral Cancer

V. Teeth of Animals

Questions

How often should the teeth be brushed?
What are the incisors and canines used for? The molars and premolars?
What are the four kinds of tissues that make up a tooth?
When should children start going to a dentist?
What are some of the causes of malocclusion?
When does dental decay result in a toothache?
How does eating sugary foods contribute to dental decay?
What is dental floss used for?
What does the periodontal ligament do?
What is the chief cause of periodontal diseases?

Reading and Study Guide

See *Teeth* in the RESEARCH GUIDE/INDEX, Volume 22, for a *Reading and Study Guide*.

CRUSTACEAN, *kruhs TAY shuhn,* is an invertebrate animal with many jointed legs. A crustacean has no bones. A shell called an *exoskeleton* covers its body. Crabs, crayfish, lobsters, and shrimp are crustaceans, as are barnacles, water fleas, and wood lice.

There are about 30,000 species of crustaceans. The largest crustacean, the giant spider crab of Japan, measures up to 12 feet (3.6 meters) long between its outstretched claws. The smallest species, such as copepods and water fleas, may be less than $\frac{1}{24}$ inch (1 millimeter) long. Most kinds of crustaceans live in salt water, but some inhabit fresh water. A few kinds, including certain crabs and wood lice, live on land.

Crustaceans play a major role in aquatic ecology. In most aquatic environments, diatoms and other tiny plants are the basic food producers. Many small crustaceans feed directly on these plants. The small crustaceans, in turn, serve as food for fish and other larger aquatic animals. Crustaceans thus form an important link between the food-producing plants and the larger animals in the aquatic food chain.

People in many parts of the world eat crabs, lobsters, shrimp, and other crustaceans. On the other hand, some kinds of crustaceans cause problems for people. For example, certain marine wood lice burrow into, and eventually destroy, wooden wharves. Barnacles attach themselves to the hulls of ships and greatly reduce the vessels' speed. Certain crabs and other crustaceans damage rice crops by burrowing into the dikes that surround rice paddies, or by eating the young plants.

The Body of a Crustacean

Outer Body. The body of most adult crustaceans has three main parts, each of which consists of many segments. These three parts are (1) the head, (2) the thorax, and (3) the abdomen.

Crustaceans have two pairs of antennae, which extend from the head. The head also includes the mouth, three pairs of jaws, and the eyes. The eyes may be even with the surface of the head or at the end of stalks.

Each segment of the thorax has a pair of legs. Most crustaceans have 6 to 14 pairs of legs. A few species have more, and some have less. Crustaceans use some of their legs mainly for swimming or walking. Other legs may be pincers used for catching food, for fighting, or for other activities.

The abdomen of most species of crustaceans lacks legs. But *malacostracans,* a major group that includes lobsters and shrimp, have small abdominal legs. These legs are used for swimming, for breathing, and, in the females of some species, for carrying eggs. Many malacostracans also have a flattened tail, which they snap rapidly to swim backward.

A crustacean's exoskeleton protects and supports the internal organs. The exoskeleton may be soft or very hard. It is soft and thin at the joints to allow for bending. Some species have a shield of exoskeleton called a *carapace* that extends from the back of the head over the thorax.

Internal Organs of crustaceans resemble those of insects (see INSECT [Internal Organs]). In most kinds of crustaceans, a heart pumps the blood throughout the body. Some small species have no heart, and their body movements promote circulation of the blood.

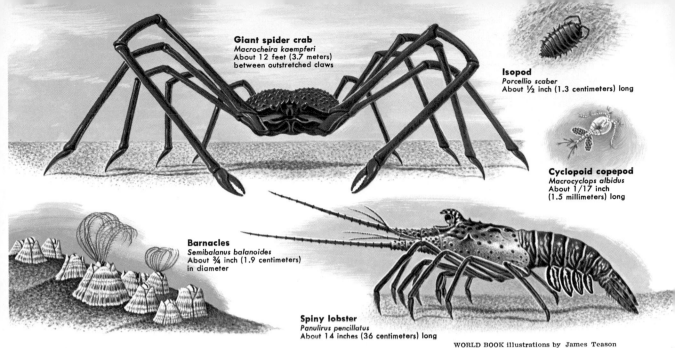

Giant spider crab
Macrocheira kaempferi
About 12 feet (3.7 meters)
between outstretched claws

Isopod
Porcellio scaber
About ½ inch (1.3 centimeters) long

Cyclopoid copepod
Macrocyclops albidus
About 1/17 inch
(1.5 millimeters) long

Barnacles
Semibalanus balanoides
About ¾ inch (1.9 centimeters)
in diameter

Spiny lobster
Panulirus pencillatus
About 14 inches (36 centimeters) long

WORLD BOOK illustrations by James Teason

Crustaceans include many kinds of animals that vary in size and physical features. The largest crustacean, the giant spider crab, measures up to 12 feet (3.6 meters) long between its outstretched claws.

A crustacean's digestive system has three main parts. In malacostracans, food is ground up in the *foregut* and is further digested in the *midgut*, or stomach. The *hindgut*, or intestine, compacts and stores undigested materials until they are eliminated from the body.

Crustaceans have a small brain. It is connected to a nerve cord that extends along the underside of the body. Clusters of nerve cell bodies along the cord have some control over various activities.

Most crustaceans, unlike land-dwelling insects, breathe through gills. However, most small species have no gills. They breathe through their skin.

Senses. Most adult crustaceans have a pair of *compound eyes*. These eyes have many separate lenses and can easily detect movement (see COMPOUND EYE). Many species also have a *simple eye*, which senses light but does not form an image. Most young crustaceans, and the adults of copepods and a few other species, have only a simple eye.

Tiny hairlike *setae* cover various parts of the body. Certain of them are sensitive to touch, smell, and taste. These sensory setae are concentrated on the antennae, mouth parts, and pincers.

The Life of a Crustacean

Reproduction. Among most species of crustaceans, the male deposits sperm on the female's shell. The sperm then fertilizes the eggs as the female lays them. The number of eggs ranges from a few to many thousand. In most species, the female carries the eggs on certain parts of her body until they hatch.

Growth and Development. Most kinds of crustaceans hatch as *larvae*, which are immature animals that do not resemble the adults. The larvae go through several body changes before they look like their parents. In a few species, including beach hoppers and wood lice, the young hatch as miniature adults.

A crustacean's exoskeleton does not expand, and so the growing animal repeatedly sheds its old shell and grows a new, larger one. The shedding process is called *molting*. Before molting begins, a soft, thin new exoskeleton forms beneath the old shell. The old exoskeleton then splits, and the animal works its way out of it. The crustacean soon swells to a larger size before the new shell hardens.

With each molt, a larva adds segments and legs and becomes increasingly like an adult. In some species, the body form may change completely in a single molt. Many kinds of crustaceans continue to molt throughout life, but others stop after reaching maturity.

If certain parts of a crustacean's body are damaged or lost, they may be repaired or replaced through a

The Body of a Shrimp

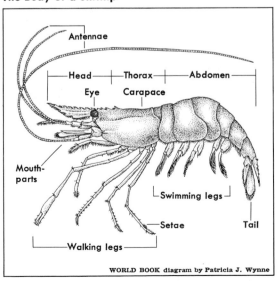

WORLD BOOK diagram by Patricia J. Wynne

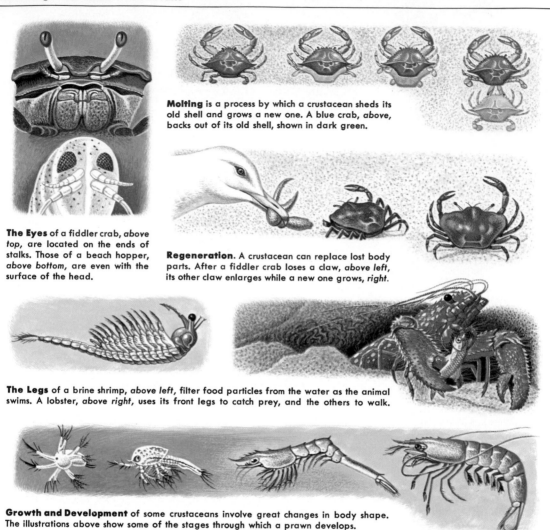

Molting is a process by which a crustacean sheds its old shell and grows a new one. A blue crab, *above*, backs out of its old shell, shown in dark green.

The Eyes of a fiddler crab, *above top*, are located on the ends of stalks. Those of a beach hopper, *above bottom*, are even with the surface of the head.

Regeneration. A crustacean can replace lost body parts. After a fiddler crab loses a claw, *above left*, its other claw enlarges while a new one grows, *right*.

The Legs of a brine shrimp, *above left*, filter food particles from the water as the animal swims. A lobster, *above right*, uses its front legs to catch prey, and the others to walk.

Growth and Development of some crustaceans involve great changes in body shape. The illustrations above show some of the stages through which a prawn develops.

process called *regeneration*. After a crustacean loses an antenna, a claw, or a leg, a replacement for the part may develop and appear during the next molt. The replacement part is small at first. It enlarges with successive molts. Some crustaceans, such as crabs and lobsters, can voluntarily detach a limb that has been caught by an enemy.

Food and Habits. Some kinds of crustaceans live as parasites on other animals. Others, including crabs, crayfish, and lobsters, prey on various water creatures. Many of these species also eat the remains of animals and plants. Copepods, water fleas, and the larvae of various crustaceans drift through the water and feed on floating microscopic plants. In turn, these crustaceans are eaten by barnacles, krill, and other crustaceans, and by many kinds of fish. Krill, in turn, are eaten by certain whales. Various other crustaceans become the prey of birds and land mammals.

Crustaceans live in a variety of habitats. Some drift through the water constantly. Others prowl along the bottom of a body of water and hide among rocks or weeds. Some find shelter in a sponge or coral, or inside the shell of a mollusk. Crabs and some other crustaceans burrow into mud or sand for safety. Barnacles attach themselves to rocks along the seashore, as well as to turtles, whales, ships, and wharves. Most land crustaceans live under rocks or fallen leaves, or in burrows and other damp places.

Scientific Classification. Crustaceans make up the class Crustacea, phylum Arthropoda. Crabs, crayfish, lobsters, shrimp, and wood lice belong to the subclass Malacostraca. Barnacles and copepods are in the subclass Maxillopoda, and water fleas belong to the subclass Branchiopoda.   WILLIAM A. NEWMAN

Related Articles in WORLD BOOK include:

Arthropod	Crab	Hermit Crab	Shrimp
Barnacle	Crayfish	Krill	Water Flea
Blue Crab	Fiddler Crab	Lobster	Wood Louse
Copepod			

NERVOUS SYSTEM is an internal communications network that enables an animal to adjust to changes in its environment. Almost all animals, except the simplest kinds, have some type of nervous system.

Animals without a backbone have a nervous system that ranges from a simple net of nerves to a highly organized system of nerve cords and a primitive brain. In human beings and other animals with backbones, the nervous system consists of the brain, the spinal cord, and the nerves. This article deals mainly with the human nervous system.

The human nervous system—especially the highly developed brain—makes people different from all other animals. The human brain functions much like a complicated computer that enables people to speak, solve difficult problems, and produce creative ideas.

The nervous system provides pathways by which information travels from a person's surroundings to the brain. The brain then sends instructions to various muscles via other pathways so that the body can respond to the information. The nervous system also regulates internal functions, such as breathing, digestion, and heartbeat. All of a person's movements, sensations, thoughts, and emotions are products of his or her nervous system.

How the Nervous System Works

The nervous system is made up of billions of special cells called *neurons* or *nerve cells*. Cordlike bundles of neuron fibers are called *nerves*. The nerves form a network of pathways that conduct information rapidly throughout the body.

A person's reaction to a situation may take only an instant, but it involves many complicated processes within the nervous system. For example, what happens in the nervous system of a person who sees a wild tiger and, an instant later, turns and runs away?

Specialized neurons called *receptors* are located in the ears and eyes and the other sense organs of the body. The receptors translate events in a person's surroundings—such as the sight of a tiger—into nerve messages, which are known as *impulses*. Nerve impulses travel along nerve fibers at speeds of 3 to 300 feet (0.9 to 90 meters) per second.

The receptor cells in the eyes respond to light rays that reflect off the tiger and translate the rays into a pattern of nerve impulses. These impulses then travel through neurons called *sensory neurons* and *association neurons*. The sensory neurons carry information from receptors in the sense organs to the association neurons, which are in the brain and the spinal cord.

The neurons in the brain receive the impulses, analyze and interpret the message, and decide what action should be taken. A message consisting of the sight of a wild tiger is, of course, interpreted as danger. The person's brain immediately sends out a message—"Run!"—in the form of nerve impulses.

Next, the impulses travel through *motor neurons*. These nerve cells carry messages from the brain to the muscles and glands, which are called *effectors*. The effectors carry out the brain's instructions. As a result, the leg muscles respond and the person runs away. At the same time, the brain sends messages to various other parts of the body. For example, it sends messages to the heart to beat faster and send more blood to the leg muscles.

Divisions of the Nervous System

The nervous system has three main parts, the *central nervous system*, the *peripheral nervous system*, and the *autonomic nervous system*. Each has special functions.

The Central Nervous System functions as a "main switchboard" that controls and coordinates the activities of the entire nervous system. The central nervous system consists of the *brain* and the *spinal cord*.

The brain is an extremely complicated organ. It consists of three principal parts, the *cerebrum*, the *cerebellum*, and the *brain stem*. This article provides basic information about the brain. For more detailed information on the brain and how it works, see the WORLD BOOK article on BRAIN.

The cerebrum makes up about 85 per cent of the brain and is the most complex part. It is above the cerebellum and the brain stem and almost surrounds them. Human beings have a highly developed cerebrum that directs their hearing, sight, and touch and their ability

How the Nervous System Works

The nervous system enables us to adjust to changes in our surroundings. Such *neurons* (nerve cells) as the *receptors* in the eyes translate information from the environment into nerve impulses. *Sensory neurons* carry the impulses to *association neurons* in the brain and spinal cord. *Motor neurons* then carry instructions from the brain to muscles, internal organs, and other body parts called *effectors*.

WORLD BOOK diagrams by Lou Bory Associates

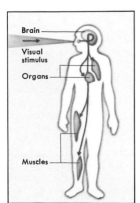

Brain
Visual stimulus
Organs
Muscles

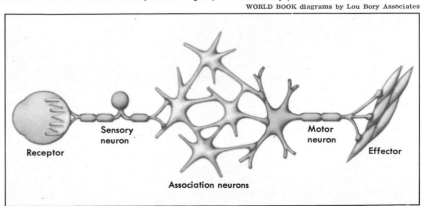

Receptor
Sensory neuron
Association neurons
Motor neuron
Effector

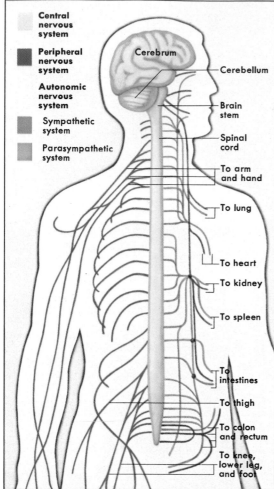

The Human Nervous System has three main parts: (1) the *central nervous system*, (2) the *peripheral nervous system*, and (3) the *autonomic nervous system*, which consists of *sympathetic* and *parasympathetic* divisions. This simplified diagram shows only major nerves. It illustrates peripheral nerves only on the left side of the figure and autonomic nerves only on the right.

Diagram labels:

Central nervous system
Peripheral nervous system
Autonomic nervous system
Sympathetic system
Parasympathetic system

Cerebrum
Cerebellum
Brain stem
Spinal cord
To arm and hand
To lung
To heart
To kidney
To spleen
To intestines
To thigh
To colon and rectum
To knee, lower leg, and foot

WORLD BOOK diagram by Lou Bory Associates

to think, use language, and feel emotions. The cerebrum is also the center of learning.

The cerebellum, which is about the size of an orange, is slightly above the brain stem. It helps maintain the body's sense of balance and coordinates muscular movements with sensory information.

The brain stem is a stalklike structure that is connected to the spinal cord at the base of the skull. The brain stem contains neurons that relay information from the sense organs. Many neurons that regulate automatic functions, such as balance, blood pressure, breathing, and heartbeat, are also in the brain stem.

The spinal cord is a cable of neurons that extends from the neck about two-thirds of the way down the backbone. The backbone surrounds and protects the spinal cord. The spinal cord contains pathways that carry sensory information to the brain. It also has path-

ways that relay commands from the brain to the motor neurons.

The Peripheral Nervous System carries all the messages sent between the central nervous system and the rest of the body. The peripheral nervous system consists of 12 pairs of nerves that originate in the brain, plus 31 pairs of nerves of the spinal cord. These cranial and spinal nerves serve as "telephone wires" that carry messages to and from every receptor and effector in the body.

The Autonomic Nervous System is a special part of the peripheral nervous system. The autonomic nervous system regulates such automatic bodily processes as breathing and digestion without conscious control by the brain. This constant regulation enables the body to maintain a stable internal environment.

The autonomic nervous system has two parts, the *sympathetic system* and the *parasympathetic system*. The sympathetic system responds to the body's needs during increased activity and in emergencies. The actions of the sympathetic system include speeding up the heartbeat, sending additional blood to the muscles, and enlarging the pupils of the eyes to use all available light.

The parasympathetic system, in general, opposes the actions of the sympathetic system. The parasympathetic system's functions include slowing down the heartbeat, diverting blood from the muscles to the stomach and intestines, and contracting the pupils of the eyes. The balance of activity between the two systems is controlled by the central nervous system.

Parts of a Neuron

A neuron has three basic parts, the *cell body*, the *axon*, and the *dendrites*. A thin *nerve membrane* surrounds the entire cell.

The Cell Body of a neuron is a ball-shaped structure about 1/1000 of an inch (.025 millimeter) wide. Each neuron cell body is a center for receiving and sending nerve impulses. The cell body is also responsible for making proteins and using energy for the maintenance and growth of the nerve cell.

The vast majority of neuron cell bodies are within the central nervous system, where incoming messages are combined and outgoing messages are produced. The few neuron cell bodies outside the central nervous system are grouped into clusters called *ganglia*. The best-known ganglia are parts of the autonomic nervous system.

The Axon, also called the *nerve fiber*, is a tubelike extension of a neuron cell body. The axon is specialized to carry messages. An axon of one neuron may have enough branches to make contact with as many as 1,000 other neurons.

Most axons in the central nervous system are less than 1/25 of an inch (1 millimeter) long. However, many axons in the peripheral nervous system are longer, and some are much longer. For example, the axons that extend from the spinal cord to the muscles in the feet may be 30 to 40 inches (76 to 100 centimeters) long.

The structures commonly called *nerves* are actually bundles of axons lying next to one another in a cordlike formation. Nerves can be made up of the axons of motor neurons or sensory neurons, or of both.

Some axons are covered by a sheath of a white,

Neurons and Nerves A neuron, *left*, has three basic parts. The *cell body* serves as the control center for the cell's activities. The *axon* is a tubelike extension that carries messages. The *dendrites* are shorter extensions specialized to receive messages. A nerve, *right*, consists of a cordlike bundle of axons from several neurons. The nerve shown runs from the spinal cord to a muscle.

WORLD BOOK diagrams by Lou Bory Associates

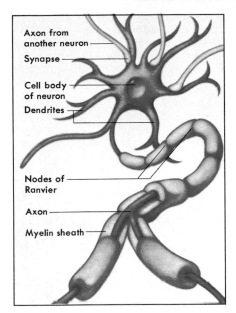

Axon from another neuron
Synapse
Cell body of neuron
Dendrites
Nodes of Ranvier
Axon
Myelin sheath

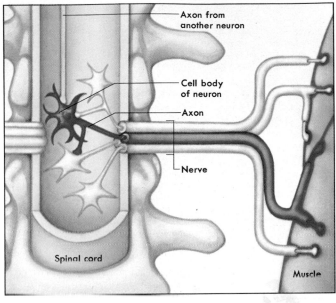

Axon from another neuron
Cell body of neuron
Axon
Nerve
Spinal cord
Muscle

fatty substance called *myelin*. The myelin increases the speed of impulses along the axons. Myelin also causes the distinction between the *gray matter* and *white matter* in the nervous system. Gray matter consists largely of *unmyelinated axons* (axons without myelin sheaths) and neuron cell bodies. White matter is made up mostly of axons that have white sheaths of myelin.

The Dendrites of a neuron are branching, tubelike extensions of the cell body that form a pattern resembling the limbs of a tree. Most neuron cell bodies have about six main dendrites, each of which is two or three times as thick as the axon of the cell. The distance between the cell body and the tips of the dendrites is about 1/50 of an inch (0.5 millimeter).

Dendrites are specialized structures for receiving impulses, mostly from the axon of another neuron. Dendrites and axons do not quite touch each other. In almost all cases, they are separated by an extremely narrow space called the *synaptic cleft*, over which nerve impulses are transmitted. These places where one neuron communicates with another are called *synapses*.

How Messages Are Routed

Simple Pathways. Much of the work of the nervous system depends upon established pathways between neurons. These pathways are called *neural circuits*. The simplest kind of neural circuit is a *reflex*. A reflex is an automatic and involuntary response to a certain stimulus. Simple reflexes do not involve the brain. Impulses in a reflex action follow a simple pathway that goes through the spinal cord and links a receptor and an effector.

One of the simplest reflexes is the *knee jerk reflex*. A tap on the tendon below the kneecap stretches the muscle there, and this action stimulates special receptors to produce an impulse. The impulse travels through a sensory neuron, over an axon to the spinal cord, and through a synapse to a motor neuron. There, a second impulse is generated. The second impulse travels over the axon of a motor neuron back to the muscle that was stretched. The impulse causes the muscle cells to contract and the leg to jerk.

Complex Pathways. Many reflexes are more complicated. They involve at least one association neuron between the sensory and motor neurons. The association neuron, in turn, may be connected with many complex neural pathways, some of which may lead to the brain. A common but complex reflex is involved in withdrawing from a painful stimulus. For example, if a person steps on a sharp object, the immediate response is to lift the foot. In addition, association neurons stimulate the muscles of the other leg to adjust and maintain balance. Interconnecting neural pathways to the brain also may be stimulated so that the person becomes aware of what has happened.

Reflexes alone cannot account for the vast number and variety of actions performed by human beings. People, as well as some other kinds of animals, can learn new behavior patterns. Voluntary muscular movements necessary for learning new skills travel along complex nerve pathways that extend from the brain throughout the body. Complicated actions, such as riding a bicycle or walking, eventually can be performed without constant, conscious control after they have been learned.

How Neurons Carry Impulses

During the 1800's, scientists discovered that nerve impulses involve electrical charges. They assumed a nerve impulse was simply an electric current flowing through nerves. By the 1900's, researchers had learned that different concentrations of certain ions in neurons and in their surrounding fluids create a potential electrical charge. It was also learned that nerve cell membranes have pores that allow only certain substances to pass through. Scientists then theorized that a nerve impulse was an electrochemical process controlled by the nerve cell membrane.

In the 1930's, researchers developed techniques to test the *membrane theory of nerve conduction*, which is the theory discussed in this section. The membrane theory is the accepted explanation of how neurons carry impulses.

The Beginning of an Impulse. A nerve cell membrane has special protein molecules that control the opening and closing of its pores. When at rest, the membrane keeps the concentration of sodium ions in the neuron very low. The membrane also keeps the concentration of potassium ions and negative organic ions much higher in the cell than in the surrounding fluids. These differences in ion concentration make the inside of the neuron more negative than the outside, and so the membrane is said to be *polarized*. The resulting voltage difference across the membrane is called the *resting potential*.

A chemical, electrical, or mechanical stimulus applied to a neuron can affect the membrane's porosity and change the resting potential. The stimulus can cause the membrane's pores to open and allow more sodium ions into the cell. The increase in sodium ions makes the inside of the cell positively charged, and this voltage change is called a *depolarization*.

When a stimulus causes a neuron to depolarize, the neuron is said to *fire*. The firing of a neuron is the beginning of a nerve impulse. A stimulus must be of a certain intensity, called the *threshold voltage*, for a neuron to fire.

All impulses from a particular neuron have the same size and duration, no matter how large the stimulus that caused the neuron to fire. The fact that neurons fire at maximum strength or not at all is called the *all-or-nothing phenomenon*. The brain probably detects the intensity of a stimulus by the frequency of impulses generated and the number of nerve fibers stimulated.

Conduction Along the Axon. The inside of an axon is filled with a solution that can conduct an electric charge. Depolarizations in one area of an axon spread through the solution to neighboring areas all along the axon. This wave of depolarizations is called an *action potential*.

If the axon of a neuron has no myelin sheath, the nerve impulse sweeps continuously along the axon, like fire along a firecracker fuse. But in a myelinated axon, nerve impulses can occur only at the *nodes of Ranvier*. The nodes of Ranvier are areas along an axon where the myelin sheath is interrupted at regular intervals. The impulse hops from node to node.

Transmission Across Synapses. Certain chemicals, called *neurotransmitters*, transmit nerve impulses across synapses. When an impulse reaches the end of an axon, a neurotransmitter is released into the synaptic cleft. The neurotransmitter moves to the dendrites of the next nerve cell and causes certain pores of the nerve membrane to open. Ions move through these pores, and a voltage change, called a *postsynaptic potential*, results.

Transmission of a Nerve Impulse

The transmission of a nerve impulse is an electrochemical process. Most scientists believe the neuron membrane controls this process by selectively allowing ions to enter and leave the cell. These diagrams show how a motor neuron carries a message from an association neuron to an effector.

WORLD BOOK diagrams by Lou Bory Associates

A Resting Neuron is *polarized*—that is, its inside is more negative than its outside. The membrane maintains the polarity by restricting the flow of ions in and out of the cell.

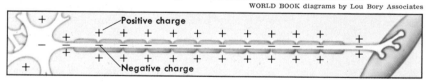

Positive charge
Negative charge

The Impulse Begins when neurotransmitters from the association neuron affect the porosity of the motor neuron's membrane. The change in porosity results in depolarization.

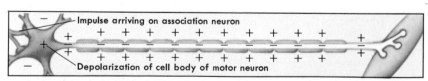

Impulse arriving on association neuron
Depolarization of cell body of motor neuron

The Impulse Spreads down a myelinated axon as the depolarization hops from one node of Ranvier to the next. The impulse shown has traveled nearly halfway down the axon.

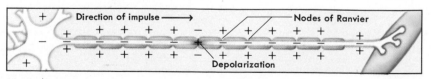

Direction of impulse ⟶
Nodes of Ranvier
Depolarization

Chemical Transmitters are released by specialized structures when the impulse reaches the end of the neuron. These chemicals stimulate the effector, in this case a muscle.

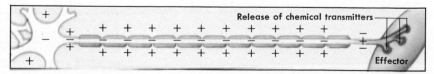

Release of chemical transmitters
Effector

The postsynaptic potential is either *excitatory* or *inhibitory*. An excitatory postsynaptic potential spreads to the axon of a nerve cell and tends to produce another action potential. An inhibitory postsynaptic potential tends to prevent the axon from producing another action potential. Not every impulse that reaches a synapse is transmitted to the next neuron. The synapses thus help regulate and route the constant flow of nerve impulses throughout the nervous system.

Disorders of the Nervous System

The nervous system can be damaged by injury and disease. Axons in the central nervous system cannot regrow after being damaged, but nerves in the peripheral nervous system may recover. Severely damaged nerve cells that die cannot be replaced.

Most neurons that perform a specific job are grouped together in the brain. Because of this grouping arrangement, called *localization of function*, damage to one area of the brain may affect only certain abilities and leave others intact. In some cases, undamaged areas of the brain gradually assume control of functions lost when another area of the brain was damaged. This action is called *recovery of function*.

The most common serious disorder of the nervous system is *stroke*. A stroke occurs if the blood supply to a certain area of the brain is cut off, resulting in the death of nerve cells. Stroke victims may lose the ability to perform functions controlled by the damaged area of the brain, such as speaking or moving a limb. Stroke victims may eventually recover some lost functions. But if respiration or some other vital function is affected, a stroke can be fatal.

The most common infectious diseases that affect the nervous system are mild virus infections that last only a few days and may produce headaches. More serious infectious diseases, such as *encephalitis* and *meningitis*, are caused by certain bacteria and viruses. Encephalitis is an inflammation of the brain, and meningitis is an inflammation of the membranes covering the brain and spinal cord. See ENCEPHALITIS; MENINGITIS.

The cause of *multiple sclerosis*, a disease of the nervous system, is not known. Multiple sclerosis causes axons in various areas of the central nervous system to lose their myelin sheaths. As a result, these axons cannot conduct nerve impulses properly.

Another disorder of the nervous system is *epilepsy*. Victims of epilepsy suffer seizures that can cause muscle convulsions and a change in, or loss of, consciousness. An epileptic seizure occurs if most of the neurons in one area of the brain produce bursts of impulses at the same time. Physicians prescribe drugs to reduce the number of seizures or to prevent them completely.

Before the development of vaccines to prevent *poliomyelitis*, this virus disease of the nervous system was widespread. The polio virus can destroy motor neurons in the spinal cord and brain stem, leading to paralysis in some cases.

Some disorders of the nervous system can lead to mental illness or mental retardation. For information about these conditions, see the articles on MENTAL ILLNESS and MENTAL RETARDATION.

The Nervous System in Other Animals

In Vertebrates. All vertebrates, including other mammals, as well as amphibians, birds, fish, and reptiles, have nervous systems much like the human nervous system. The neurons of these animals are about the same size and shape as human neurons.

The size of a specific area of the brain may indicate the importance of the function of that area for the animal. For example, dogs have a larger and better developed area for smell than do human beings. In contrast, human beings have a larger and more highly developed *cerebral cortex* than other animals. The cerebral cortex is the outer surface of the cerebrum, where such complicated skills as delicate motor control and the use of language are coordinated.

In Invertebrates. Most species of invertebrates that consist of more than one cell have some sort of nervous system. Many of the neurons of these animals are larger than those of the human nervous system. In hydras and some other simple invertebrates, the nervous system may be a *nerve net*, in which nerve cells are spread throughout the organism. There is no distinction between axons and dendrites in nerve net systems, and impulses travel in all directions from the point of stimulation.

Other invertebrates, including worms and insects, have more complicated, centralized nervous systems. These systems consist largely of concentrations of neurons that form a nerve cord. Ganglia along the cord serve as centers for organizing and integrating various activities of the animals. Clusters of ganglia in the front end of the body act as a primitive "brain." Many insects also have such ganglia in the thorax region. These ganglia coordinate motor activities. The mechanisms of nerve impulses and synaptic potentials in higher invertebrates are the same as those in the human nervous system.

CHARLES F. STEVENS

See also *Nervous System* in the RESEARCH GUIDE/INDEX, Volume 22, for a *Reading and Study Guide*.

People in Science

Like people in any vocation, scientists often pursue a hobby that is an extension of their life's work. For nonscientists, a hobby can be an entry into the world of science. This section, which recognizes outstanding scientists, also describes how amateurs can sometimes contribute to the field.

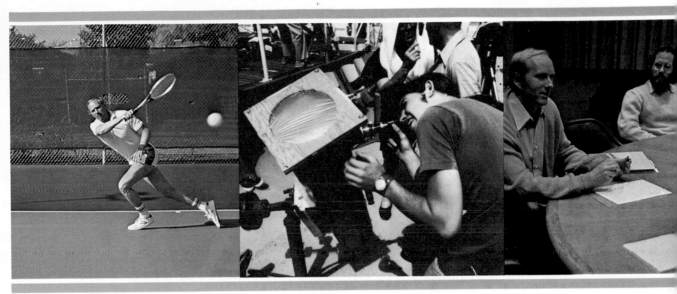

Ronald L. Graham

By Gina Bari Kolata

This versatile research mathematician not only finds time for problem solving, music, and sports, but also for aiding and inspiring both students and colleagues

It is lunchtime on the sunny California campus of Stanford University, and a crowd of mathematicians, other scientists, and students gathers around mathematician Ronald L. Graham, who is spending the fall 1979 semester as a visiting professor in Stanford's Computer Science Department. He is about to give a lesson in a subject he considers one of his specialties – juggling. Graham confidently tosses several colorful balls into the air and keeps them going with the ease of an expert, which he is. At one time, he served as president of the International Jugglers Association, and he estimates he has taught about 1,000 persons to juggle.

Graham regards learning the skills of juggling and his other hobbies – gymnastics, music, trampoline, tennis, and table tennis – as being similar to learning mathematics. "The whole philosophy of learning a physical or mental skill is the same," he says. "You break a complicated skill – whether it is juggling or calculus – into much simpler parts. Then you work on the parts. Finally, after you have mastered the parts, you put the parts together. For example, when

With one hand behind his back, Graham evens the odds in a juggling contest with students at Stanford.

you juggle, you start with one ball. You work on the skill of throwing and catching that ball. When you've learned to throw and catch it accurately, you add a second ball. With mathematics, it's the same thing. Before you can learn to solve calculus problems, you must build your mathematical skills step by step."

Graham's career is devoted to mathematical research. His current job is head of the Discrete Mathematics Department of Bell Laboratories at Murray Hill, N.J. He also is an elected member of the Executive Committee of the American Mathematical Society, secretary of the mathematics section of the American Association for the Advancement of Science, and he publishes about 15 scientific papers each year. In 1972, Graham won the prestigious Polya Prize awarded by the Society for Industrial and Applied Mathematics. (George Polya, a Hungarian-born mathematician, pioneered combinatorics, the kind of math used in computer science.) Graham's colleague, mathematician Persi Diaconis of Stanford University, says that "people in his field speak of Ron Graham with a special awe."

As a boy, Graham dreamed of becoming an astronomer. But he says his love of mathematics also developed very early. He enjoyed arithmetic in elementary school. While in the fifth grade, he learned how to find square roots of numbers, then tried to use the basic idea of the square-root method to find cube roots. Although it did not work, this small failure did not discourage him from setting out on a lifelong exploration of the world of math.

The author:
Gina Bari Kolata is a senior science writer for *Science* magazine.

Graham took a beginning algebra course in the seventh grade, but soon became bored because he could do all the problems. His teacher gave him a book about calculus and introduced him to differential equations. From then on, his involvement with math deepened.

Ron Graham was born on Halloween, 1935, in Taft, Calif., a town about 241 kilometers (150 miles) northwest of Los Angeles. Graham's father worked in the oil fields near Taft until Graham was 6 years old. Then the family moved to Savannah, Ga., where his father worked in the shipyards for a short time before the family moved back to California. From then on, they shuttled between Georgia and California as his father kept changing jobs. After reaching school age, Graham never lived in any town for more than 1½ years. Eventually, his father joined the United States Merchant Marine and his parents were divorced. His mother moved to Florida, taking along with her Graham and his younger brother and sister.

Despite this unsettled life, Graham worked hard in school and did well. He did so well on achievement tests in high school that he won a Ford Foundation scholarship. It entitled him to enter any one of four universities that had special programs allowing gifted youngsters to enroll without graduating from high school. He chose to attend the University of Chicago.

To be 15 years old and a student at the University of Chicago was both stimulating and humbling, Graham says. "Normally, each young person who entered college at such an early age was considered the best student in their little town. But when all those kids were put together, suddenly some had to face the fact that they were not the best in this college grouping."

But college gave Graham his first real opportunity to make friends and enjoy sports. He was small for his age and had also skipped grades in school. "Because we moved so often," he says, "I was always the new kid at school and – even though I'm now 6 feet 2 inches – the littlest kid." So he never was asked to participate in team sports. At the University of Chicago, however, he discovered gymnastics and juggling, sports in which being small is not a drawback. For the first time, he was accepted and respected for his physical abilities.

Graham entered the University of Chicago in 1951, with the idea of becoming a mathematician. At that time, the university admitted talented students up to two years before they were to graduate from high school and gave them degrees as soon as they completed a program that entailed reading original works in the sciences and the humanities. "That meant reading Newton for physics and Darwin for biology," Graham says. The program was designed to provide a well-rounded education. As a result, even though he was a science major, Graham took no mathematics and very few science courses because he had placed so high in his science and mathematics achievement tests. Instead, he concentrated mainly on humanities, an area in which he did not do as well on the tests.

Graham the teacher broadcasts a math course, *above,* over closed-circuit television. With his teaching assistants, *top right,* Graham tackles the paperwork of final exams. Later he pauses to answer students' questions, *above right.*

After three years in this program, Graham faced a turning point in his academic career. He ran into financial problems because his scholarship had expired. His father offered to help him financially, but only if he transferred to the University of California, Berkeley. And so Graham returned to California.

His college adviser said it would be easier for him to be accepted by the university's electrical engineering department than its mathematics department because he had no math course credits from Chicago. So he became an electrical engineering major. In the more traditional program at Berkeley, he had to take the required elementary science and engineering courses before getting into advanced studies. "After spending one year at Berkeley, I had completed four years of college," he says, "but I was not even close to a degree. And in those days, after four years of college without getting a degree, you became eligible for the military draft."

Rather than waiting to be drafted into the Army, he enlisted in the U.S. Air Force in 1955 because it promised better benefits. He was trained as a communications specialist. "This actually meant typing and sending messages," says Graham. He understood that the best student in his communications class of 100 was to be given his choice of assignments, so Graham worked like a fiend and was soon the star of the class. But he discovered that being best was not what really counted. "Those who got the good assignments," he says, "were friends with the people who made the assignments." To his dismay, Graham was sent to Alaska.

He was stationed at a large Air Force base about 42 kilometers (26 miles) from Fairbanks. Life there is bleak, especially during the winter. Fortunately, Graham obtained permission to attend the University of Alaska, about 52 kilometers (32 miles) away. "School was a real outlet," he says. He signed up to work from 7 P.M. to midnight so he could attend school during the day. Graham commuted between the base and the university by bus.

But Graham still could not major in mathematics. The university was not accredited to award math degrees. It offered only basic mathematics courses to students majoring in other disciplines. So Graham chose physics and, finally, seven years after he began college, he received a B.S. degree in 1958.

He left the Air Force in 1959, at the age of 23, and then life began to run more smoothly. Graham returned to the University of California, Berkeley, as a graduate mathematics student. There he earned his spending money as a professional trampolinist, a member of a group that performed in a circus, at supermarket openings, and in schools. At Berkeley, he met and married a classmate, math major Nancy Young. In 1962, Graham received a Ph.D. degree from the University of California and accepted a job at Bell Laboratories. He and Nancy moved to New Jersey. They had two children — a girl, Cheryl, who is now 18, and a boy, Marc, who is now 13.

Graham and a Stanford colleague, Persi Diaconis, ponder a problem in advanced mathematics.

Graham the athlete slams a return across the tennis court, *above.* He also applies his finely tuned reflexes to more exotic sports, ranging from juggling balls in his Bell Labs office, *opposite page left,* to throwing a boomerang on an athletic field, *opposite page right.*

Marc, like Graham when he was Marc's age, says he wants to be an astronomer. "Math's OK," he concedes, but he does not consider it his main interest. Neither of his parents ever indicated that mathematics might be difficult, and Marc never found it so.

Cheryl's interests are more artistic than scientific. She wants to be a writer for radio or television. Nonetheless, she had no trouble learning mathematics and is currently taking calculus, the most advanced mathematics course taught in her high school. Her father always helped and encouraged her to learn mathematics, but he never pushed her to become a mathematician. He also encouraged her to learn other skills, and in 1974 she won the trampoline competition in the New Jersey State Championships. Cheryl says her father's greatest influence on her life has been in teaching her self-discipline, partly by his own example.

Cheryl and Marc had the advantage of learning about the enormous scope and power of mathematics from their father. When Marc was 10, his father showed him how mathematics can simplify a difficult problem. The problem involved trying to cover a chessboard with dominoes. The chessboard is made up of 32 black squares alternating with 32 white squares, and each square measures 1 by 1 inch. Each domino is 2 inches by 1 inch. It is easy to see that you can cover the board exactly by lining up 32 of these dominoes in 4

rows, with each row containing 8 dominoes. Now, suppose you cut one square out of the upper left-hand corner of the board and one square out of the lower right-hand corner of the board. Can you still cover the board exactly with 31 dominoes?

"You might try to find out," Graham says, "by physically arranging the dominoes in all possible positions on the board. But this is a long process because there are so many possible combinations of dominoes, and you are never sure if you've really tried them all."

Graham explains that it is easy to solve the problem by using a type of mathematical logic. The square you removed from the upper left-hand corner of the board is the same color as the one you removed from the lower right-hand corner. If these two squares are white, you are left with 32 black squares and 30 white squares on the board. Each domino must cover one black square and one white square, simply because that is the nature of the chessboard pattern. By breaking the problem down to these elements, the answer becomes obvious — it cannot be done. It is impossible to cover 32 black and 30 white squares with 31 dominoes, because each domino must cover one black and one white square.

The mathematics most people are exposed to in high school, or even in college, is really just the tip of the iceberg, according to Graham. Mathematics is a catchall term for an enormous number of

Graham *the* researcher checks *some* figures in his *office,* top, then gets *tog*ether with his st*aff, a*bove, to discuss t*heir* projects.

disciplines. Some mathematicians work with computers. Others study the logical foundations of mathematics and never work with numbers. Mathematics covers such a broad area that, very often, mathematicians with different specialties cannot communicate with one another. They do not understand the problems the others are working on.

But some common quality makes all of these fields mathematics. "The essence of mathematics is the search for order and structure," explains Graham. "Mathematicians can deal with numbers, or with geometrical figures, or even with concepts. What unites them is their search for patterns."

Graham's work often focuses on problems that arise at the boundary between mathematics and computer science. For example, he looks for solutions to a group of problems called "hard" problems. These problems are generally easy to state and occur in countless practical situations. But the only known ways guaranteed to solve most of these problems would involve so many trillions of calculations that they would require centuries of computer time. However, researchers have shown that if they could find a short cut to solving one hard problem, they could adapt that short cut to solve them all.

One of the best-known examples of hard problems is the traveling salesman problem — find the shortest tour of a group of cities in which each city is visited only once. This problem turns up in a number of everyday situations. Telephone companies, for example, must solve a traveling salesman problem to plan collections from the coin boxes of pay telephones. Yet there is no easy way to solve this kind of problem short of measuring the distances of all possible routes between cities and then comparing all of the possible combinations of these routes to find the shortest combination. For a tour of only 60 cities, for example, it would take a computer billions of centuries to test all of the possible route combinations.

Another hard problem involves objects of different weights that must be divided into two or more groups so that the groups are as equal in weight as possible. Graham explains that this becomes a scheduling problem if you substitute the word "time" for "weight." How can you assign tasks, each of which takes a certain length of time, to several workers so that the workers complete all the tasks in the shortest possible time? Once again, the only known way to solve this problem is to try all the possibilities. Again, this can take an enormous amount of computer time when there are many tasks.

Graham devised a method that allows mathematicians at least to begin dealing with hard problems. His method is called a "worst-case analysis" because it tells what happens in the worst of all circumstances using some particular technique. This is now a major thrust in research on solutions to hard problems. Graham first applied his worst-case analysis to a weighing problem. Suppose you want to divide a group of objects into two piles being as equal in weight as possible. One way to do this would be to first arrange the weights in

Graham swaps ideas with a Bell Labs engineer on a problem involving
an electron-beam device used in making integrated circuits.

Graham shares a playful moment with his son, Marc, and daughter, Cheryl, on the sundeck of his New Jersey home.

decreasing order. Then put the heaviest weight in the first pile and the next heaviest weight in the second pile. Thereafter, add each weight to the pile that weighs the least at that point.

If you follow this grouping pattern with five objects weighing, for example, 3, 3, 2, 2, and 2 pounds, one pile will consist of objects weighing 3, 2, and 2 pounds; the other pile, 3 and 2 pounds. The heaviest pile, then, has a total weight of 7 pounds; the lightest, 5 pounds. This is the worst solution this method will produce. In this simple case, it is easy to find the best solution — one pile of objects weighing 3 and 3 pounds and the other of objects weighing 2, 2, and 2 pounds. Note that the heaviest pile of the best solution weighs 6 pounds and that of Graham's solution weighs 7 pounds; the ratio between the two is 7 to 6. Graham has shown that no matter how complicated such a problem is, this ratio will hold. Worst-case analysis is important in such complicated problems as scheduling tasks and work shifts for thousands of employees in a factory.

Graham shared the 1972 Polya Prize for his work in a branch of mathematics called Ramsey theory. The theory was named after Frank P. Ramsey, brother of the former archbishop of Canterbury. Before his death at age 26, Ramsey began to develop the mathematical branch that bears his name. "The basic philosophy of Ramsey theory," Graham says, "is that complete randomness is impossible. There is always structure somewhere." For example, a simple result in Ramsey theory states that the numbers 1 through 101 arranged in any order will always contain, interspersed among the entire 101 numbers, 11 numbers which are in increasing order or 11 numbers which are in decreasing order.

Another example of Ramsey theory deals with relationships among pairs of objects, ranging from dots on paper to people in a crowd. Any two dots can either be connected by a line or not connected. Any two persons can either know each other or be strangers. Ramsey theory tells us that, in any collection of six dots, we are guaranteed of always finding either three dots with all pairs connected or three dots with none of the pairs connected. Likewise, Ramsey theory states that in any randomly selected group of six people, there will always be either three people who all know each other or three people who are complete strangers.

According to Graham, Ramsey theory problems get very hard very fast. For example, to guarantee that a group of people will contain four who either all know one another or are all complete strangers, the group must consist of at least 18 persons. But no one has any idea of exactly how many people must be in a randomly selected group to guarantee that at least five of these people will either all know one another or be strangers.

Graham shared the Polya Prize for work on Ramsey theory with Bruce L. Rothschild of the University of California, Los Angeles, and Klaus Leeb of the University of Erlangen in West Germany. In a joint paper, these three mathematicians showed that a much larger collection of mathematical structures have Ramsey properties than anyone had suspected. Ramsey theory is not very useful in solving

Cheryl and Marc receive a lesson from their father in the dangerous but graceful art of trampoline gymnastics.

In a quiet moment alone, Graham applies to music the same powers of learning and concentration that make him a proficient athlete and a great mathematician.

practical problems, but Graham believes that the new ways in which he learns to think in the process of solving Ramsey-type problems help him in solving practical problems.

At Bell Laboratories, Graham works on practical problems that have stumped researchers in other areas of the laboratories. For example, he has worked on problems involving the creation of more intense laser beams. This work is important because telephone companies are beginning to use systems for transmitting voice and data signals on beams of light through thin glass fibers, rather than on electrical impulses through copper wire. Lasers are used to generate the light beams at the transmission ends of the fibers and boost, or strengthen, them at regular intervals as they travel along the fibers. With a more intense laser beam, the light will travel farther through a fiber before it needs to be boosted.

Graham's unusual college experience has proved to be a real asset in his position at Bell Laboratories. Henry O. Pollak, director of the Mathematics and Statistics Research Center, believes that Graham's undergraduate training in physics and engineering helps him communicate with engineers and systems developers and planners. Mathematicians and engineers use different kinds of jargon, or specialized terms, so they often find it difficult to communicate even when they are talking about the same things. "Ron is bilingual in the languages of mathematics and engineering," says Pollak.

Although people often think of mathematicians as isolated thinkers, doing little besides working alone in tiny rooms with their pencils and pads of paper, this is not the case. Like many mathematicians, Graham collaborates a great deal with other mathematicians and scientists. A clear and articulate speaker, he gives about 20 talks a year. He also attends 10 to 15 scientific meetings a year and enjoys traveling and socializing with other researchers. "I find new places and new people stimulating," he says. "With personal contact, you can find out what the current problems are. If you wait and read the journals, you will be two years behind."

A typical day for Graham at Bell Laboratories is hectic and usually leaves him little time for his own research. He must constantly attend to various letters and telephone calls. Often his correspondence concerns his duties as a member of the editorial boards of 21 scientific publications. He consults with people in his department on problems they encounter in their work. He also spends time with scientists and engineers from other departments at Bell Laboratories who have problems they hope Graham and his group can solve. So Graham does most of his research at night or on airplanes when he travels, because this mathematical research requires quiet, uninterrupted stretches of time.

Graham finds the creative aspects of mathematics research truly exciting. Even when he is not consciously wrestling with a problem, a part of his brain is working on it. Often the solution comes to him out of the blue, when he least expects it. "It's almost as though your brain has a life of its own," he says. "You think about a difficult problem during the day, go to sleep, then wake up the next morning and things are much clearer. It's as though sleep gives the brain a chance to reorganize the information that has come in."

Diaconis was quite impressed with the amount of work that Graham managed to produce at Stanford University. "I asked him a question one day," Diaconis says. "Soon he returned with a large folder containing 40 or 50 pages of calculations."

Calculations aid Graham in searching for structures. He breaks down a general problem, then looks over his calculations to see whether they have something in common, some pattern that keeps recurring. When he sees the patterns emerge, complex problems begin to fall into place and become more manageable.

In order to detect these often subtle patterns, Graham stresses that it is crucial to keep an open mind — to be willing to look at problems in unusual ways. "I think it is important to try to keep your brain flexible," he says. To do this, he constantly learns new skills. For example, he studied Chinese for two years and then turned to learning to play the piano. He even bought a portable electric piano so he can practice at least one hour each day even on trips.

His list of skills seems endless. Besides music, juggling, trampoline, and gymnastics, he is fond of bowling, jogging, tennis, table tennis, throwing a boomerang, running in marathon races, and skating. Learning all these skills, Graham says, reflects his desire to keep using different parts of his brain. "It just makes you look at things from a different point of view. Things are moving so fast that much of the knowledge you have now will probably be obsolete in 10 years. But if you keep yourself familiar with how to break down complicated tasks into simpler skills and then practice putting those skills together, you can continue to learn," Graham explains.

Graham is greatly disturbed by evidence that students today may not be learning to learn. In particular, he mentions a recent survey showing that the ability of high school students to solve simple mathematical problems is decreasing. He believes that students who fail to learn basic mathematics are permanently handicapped in their ability to function in the world. "As I look around, I see mathematics everywhere," he says. "Take juggling, for example. Some patterns are possible only with an even number of balls, some only with an odd number of balls. Why? Because we only have two hands. Jugglers usually divide an even number of balls between their two hands, throwing and catching half with one hand and half with the other. When they work with an odd number of balls, they usually throw all the balls from one hand to the other. If we had three hands," he says, "we would use entirely different patterns."

The fact that most students dislike math is nothing new, but Graham suspects that current low test scores may be related to the advent of the new math in the 1960s. This experiment in teaching mathematics to elementary and high school students was designed by educators who believed that mathematics, as it was then taught, was old-fashioned. All the sciences were developing and changing, and so should mathematics. Students in physics classes learned about discoveries in quantum mechanics and relativity. Biology students studied genes and deoxyribonucleic acid (DNA). But mathematics students were taught as though nothing new had happened since Sir Isaac Newton developed calculus 300 years before.

To modernize mathematics, educators decided to introduce some abstract 20th-century concepts, such as set theory. These concepts, however, were foreign to many teachers. Graham believes that all too often the teachers communicated their dislike, distrust, and misunderstanding of the new math to their students. Parents also were confused by the new math, and many were afraid even to try to help their children with their homework. As a result, many students felt alienated by their math courses, failing to see how mathematics could apply to their lives.

In addition, Graham explains, the new math was often dull. "It did not lend itself to interesting exercises and examples. It wasn't a very good playground for students to have fun."

But, according to Graham, even students not exposed to the new math have felt put off by mathematics because most teachers do not feel much enthusiasm for any kind of math. "Teachers often take just a few math courses and look upon mathematics as a chore," Graham says. "For me, mathematics is exciting and alive, and there's always something new around the corner." Graham believes it should be possible to teach mathematics in a way that is more fun at the elementary levels. Students could analyze games or work with mathematical models of real-life situations. His idea is not to turn everyone into mathematicians—he simply wants everyone to be comfortable with math. "Mathematics is at the base of almost all technical areas," he says. "If you don't feel comfortable with mathematics, these areas will always be difficult."

Graham makes his own efforts to show students the excitement of mathematics. He gives talks to high school students and writes popular articles about various new developments in the field to dispel the popular impression that "mathematics is dead and buried in textbooks." In his talks, he shows how mathematics applies to many problems in the world, from creating or breaking secret codes to developing computer programs and even to scheduling classes or homework efficiently. He finds that most of the students he talks with are amazed that mathematics can be so lively.

With all of his activities, Graham's colleagues continually ask themselves how he finds time to do any research. "I think he works 24-hour shifts," remarks Fan Chung, a member of Graham's research group at Bell Laboratories.

Yet Graham never seems harried. He always acts as though he has all the time in the world for each person who wants to talk with him. Chung believes that she is a much better mathematician for having worked with Graham. He encouraged her to try more challenging problems than she had ever approached before, and he helped her develop a feeling for the kinds of problems that might be of the most interest to her. "He makes people feel free to go to him for help," she says. "Ron guided me into a new level of mathematics, and I'm not the only one for whom he did this."

Pollak agrees. "One of Ron's responsibilities at Bell Laboratories is to guide people in interesting directions. He is very, very good at this. He is willing to take the time and he is good at working with people. He is full of ideas and doesn't mind sharing them."

Graham says that, out of necessity, he developed the knack of changing gears quickly. "If you let yourself think that there's so much to do that you can never do it all, you might get bogged down and wind up not doing anything," he says.

Nevertheless, mathematics research for him is not an on-again off-again process. "Part of your brain is always running," he says. So, as Graham the juggler performs before the crowd at Stanford University, or Graham the pianist practices music, it is highly likely that, simultaneously, Graham the mathematician is solving problems in some corner of his mind.

The Secular Stargazers

By William J. Cromie

**Although most amateur astronomers study the
nighttime sky as a hobby, some make discoveries
that extend our understanding of the universe**

It seemed to Donald Machholz that he had just gone to bed when the
clanging alarm clock aroused him at 1 A.M. on Tuesday morning,
Sept. 12, 1978. The sky outside his window was clear. So he forced
back the urge to slide deeper under the blanket, got up, dressed, and
drove to the 1,110-meter (3,300-foot) level of Loma Prieta, a mountain about 30 minutes from his home in Los Gatos, Calif. On a wide
section of dirt road, he set up a 25.4-centimeter (10-inch) reflecting
telescope, which he had designed and built mostly by himself.

At 5:16 A.M., he suddenly saw a faint, unfamiliar patch of diffuse
light just south of the star Sirius. The star charts and the catalog that
he carried with him showed that no *nebula* (a glowing mass of dust
and gas) should be in that area. Machholz looked through his
telescope again. The fuzzy patch clearly was not a nebula. "With all
the basic checks done," he recalls, "I allowed myself to get excited
and started jumping around."

The 26-year old Machholz went home and sent a telegram announcing his find to the Harvard-Smithsonian Center for Astrophysics in Cambridge, Mass., which serves as the international clearing house for astronomical discoveries. The center arranges for professional astronomers to check out discoveries reported by amateurs such as Machholz.

The next morning, he arose at 2 A.M. and went out to check the sky again. "His" patch had moved a little since the previous day. Only a comet would have changed position in that brief time span. But had he been the first to see it?

Machholz went to his job at a Los Gatos optical laboratory where he makes eyeglass lenses. All day he wondered and worried about that comet. On Thursday morning, the telephone rang. It was Brian G. Marsden, astronomer at the Harvard-Smithsonian Center, who also serves as director of the International Astronomical Union's Central Bureau of Astronomical Telegrams. "The comet has been confirmed," Marsden said. "It is now known as Comet Machholz, 1978 l." (l means that it was the 12th comet found in 1978.) Later, Machholz received a plaque and a cash prize from a New Jersey telescope distributor. But more important, after 1,700 hours of searching in more than 3½ years, he had done what he set out to do—achieve immortality in the heavens.

Machholz is one of an estimated 2 million to 3 million amateur astronomers throughout the world. He is at one end of a spectrum. At the other end are the many people whose "astronomy" consists of standing in the backyard and watching the moon rise, or trying to pick out a constellation or two.

"Most amateurs watch, not study, the sky," comments Norman Sperling, an assistant editor of *Sky and Telescope,* one of the popular astronomy magazines. "We go inside when it gets too cold, or won't bother to get up to see an early-morning planet. Most people are into astronomy more for the fun and beauty and less to pursue discovery. I've been a stargazer for 22 years, and I still think that a clear night sky is the most beautiful sight on earth. It's a sight everyone can enjoy without a telescope or knowledge. But telescopes and knowledge make it more interesting and more meaningful."

The author:
William J. Cromie is a free-lance science writer and executive director of the Council for the Advancement of Science Writing.

What can you see when you study the night sky? In most areas you can see 2,000 to 3,000 stars with the unaided eye. These are stars with a magnitude of six or less. Magnitude is a numbering system for comparing brightness; the brighter a star or planet, the lower its magnitude number. A star of one magnitude is 2½ times brighter than a star of the next highest magnitude. This means that Sirius, a first-magnitude star, is about 250 times brighter than Polaris, a sixth-magnitude star. In clear areas in western North America, such as parts of Arizona or Alberta, Canada, it is possible to see stars of magnitude seven on a clear night. In a city, the pollution and bright lights limit you to seeing stars of magnitude four or brighter.

Long the subject of poem and song, the romantic moon takes on a new, unfamiliar pattern, *below,* when seen through binoculars that magnify its image seven times.

Planets and meteors can be seen by the unaided eye from almost anywhere on a clear night. You can see as many as five planets — Mercury, Venus, Mars, Jupiter, and Saturn. They are easily distinguished from bright stars because planets do not twinkle. Many amateurs enjoy looking for meteors. Meteor showers, such as the Leonid shower which takes place every November, are among the most spectacular sights in the night sky.

Astronomers divide the sky into 88 regions, or constellations, many of them named for an imaginary figure, such as the Great Bear (which includes the Big Dipper) or Orion, the Great Hunter. Amateurs get acquainted with the sky by learning the shapes and positions of the constellations. Without a telescope, you can see about 60 constellations, including the 12 zodiac groups — the origin of the "signs" used by astrologers to cast horoscopes. There are many good star charts to help beginners find their way in the sky.

A pair of good binoculars will bring hundreds of thousands of stars into view. Seen through 7x50 binoculars, objects become seven times larger than when seen with the naked eye. (The 50 refers to the diameter, or aperture, of the lenses in millimeters.) You can see stars that have a magnitude as low as 10. You can see open clusters — loose aggregates of several dozen to several hundred stars — and globular clusters — dense groups of 50,000 to 1 million stars. With binoculars, you can also see nebulae.

You may be surprised at what binoculars can show you about the planets. Venus sometimes will appear as a crescent. You can see, next to Jupiter, four pinpoints of light that represent its largest moons. With luck, you may spot a few of the largest asteroids, or minor planets, that orbit between Mars and Jupiter.

You also can get a good look at some of the brighter comets. In fact, many new comets have been discovered by amateurs searching the sky with binoculars. George E. D. Alcock, a retired British school-teacher and amateur astronomer, has discovered comets using 25x105 binoculars mounted on a tripod. Alcock also uses 15x80 binoculars to sweep the sky in search of novae, or "new" stars, which suddenly become brighter when their outer regions explode. They then gradually fade over a period of weeks, or even years.

After studying the night sky with binoculars, you may want to borrow or buy a telescope. There are two types of telescopes. A refracting telescope uses lenses to gather the light. A reflecting telescope uses focusing mirrors. Each has a set of small lenses that serve as an eyepiece. A 15-centimeter (6-inch) aperture reflecting telescope is popular. It magnifies up to 250 times and can be carried from place to place with relative ease. "Such an instrument lets you see millions of stars and other objects — more things than you can study in a lifetime," says Gary A. Becker of the Lehigh Valley Amateur Astronomical Society in Allentown, Pa. You can study craters and valleys on the moon; details of planets, such as the surface of Mars; comets; novae; and other objects that are trillions of kilometers away. With the proper filters and screens, you can watch the eruptions and other changes on the sun.

"Astronomy is one, if not the only, science in which the amateur can carry out useful research," says Patrick Moore, British writer, broadcaster, and amateur astronomer. "He cannot produce new theories of the universe. But he can and does discover comets and novae, make valuable observations of the planets, and keep a close watch on some types of variable stars."

People of all ages and occupations become amateur astronomers — elementary and high school students, college professors, members of the clergy, engineers, politicians, dentists, physicians, salespersons, secretaries, musicians, and physicists and other scientists. In some cases, amateurs turn professional. Clyde W. Tombaugh, the astronomer at Lowell Observatory in Flagstaff, Ariz., who discovered the planet Pluto in 1930, began his career as an amateur. So did two leading Russian astronomers, Pavel Parenago and Boris Kukarkin, who became experts in variable stars. A survey conducted by *Star and Sky* magazine in 1979 put the number of amateur astronomers in the United States at 300,000. Sperling believes that the number may be as high as 1 million if you count "everyone who spends an occasional dollar on the hobby and reads at least some of the articles in an astronomy magazine. However," he adds, "no more than a few thousand own really large telescopes and examine the sky frequently. People like Machholz, who watch the sky night after night and actually contribute to the science, probably do not exceed several hundred in number."

Most people prefer to enjoy their celestial hobby, interest, or passion alone or with a few friends. In the United States, star watchers are scattered among some 200 local clubs, and membership in these clubs totals only about 12,000. The clubs offer a variety of activities including lectures, courses, instruction in telescope making, local and foreign field trips, and social events. Some of the clubs give awards and scholarships.

Members of New York City's Amateur Astronomers Association look at the sky from the 86th floor of the Empire State Building and have "star parties" on isolated beaches on Long Island and the New Jersey shore. The Lehigh Valley Amateur Astronomical Society operates its own observatory on a 1.7-hectare (4.3-acre) site atop a 480-meter (1,600-foot) hill near Allentown. The East Bay Amateur Astronomers collect data for the professionals at the University of

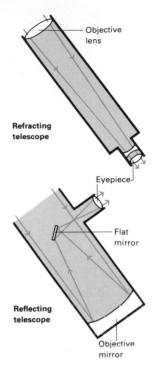

The Eye's Extension
A refracting telescope, *top,* magnifies an object with a combination of lenses. A reflecting telescope, *above,* uses mirrors for this purpose.

The constellation Orion, *above,* when seen through seven-power binoculars, *right,* is not only magnified, but also its close-together stars are resolved or separated, so that they can be seen individually.

A homemade reflecting telescope, *right,* is admired at a telescope makers' convention. Amateur astronomers build instruments as diverse as a diffraction spectroscope, *below,* an aluminized box for viewing solar eclipses, *opposite page, left,* and a dome-covered, 20-inch reflecting telescope, *opposite page, right,* that is owned by an amateur club in Lehigh, Pa.

California, Berkeley. The university provides equipment with which the club members, including high school students, watch young stars, study the moons of Jupiter, and monitor air pollution.

There are several regional amateur organizations in the United States. The East Bay club and about 40 others in the Western states belong to the Western Amateur Astronomers. In the rest of the United States, about 150 clubs form the Astronomical League. These associations conduct annual conventions, help new clubs to organize, provide lectures, slides, and publications, and campaign against light pollution. (Brilliantly lighted cities make it difficult to see the stars.) They also note the quality of the equipment sold to amateurs.

Many clubs have divisions and special courses for amateur telescope makers. The Amateur Astronomers Association maintains a well-equipped mirror-making and testing shop in the basement of the Hayden Planetarium in New York City. Telescope-making courses are very popular and draw people from 10 to 80 years of age. Members of the Lehigh Valley club constructed their own planetarium projector, observatory buildings, and telescopes, including a 50-centimeter (20-inch) instrument in a two-story building. This telescope and its building rank among the largest installations in the world built and operated by amateurs. Among other purposes, it is used to observe variable stars in a cooperative program with Villanova University in Villanova, Pa. Variable stars are stars whose brightness increases and decreases, sometimes on a regular cycle.

Virtually all beginning telescope makers, whether they take a course or not, begin by reading about the subject. The most popular is *All About Telescopes,* a book by Sam Brown (third edition published in 1976 by Edmund Scientific Co.). Usually, the novice starts with a six-inch or smaller reflecting telescope. The first and most important piece to make is the primary, or objective, mirror, which gathers the light and enlarges the image. It is made by grinding a piece of glass into a parabolic curve with an abrasive powder, using another piece of glass as a grinding "tool."

The parabolic mirror is placed into a holder, as is a second, flat mirror. The amateur then mounts the two mirrors in a tube or other rigid framework. Some people buy the tube; others build a long, rectangular, open-ended box out of wood. The eyepiece lenses, which the amateur can either make or buy, are mounted at the side of the tube. The mirror-and-lens assembly is placed on a mount, often a simple tripod.

A six-inch reflector can be made for less than $200. "You can buy one for $250, but it probably will not be as good as the one you make if you do even an average job," says Richard Mazziotti, an amateur who teaches telescope making to members of the Amateur Astronomers Association in New York City. Amateurs who build instruments larger than eight inches usually mount these permanently. Some people even build small observatories in their backyards, complete with a movable roof or a rotating dome with a viewing slot.

Grinding the objective mirror to its proper curvature is the most important and most difficult step in making a telescope.

The bigger, more complicated instruments, like professional telescopes, have electrical devices that compensate for the earth's rotation. As you look through a simple telescope, you will notice that the object you are observing drifts slowly across the field of view and the telescope has to be constantly readjusted, which is a great nuisance. A motor drive, fitted between the telescope and its mount, holds the field of view "steady."

Amateur and professional astronomers in the United States may cooperate on projects, but they rarely work side by side, publish their findings together, or socialize. The Astronomical Society of the Pacific, with headquarters in San Francisco, has both professionals and amateurs in its ranks. Its 5,000 members come from all over the world and include about 1,500 professionals from 54 nations. The professionals publish the results of their research in the society's technical journal, *Publications of the Astronomical Society of the Pacific,*

while both amateurs' and professionals' activities are reported in *Mercury* magazine.

In other countries, amateurs and professionals are more closely affiliated. Canadian amateurs can join the Royal Astronomical Society of Canada (RASC), which includes 20 per cent of Canada's professionals. The RASC has 18 centers throughout the country, with the 800-member Toronto group being the largest. Great Britain has national clubs for both beginning and advanced amateurs. The amateur British Astronomical Society includes professionals from many nations.

In Russia, both amateurs and professionals belong to the 6,000-member All-Union Astronomical and Geodetic Society, which has branches in 60 cities. Poland's Society of Amateur Astronomers has 3,000 members. Amateurs' research is coordinated by the society's 200 professionals. Amateurs also are very active in Australia, Belgium, France, West Germany, Hungary, Italy, Japan, and Spain.

Professional astronomers depend on amateurs in a number of ways. "Amateurs discover more of the bright comets and novae than professionals because they spend more time looking at the sky and know it better," explains Carlson R. Chambliss, a professional astronomer. Professionals who observe the sky do so with auxiliary equipment — photometers, spectrometers, cameras — as well as tele-

397

scopes. The faint comets and novae are found, for example, by examining photographic plates.

Japanese amateurs lead the comet sweepstakes with the largest number of discoveries in the past 25 years. The individual record, however, is held by Leslie C. Peltier, a retired furniture maker from Delphos, Ohio. He started watching the sky in 1918 when he was 16, and now has 13 comet discoveries to his credit. William Bradfield, an Australian, boasts of 10 finds, all in the Southern Hemisphere.

George Alcock spent six years looking through binoculars from his backyard in Farcet, England, memorizing the patterns of stars down to magnitude 8. His perseverance resulted in the discovery of four comets — two in one week — and three novae. As a by-product of his acquaintance with the heavens, Alcock has found many errors and

Amateur Astronomy Organizations

So you want to become an amateur astronomer. Fortunately, you do not need an expensive telescope or extensive knowledge. The beauty of the universe is free, and enjoying it can cost as little or as much as you want to spend in time or money.

You can study the sky by eye or with binoculars, and learn much about what you see from THE WORLD BOOK ENCYCLOPEDIA, books and magazines on the subject, and star guides.

You can also find out about what is going on in astronomy by reading *Sky and Telescope, Astronomy,* or *Star and Sky.* Most public and many school libraries subscribe to one or more of these magazines.

If you want to go beyond this, you should consider joining a club. In most areas, you can locate one within commuting distance. There you can meet others who share your interest, find out what activities are available, and obtain advice on buying and using, or even making, a telescope.

To locate the nearest club, check with your local planetarium or the science department of a local high school or college. For information about the regional organizations listed in the margin at the left, send a stamped, self-addressed envelope to the one nearest to you and ask for information.

The Astronomical Society of the Pacific publishes a directory of amateur astronomy groups, observatories, museums, and courses taught in the northern California area.

About one-third of the amateur astronomy clubs have junior groups for high school and junior high school students. But all the clubs welcome younger members. The Boy Scouts of America have Explorer posts that specialize in astronomy; these usually are affiliated with amateur clubs. Most club dues are between $15 and $20 a year, less for junior members.

Many astronomy clubs own instruments that beginners can borrow on meeting nights or rent for a longer period. For example, the Lehigh Valley Amateur Astronomical Society rents small telescopes for about $5 a month.

Before you buy a telescope, try several different kinds so that you can decide what is best for your needs. No instrument is equally good for viewing all the objects in the sky. Some are awkward to use and can literally give you a pain in the neck.

Borrow different instruments from club members and try them out. Then discuss the advantages and disadvantages with experienced amateurs. The right kind of telescope can be a rewarding investment in a fascinating hobby.   [W. J. C.]

omissions in star charts and catalogs that are compiled by professional observatories.

Japanese astronomers Kantero Osada and Minoru Honda discovered Nova Cygni in 1975. The night that the nova blazed to life, Ben Mayer, an amateur who owns a light-designing company in Los Angeles, had hooked up an automatic camera to his lawn-sprinkler timer to photograph meteors. The next morning, when he developed the film and found no meteors, Mayer threw the film into a wastebasket. That evening he went out to watch the sky with some friends, and they told him about the discovery of Nova Cygni. Realizing that he might have photographs of the new star, Mayer drove 32 kilometers (20 miles) to a telephone and called home. "Did you empty the wastebaskets yet?" he asked his teen-age son. "No," came the guilty reply, "but I'll do it right away." Young Mayer was then startled to hear his father yell, "Don't touch them!"

Mayer rushed home, re-examined the film, and found a sequence of 14 photographs that showed the star erupting into view. He sent the film to Harvard University and was, in his words, "catapulted from wastebasket to fame."

In 1979, Mayer organized a national amateur effort to search for novae photographically. About 100 observers are assigned sections of the sky to patrol. Each amateur photographs his or her sections about a week apart. The photos are compared using two slide projectors. By "blinking," or superimposing, the one star field on the other, observers spot new objects. Mayer calls his project "Problicom" (project blink comparison).

W hen novae appear, they throw off part of themselves as glowing gas. Most increase 10,000 to 100,000 times in brightness, and they are exciting objects to watch. Even more thrilling are supernovae — violent explosions that cause stars to increase as much as a billion times in brightness in a few days. Most of these cataclysms occur in galaxies that lie vast distances from our Milky Way.

It requires careful, systematic observation, familiarity with the appearance of galaxies, and good luck to discover a supernova. Gus E. Johnson, a schoolteacher in Swanton, Md., spent 20 years developing the skill and familiarity. Then on the night of April 18-19, 1979, he got lucky. Through his telescope he saw a glow as bright as a million suns in the galaxy NGC 4321 in the constellation Coma Berenices. Johnson called Brian Marsden, who cabled the McGraw Hill telescope operators at Kitt Peak National Observatory in Arizona, and the Asiago Observatory in Italy. When these observatories confirmed the sighting, Johnson became the second amateur in this century to discover a supernova. Jack Bennett, a South African, made the first discovery in 1968.

Novae and supernovae are variable stars, and a special amateur group devotes itself to watching these flickering beacons. The American Association of Variable Star Observers (AAVSO), with head-

Dennis Milon, who used a four-inch reflector telescope, *top,* to find Comet 1975h, *above,* is one of many amateur astronomers who discover events in the heavens.

quarters in Cambridge, Mass., has 1,100 members who make observations for professionals. "Stars become variable [in brightness] at certain important ages in their lifetime, particularly at birth and near death," explains Janet A. Mattei, director of AAVSO. "By continuously monitoring these stars, you can learn something about their mass, composition, and life history. However, the number of known variable stars, about 20,000, far exceeds the number of professional astronomers available to watch them. This is where amateurs can contribute. About 15,000 observations are made annually, mainly by 500 of our most active members."

Professional astronomers and the National Aeronautics and Space Administration (NASA) use AAVSO observations to find out which variable stars to watch. A series of unmanned space laboratories known as High Energy Astronomy Observatories (HEAO) has been surveying the universe for sources of X rays since 1977. Variable stars emit detectable X rays at their maximum brightness but not when they dim to normal radiance. Professional astronomers with experiments aboard the HEAO satellites ask AAVSO to tell them which variables are shining at maximum brightness. Then the scientists ask NASA to maneuver the space probe to check these stars. Occasionally, when the orbiting observatories detect a source of X rays, professionals call AAVSO to find out what can be seen out there. As an example of this cooperation in 1980, AAVSO and the Royal Astronomical Society of New Zealand were participating in a study of dwarf novae in conjunction with HEAO-2.

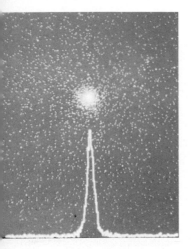

X-ray photo of variable star SS Cygnia was taken at a peak in the star's cycle by the Einstein Orbiting Observatory as a result of information supplied by the American Variable Star Observers, an amateur organization in Cambridge, Mass.

Some variables exist in pairs. When they flare up, hot gases may cross millions of kilometers of space from one star to the other. This produces bursts of X rays, ultraviolet, and other types of radiation. In January 1978, NASA launched an instrumented satellite called International Ultraviolet Explorer to study, among other things, this spectacular celestial transfer of star dust. Instead of wasting time, money, and effort searching for stars to measure, NASA's satellite operators contact amateurs, who have already accidentally found such stars, to determine how to orient the spacecraft. "It is extremely exciting and satisfying," comments Mattei, "to know that an amateur with a six- or eight-inch telescope in his or her backyard and a little training can tell scientists and NASA where to point satellites to obtain the maximum amount of information about the universe."

AAVSO trains amateurs as young as 16 years of age to monitor variable stars. It also maintains a division that observes sunspots and solar flares. Records of sunspot activity compiled and published by the association form a historical record that can be used by researchers to correlate changes in the sun with events on earth, such as severe droughts and temperature changes. Solar flares disrupt long-distance communications, produce power surges that result in blackouts, and cause magnetic compasses to go awry and migrating birds to lose their way.

Irene Gordon counts sunspots on her backyard optical telescope through special filters located on a hill in Nazareth, Pa. Looking at the sun can damage the eyes, so this work requires care. Observations made by Gordon and other sun watchers go to the National Oceanic and Atmospheric Administration (NOAA) in Boulder, Colo., which makes them available to professional scientists.

At night, Irene's husband Roger, a telescope salesman, takes over the Gordon telescope to watch the planets and the moon. He belongs to another amateur specialty group — the 800-member Association of Lunar and Planetary Observers. Other amateur organizations specialize in surveying meteors and in occultations. When a planet, moon, or asteroid passes between earth and a star, it momentarily occults, or blocks out, the starlight. A close watch on the edge of the planetary body at this time reveals details about its atmosphere, *topography* (mountains and valleys), and other characteristics. Professional astronomers discovered the rings around Uranus in 1977 when the light of star SAO 158687 was seen to blink on and off before the planet blocked the star from view.

On the night of June 7, 1978, both professionals and amateurs watched the asteroid Herculina as it moved in front of star SAO 120774. The asteroid, 216 kilometers (135 miles) in diameter, is one of thousands of small planets that orbit the sun between Mars and Jupiter. James H. McMahon, a metallurgical engineer from China Lake, Calif., received details on the impending event from the amateur International Occultation Timing Association.

As he watched through his 10-centimeter (4-inch) instrument in the Mojave Desert, McMahon saw the star flicker on and off several times *after* Herculina passed. He alerted professionals at the Lowell Observatory in Flagstaff. They had not noticed the secondary extinctions. But they rechecked their data and found that light levels recorded by a photometer showed that the starlight had blinked on and off after the asteroid passed. The best explanation is that the secondary occultations were caused by a satellite orbiting Herculina.

Not all professionals or amateurs agree with this explanation, however. Nevertheless, McMahon's work stands as a good example of what an experienced and dedicated amateur can do with a modest telescope. In August 1979, the Astronomical Society of the Pacific gave McMahon its Amateur Achievement Award.

While the Alcocks, Machholzes, and McMahons make the discoveries and contributions to science, most amateurs are content to enjoy astronomy in a more leisurely way. They keep a telescope in the backyard, basement, or hall closet and occasionally take it out and look at Orion or the moon. "We have a lot of fun in amateur astronomy," says Cliff W. Holmes, a bakery salesman who is vice-president of the Western Amateur Astronomers. "Some of us make valuable contributions to science, most of us enjoy the mystery and beauty of the universe, and all of us have a good time."

Awards
And Prizes

A listing and description of the year's major awards and prizes in science, and the men and women who received them

Earth and Physical Sciences

Chemistry. Major awards in the field of chemistry included:

Nobel Prize. Professor Herbert C. Brown of Purdue University in Lafayette, Ind., and Professor Emeritus Georg Wittig of Heidelberg University in West Germany shared the 1979 Nobel prize in chemistry. They won the $190,000 prize for devising ways to induce chemical reactions for the mass production of important pharmaceuticals and industrial chemicals.

Brown linked compounds of boron and hydrogen with many large molecules to synthesize biologically active substances. Wittig used compounds of phosphorus for the same purpose.

Cope Award. Gilbert Storck a professor at Columbia University won the Arthur C. Cope Award in 1980 for outstanding achievement in organic chemistry. Storck received the $10,000 prize and $10,000 research grant for developing basic techniques used to synthesize important natural products.

Perkin Medal. Herman F. Mark, dean emeritus, Polytechnic Institute of New York, was awarded the Perkin Medal in 1980. Mark is recognized as an international pioneer in the development of polymer science.

Petroleum Chemistry Award. William A. Pryor, professor of chemistry at Louisiana State University in Baton Rouge, won the 1980 American Chemical Society (ACS) Award in Petroleum Chemistry. Pryor received the $5,000 prize for his significant research on the reactions of hydrocarbons, sulfur compounds, free radicals, and initiators of polymerization.

Priestley Medal. Milton Harris of Washington, D.C., an expert in fiber and polymer chemistry, received the 1980 Priestley Medal. The award, highest honor given by the ACS, recognizes distinguished contributions to chemistry.

Harris initiated research that led to development of the cold permanent wave, shrinkproof wool, and improved shaving creams and lotions. He founded the Harris Research Laboratories in Washington, D.C., in 1945 and was director of research for the Gillette Company from 1956 to 1966.

Herbert C. Brown   Georg Wittig

Earth and Physical Sciences

Continued

Physics. Awards presented during the year recognizing major works in physics included.

Nobel Prize. A Pakistani and two Harvard University physicists shared the 1979 Nobel prize for physics. Abdus Salam, head of the International Center for Theoretical Physics in Trieste, Italy, shared the award with Harvard researchers Steven Weinberg and Sheldon L. Glashow.

The three were honored for separate, but complementary, research on the Weinberg-Salam Theory of Weak Interactions. This theory is considered a major advance in understanding three fundamental forces of nature: electromagnetism; the strong interaction, which holds atomic nuclei together; and the weak interaction, which causes radioactive decay in certain kinds of atomic nuclei.

Difficulty arose in applying the theory because only three of the fundamental particles called quarks were known. But Glashow's research on a fourth, the "charmed" quark, helped overcome the difficulty.

Buckley Prize. Dean E. Eastman, manager of the Photoemission and Surface Group at the IBM Thomas J. Watson Research Center in Yorktown Heights, N.Y., and William E. Spicer, professor of electrical engineering at Stanford University in California, shared the 1980 Oliver E. Buckley Solid State Physics Prize. They were honored for developing and applying photoelectron spectroscopy as a tool in studying bulk and surface electronic structure in solids.

Fermi Award. Harold M. Agnew and Wolfgang K. H. Panofsky shared the $25,000 Enrico Fermi Award in 1979 for achievement in the development, use, and control of atomic energy. Agnew worked with the Fermi group that achieved the first nuclear fission reaction in 1942. Panofsky, director of the Stanford Linear Accelerator Center, uncovered the nature of an elementary particle, the pi-meson.

Heineman Prize. James G. Glimm of Rockefeller University and Arthur M. Jaffe of Harvard shared the 1980 Dannie Heineman Prize for Mathemat-

Sheldon Glashow (left) and Steven Weinberg

Abdus Salam

ical Physics. The award, administered jointly by the American Institute of Physics (AIP) and the American Physical Society (APS), was for their joint contributions to quantum field theory.

Luck Award. Professor Conyers Herring of the Stanford University Department of Applied Physics was awarded the James Murray Luck Award in 1980. The $5,000 award was made by the National Academy of Sciences for "a career of service to the scientific community and particularly its review literature."

Oersted Medal. Professor Gerald Holton, a member of the Harvard University faculty since 1945, received the Oersted Medal for the teaching of physics in 1980. The award is given annually by the American Association of Physics Teachers.

Geosciences. Awards for important work in the geosciences during the year included:

Bowie Medal. Charles A. Whitten, who retired as chief geodesist of the U.S. Coast and Geodetic Survey (now the National Ocean Survey) in 1972, received the William Bowie Medal in 1980. The award, by the American Geophysical Union, was in recognition of Whitten's outstanding contributions to fundamental geophysics and his unselfish cooperation with other researchers. Whitten is known for his work in the use of large-scale computers for geodetic adjustments.

Day Medal. Professor Harry G. Thode of McMaster University in Hamilton, Canada, received the Arthur L. Day Medal in 1980. The Geological Society of America award honored Thode for outstanding contributions in geochemistry and cosmochemistry, as well as in other research.

Penrose Medal. Hollis D. Hedberg, emeritus professor of geology at Princeton University and for many years a geologist for the Gulf Oil Corporation, received the Penrose Medal in 1980. Hedberg was a leader in the completion in 1976 of the International Stratigraphic Guide, a 20-year project. The system of stratigraphic classification for the earth's geological strata has received international recognition. He is also known for pioneering work on the compaction of sediments.

Medicine. Major awards in the medical sciences include the following:

Nobel Prize. Physicist Allan M. Cormack of Tufts University in Medford, Mass., and Godfrey N. Hounsfield of the EMI, Limited, research staff in Great Britain shared the 1979 Nobel prize in physiology or medicine for developing the computerized axial tomograph (CAT) scanner. This device provides clear X-ray pictures of sections, or slices, of the body and in much greater detail than do other photographic techniques.

Cormack began studying limitations of X-ray methods in his native South Africa. In 1963, after coming to the United States, he published his findings on how radiation is affected by the material through which it passes.

Hounsfield invented an EMI device to make two-dimensional X-ray pictures, and the CAT scanner was developed from that. The device takes pictures from a tube that rotates 360 degrees, and the pictures are then greatly clarified and improved by computer processing.

Hazen Award. Jesse Roth, chief of the diabetes branch of the National Institute of Arthritis, Metabolism, and Digestive Diseases in Bethesda, Md., won the first Lita Annenberg Hazen Award in 1979. Roth received half of the $100,000 award. The remainder finances young physicians chosen to work with Roth in biomedical research. Roth made important advances in showing why diabetes can exist despite an excess of insulin.

Gairdner Awards. Claude Fortier of Laval University in Quebec, Canada, received the $25,000 Gairdner Foundation Wightman Award for contributions to Canadian medicine as a scientist, teacher, and government adviser. In addition, six medical researchers working in Canada, Great Britain, and the United States received $10,000 Gairdner Foundation International Awards in 1979.

The $10,000 awards went to James W. Black of the Wellcome Research Laboratories in Kent, England, for his work in identifying amine receptors and developing the receptor-blocking drugs Propanolol and Cimetidine; George F. Cahill, Jr., of Harvard Medical School in Boston for work on the

Life Sciences

Allan M. Cormack

Godfrey N. Hounsfield

interrelationships of hormones and body fuels in differing human nutritional states; Walter Gilbert of Harvard for researching on gene replication and regulation, and for developing methods of sequencing deoxyribonucleic acid (DNA); Elwood V. Jensen of the University of Chicago for discovering steroid receptors and developing tests for endocrine treatment for breast cancer; Frederick Sanger of the University of Cambridge in England for perfecting DNA sequencing methods and contributing to new concepts of gene structure; and Charles Scriver of McGill University/Montreal Children's Hospital Research Center for his research on genetic disease.

Lasker Awards. Three scientists and a blind health administrator won 1979 Albert Lasker Awards. Psychobiologist Roger W. Sperry of the California Institute of Technology (Caltech) in Pasadena received $15,000 for discovering the functions of the brain's left and right hemispheres and how the hemispheres interact.

Walter Gilbert, Harvard University molecular biologist, and Frederick Sanger of England's Medical Research Council Laboratory of Molecular Biology shared a $15,000 award. Gilbert and Sanger independently devised ways to sequence deoxyribonucleic acid (DNA), the basic genetic material in all living things. To break DNA molecules into fragments so that their sequence could be determined, Gilbert used chemicals and Sanger used enzymes.

A $15,000 special public service award went to Sir John Wilson of Great Britain. Wilson, blind since youth, is director of the Royal Commonwealth Society for the Blind and president of the International Agency for the Prevention of Blindness.

Biology. Among the awards presented in biology were the following:

Franklin Medal. G. Evelyn Hutchinson, Sterling Professor of Zoology Emeritus at Yale University, received the 1979 Franklin Medal, highest award of The Franklin Institute of Philadelphia. Hutchinson was cited for developing the concept of the ecological niche — the role each living thing plays in its surroundings — and for other research work.

Horwitz Prize. Molecular biologists Walter Gilbert of Harvard and Frederick Sanger of Cambridge University in England shared the $22,000 Louisa Gross Horwitz Prize in 1979. Gilbert and Sanger were honored for research that laid the experimental groundwork for the great explosion of knowledge in the field of genetics that occurred during the 1970s.

Gilbert took part in 1960 in one of the first demonstrations of messenger ribonucleic acid (mRNA), the chemical substance that carries instructions for life between the cell nucleus and the cytoplasm, where new proteins are produced. Later, he helped to explain interrelationships between gene structure and function, including how genes are turned on and off.

Sanger was honored for his research on how the RNA and DNA molecules transfer inheritable characteristics from one generation to the next. See Medicine (Lasker Awards) in column 1 on this page.

Mitchell Prize. Paul R. Ehrlich, biologist and professor of population studies at Stanford University, won the $10,000 first prize in the $100,000 Mitchell Prize program. Sponsored by the Mitchell Energy & Development Corporation, the University of Houston System, and Aspen Institute for Humanistic Studies, this competition is designed to stimulate original thinking on issues related to population growth. Eight $5,000 awards were also made as part of the Mitchell program, which is held biennially.

3M Life Sciences Award. Biochemist Arthur B. Pardee of Harvard's Sidney Farber Cancer Institute won the 1980 3M Life Sciences Award. Farber was cited for experiments opening new areas of investigation and work on the feedback control of enzymes, which shed new light on the chemistry of living organisms.

U.S. Steel Foundation Award. Philip Sharp, professor at the Massachusetts Institute of Technology (M.I.T.) Center for Cancer Research and Department of Biology, won the 1980 U.S. Steel Foundation Award in Molecular Biology. Sharp received the $5,000 prize for his pioneering contributions to the understanding of mRNA biogenesis in mammalian cells.

Aerospace. The highest awards in the aerospace sciences included:

Collier Trophy. Paul B. MacCready, Pasadena, Calif., aeronautical engineer, won the 1979 Robert J. Collier Trophy for designing and building the *Gossamer Condor* and the *Gossamer Albatross,* two highly unusual human-powered aircraft.

The *Gossamer Condor* made the first human-powered flight in 1977 and won a $95,000 Kremer Prize. Powered by cyclist Bryan Allen, it flew 2.16 kilometers (1.35 miles) over a figure-eight course at Shafter, Calif. (see FLIGHT OF THE GOSSAMER CONDOR, *Science Year,* 1979). The *Gossamer Albatross,* also powered by Allen, flew 35 kilometers (22 miles) across the English Channel on June 12, 1979, in 2 hours 49 minutes to win a $220,000 Kremer Prize.

Goddard Astronautics Award. Robert Parks, assistant laboratory director at the Jet Propulsion Laboratory (JPL) in Pasadena, Calif., won the 1980 Goddard Astronautics Award. Parks was honored "for outstanding achievement and inspired leadership in his direction at JPL of flight projects from *Mariner 2* to *Voyager.*"

Longstreth Medal. Paul MacCready and his associate Peter Lissaman won the 1979 Longstreth Medal for the design and construction of the *Gossamer Condor* and the *Gossamer Albatross.* MacCready designed and built the craft. Lissaman helped him deal with the more sophisticated aspects of the aerodynamics involved in the project.

Astronomy. Major awards in astronomy during the year included:

Amateur Achievement Award. Frank Bateson, a retired New Zealand accountant, won the 1980 Amateur Achievement Award of the Astronomical Society of the Pacific. Bateson has made more than 100,000 observations of variable stars. For more information on the activities and contributions of amateur astronomers, see THE SECULAR STARGAZERS.

Bruce Medal. George Herbig, a Lick Observatory astronomer and professor at the University of California, Santa Cruz, won the 1980 Catherine Wolfe Bruce Medal for distinguished service in astronomy. Herbig is noted for his work on extremely young stars and on the peculiar nebulous knots called Herbig Hare objects.

Heineman Prize for Astrophysics. Joseph H. Taylor, Jr., professor of astronomy at the University of Massachusetts, received the first Dannie Heineman Prize for Astrophysics in 1980. The new prize, awarded jointly by the American Institute of Physics and the American Astronomical Society, went to Taylor for his discoveries of new pulsars, his studies of pulsar radiation and pulsar distribution, and his use of pulsar data to explain fundamental physical laws.

Draper Medal. W. W. Morgan, professor emeritus at the University of Chicago's Yerkes Observatory in Williams Bay, Wis., received the Henry Draper Medal in 1980. The award honored Morgan for his pioneering research in spectral classification, which enabled scientists to measure the distances of stars and the structure of our galaxy more accurately.

Merrill Award. Robert N. Clayton, chairman of the University of Chicago Department of the Geophysical Sciences, received the George P. Merrill Award in 1980. Clayton was honored for "his pioneering measurements of isotopic *heterogeneities* [dissimilarities] in extraterrestrial materials."

Russell Lectureship. Jeremiah Ostriker, professor of astrophysics at Princeton University in New Jersey, received the Henry Norris Russell Lectureship in 1980. The lectureship is awarded annually by the American Astronomical Society on the basis of eminence in astronomical research.

Ostriker was honored for his many scientific contributions to a wide variety of astrophysical subjects. The citation singled out his research work on "compact objects, the theory of the interstellar medium, and the structure and evolution of galaxies."

Warner Prize. Paul C. Joss, associate professor of physics at M.I.T., won the Helen B. Warner Prize in 1980. The Warner Prize is awarded annually for significant contributions to astronomy during the five years immediately preceding the award. Joss was honored by the American Astronomical Society for "his distinguished contribution to theoretical astrophysics, particularly for his work on the theory of X-ray stars."

Space and Other Awards

Continued

The 20 winners of the National Medal of Science were honored by President Jimmy Carter at the White House in January.

Science and Humanity Awards received during 1979 and 1980 included the following:

National Medal of Science. President Jimmy Carter awarded the National Medal of Science to 20 researchers on Jan. 14, 1980. Those honored were:

Robert H. Burris, biochemist, University of Wisconsin; Elizabeth C. Crosby, anatomist, University of Michigan; Joseph L. Doob, mathematician, University of Illinois, Urbana; Richard R. Feynman, physicist, Caltech; Donald E. Knuth, computer science, Stanford; Arthur Kornberg, biochemist, Stanford; Emmett N. Leith, electrical engineer, Michigan; Herman F. Mark, chemist, Polytechnic Institute of New York; Raymond D. Mindlin, engineer, Columbia University; Robert N. Noyce, research engineer, Intel Corporation, Santa Clara, Calif.; Severa Ochoa, biochemist, Roche Institute of Molecular Biology, Nutley, N.J.; Earl R. Parker, metallurgist, University of California, Berkeley; Edward M. Purcell, physicist, Harvard; Simon Ramo, engineer, TRW Incorporated, Redon-

do Beach, Calif.; John H. Sinfelt, chemist, Exxon Corporate Research Laboratories, Linden, N.J.; Lyman Spitzer, Jr., astronomer, Princeton University; Earl R. Stadtman, biochemist, National Heart, Lung, and Blood Institute; George L. Stebbins, Jr., geneticist, University of California, Davis; Paul A. Weiss, biologist, Rockefeller University; and Victor F. Weisskopf, physicist, M.I.T.

Founders Medal. David Packard, board chairman of the Hewlett-Packard Company, was awarded the Founders Medal in 1979. Packard was honored by the National Academy of Engineering for his pioneering role in the engineering, manufacturing, and marketing of advanced electronic technology and also for his leadership in public service.

Packard was a founder of Hewlett-Packard in 1939. He served as U.S. deputy secretary of defense in 1969, 1970, and 1971. He has also served on the Stanford University Board of Trustees and as a director of several business organizations. [Joseph P. Spohn]

Major Awards and Prizes

Award winners treated more fully in the first portion of this section are indicated by an asterisk (*)

AAAS-Newcomb Cleveland Prize: Patrick M. Cassen, Stanton J. Peale, Ray T. Reynolds

AAAS-Socio-Psychological Prize: Ronald S. Wilson

ACS Award for Nuclear Chemistry: Arthur Poskanzer

*ACS Award in Petroleum Chemistry: William A. Pryor

Allan Award (genetics): F. Clarke Fraser

*Amateur Achievement Award (astronomy): Frank Bateson

American Physical Society (APS) High Polymer Physics Prize: Marshall Fixman

Apker Award (physics): Louis A. Bloomfield

APS International Prize for New Materials: Pol E. Duwez, William Klement, Jr., Ronald H. Willens

APS Prize for Industrial Applications of Physics: Andrew H. Bobeck

*Arthur L. Day Medal (geophysics): Harry G. Thode

Bertner Memorial Award (cancer research): T. C. Hsu

Bingham Medal (rheology): William W. Graessley

Borden Award (pediatrics): Abraham M. Rudolph

*Bowie Medal (geophysics): Charles A. Whitten

Brewer Trophy (aviation): Paul H. Poberezny

Broida Prize (physics): Robert W. Field

*Bruce Medal (astronomy): George Herbig

*Buckley Solid State Physics Prize: Dean E. Eastman, William E. Spicer

Carski Award (teaching): Warren Litsky

Clamer Medal (metallurgy): George R. Irwin

*Collier Trophy (astronautics): Paul B. MacCready

*Cope Award (chemistry): Gilbert Storck

Damashek Award (hematology): Yust Wai Kan

Delmer S. Fahrney Medal (telecommunications): Peter Fortescue

*Draper Medal (astronomy): W. W. Morgan

Earle K. Plyler Prize (physics): Walter Gordy

Elliott Cresson Medal (chemistry): Steven Weinberg

E. Mead Johnson Award (pediatrics): Philip L. Ballard

Ewing Medal (geophysics): J. Tuzo Wilson

*Fermi Award (energy): Harold M. Agnew, Wolfgang K. H. Panofsky

Flexner Award (medical education): Julius H. Comroe

*Founder's Medal (engineering): David Packard

*Franklin Medal: G. Evelyn Hutchinson

*Gairdner Awards (medicine): Wightman Award, Claude Fortier; Individual Awards, James W. Black, George F. Cahill, Jr., Walter Gilbert, Elwood V. Jensen, Frederick Sanger, Charles R. Scriver

Garvan Medal (chemistry): Helen M. Free

Gibbs Brothers Medal (marine engineering): Matthew G. Forrest

*Goddard Astronautics Award: Robert Parks

Gold Air Medal: Ben L. Abruzzo, Maxie L. Anderson

*Hazen Award (medicine): Jesse Roth

*Heineman Prize for Astrophysics: Joseph H. Taylor, Jr.

*Heineman Prize for Mathematical Physics: James G. Glimm, Arthur M. Jaffe

Horton Award (geophysics): William G. Ackermann

*Horwitz Prize (biology): Walter Gilbert, Frederick Sanger

Howard N. Potts Medal (chemistry): Seymour R. Cray, Richard T. Whitcomb

Ipatieff Prize (chemistry): Denis Forster

Isakson Prize (physics): David L. Dexter

Klumpke-Roberts Award (astronomy): Walter Sullivan

*Lasker Awards (medical research): Walter Gilbert, Frederick Sanger, Roger W. Sperry, Sir John Wilson

Leo Szilard Award (physics): F. Sherwood Rowland

Lilly Award (microbiology): Christopher T. Walsh

*Longstreth Medal: Paul B. MacCready, Peter Lissaman

*Luck Award (scientific reviewing): Conyers Herring

Macelwane Award (geophysics): Lawrence Grossman, Thomas W. Hill, Norman H. Sleep

Mees Medal (optics): Koichi Shimoda

*Merrill Award (astronomy): Robert N. Clayton

Michelson Medal (optics): Richard G. Brewer

*Mitchell Prize: Paul R. Ehrlich, Robert L. Chianese, Edward T. Clark, John Coletta, Arthur A. Few, Jr., James Garbarino, Michael Gibbons, David Hopcraft, George Modelski, Dillard Tinsley

NAS Award in Aeronautical Engineering: James T. McDonnell

NAS Award in Applied Mathematics and Numerical Analysis: George F. Carrier

NAS Award in Chemical Sciences: Frank H. Westheimer

NAS Award for Environmental Quality: Gilbert F. White

NAS Public Welfare Medal: Walter Sullivan

*National Medal of Science: Robert H. Burris, Elizabeth C. Crosby, Joseph L. Doob, Richard P. Feynman, Donald E. Knuth, Arthur Kornberg, Emmett N. Leith, Herman F. Mark, Raymond D. Mindlin, Robert N. Noyce, Severa Ochoa, Earl R. Parker, Edward M. Purcell, Simon Ramo, John H. Sinfelt, Lyman Spitzer, Jr., Earl R. Stadtman, George L. Stebbins, Jr., Paul A. Weiss, Victor F. Weisskopf

*Nobel Prize: chemistry, Herbert C. Brown, Georg Wittig; physics, Sheldon L. Glashow, Abdus Salam, Steven Weinberg; physiology or medicine, Allan M. Cormack, Godfrey N. Hounsfield

*Oersted Medal (physics teaching): Gerald Holton

Oppenheimer Memorial Prize (physics): Richard H. Dalitz

*Penrose Medal (geology): Hollis D. Hedberg

*Perkin Medal (chemistry): Herman F. Mark

Pfizer Award: Frederick C. Hartman

Pierce Prize (astronomy): Jack Baldwin

*Priestley Medal (chemistry): Milton Harris

Richardson Medal (optics): William P. Ewald

*Russell Lectureship: Jeremiah Ostriker

R. W. Woods Prize (optics): Peter Franken

Stuart Ballantine Medal: Benjamin Abeles, George D. Cody, Marcian E. Hoff, Jr.

*3M Life Sciences Award (biology): Arthur B. Pardee

Trumpler Award (astronomy): James Liebert, Luis Rodriguez

*U.S. Steel Foundation Award (molecular biology): Philip A. Sharp

Waksman Award (microbiology): Julius Adler

*Warner Prize (astronomy): Paul C. Joss

Welch Award (physics): Gert Ehrlich

Wetherill Medal: Elias Burstein

Wilson S. Stone Memorial Award (cancer research): Marc S. Collett, Peter T. Lomedico

Wright Brothers Memorial Trophy: T. A. Wilson

Deaths of Notable Scientists

Ernst B. Chain

Werner Forssmann

Erich Fromm

Notable scientists and engineers who died between June 1, 1979, and June 1, 1980, are listed below. An asterisk (*) indicates that a biography appears in *The World Book Encyclopedia.*

Blodgett, Katharine B. (1898-Oct. 12, 1979), chemist who in 1939 developed the nonreflecting coating for glass now used in virtually all camera lenses.

Bosworth, David M. (1897-July 11, 1979), orthopedic surgeon noted for his research in bone and joint tuberculosis. He developed 27 surgical procedures.

Bullard, Edward (1908-April 3, 1980), British geophysicist whose theories of continental drift and the movement of land masses helped clarify the processes involved in earthquakes.

Carpenter, Rhys (1889-Jan. 2, 1980), archaeologist, was an authority on the ways in which alphabets were transmitted among different cultures, and on the cultural geography of the Mediterranean region. His books are standard references for classical scholars.

***Chain, Ernst B.** (1906-Aug. 12, 1979), British biochemist who shared the 1945 Nobel prize for physiology or medicine for discovering penicillin.

DeHaven, Hugh (1895-Feb. 13, 1980), engineer, pioneer in research on automobile- and plane-crash injuries. As early as 1952, he urged the use of collapsible steering wheels, safety belts, and "soft" instrument panels in cars.

***Forssmann, Werner** (1904-June 1, 1979), German surgeon and urologist, was co-winner of the 1956 Nobel prize for medicine or physiology for his work on cardiac catheterization.

Frisch, Otto R. (1904-Sept. 22, 1979), Austrian-born nuclear physicist who coined the term *nuclear fission.*

***Fromm, Erich** (1900-March 18, 1980), German-born psychoanalyst who led a movement away from orthodox Freudian thought. Fromm theorized that response to social conditions is the major factor in human psychological development. His many books include *The Art of Loving* (1956).

Gantt, William H. (1893-Feb. 26, 1980), psychologist who pioneered in behavioral psychology. His work on conditioned heart reflexes in animals led to a better understanding of the causes of high blood pressure.

Gifford, William E. (1920-March 9, 1980), engineer, co-inventor of the Gifford-McMahon refrigeration cycle, which increased the availability of very low temperatures to science.

Gilbert, David S. (1940-Dec. 11, 1979), biologist whose work on the structural properties of axons, the long, thin extensions of nerve cells, provided a standard reference for research on biochemical filaments.

Harrison, George R. (1898-July 27, 1979), physicist, was dean of science at Massachusetts Institute of Technology (M.I.T.) in Cambridge from 1942 to 1964. He was noted for his contributions to the use of optical spectroscopy in studying the complexities of the atom. His wavelength tables, recorded and compiled in the 1930s, are used throughout the world as the basic spectrograph reference.

Heizer, Robert F. (1915-July 18, 1979), anthropologist whose research in Mexico and Central America increased understanding of ancient civilizations in North America.

Ingelfinger, Franz J. (1910-March 1, 1980), German-born physician noted for his research in gastroenterology. He was editor of the *New England Journal of Medicine* from 1967 to 1977.

Kennedy, George C. (1919-March 18, 1980), geologist who invented a piston-cylinder apparatus that enabled scientists to reproduce the earth's internal pressures and temperatures.

Kowarski, Lew (1907-July 27, 1979), Russian-born French nuclear physicist, was the last survivor of the team headed by Frédéric Joliot-Curie that explored the possibility of creating a nuclear chain reaction in 1939. He directed the construction of the first atomic pile in Canada in 1944 and played a leading role in the development of the European Organization for Nuclear Research (CERN).

Linton, Robert R. (1900-July 21, 1979), vascular surgeon who developed the tourniquet clamp and the Linton balloon, which controls bleeding in neck arteries.

***Lynen, Feodor** (1911-Aug. 6, 1979), West German biochemist, co-winner of the 1964 Nobel prize for physiology or medicine for his work on cholesterol and fatty acid metabolism.

Markham, Roy (1916-Nov. 16, 1979), British biochemist who was noted for his pioneering use of the electron mi-

Deaths of Notable Scientists

Continued

Feodor Lynen

William H. Stein

Robert B. Woodward

croscope in determining the measurements and structure of virus particles.

Mauchly, John W. (1907-Jan. 8, 1980), physicist and engineer who co-invented the first practical electronic digital computer, ENIAC, in 1946. He also co-developed UNIVAC I in 1951.

McMeekin, Thomas L. (1900-Nov. 11, 1979), chemist, was noted for his work on the physical chemistry of amino acids, peptides, and a variety of related molecules.

Payne-Gaposchkin, Cecelia H. (1900-Dec. 6, 1979), British-born astronomer, was noted for her studies of variable stars. She was the first woman to hold a tenured professorship at Harvard University in Cambridge, Mass.

Plaskett, Harry H. (1893-Jan. 26, 1980), British astronomer whose work on the emission spectra of gaseous nebulae led to a better understanding of the mechanisms of stellar spectral lines.

Rappaport, Paul (1922-April 21, 1980), physicist, noted for his research on energy conversion and solar cells.

Rhine, Joseph B. (1895-Feb. 20, 1980), psychologist, who pioneered in psychic studies and coined the term *extrasensory perception*. He headed the Parapsychology Laboratory at Duke University from 1940 to 1965.

Roberts, Richard B. (1910-April 4, 1980), physicist and microbiologist who was the principal contributor to the discovery of delayed neutrons, the basis for atomic reactors. As a microbiologist, he discovered the key chemical processes for cell duplication.

Rosenblad, Kurt E. (1899-July 9, 1979), engineer and inventor who developed the spiral heat exchanger used in the pulp and paper industries.

Sauer, Louis W. (1885-Feb. 10, 1980), pediatrician who in 1932 developed the multiple vaccine used to protect children against whooping cough, diphtheria, and tetanus.

Sisler, Frederick D. (1916-March 2, 1980), microbiologist who in 1961 developed the biochemical fuel cell used in extracting electrical power from organic waste.

Soderberg, C. Richard (1895-Oct. 17, 1979), Swedish-born mechanical engineer, a pioneer in the development of the turbine engine.

Stein, William H. (1911-Feb. 2, 1980), biochemist, was co-winner of the 1972 Nobel prize for chemistry for his work on the chemistry of enzymes.

Sugiura, Kanematsu (1892-Oct. 21, 1979), Japanese-born chemist, a pioneer in the development of chemotherapy in the treatment of cancer.

Tarnower, Herman (1910-March 10, 1980), cardiologist who achieved worldwide fame as the author of *The Complete Scarsdale Medical Diet* (1979).

*****Tomonaga, Sin-itiro** (1906-July 8, 1979), Japanese physicist who shared the 1965 Nobel prize for physics for work in quantum electrodynamics.

Velikovsky, Immanuel (1895-Nov. 17, 1979), Russian-born psychiatrist whose unorthodox theories on cosmic evolution outraged many scientists. His most striking forecasts included the high temperatures on Venus, the surface residual magnetism in moon rocks, the sun's electrical charge, and the craters on Mars.

Wallis, Sir Barnes N. (1887-Oct. 30, 1979), British aeronautical engineer who designed the "skipping bomb" used to destroy German dams on the Ruhr River in World War II.

Watts, George W. (1911-March 29, 1980), chemist on the Manhattan Project who played a major role in isolating and purifying the uranium used in the first atomic bomb.

White, Milton G. (1910-Oct. 16, 1979), physicist, was a leader in the development and use of particle accelerators for physics research. He designed and guided the construction of Princeton University's first cyclotron.

Woodward, Robert B. (1917-July 8, 1979), organic chemist who won the 1965 Nobel prize for chemistry for demonstrating that such complex compounds as chlorophyll, quinine, cortisone, and cholesterol could be made in the laboratory. Woodward's research also helped to determine the molecular structure of penicillin, terramycin, and strychnine.

Wynn-Williams, C. E. (1903-Aug. 30, 1979), British mathematician and physicist who pioneered the use of radio electron tubes and amplifiers in nuclear and radiation physics. He also helped develop the basic techniques of constructing electronic computers. He worked on code-breakers during World War II, including the Enigma cipher machine. [Irene B. Keller]

Index

This index covers the contents of the 1979, 1980, and 1981 editions of *Science Year*, The World Book Science Annual.

Each index entry is followed by the edition year in *italics* and the page numbers:

   Lymphocytes, inflammation, *Special Report, 81*-58, *80*-293, *79*-294

This means that information about lymphocytes begins on the page indicated for each of the editions.

An index entry that is the title of an article appearing in *Science Year* is printed in boldface italic letters: ***Archaeology.*** An entry that is not an article title, but a subject discussed in an article of some other title, is printed: **Plutonium.**

The various "See" and "See also" cross references in the index are to other entries within the index. Clue words or phrases are used when the entry needs further definition or when two or more references to the same subject appear in *Science Year*. These make it easy to locate the material on the page.

   Neuroscience, *81*-306, *80*-311, *79*-311, brain nutrition, *Special Report, 80*-87.

   See also **Brain; Nervous system.**

The indication *"il."* means that the reference is to an illustration only, as:

   Orion, *il., 81*-393

Index

A

Absorption lines: cosmology, *81*-246; interstellar medium, *Special Report, 81*-160

Accretion disk: star birth, *Special Report, 79*-66

Acetylcholine, *80*-89

Acid phosphatase, *79*-297

Acid rain: environment, *Close-Up, 81*-276

Acne, *80*-299

Acoustic microscope, *79*-330; *il., 81*-249

Acrylonitrile: environment, *79*-280

Actin: inflammation, *Special Report, 81*-67

Acupuncture, *il., 80*-339

Addiction: drugs, *81*-261

Additives, food: psychology, *81*-326

Adenine: split genes, *Special Report, 81*-198

Adenosine triphosphate: swimming, *Special Report, 81*-37

Adenovirus 2: genetics, *79*-281; split genes, *Special Report, 81*-200

Adrian, Lord Edgar Douglas: deaths, *79*-394

Aegyptopithecus: anthropology, *81*-232

Aeronautics: *Gossamer Condor, Special Report, 79*-85

Aerosols: technology, *79*-346

Aerospace: awards and prizes, *81*-406, *80*-392, *79*-391

Afar: *Special Report, 79*-43

Aging: botany, *80*-256; internal medicine, *81*-297

Agnew, Harold M., *81*-403

Agriculture, 81-226, *80*-226, *79*-226; arid lands, *Special Report, 79*-157; chemistry, *80*-260; microbiology, *80*-310; Negev, *Special Report, 80*-127; New World archaeology, *81*-237; Old World archaeology, *81*-233; acid rain, *Close-Up, 81*-276; water buffalo, *Special Report, 80*-73. See also **Botany; Chemical Technology; Climate; Food; Nutrition.**

Air pollution: transportation, *81*-332. See also **Automobile; Climate; Environment; Pollution.**

Air pressure: hurricane, *Special Report, 81*-91

Airbags, *79*-347

Airflow: heat absorption, *Close-Up, 81*-323

ALA-synthetase: liver, *Special Report, 79*-175

Alamo: archaeology, *81*-236

Alaska: environment, *80*-281

Albedo: asteroids, *Special Report, 79*-147

Alcohol: botany, *80*-256; *il., 80*-312; liver, *Special Report, 79*-177; nutrition, *81*-310

Alder aphids: zoology, *79*-349

Alfvén waves: solar wind, *Special Report, 80*-21

Allende meteorite, *79*-285

Allergies: biochemistry, *79*-249; immunology, *80*-295

Allogenic effect factor (AEF): immunology, *81*-292

Aluminum: geochemistry, *81*-283

Alvarez, Walter C.: deaths, *80*-394

Alveolar bone: dentistry, *81*-294

Alvin: Atwater, Tanya, *80*-356; Galapagos Rift Valley, *Special Report, 79*-14; geophysics, *81*-286; oceanography, *81*-311, *80*-316

Amalthea: Jupiter, *Special Report, 81*-50

Amateur astronomy: *Special Report, 81*-389

American Sign Language, *81*-325

Amino acids: anthropology, *81*-232; chemical ecology, *Special Report, 81*-18; chemistry, *81*-258; nutrition, *79*-315; split genes, *Special Report, 81*-199

Amniocentesis, *81*-296

Amoco Cadiz: environment, *79*-280; oil spill, *Special Report, 81*-71

Amor asteroids: asteroids, *Special Report, 79*-146

Amphetamine, *81*-137

Anastomosis: surgery, *80*-300

Anatomy: collision research, *Special Report, 80*-143

Anderson, Philip W.: awards, *79*-387

Angina pectoris: medicine, *80*-299

Anglerfish: zoology, *80*-350

Angus: geophysics, *81*-286

Animal behavior: ecology, *80*-271, *Close-Up, 80*-266; light, *Special Report, 79*-113; navigation, *Special Report, 81*-114; oceanography, *81*-311; psychology, *81*-325, *79*-333; swimming, *Special Report, 81*-28; water buffalo, *Special Report, 80*-77; zoology, *81*-333, *80*-349, *79*-248

Animal vaccines: agriculture, *80*-229

Anisotropy: cosmology, *79*-245

Anopheles **mosquito:** malaria, *Special Report, 79*-71

Ant: chemical ecology, *Special Report, 81*-20; zoology, *81*-333, *79*-349

Antarctica: oceanography, *79*-316

Anthropology, 81-230, *80*-229, *79*-230; *Books of Science, 79*-250; early man in Afar, *Special Report, 79*-43; forensic science, *Special Report, 81*-111; Mead, Margaret, *Close-Up, 80*-232; museum, *Special Report, 81*-146. See also **Archaeology.**

Antibaryon, *81*-174

Antibiotics: biochemistry, *80*-249; drugs, *81*-263

Antibodies: immunology, *81*-293, *79*-295; inflammation, *Special Report, 81*-59

Anticyclone system: hurricane, *Special Report, 81*-91

Antigens: immunology, *79*-294; inflammation, *Special Report, 81*-59

Antimatter: cosmology, *81*-246; physics, *80*-323; quantum chromodynamics, *Special Report, 81*-173

Antiproton: cosmology, *81*-246; elementary particles, *81*-317

Antiquarks: elementary particles, *81*-315, *79*-321; physics, *80*-323

Apes: anthropology, *81*-231, *79*-230; psychology, *81*-325

Aphid: zoology, *79*-349

Apollo asteroids: asteroids, *Special Report, 79*-146

Apollo-Soyuz Test Project: space shuttle, *Special Report, 79*-40

Appetite: neuroscience, *80*-311

Aquasol: technology, *79*-346

Archaebacteria: microbiology, *79*-310

Archaeology, 81-233, *80*-237, *79*-233; *Books of Science, 80*-253; Negev, *Special Report, 80*-131; New World, *81*-235, *80*-237, *79*-235; Old World, *81*-233, *80*-234, *79*-233; *Special Report, 80*-99. See also **Anthropology; Geoscience.**

Archaeopteryx: paleontology, *80*-292

Archiméde: *Special Report, 79*-16

Arctic Ocean: oceanography, *81*-310; paleontology, *81*-288

Arctic Wildlife Range: environment, *80*-281

Arethusa: asteroids, *Special Report, 79*-148

Argon: geochemistry, *80*-286

Argyrodes: zoology, *81*-335

Ariane: space exploration, *81*-329

Arid land: *Special Report, 79*-157

Army ant: zoology, *81*-333

Artery, *il., 80*-53

Arthritis: medicine, *80*-297

Artificial blood: *Close-Up, 81*-295

Artificial food coloring: psychology, *81*-326

Artificial gene. See **Recombinant DNA.**

Artificial insemination: public health, *80*-336

Artificial organs: liver, *Special Report, 79*-180

Artificial spine: surgery, *81*-298

Artificial-voice machine: technology, *79*-345

Aspirin: drugs, *81*-262, *80*-267

Asteroids: Jupiter, *Special Report, 81*-50; *Special Report, 79*-143

Asthma: chemistry, *81*-257

Astronomy: amateur, *Special Report, 81*-389; asteroids, *Special Report, 79*-143; awards and prizes, *81*-406, *80*-392, *79*-391; *Books of Science, 80*-253, *79*-250; cosmology, *81*-245, *80*-247, *79*-246; Einstein, Albert, *80*-408; extraterrestrial life, *Special Report, 80*-57; high-energy, *81*-243, *80*-245, *79*-243; interstellar medium, *Special Report, 81*-156; Jupiter, *Special Report, 81*-41; planetary, *81*-238, *80*-240, *79*-238; shrinking sun, *Close-Up, 81*-242; solar wind, *Special Report, 80*-13; star birth, *Special Report, 80*-99, *79*-57; stellar, *81*-240, *80*-243, *79*-241. See also **Space Exploration.**

Athabasca tar sands, *81*-183

Atherosclerosis: cell receptors, *Special Report, 80*-44; nutrition, *81*-308

Atlas Centaur: space exploration, *79*-344

Atmosphere. See **Climate;** *Meteorology;* **Weather.**
Atmospheric science: *Books of Science,* 79-250
Atomic and molecular physics. See *Physics* (atomic and molecular).
Atomic reactor. See **Nuclear power plants.**
Atrazine: agriculture, *81*-227
Atrium buildings: fires, *Special Report, 79*-208
Atwater, Tanya: biography, *80*-356
Augite, *il., 81*-284
Austen, K. Frank: awards and prizes, *79*-389
Australia: anthropology, *81*-231
Australian antigen: liver, *Special Report, 79*-180
Australopithecines: anthropology, *80*-229; early man in Afar, *Special Report, 79*-44
Australopithecus afarensis: anthropology, *80*-229
Autoimmune diseases: immunology, *80*-293; inflammation, *Special Report, 81*-68
Autoionizing Rydberg states: atomic and molecular physics, *79*-320
Automobile: chemical technology, *80*-257, *79*-255; collision research, *Special Report, 80*-141; electronics, *79*-272; environment, *79*-277; transportation, *80*-347, *79*-347. See also **Air pollution; Transportation.**
Avdat: agriculture in arid lands, *Special Report, 79*-158
Aviation: collision research, *Special Report, 80*-150; Gossamer Condor, *Special Report, 79*-85; meteorology, *79*-305; technology, *80*-345
Awards and Prizes, 81-402, *80*-386, *79*-387

B

B-DNA: biochemistry, *81*-249
B-lactamase: biochemistry, *81*-250
B quark: elementary particles, *81*-316
B star: star birth, *Special Report, 79*-58
Baby: nutrition, *Close-Up, 80*-314
Bacteria: agriculture, *81*-226; biochemistry, *81*-250, *80*-249; botany, *80*-256; dentistry, *79*-296; drugs, *Close-Up, 81*-263; Galapagos Rift Valley, *Special Report, 79*-26; geochemistry, *81*-281; inflammation, *Special Report, 81*-58; microbiology, *80*-308, *79*-308; nutrition, *80*-314; oceanography, *81*-311
Bacterial chemosynthesis: oceanography, *81*-312
Bacteriology. See **Bacteria; Biology; Microbiology.**
Barbiturates: public health, *80*-337
Barley: agriculture, *81*-230, *79*-226, *Special Report, 79*-169
Barnard's Star: extraterrestrial life, *Special Report, 80*-58
Barosaurus: dinosaur, *Close-Up, 81*-290

Baryon: quantum chromodynamics, *Special Report, 81*-174
Basic research: science policy, *80*-337
Basilosaurus: paleontology, *79*-292
Bateson, Frank: awards and prizes, *81*-406
Batteries: solid-state physics, *80*-330; transportation, *81*-331
BCG: malaria, *Special Report, 79*-83
Béarnaise, sauce: chemistry, *Close-Up, 81*-256
Becklin-Neugebauer (BN) object: star birth, *Special Report, 79*-57; stellar astronomy, *79*-241
Bedouins: *Close-Up, 81*-322
Bee: animal navigation, *Special Report, 81*-116
Beetle, bombardier: chemical ecology, *Special Report, 80*-12
Behavior: science policy, *Close-Up, 79*-338. See also **Animal behavior.**
Benzene: environment, *79*-280
Benzodiazepines: public health, *80*-337
Bernoulli's principle: swimming, *Special Report, 81*-35
Beta decay: nuclear physics, *80*-325
Beta-galactosidase: biochemistry, *79*-248
Beta-globin: microbiology, *81*-305
Bible: Negev, *Special Report, 80*-131
Big bang: cosmology, *81*-245, *80*-247; interstellar medium, *Special Report, 81*-158
Bighorn Medicine Wheel: archaeoastronomy, *Special Report, 80*-108
Bile: liver, *Special Report, 79*-172
Bile duct: medicine, *80*-302
Bilirubin: liver, *Special Report, 79*-177
Binary pulsar: stellar astronomy, *81*-241
Binary star: interstellar medium, *Special Report, 81*-161; stellar astronomy, *81*-242
Biochemistry, 81-247, *80*-249, *79*-247; chemistry, *80*-262; *Close-Up, 80*-250; extraterrestrial life, *Special Report, 80*-62; genetics, *80*-282; medicine, *80*-297; nutrition, *80*-314; nutrition and the brain, *Special Report, 80*-87; schizophrenia, *Special Report, 81*-134. See also **Amino acids; Biology;** *Chemistry;* **DNA; Enzymes; Hormone; Plant.**
Biological clock: animal navigation, *Special Report, 81*-124; animals and light, *Special Report, 79*-114
Biology: awards and prizes, *81*-405, *80*-390, *79*-389; *Books of Science, 81*-251, *80*-253, *79*-250; cell receptors, *Special Report, 80*-42; embryo transplants, *Special Report, 80*-185; extraterrestrial life, *Special Report, 80*-57; Galapagos Rift Valley, *Special Report, 79*-24; interferon, *Special Report, 80*-115; split genes, *Special Report, 81*-197. See also *Biochemistry; Botany;* **Cell;** *Ecology;* **Enzymes;** *Genetics; Microbiology; Zoology.*

Biophysics: collision research, *Special Report, 80*-143; synchrotron, *Special Report, 80*-180
Birds: animal navigation, *Special Report, 81*-116; birdsong, *Special Report, 80*-28; oil spill, *Special Report, 81*-79; paleontology, *80*-292; zoology, *81*-337
Birdsong: *Special Report, 80*-28; zoology, *79*-350
Bismuth: physics, *79*-319
Bite marks: forensic science, *Special Report, 81*-106
Bitumen: tar sands, *Special Report, 81*-188
Black-backed oriole, *81*-337
Black holes: Einstein, Albert, *80*-408
Bladder: surgery, *81*-299
Blindness: surgery, *81*-299
Blister: disorders, *Consumer Science, 81*-345
Blodgett, Katharine B.: deaths, *81*-409
Blokhintsev, Dmitrii I., *80*-394
Blood: forensic science, *Special Report, 80*-107; inflammation, *Special Report, 81*-58; medicine, *Close-Up, 81*-295; nutrition, *80*-314; surgery, *80*-303
Blood clots: surgery, *79*-302
Blood pressure: nutrition and the brain, *Special Report, 80*-97
Blood sugar: internal medicine, *81*-296
Blood test: electronics, *80*-275
Bluegill sunfish: zoology, *80*-352
BN object: star birth, *Special Report, 79*-57
Bode's law: asteroids, *Special Report, 79*-144
Bodo (Ethiopia): anthropology, *80*-233
Body identification: forensic science, *Special Report, 81*-111
Bollworm: chemical technology, *80*-260
Bombardier beetle: chemical ecology, *Special Report, 81*-12
Bonaire reef: Earthwatch, *80*-385
Bone destruction: dentistry, *81*-294
Bone fractures: medicine, *81*-297, *80*-301
Bone marrow: microbiology, *81*-304
Books of Science, 81-251, *80*-253, *79*-250
Bornean bearded pig: anthropology, *79*-232
Bosworth, David M.: deaths, *81*-409
Botany, 81-253, *80*-255, *79*-252; agriculture, *80*-226; chemistry, *80*-260; *Close-Up, 79*-253; ecology, *80*-270; museum, *Special Report, 81*-146. See also **Agriculture; Plant.**
Bowie Medal, *81*-404, *80*-388
Brackett alpha: star birth, *Special Report, 79*-69
Brackett gamma: star birth, *Special Report, 79*-69
Brain: *Books of Science, 79*-250; neuroscience, *81*-306, *80*-311; nutrition, *Special Report, 80*-87; schizophrenia, *Special Report, 81*-130. See also **Neuroscience; Psychology.**

Index

Index

Index

Lymphokine: inflammation, *Special Report, 81*-59
Lyon: archaeology, *80*-234
Lysosome: shock, *Close-Up, 80*-250

M

MacCready, Paul B.: awards, *81*-406
Macedonia: archaeology, *79*-233
Macroevolution: *Special Report, 80*-197
Macrophage: immunology, *81*-293; inflammation, *Special Report, 81*-58
Magma: geology, *81*-285, *79*-288; geophysics, *81*-286
Magnetic bubble memory: electronics, *80*-272
Magnetic dipole radiation: physics, *79*-320
Magnetic field: drugs, *79*-267; planetary astronomy, *81* 238; solar wind, *Special Report, 80*-14
Magnetic fusion, *79*-326
Magnetic mirror device: plasma physics, *81*-320
Magnetism: animal navigation, *Special Report, 81*-116; zoology, *80*-349
Magnetite: animal navigation, *Special Report, 81*-125
Magnetohydrodynamic generator: energy, *80*-277
Magnetosphere: Jupiter, *Special Report, 81*-46; planetary astronomy, *81*-238
Main-sequence star: star birth, *Special Report, 79*-58
Malaria: immunology, *81*-293; *Special Report, 79*-71
Mammoth: Earthwatch, *80*-371
Manganese, *il., 81*-282
Mangrove: zoology, *80*-350
Manic-depressive psychosis: schizophrenia, *Special Report, 81*-131
Manicouagan meteorite, *80*-288
Mantle: geology, *81*-283; geophysics, *81*-288
Manton, Sidnie: deaths, *80*-395
Marijuana: drugs, *81*-261; neuroscience, *80*-311
Marine life: oceanography, *81*-310, *79*-316; oil spill, *Special Report, 81*-72
Mars: planetary astronomy, *81*-239
Marwick, John: deaths, *80*-395
Maser: Einstein, Albert, *80*-405
Mass, neutrino: physics, *81*-316
Mastectomy: breast cancer, *Consumer Science, 81*-352
Mathematics: Books of Science, *80*-254; electronics, *Close-Up, 80*-274; Fourier Transforms, *Special Report, 81*-208; Graham, Ronald L., *81*-373
Mauchly, John W.: deaths, *81*-410
Mauna Kea, *il., 79*-236
Maunder Minimum: stellar astronomy, *80*-243, *79*-241
Maya: New World archaeology, *81*-236

Mead, Margaret: *Close-Up, 80*-232; deaths, *80*-395
Medicine, *81*-294, *80*-295, *79*-296; awards and prizes, *81*-404, *80*-389, *79*-389; Books of Science, *80*-254; cell receptors, *Special Report, 80*-42; *Close-Up, 81*-295, *80*-298, *79*-299; dentistry, *81*-294, *80*-295, *79*-296; drugs, *80*-266; electronics, *81*-270, *80*-275; genetics, *80*-282; immunology, *80*-293; interferon, *Special Report, 80*-115; internal *81*-294, *79*-297; public health, *80*-335; surgery, *81*-298, *80*-300, *79*-301; technology, *80*-346. See also **Disease; *Public Health.***
Medicine wheel: archaeoastronomy, *Special Report, 80*-108
Mefloquine: malaria, *Special Report, 79*-77
Megaliths, *80*-101
Meltdown: energy, *80*-276; environment, *80*-279
Memory: psychology, *80*-331
Menard, H. William, *80*-364
Meningitis: internal medicine, *79*-297
Menopause: and smoking, *79*-336; internal medicine, *81*-297
Mental illness: schizophrenia, *Special Report, 81* 120
Merritt, H. Houston: deaths, *80*-395
Meson: elementary particles, *81*-315, *79*-324; quantum chromodynamics, *Special Report, 81* 174
Messenger RNA: biochemistry, *81*-247, *80*-251; microbiology, *80*-308; split genes, *Special Report, 81*-200
Messerschmitt, Willy: deaths, *80*-395
Metabolism: drugs, *80*-266
Metal electrides: chemistry, *81*-257
Metal-metal bonds: chemistry, *79*-261
Metal-semiconductor junction: solar cells, *Special Report, 79*-106
Metal sulfide: geophysics, *81*-287
Metamorphosis: ecology, *79*-269
Metaponto (Greece): archaeology, *81*-233
Meteorites: geology, *80*-288; geoscience, *Close-Up, 79*-285
Meteorology, *81*-301, *80*-304, *79*-304; agriculture, *80*-228; hurricane, *Special Report, 81*-88. See also **Climate; Weather.**
Meteosat: meteorology, *79*-307
Methane-forming bacteria: microbiology, *79*-310
Methotrexate (MTX), *81*-304, *80*-251
Mexico: archaeoastronomy, *Special Report, 80*-110; geology, *80*-289; geophysics, *80*-289
Microbiology, *81*-304, *80*-308, *79*-308
Microcircuits, *il., 81*-269; synchrotron, *Special Report, 80*-183
Microcomputers: communications, *79*-265; electronics, *79*-272; personal computers, *Special Report, 79*-186
Microspheres: drugs, *79*-267
Microsurgery, *il., 81*-300
Microtubules: inflammation, *Special Report, 81*-67

Microwave energy: communications, *79*-263; electronics, *81*-270
Mid-Atlantic Ridge: Galapagos Rift Valley, *Special Report, 79*-16; geology, *79*-288
Migration: animal navigation, *Special Report, 81*-116
Mileage: chemical technology, *79*-255
Milk: nutrition, *Close-Up, 80*-314
Milky Way: cosmology, *79*-245
Mimicry: zoology, *79*-248
Mind. See **Brain; *Psychology.***
Mining: tar sands, *Special Report, 81*-183
Mirror magnet reactor: plasma physics, *81*-320
Misar: electronics, *79*-272
Mitochondria, *81*-247, *80*-250
Mixed function oxidase system: liver, *Special Report, 81*-173
Molecular sieve: chemistry, *79*-262
Molecule: atomic and molecular physics, *80*-320
Monarch butterfly, *81*-336
Monazite: physics, *81*-323
Mondrian display: neuroscience, *81* 307
Monkey: psychology, *Close-Up, 80*-332
Monopole mode: nuclear physics, *79*-325
Moog synthesizer: Fourier Transforms, *Special Report, 81*-221
Moon. See headings beginning **Lunar. . . .**
Moray eel, *il., 79*-353
Morgan, W. W.: awards and prizes, *81*-406
Morro Rock: geophysics, *80*-290
Mosasaurs: paleontology, *79*-292
Mosquitoes: malaria, *Special Report, 79* 71
Multiple Mirror Telescope Observatory, *80*-244; *il., 80*-243
Multiple myeloma, *81*-298
Multiple sclerosis: immunology, *81*-293
Muon neutrino, *81*-316
Murchison, *il., 79*-151
Murphy, Gardner: deaths, *80*-395
Muscle: swimming, *Special Report, 81*-37
Museum: *Special Report, 81*-141
Mutation: drugs, *Close-Up, 81*-263; macroevolution, *Special Report, 80*-200
MWC 349: stellar astronomy, *79*-241
Myocardial depressant factor: shock, *Close-Up, 80*-250
Myosin: inflammation, *Special Report, 81*-67

N

N-type semiconductor: solar cells, *Special Report, 79*-103; solid-state physics, *79*-329
Nabataean Empire: Negev, *Special Report, 80*-132
Nabataeans: agriculture, *Special*

Index

80-279; science policy, 80-339; transportation, 79-347
Safflower: agriculture, 81-229
Salam, Abdus: awards, 81-403
Salpae: oceanography, 79-316
Salt: nutrition, 81-310
Salt water: agriculture, 79-226
Salyut 6: space exploration, 81-329, 80-343, 79-343
San Andreas Fault, 80-286, 366
Sanger, Frederick: awards, 81-405
Sangihe Plate: geology, 81-283
Satellite: astronomy, 80-242; energy, 79-276; Jupiter, *Special Report,* 81-41; planetary astronomy, 81-238
Satellite, communications: communications, 79-263
Saturn: planetary astronomy, 81-238; space exploration, 81-331
Sauce Béarnaise: chemistry, *Close-Up,* 81-256
Sauer, Louis W.: deaths, 81-410
Sauropod: dinosaur, *Close-Up,* 81-290
Sawfly: chemical ecology, *Special Report,* 81-24
Sawyer, Ralph: deaths, 80-395
Scanning acoustic microscope, 79-330
Scanning electron microscope (SEM): forensic science, *Special Report,* 81-103
Scanning/spot-beam: communications, 79-263
Schizont: malaria, *Special Report,* 79-73
Schizophrenics: neuroscience, 79-311; *Special Report,* 81-129
Science and Humanity Awards: 81-407
Science Policy, 80-337, 79-337; *Close-Up,* 80-339, 79-338. See also *Ecology. Space Exploration; Transportation.*
Science Service: Science Talent Search, 79-375
Science Talent Search: *People in Science,* 79-373
Scott's oriole: zoology, 81-337
Sea-floor spreading: Atwater, Tanya, 80-362; geology, 81-283. See also *Continental drift; Plate tectonics.*
Sea worm: oceanography, 80-318
Seat belts: collision research, *Special Report,* 80-146
Secondary hypertension: internal medicine, 81-294
Sedimentary rock: petroleum, *Essay,* 79-404
Seismic boomer, *il.,* 81-285
Seismic monitoring: geophysics, 80-289
Selarcryn: drugs, 80-268
Semiconductors: solar cells, *Special Report,* 79-102; solid-state physics, 79-329
Sencor: agriculture, 81-227
Sensory perception: neuroscience, 81-306
Sequenator: chemistry, 81-258
Serotonin: nutrition and the brain, *Special Report,* 80-89
Serum, blood: inflammation, *Special Report,* 81-58

Serum hepatitis: liver, *Special Report,* 79-179
SETI: *Special Report,* 80-66
Seychelles Plateau: geology, 81-285
Shark: paleontology, 79-291
Shear flow: turbulence, *Special Report,* 79-129
Shear stress: geophysics, 81-288
Shigella: drugs, *Close-Up,* 81-263
Shingles: interferon, *Special Report,* 80-121
Shipwreck, ancient: Old World archaeology, 81-234
Shiva: plasma physics, 79-328
Shock: chemistry, 81-257; *Close-Up,* 80-250
Shroud of Turin: *Close-Up,* 80-236; Old World archaeology, 79-235
Siabon: anthropology, 81-231
Siberia: geology, 80-287; Lake Baikal, *Special Report,* 80-155
Sickle cell anemia, 81-305, 80-250
Siegbahn, Karl: deaths, 80-395
Signature verification, *il.,* 80-346
Silicon: chemistry, 81-256; solar cells, *Special Report,* 79-103
Sine wave: Fourier Transforms, *Special Report,* 81-210
Single-lens reflex camera: *Consumer Science,* 81-347
Sivapithecus: anthropology, 79-230
Skin: disorders, *Consumer Science,* 81-344
Skull: dinosaur, *Close-Up,* 81-291
Skylab: solar wind, *Special Report,* 80-15; space exploration, 81-330, 80-342, 79-343; space shuttle, *Special Report,* 79-38
Sleeping pills: public health, 80-337
Slow-reacting substance (SRS): chemistry, 81-257
Slow-twitch muscle fibers: swimming, *Special Report,* 81-37
Smalltalk: personal computers, *Special Report,* 79-188
Smog: chemistry, 79-261
Smoke: fires, *Special Report,* 79-206
Smoking: drugs, 80-266; public health, 81-327, 79-335
Snail darter: environment, 80-281, 79-281
SO Galaxies: cosmology, 80-247
Social Darwinists: science policy, *Close-Up,* 79-338
Sociobiology: neuroscience, 81-307; science policy, *Close-Up,* 79-338
Sodium: geochemistry, 81-282; internal medicine, 81-294; Lake Baikal, *Special Report,* 80-164
Sodium fluorosilicate: chemistry, 81-256
Solar cells: chemistry, 81-256, 80-260; physics, 79-329; *Special Report,* 79-101
Solar collector: solar cells, *Special Report,* 79-101
Solar energy: agriculture, 81-230; chemistry, 81-255; energy, 81-272, 79-276; science policy, 79-340
Solar greenhouses: agriculture, 79-228
Solar heating, 80-347
Solar Maximum Mission Observatory satellite, 81-331

Solar neutrino: elementary particles, 81-316
Solar satellite: energy, 79-276
Solar system: asteroids, *Special Report,* 79-143; Jupiter, *Special Report,* 81-41
Solar wind: *Special Report,* 80-13
Solid-State Physics, 81-321, 80-329, 79-329
Solvation cage: lasers, *Special Report,* 79-217
Somatostatin: biochemistry, 79-247
Song sparrow: zoology, 79-350
Sound generator, *il.,* 81-303
Sound recording: technology, 80-345
Sound spectrography: birdsong, *Special Report,* 80-31
Sound synthesizer: technology, 79-345
Soyuz: space exploration, 80-343
Space Exploration, 81-329, 80-342, 79-342; space shuttle, *Special Report,* 79-28. See also **Astronomy (planetary).**
Space shuttle: energy, 79-276; space exploration, 81-329, 80-342, 79-342; *Special Report,* 79-28
Space station, *il.,* 79-36. See also **Space Exploration.**
Spacelab, 80-342, 79-37, 343
Speaker, stereo: *Consumer Science,* 81-349
Speaker-activated video-display terminal: electronics, 81-270
SPEAR. See **Stanford Positron-Electron Accelerating Ring.**
Spectrogram, *il.,* 80-32
Spectrometer, energy loss, 81-319
Spectrometer, Fourier, 81-210
Speech: birdsong, *Special Report,* 80-28
Speech recognition device: electronics, 81-269
Speech synthesis: electronics, 81-268; *il.,* 79-272
Sperry, Roger W.: awards and prizes, 81-405
Sphincter muscle: surgery, 81-299
Spicer, William E.: awards and prizes, 81-403
Spider: zoology, 81-335
Spine, artificial: surgery, 81-298
Spiral galaxies: cosmology, 81-245, 80-247
Split genes: genetics, 79-281; *Special Report,* 81-197
Sporozoites: malaria, *Special Report,* 79-73
Sprinkler system: fire, *Special Report,* 79-202
SS Cygnia, *il.,* 81-400
Stakman, Elvin: deaths, 80-395
Standard light-rail vehicles (SLRV): transportation, 79-348
Stanford Positron-Electron Accelerating Ring (SPEAR), 80-171
Star, 80-245; amateur astronomy, *Special Report,* 81-390; extraterrestrial life, *Special Report,* 80-57; interstellar medium, *Special Report,* 81-158; nuclear physics, 81-319
Stein, William H.: deaths, 81-410

Index

Acknowledgments

The publishers of *Science Year* gratefully acknowledge the courtesy of the following artists, photographers, publishers, institutions, agencies, and corporations for the illustrations in this volume. Credits should be read from top to bottom, left to right, on their respective pages. All entries marked with an asterisk (*) denote illustrations created exclusively for *Science Year*. All maps, charts, and diagrams were prepared by the *Science Year* staff unless otherwise noted.

Cover

Kenneth Lorenzen

Advisory Board

7 Stanford University; Harvard University; Cornell University; Argonne National Laboratory; Harvard University; State University of New York at Stony Brook; Duke University Medical Center

Special Reports

10 Colin Bidgood*; Dennis Brack, Black Star; Martin B. Hyatt
11 George Kelvin*; Alain Majani, Sygma
12-17 Thomas Eisner
19 Benjamin R. Goode*; Thomas Eisner; Thomas Eisner; Thomas Eisner
20-23 Thomas Eisner
26 Fred Zimmerman, Black Star; James E. Counsilman; James E. Counsilman; James E. Counsilman
27 James E. Counsilman
29 British Museum (Mansell Collection)
30-32 John Dawson*
33-34 James E. Counsilman
36 Human Performance Laboratory, Ball State University, Muncie, Indiana
37 James E. Counsilman
38 Focus on Sports
40 Jet Propulsion Laboratory
43 J. R. Eyerman; James Teason*
44 James Teason*
46 Jet Propulsion Laboratory
47 James Teason*
49 James Teason*; Jet Propulsion Laboratory; Jet Propulsion Laboratory; Jet Propulsion Laboratory; Jet Propulsion Laboratory
51 Jet Propulsion Laboratory
52 Jet Propulsion Laboratory; James Teason*; Albert Moldvay
56-65 Stephen Boswick*
66 Morris J. Karnovsky, M.D., Harvard Medical School; Morris J. Karnovsky, M.D., Harvard Medical School; Ralph Snyderman, M.D., Duke University Medical Center
70 © 1978 John Launois, Black Star
74 © 1978 Martin Rogers, Woodfin Camp, Inc.
75 I. Beames, Ardea London; Eric Schneider
76 Liz and Tony Bomford, Ardea London; Mark Antman, Fotogram Agence Photographique
77 © 1978 John Launois, Black Star; Mark Antman, Fotogram Agence Photographique
79 M.O. Hayes (Research Planning Institute, Inc.); Erich R. Gundlach (Research Planning Institute, Inc.)
81 Rebecca Harrington
82 Rebecca Harrington; James Lake; Rebecca Harrington
84 Erich R. Gundlach (Research Planning Institute, Inc.)
86 NASA
90 Tim Chapman, *Miami Herald;* Sipa from Black Star; National Hurricane Center, NOAA; Alain Majani, Sygma; Ken Hawkins, Sygma; William Strode, Woodfin Camp, Inc.
92-93 Patrick Maloney*
94-95 National Oceanic and Atmospheric Administration
96 National Hurricane and Experimental Meteorological Laboratory and NOAA; Technical Sergeant Eddings, U.S. Air Force
97 Flip Schulke, Black Star
98 T. Theodore Fugita

100 Bureau of Scientific Services, Illinois Department of Law Enforcement, Joliet, Illinois (Steve Hale*); Alabama Department of Forensic Sciences; Betty Pat Gatliff
103 Bureau of Scientific Services, Illinois Department of Law Enforcement, Joliet, Illinois (Steve Hale*); The Aerospace Corporation
104 H. R. Campbell, Jr., D.D.S.
105 Bureau of Scientific Services, Illinois Department of Law Enforcement, Joliet, Illinois (Steve Hale*); Bureau of Scientific Services, Illinois Department of Law Enforcement, Joliet, Illinois (Steve Hale*); Bureau of Scientific Services, Illinois Department of Law Enforcement, Joliet, Illinois (Steve Hale*); Skip Palenik, McCrone Research Institute, Chicago
107 Herbert Leon MacDonnell, Laboratory of Forensic Science, Corning, New York; Mark D. Stolorow
108 Ken Firestone
109 Betty Pat Gatliff; Stanley Rhine, University of New Mexico
111 Bureau of Scientific Services, Illinois Department of Law Enforcement, Joliet, Illinois (Steve Hale*); Alabama Department of Forensic Sciences; Walter C. McCrone, McCrone Research Institute, Chicago; Bureau of Scientific Services, Illinois Department of Law Enforcement, Joliet, Illinois (Steve Hale*)
112 Michael Charney, Center of Human Identification, Colorado State University
114-115 Britt Taylor Collins*
117 Martin B. Hyatt; Kenneth Lorenzen
118 Kenneth Lorenzen; Steve Hale*; Steve Hale*
119 Britt Taylor Collins*
120-121 Steve Hale*
122 Britt Taylor Collins*
123 Russell A. Charif
124 Charles Walcott; Steve G. Henry, Department of Geological Sciences, University of Michigan
126 Jeff Foott, Bruce Coleman Inc.; Jeanne A. Mortimer
128-133 John Zielinski*
136-137 John Zielinski*
140-141 Field Museum of Natural History (Steve Hale*)
143 Wide World
144 Field Museum of Natural History (Steve Hale*); Kjell B. Sandved, Smithsonian Institution; Kjell B. Sandved, Smithsonian Institution
145 Field Museum of Natural History (Steve Hale*)
146 Kjell B. Sandved, Smithsonian Institution
147-149 Field Museum of Natural History (Steve Hale*)
151 Kjell B. Sandved, Smithsonian Institution; Field Museum of Natural History (Steve Hale*)
152-153 Field Museum of Natural History (Steve Hale*)
154 Field Museum of Natural History (Dan Miller*)
157 Tim Casady (foreground)
159 Colin Bidgood*
160 Royal Observatory, Edinburgh, Scotland
162-163 Colin Bidgood*
164-165 Base photo from Carl Heiles, University of California, Berkeley and Edward Jenkins, Princeton University
166 Colin Bidgood*
168 Kitt Peak National Observatory; A.H. Rots and W.W. Shane with the Westerbork Synthesis Radio Telescope (the Netherlands), picture was produced on the Image Recording System of the National Radio Astronomy Observatory (USA)
170-177 Mike Hagle*
178 Leonard Morgan*; Mike Hagle*
179 Leonard Morgan*
180 Mike Hagle*
182 Syncrude Canada Ltd.; © Doug Wilson, Black Star; © Doug Wilson, Black Star
183 © Doug Wilson, Black Star; Dennis Brack, Black Star

Typography
Display — Univers
Text — Baskerville Linotron
Black Dot Computer Typesetting
Corporation, Chicago

Offset Positives
Collins, Miller, & Hutchings, Chicago
Capper, Inc., Knoxville, Tenn.
Liberty Photo Engraving
Company, Chicago

Printing
Kingsport Press, Inc., Kingsport, Tenn.

Binding
Kingsport Press, Inc., Kingsport, Tenn.

Paper
Text
Childcraft Text, Web Offset (basis 50 & 55 pound)
Mead, Escanaba, Mich.

Cover Material
10 point Lexotone
Holliston Mills, Inc., Kingsport, Tenn.
10 point Graphitek-C
James River Graphics, Holyoke, Mass.
Cabra
Parimco Products, Inc., N.Y., N.Y.

Cyclo-teacher® The easy-to-use learning system

Features hundreds of cycles from seven valuable learning areas

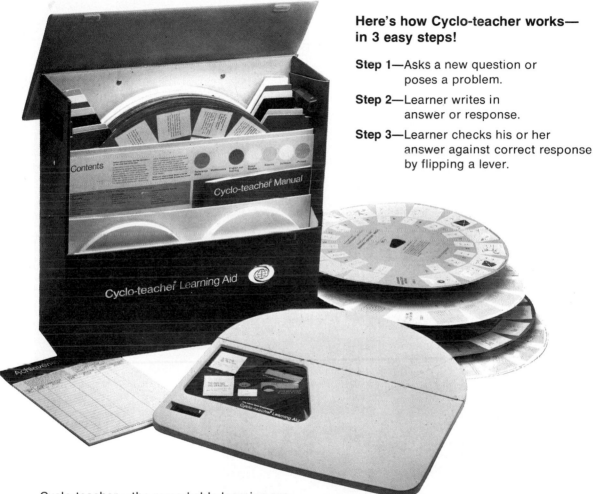

Here's how Cyclo-teacher works—in 3 easy steps!

Step 1—Asks a new question or poses a problem.

Step 2—Learner writes in answer or response.

Step 3—Learner checks his or her answer against correct response by flipping a lever.

Cyclo-teacher —the remarkable learning system based on the techniques of programmed instruction —comes right into your home to help stimulate and accelerate the learning of basic skills, concepts, and information. Housed in a specially designed file box are the Cyclo-teacher machine, Study Wheels, Answer Wheels, a Manual, a Contents and Instruction Card, and Achievement Record sheets.

Your child will find Cyclo-teacher to be a new and fascinating way to learn —much like playing a game. Only, Cyclo-teacher is much more than a game —it teaches new things

. . . reinforces learning . . . and challenges a youngster to go beyond!

Features hundreds of study cycles to meet the individual needs of students —your entire family —just as *Science Year* is a valuable learning aid. And, best of all, lets you track your own progress —advance at your own pace! Cyclo-teacher is available by writing us at the address below:

These beautiful bookstands–

specially designed to hold your entire program,
including your editions of *Science Year*.

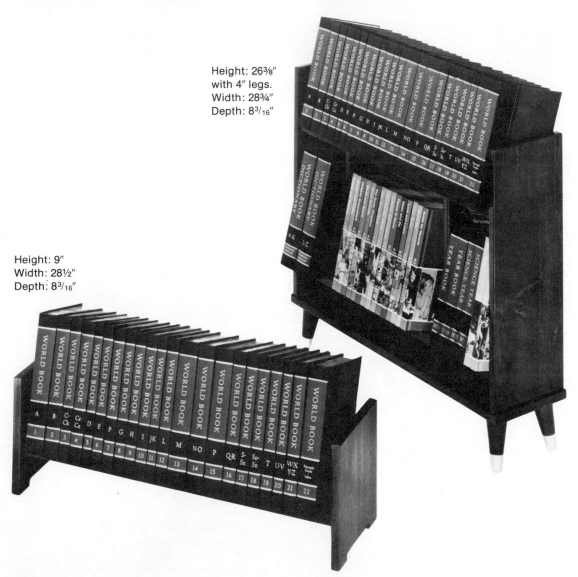

Height: 26⅜″
with 4″ legs.
Width: 28¾″
Depth: 8³/₁₆″

Height: 9″
Width: 28½″
Depth: 8³/₁₆″

Most parents like having a convenient place to house their *Science Year* editions and their *World Book Encyclopedia*. A beautiful floor-model bookstand —constructed of solid hardwood —is available in either walnut or fruitwood finish.

You might prefer the attractive hardwood table racks, also available in either walnut or fruitwood finish. Let us know by writing us at the following address:

Science Year
Post Office Box 3737
Chicago, IL 60654